McDougal Littell

CLASSZONE

Visit **classzone.com** and get connected.

ClassZone resources provide instruction, planning and assessment support for teachers.

Help with the Math

- @Home Tutor enables students to focus on the math and be more prepared for class, using animated examples and instruction.
- Extra examples similar to those in the book provide additional support.
- Hints and Homework Help offers assistance solving select homework exercises.

Practice, Practice, Practice

- eWorkbook includes interactive worksheets with additional practice problems.
- Problem of the Week features a new problem to solve every week.

Games and Activities

- Crossword puzzles, memory games, and other activities help students connect to essential math concepts.
- Math Vocabulary Flipcards are a fun way to learn math terminology.

Animated Math

- Engaging activities with animated problem-solving graphics support each lesson.

State-Specific Resources

- Select your state and access state-specific resources

You have immediate access to the the online version of the textbook and ClassZone resources at **www.classzone.com**

M C D T K A S T M S M Z

Use this code to create your own user name and password.

McDougal Littell
Where Great Lessons Begin

Littell

McGEORGIA HIGH SCHOOL

ATHEMATICS 3

er's Edition

McDougal Littell

A DIVISION OF HOUGHTON MIFFLIN COMPANY

Evanston, Illinois • Boston • Dallas

Teacher's Edition Contents

Georgia Mathematics 3 Teacher's Edition

Correlation to Georgia Process Standards for Mathematics 3

The table below is a correlation of *Georgia High School Mathematics 3* to

Correlation to Standards

Correlation of *McDougal Littell Georgia High School Mathematics 3* to the Georgia Performance Standards for Mathematics 3

ALGEBRA

Students will investigate exponential, logarithmic and polynomial functions of degree higher than 2. Students will understand matrices and use them to solve problems.

Georgia Performance Standard		Lesson/Activity
MM3A1	Students will analyze graphs of polynomial functions of higher degree.	
MM3A1a	Graph simple polynomial functions as translations of the function $f(x) = ax^n$.	Lesson 2.2
MM3A1b	Understand the effects of the following on the graph of a polynomial function: degree, lead coefficient, and multiplicity of real zeros.	Lesson 2.1, Investigating Math Activity 2.7, Lesson 2.8
MM3A1c	Determine whether a polynomial function has symmetry and whether it is even, odd, or neither.	Lesson 2.1, Lesson 2.2
MM3A1d	Investigate and explain characteristics of polynomial functions, including domain and range, intercepts, zeros, relative and absolute extrema, intervals of increase and decrease, and end behavior.	Lesson 2.1, Lesson 2.2, Investigating Math Activity 2.7, Lesson 2.8, Technology Activity 2.8
MM3A2	Students will explore logarithmic functions as inverses of exponential functions.	
MM3A2a	Define and understand properties o	
MM3A2b	Extend properties of exponents to i exponents.	
MM3A2c	Define logarithmic functions as inve exponential functions.	
MM3A2d	Understand and use properties of lo extending laws of exponents.	
MM3A2e	Investigate and explain characterist exponential and logarithmic functio domain and range, asymptotes, zero intervals of increase and decrease, a change.	
MM3A2f	Graph functions as transformations $f(x) = \log x, f(x) = e^x, f(x) = \ln x$.	

The correlation charts on pages GA13–GA17 of this Teacher's Edition and pages ix–xii in the Student Edition indicate where each Georgia Standard for Mathematics 3 is covered.

The Georgia Performance Standards for Mathematics 3 that correlate to the content of each activity or lesson are given at point of use in the Student Edition.

Georgia Performance Standards

MM3A2a Define and understand the properties of *n*th roots. ☑

Investigating Math Activity

Ra

M

LESSON 2.5 Apply the Remainder and Factor Theorems

Georgia Performance Standards: MM3A3a, MM3A3d

Goal Use theorems to factor polynomials.

Vocabulary

Polynomial long division can be used to divide a polynomial $f(x)$ by a divisor polynomial $d(x)$, producing a quotient polynomial $q(x)$ and a remainder polynomial $r(x)$.

Synthetic division can be used to divide any polynomial by a divisor of the form $x - k$.

Remainder Theorem: If a polynomial $f(x)$ is divided by $x - k$, then the remainder is $r = f(k)$.

Factor Theorem: A polynomial $f(x)$ has a factor $x - k$, if and only if $f(k) = 0$.

Example 1 Use polynomial long division

Divide $f(x) = x^3 + 2$ by $x + 1$ using long division.

Solution

$$
\begin{array}{r}
x^2 - x + 1 \\
x + 1 \overline{)x^3 + 0x^2 + 0x + 2}
\end{array}
$$

$\underline{x^3 + x^2}$	Multiply divisor by $x^3/x = x^2$.
$-x^2 + 0x$	Subtract.
$\underline{-x^2 - x}$	Multiply divisor by $-x^2/x = -x$.
$x + 2$	Subtract.
$\underline{x + 1}$	Multiply divisor by $x/x = 1$.
1	Subtract.

$\dfrac{x^3 + 2}{x + 1} = x^2 - x + 1 + \dfrac{1}{x + 1}$

Example 2 Use synthetic division

Divide $f(x) = x^3 + 2$ by $x + 1$ using synthetic division.

Write $x + 1$ in the form $x - k$: $x + 1 = x - (-1)$. So, write -1 to the left of the coefficients of $f(x)$, as shown.

$$
\begin{array}{r|rrrr}
-1 & 1 & 0 & 0 & 2 \\
& & -1 & 1 & -1 \\
\hline
& 1 & -1 & 1 & 1
\end{array}
$$

coefficients of quotient ⟶   ⟵ remainder

So, $\dfrac{x^3 + 2}{x + 1} = x^2 - x + 1 + \dfrac{1}{x + 1}$, which is the same result as in Example 1.

Georgia Mathematics 3
Notetaking Guide

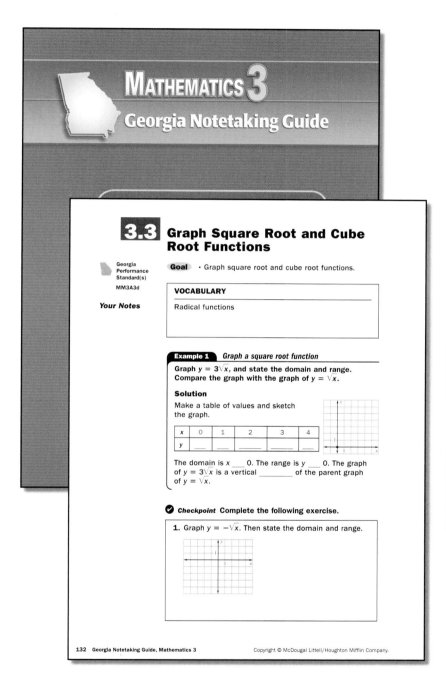

The Notetaking Guide contains a lesson-by-lesson framework that allows students to take notes on and review the main concepts of each lesson in the textbook.

Each Notetaking Guide lesson features worked-out examples, Checkpoint exercises after examples, and Practice exercises at the end of the lesson. Each example has a number of write-on lines for students to fill in.

The Georgia Performance Standards for Mathematics 3 that correlate to a lesson are listed at the beginning of the lesson.

Georgia Assessment Resources

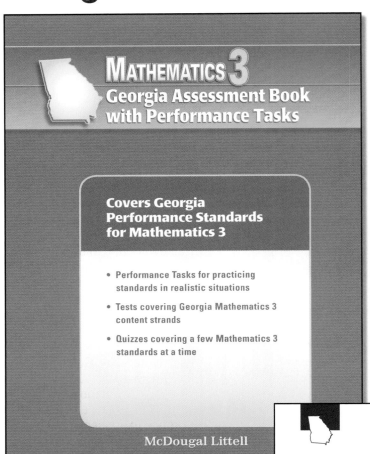

The sequence and organization of the assessment items in *Georgia Assessment Book with Performance Tasks: Mathematics 3* corresponds to the organization of topics in *Georgia High School Mathematics 3*.

Performance Tasks give students an opportunity to solve realistic multi-step problems. Assessment items also include tests covering Mathematics 3 content strands, and quizzes that cover a few standards at a time.

Georgia Mathematics 3 Test Preparation and Practice provides practice for every Georgia Performance Standard for Mathematics 3. It prepares students for future testing situations when they will be asked to meet the Georgia Performance Standards.

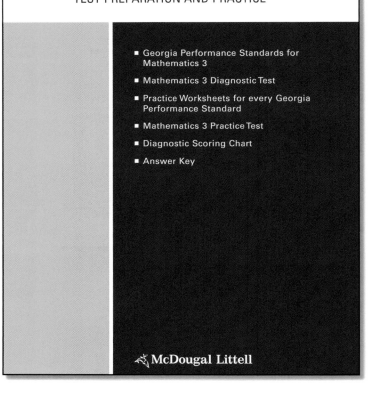

Georgia Technology Resources

Teaching the Lesson

Activity Generator CD-ROM
- Leveled activities (A, B, C) for most lessons
- Teaching commentary to guide students from concrete to abstract

@HomeTutor
- Animated examples and instruction
- Self-scoring exercises
- Customized student progress reports

eEdition
- Electronic version of the text
- CD-ROM and online formats

Assessment

McDougal Littell Assessment System
- Innovative standards-based system
- Helps you test, score, report, reteach
- Tests and answer sheets can be printed on plain paper

Test Generator

Correlation to Technology Resources

The table below lists the Test Generator lessons and @HomeTutor lessons as well as the Activity Generator activities that correspond to the lessons in *Georgia High School Mathematics 3*.

Student Edition Lesson	Test Generator and @HomeTutor Lesson	Activities from Activity Generator
1.1 Use Problem Solving Strategies and Models	Alg. 2 1.5	Exploring Problem Solving Strategies
1.2 Solve Linear Systems by Graphing	Alg. 2 3.1	Solving Linear Systems Using Tables
1.3 Solve Linear Systems Algebraically	Alg. 2 3.2	Solving Systems of Linear Equations
1.4 Graph Linear Inequalities in Two Variables	Alg. 2 2.8	Exploring Graphs of Linear Inequalities
1.5 Graph Systems of Linear Inequalities	Alg. 2 3.3	Graphing Systems of Linear Inequalities
1.6 Linear Programming	n/a	Exploring Linear Programming
1.7 Solve Systems of Linear Equations in Three Variables	Alg. 2 3.4	Graphing Linear Equations in Three Variables
1.8 Perform Basic Matrix Operations	Alg. 2 3.5	Organizing Data in Matrices
1.9 Multiply Matrices	Alg. 2 3.6	Multiplying Matrices
1.10 Evaluate Determinants and Apply Cramer's Rule	Alg. 2 3.7	Algebra Game: Finding Determinants
1.11 Use Inverse Matrices to Solve Linear Systems	Alg. 2 3.8	TI-Navigator*: Solving Linear Systems
1.12 Use Vertex-Edge Graphs	n/a	n/a
2.1 Evaluate and Graph Polynomial Functions	Alg. 2 5.2	End Behavior of Polynomial Functions
2.2 Translate Graphs of Polynomial Functions	n/a	n/a
2.3 Factor and Solve Polynomial Equations	Alg. 2 5.4	Algebra Game: Factoring Polynomials
2.4 Solve Polynomial Inequalities	n/a	n/a
2.5 Apply the Remainder and Factor Theorems	Alg. 2 5.5	Investigating the Remainder and Factor Theorems
2.6 Find Rational Zeros	Alg. 2 5.6	Exploring Rational Zeros
2.7 Apply the Fundamental Theorem of Algebra	Alg. 2 5.7	TI-Navigator: Exploring the Fundamental Theorem of Algebra
2.8 Analyze Graphs of Polynomial Functions	Alg. 2 5.8	Investigating Graphs of Polynomial Functions

*TI-Navigator is a registered trademark of Texas Instruments Incorporated.

Student Edition Lesson	Test Generator and @HomeTutor Lesson	Activities from Activity Generator
3.1 Evaluate *n*th Roots and Use Rational Exponents	Alg. 2 6.1	Exploring Roots and Rational Exponents
3.2 Apply Properties of Rational Exponents	Alg. 2 6.2	Algebra Game: Applying Properties of Rational Numbers
3.3 Graph Square Root and Cube Root Functions	Alg. 2 6.5	TI-Navigator: Exploring Graphs of Square Root and Cube Root Functions
3.4 Solve Radical Equations	Alg. 2 6.6	Solving Radical Equations
4.1 Graph Exponential Growth Functions	Alg. 2 7.1	Investigating Exponential Growth
4.2 Graph Exponential Decay Functions	Alg. 2 7.2	Exploring Exponential Growth and Decay
4.3 Use Functions Involving *e*	Alg. 2 7.3	Compounding Interest
4.4 Evaluate Logarithms and Graph Logarithmic Functions	Alg. 2 7.4	Evaluating Logarithms and Graphing Logarithmic Functions
4.5 Interpret Graphs of Exponential and Logarithmic Functions	n/a	n/a
4.6 Apply Properties of Logarithms	Alg. 2 7.5	Exploring Properties of Logarithms
4.7 Solve Exponential and Logarithmic Equations	Alg. 2 7.6	Solving Exponential and Logarithmic Equations
4.8 Solve Exponential and Logarithmic Inequalities	n/a	Algebra Game: Exponential and Logarithmic Inequalities
4.9 Write and Apply Exponential and Power Functions	Alg. 2 7.7	Modeling Data with an Exponential Function
5.1 Graph and Write Equations of Parabolas	Alg. 2 9.2	Modeling Parabolas
5.2 Graph and Write Equations of Circles	Alg. 2 9.3	Graphing and Writing Equations of Circles
5.3 Graph and Write Equations of Ellipses	Alg. 2 9.4	Modeling an Ellipse
5.4 Graph and Write Equations of Hyperbolas	Alg. 2 9.5	Modeling a Hyperbola
5.5 Translate and Classify Conic Sections	Alg. 2 9.6	Exploring Intersections of Planes and Cones
5.6 Solve Quadratic Systems	Alg. 2 9.7	Visualizing Solutions of Quadratic Systems
5.7 Use Figures in Three-Dimensional Space	n/a	n/a

Student Edition Lesson	Test Generator and @HomeTutor Lesson	Activities from Activity Generator
6.1 Construct and Interpret Binomial Distributions	Alg. 2 10.6	Constructing and Interpreting a Histogram
6.2 Use Normal Distributions	Alg. 2 11.3	Organizing and Analyzing Data
6.3 Approximate Binomial Distributions and Test Hypotheses	n/a	Approximating Binomial Distributions
6.4 Select and Draw Conclusions from Samples	Alg. 2 11.4	Investigating Samples
6.5 Experimental and Observational Studies	n/a	Designing Surveys and Experiments

Implementing Performance Tasks

Write a power function $y = ax^b$ whose graph passes through the given points.

30. $(1, 2), (4, 256)$ **31.** $(1, 0.2), (2, 51.2)$ **32.** $(-1, -5), (3, -405)$

33. Half-life Models The half-life of nitrogen-13 is about 10 minutes. The amount A (in grams) of radioactive nitrogen-13 that remains in a sample after t minutes is given by $A = 2000\left(\frac{1}{2}\right)^{t/10}$.

   a. What is the initial amount of nitrogen-13? ($t = 0$)

   b. How much nitrogen-13 is present after half an hour?

   c. In about how many hours will 500 grams of nitrogen-13 remain?

34. Bacteria Growth A population of bacteria can be modeled by the function $P = 60e^{0.3t}$ where t is the time (in hours). Graph the model and use the graph to estimate the population after 5 hours.

35. Chemistry The pH value for a substance measures how acidic or alkaline the substance is. It is given by the formula $\text{pH} = -\log{[\text{H}^+]}$ where H^+ is the hydrogen ion concentration (in moles per liter). What is the pH value of a substance with a hydrogen ion concentration of $10^{-5.7}$ moles per liter?

36. Finance You deposit $2000 in an account that pays 3.5% annual interest compounded continuously. When will your balance exceed $2500? When will your balance double?

Performance Task

Finance

You have $500 to invest, and you are trying to decide between two different banks. The first bank pays 5% annual interest compounded monthly.

   a. Write a model giving the account balance A after t years for the first bank.

   b. Make a table of values and graph the model for the first bank. In about how many years will your balance double in the first bank?

   c. Analyze the graph in part (b). Identify the zeros of the func[tion,] the intervals for which the function is increasing and decrea[sing.] these mean in the context of the problem.

   d. A bank representative from the second bank provides the f[ollowing] your money will perform over the next 5 years if deposited scatter plot of the data. Then find an exponential model for

Time, t	1	2	3
Account balance, A	530.00	561.80	595.51

   e. If you deposit your money in the second bank, when will y[ou have] $750? Which bank seems to be the better choice? *Explain.*

> There is a Performance Task at the end of each Unit Test in *Georgia High School Mathematics 3*.

> In the *Georgia Assessment Book with Performance Tasks*, there are five Performance Tasks for each unit. Two tasks cover the first half of the unit, two tasks cover the second half of the unit, and one task covers the entire unit.

Name _____ Date _____

Performance Task for Lessons 3.1–3.2

Ge
Pe
Sta

MM
MM

Name _____ Date _____

Performance Task for Algebra: Rational Exponents and Square Root Functions

Georgia Performance Standard(s)
MM3A2a,
MM3A2b,
MM3A3d

A nursery operator wants to build a greenhouse in the shape of a half cylinder. The volume of the greenhouse is to be approximately 35,350 cubic feet.

$\ell = 100$ ft

   a. The formula for the radius r (in feet) of a half cylinder is given by

$$r = \sqrt{\frac{2V}{\pi\ell}}$$

where V is the volume (in cubic feet) and ℓ is the length (in feet). Find the radius of the greenhouse. Round the result to the nearest whole number.

   b. Beams for holding a sprinkler system are to be placed across the top of the greenhouse. The formula for the height h at which the beams are to be placed is given by

$$h = \sqrt{r^2 - \left(\frac{a}{2}\right)^2}$$

where a is the length of a beam. Rewrite h as a function of only a.

   c. The length of each beam is 25 feet. Find the height h at which the beams should be placed. Round the result to two decimal places.

   d. Show that the equation from part (b) can be written as $a = 2\sqrt{r^2 - h^2}$.

   e. Use the value of r from part (a) to graph the equation from part (d).

   f. Use the graph from part (e) to determine an appropriate domain for the equation.

   g. At what height should the beams be placed if the length of each beam is 20 feet? Use the value of r from part (a) and the equation from part (d) to solve the problem. Round the result to two decimal places.

   h. The cost of building the greenhouse is estimated to be $35,000. In order to pay for the greenhouse, the nursery operator invested money in an interest-bearing account 10 years ago at an annual percent rate of 5%. The amount of money earned can be found using the formula

$$r = \left(\frac{A}{P}\right)^{1/n} - 1$$

where r is the annual percent rate (expressed as a decimal), A is the amount in the account after 10 years, P is the initial deposit, and n is the number of years. What initial deposit would have generated enough money to cover the building cost of $35,000?

Implementing Performance Tasks

The *Georgia Assessment Book with Performance Tasks* contains five Performance Tasks per unit, and *Georgia High School Mathematics 3* contains one Performance Task per unit. The table below shows when to implement each Performance Task.

Implementing Performance Tasks		
When to Implement Performance Tasks	Performance Task from *Georgia Assessment Book with Performance Tasks: Mathematics 3*	Performance Task from *Georgia High School Mathematics 3*
After Lesson 1.6	pp. 2, 3	
After Lesson 1.12	pp. 5, 6, 11	p. 64
After Lesson 2.4	pp. 13, 14	
After Lesson 2.8	pp. 16, 17, 22	p. 106
After Lesson 3.2	pp. 24, 25	
After Lesson 3.4	pp. 27, 28, 33	p. 128
After Lesson 4.5	pp. 35, 36	
After Lesson 4.9	pp. 38, 39, 44	p. 174
After Lesson 5.4	pp. 46, 47	
After Lesson 5.7	pp. 49, 50, 55	p. 210
After Lesson 6.3	pp. 57, 58	
After Lesson 6.5	pp. 60, 61, 66	p. 238

Correlation to Georgia Process Standards for Mathematics 3

The table below is a correlation of *Georgia High School Mathematics 3* to the Georgia Process Standards for Mathematics 3. The correlation of *Georgia High School Mathematics 3* to the Georgia Performance Standards for Mathematics 3 is on pages viii–xii in the Student Edition.

Georgia Process Standard	Lesson/Activity
MM3P1 Students will solve problems (using appropriate technology).	
MM3P1a Build new mathematical knowledge through problem solving.	Lesson 1.1, **Investigating Math Activity 1.3**, Investigating Math Activity 2.7, Investigating Math Activity 3.1, Investigating Math Activity 4.4, **Investigating Math Activity 5.3, Investigating Math Activity Lesson 6.2**
MM3P1b Solve problems that arise in mathematics and in other contexts.	Lesson 1.1, Problem Solving Workshop 1.5, **Lesson 1.6**, Lesson 1.12, Lesson 2.8 (p. 99, Example 3), Problem Solving Workshop 3.2, Lesson 3.3 (p. 119, Example 3), Lesson 4.1 (p. 131, Example 4), **Problem Solving Workshop 4.1**, Lesson 4.2 (p. 136, Example 4), Technology Activity 4.2, Lesson 4.3 (p. 141, Examples 3, 4), Lesson 4.9 (p. 169, Example 2), Lesson 6.1, Technology Activity 6.1, **Lesson 6.2**, Investigating Math Activity 6.3, Lesson 6.3, Lesson 6.4, Problem Solving Workshop 6.4, Lesson 6.5, and problem-solving examples and exercises throughout
MM3P1c Apply and adapt a variety of appropriate strategies to solve problems.	**Lesson 1.1**, Lesson 1.2, Investigating Math Activity 1.3, Lesson 1.3, Lesson 1.7, Lesson 1.10, Lesson 1.11, Lesson 2.3, Problem Solving Workshop 2.3, **Lesson 2.4**, Lesson 2.5, Lesson 4.7, Lesson 4.8, **Lesson 5.6**, Technology Activity 5.6, and problem-solving examples and exercises throughout
MM3P1d Monitor and reflect on the process of mathematical problem solving.	Investigating Math Activity 1.3, **Problem Solving Workshop 1.5**, Investigating Math Activity 1.11, Lesson 2.1 (p. 69, Ex. 20), Lesson 2.5 (p. 88, Ex. 16), Unit 2 Performance Task, Problem Solving Workshop 3.2, Problem Solving Workshop 4.1, Investigating Math Activity 4.4, **Lesson 4.5 (p. 153, Ex. 10; p. 154, Exs. 12, 13)**, Unit 4 Performance Task, Problem Solving Workshop 5.2, **Investigating Math Activity 5.3**, Lesson 5.4 (p. 193, Ex. 15), Investigating Math Activity 6.3, Problem Solving Workshop 6.4, Lesson 6.5, and error analysis exercises throughout

Key references to the student edition appear in **bold type**.
Other references that apply are listed in regular type.

Correlation to Georgia Process Standards (*continued*)

Georgia Process Standard	Lesson/Activity
MM3P2 Students will reason and evaluate mathematical arguments.	
MM3P2a Recognize reasoning and proof as fundamental aspects of mathematics.	Investigating Math Activity 1.3 (p. 12, Ex. 6), Lesson 1.9 (p. 47, Ex. 13), **Lesson 1.10 (p. 52, Exs. 20, 21)**, Investigating Math Activity 1.11, Lesson 2.1 (p. 70, Ex. 17), Lesson 2.3 (p. 79, Ex. 29), Lesson 2.4 (p. 84, Exs. 19, 20), **Lesson 2.6 (p. 92, Exs. 12, 13)**, Investigating Math Activity 2.7 (p. 93, Ex. 2), Lesson 2.7 (p. 97, Exs. 23, 24), Lesson 2.8 (p. 103, Exs. 26, 27, 31), **Investigating Math Activity 3.1**, Lesson 3.1 (p. 112, Ex. 36), Investigating Math Activity 4.4, Lesson 5.2 (p. 183, Ex. 20), Investigating Math Activity 5.3, Investigating Math Activity 6.2, Investigating Math Activity 6.3
MM3P2b Make and investigate mathematical conjectures.	**Investigating Math Activity 1.3 (p. 12, Ex. 6)**, Lesson 1.9 (p. 47, Ex. 13), **Investigating Math Activity 1.11**, Investigating Math Activity 2.7 (p. 93, Ex. 2), Lesson 2.8 (p. 103, Ex. 31), **Investigating Math Activity 3.1**, Investigating Math Activity 4.4, Investigating Math Activity 5.3, Investigating Math Activity 6.2 (p. 218, Ex. 2)
MM3P2c Develop and evaluate mathematical arguments and proofs.	Investigating Math Activity 1.3 (p. 12, Ex. 6), Lesson 1.9 (p. 47, Ex. 13), **Lesson 1.10 (p. 52, Exs. 20, 21)**, **Investigating Math Activity 1.11**, Lesson 2.1 (p. 70, Ex. 17), Lesson 2.3 (p. 79, Ex. 29), Lesson 2.4 (p. 84, Exs. 19, 20), Lesson 2.6 (p. 92, Exs. 12, 13), Investigating Math Activity 2.7 (p. 93, Ex. 2), **Lesson 2.7 (p. 97, Exs. 23, 24)**, Lesson 2.8 (p. 103, Exs. 26, 27, 31), Investigating Math Activity 3.1, Lesson 3.1 (p. 112, Ex. 36), Investigating Math Activity 4.4, Lesson 5.2 (p. 183, Ex. 20), Investigating Math Activity 5.3, Investigating Math Activity 6.2, Investigating Math Activity 6.3, and error analysis exercises throughout
MM3P2d Select and use various types of reasoning and methods of proof.	Investigating Math Activity 1.3 (p. 12, Ex. 6), Lesson 1.9 (p. 47, Ex. 13), **Lesson 1.10 (p. 52, Exs. 20, 21)**, Investigating Math Activity 1.11, Lesson 2.1 (p. 70, Ex. 17), Lesson 2.3 (p. 79, Ex. 29), Lesson 2.4 (p. 84, Exs. 19, 20), Lesson 2.6 (p. 92, Exs. 12, 13), Investigating Math Activity 2.7 (p. 93, Ex. 2), **Lesson 2.7 (p. 97, Exs. 23, 24)**, Lesson 2.8 (p. 103, Exs. 26, 27, 31), **Investigating Math Activity 3.1**, Lesson 3.1 (p. 112, Ex. 36), Investigating Math Activity 4.4, Lesson 5.2 (p. 183, Ex. 20), Investigating Math Activity 5.3, Investigating Math Activity 6.2, Investigating Math Activity 6.3, and throughout

Correlation to Georgia Process Standards (*continued*)

Georgia Process Standard	Lesson/Activity
MM3P3 Students will communicate mathematically.	
MM3P3a Organize and consolidate their mathematical thinking through communication.	Lesson 1.1, Problem Solving Workshop 1.5, Investigating Math Activity 1.11, Unit 1 Performance Task, Lesson 2.2, Problem Solving Workshop 2.3, Lesson 2.4 (p. 84, Ex. 19), Lesson 2.6 (p. 92, Exs. 12, 13), Unit 2 Performance Task, Investigating Math Activity 3.1, Problem Solving Workshop 3.2, Unit 3 Performance Task, Problem Solving Workshop 4.1, **Investigating Math Activity 4.4**, Unit 4 Performance Task, Problem Solving Workshop 5.2, Investigating Math Activity 5.3, Lesson 5.4 (p. 193, Ex. 15), Unit 5 Performance Task, Investigating Math Activity 6.2 (p. 218, Ex. 2), **Investigating Math Activity 6.3**, Lesson 6.3, Lesson 6.4, Problem Solving Workshop 6.4, **Lesson 6.5**, Unit 6 Performance Task
MM3P3b Communicate their mathematical thinking coherently and clearly to peers, teachers, and others.	Lesson 1.1, Problem Solving Workshop 1.5, Investigating Math Activity 1.11, Unit 1 Performance Task, Lesson 2.2, Problem Solving Workshop 2.3, Lesson 2.4 (p. 84, Ex. 19), Lesson 2.6 (p. 92, Exs. 12, 13), Unit 2 Performance Task, Investigating Math Activity 3.1, Problem Solving Workshop 3.2, Unit 3 Performance Task, Problem Solving Workshop 4.1, **Investigating Math Activity 4.4**, Unit 4 Performance Task, Problem Solving Workshop 5.2, Investigating Math Activity 5.3, Lesson 5.4 (p. 193, Ex. 15), Unit 5 Performance Task, **Investigating Math Activity 6.2 (p. 218, Ex. 2)**, Investigating Math Activity 6.3, Lesson 6.3, Lesson 6.4, Problem Solving Workshop 6.4, **Lesson 6.5**, Unit 6 Performance Task, and throughout
MM3P3c Analyze and evaluate the mathematical thinking and strategies of others.	Lesson 1.1 (p. 4, Ex. 9), Lesson 1.2 (p. 8, Ex. 16), Lesson 1.4 (p. 19, Exs. 22, 23; p. 21, Exs. 20, 21), Lesson 1.5 (p. 25, Ex. 4), Lesson 1.6 (p. 33, Ex. 7), Lesson 2.2 (p. 75, Ex. 17), **Lesson 2.3 (p. 78, Ex. 26)**, Lesson 2.4 (p. 83, Ex. 19), Lesson 2.7 (p. 96, Ex. 17), Lesson 2.8 (p. 100, Ex. 1), Lesson 3.2 (p. 116, Ex. 19), Lesson 3.3 (p. 121, Ex. 10), Lesson 4.1 (p. 132, Ex. 13), Lesson 4.2 (p. 138, Ex. 11), Lesson 4.3 (p. 142, Ex. 10), **Lesson 4.5 (p. 153, Ex. 3)**, Lesson 5.1 (p. 178, Ex. 10), Lesson 5.2 (p. 182, Ex. 7), Lesson 5.4 (p. 192, Ex. 7), **Lesson 6.2 (p. 221, Ex. 18)**, Lesson 6.3 (p. 226, Ex. 7), Lesson 6.4 (p. 230, Ex. 16)
MM3P3d Use the language of mathematics to express mathematical ideas precisely.	Lesson 1.6, Lesson 1.10, **Lesson 2.1**, Lesson 2.2, **Lesson 2.4**, Lesson 2.8, Lesson 4.3, Lesson 4.4, Lesson 6.1, **Lesson 6.2**, and throughout

Correlation to Georgia Process Standards (*continued*)

Georgia Process Standard	Lesson/Activity
MM3P4 Students will make connections among mathematical ideas and to other disciplines.	
MM3P4a Recognize and use connections among mathematical ideas.	Unit 1 Performance Task, **Unit 2 Performance Task**, Unit 3 Performance Task, **Unit 4 Performance Task**, **Unit 5 Performance Task**, Unit 6 Performance Task, and throughout
MM3P4b Understand how mathematical ideas interconnect and build on one another to produce a coherent whole.	Throughout book. See, for example, Lessons 1.4 and 1.5 (students graph linear inequalities in two variables and then systems of such inequalities); Lessons 2.1 and 2.2 (students graph polynomial functions and then translate polynomial graphs); Lessons 3.1 and 3.2 (students learn the definition of rational exponent and then apply properties of rational exponents); Lesson 4.1–4.5 (students graph exponential and logarithmic functions and then interpret their graphs); Lessons 5.1–5.5 (students graph conic sections and then translate the graphs)
MM3P4c Recognize and apply mathematics in contexts outside of mathematics.	Lesson 1.1, Problem Solving Workshop 1.5, **Lesson 1.6**, Lesson 1.12, Unit 1 Performance Task, Problem Solving Workshop 2.3, Unit 2 Performance Task, Problem Solving Workshop 3.2, Unit 3 Performance Task, Lesson 4.1 (p. 131, Example 4), Problem Solving Workshop 4.1, Lesson 4.2 (p. 136, Example 4), Technology Activity 4.2, Lesson 4.3 (p. 141, Examples 3, 4), Unit 4 Performance Task, Problem Solving Workshop 5.2, Unit 5 Performance Task, Lesson 6.1, Technology Activity 6.1, Lesson 6.2, Investigating Math Activity 6.3, **Lesson 6.3**, **Lesson 6.4**, Problem Solving Workshop 6.4, Unit 6 Performance Task, and applications throughout
MM3P5 Students will represent mathematics in multiple ways.	
MM3P5a Create and use representations to organize, record, and communicate mathematical ideas.	Lesson 1.1, Lesson 1.8 (p. 39, Example 3; p. 41, Exs. 12–15; p. 42, Exs. 13, 14), Lesson 1.9 (p. 45, Example 4; p. 46, Ex. 15; p. 47, Exs. 13, 14), Technology Activity 1.9 (p. 48, Ex. 5), **Lesson 1.12**, Lesson 2.1 (p. 68, Example 4; p. 69, Ex. 20), Lesson 2.2, Problem Solving Workshop 2.3, Lesson 2.8, Technology Activity 2.8, Unit 2 Performance Task, Lesson 3.3, Technology Activity 3.4, Lesson 4.1, **Problem Solving Workshop 4.1**, Lesson 4.2, Technology Activity 4.2, Lesson 4.3, Lesson 4.5, **Lesson 4.8 (p. 164, Example 2)**, Lesson 5.1, Lesson 5.2, Problem Solving Workshop 5.2, Lesson 5.3, Lesson 5.4, Lesson 5.5, Lesson 5.6, Technology Activity 5.6, Lesson 5.7, and throughout

Correlation to Georgia Process Standards (*continued*)

Georgia Process Standard	Lesson/Activity
MM3P5b Select, apply, and translate among mathematical representations to solve problems.	**Lesson 1.1**, Lesson 1.2, Lesson 1.4, Lesson 1.5, Problem Solving Workshop 1.5, Lesson 1.6, Lesson 1.11 (p. 57, Exs. 17–19; p. 58, Exs. 16–18), Lesson 2.1 (p. 69, Ex. 20), Problem Solving Workshop 2.3, **Lesson 2.4 (p. 84, Ex. 22)**, Lesson 2.5 (p. 88, Ex. 15), Lesson 2.6 (p. 91, Ex. 15), Lesson 3.3 (p. 120, Ex. 17), **Lesson 4.1 (p. 133, Ex. 15)**, Lesson 4.2 (p. 138, Ex. 10), Lesson 4.5 (p. 154, Ex. 10), Lesson 4.8 (p. 167, Ex. 21), Unit 4 Performance Task, Lesson 5.2 (p. 183, Ex. 19), Lesson 5.4 (p. 193, Ex. 15), Lesson 5.5 (p. 199, Ex. 31), Unit 5 Performance Task, Lesson 6.1 (p. 215, Ex. 16), and throughout
MM3P5c Use representations to model and interpret physical, social, and mathematical phenomena.	Lesson 1.1, Lesson 1.2, Lesson 1.4, Lesson 1.5, Problem Solving Workshop 1.5, **Lesson 1.6**, Lesson 1.8 (p. 39, Example 3; p. 41, Exs. 12–15; p. 42, Exs. 13, 14), Lesson 1.9 (p. 45, Example 4; p. 46, Ex. 15; p. 47, Exs. 13, 14), Technology Activity 1.9 (p. 48, Ex. 5), Lesson 1.11 (p. 57, Exs. 17–19; p. 58, Exs. 16–18), Lesson 1.12, Lesson 2.1 (p. 68, Example 4; p. 69, Ex. 20), Lesson 2.2, Problem Solving Workshop 2.3, Lesson 2.4 (p. 84, Ex. 22), Lesson 2.5 (p. 88, Ex. 15), Lesson 2.6 (p. 91, Ex. 15), Lesson 2.8, Technology Activity 2.8, Unit 2 Performance Task, Lesson 3.3, Technology Activity 3.4, Lesson 4.1, Problem Solving Workshop 4.1, Lesson 4.2, Technology Activity 4.2, Lesson 4.3, Lesson 4.5, Lesson 4.8 (p. 164, Example 2; p. 167, Ex. 21), Unit 4 Performance Task, Lesson 5.1, Lesson 5.2, Problem Solving Workshop 5.2, Lesson 5.3, Lesson 5.4, Lesson 5.5, Lesson 5.6, **Technology Activity 5.6**, Lesson 5.7, Unit 5 Performance Task, **Lesson 6.1 (p. 215, Ex. 16)**, and throughout

Pacing the Course

The pacing chart below shows the number of days allotted for each unit. The Regular Schedule requires 160 days. The Block Schedule requires 80 days. These time frames include days for review and assessment: 4 days per unit for the Regular Schedule and 2 days for the Block Schedule.

Unit	Semester 1			Semester 2		
	1	2	3	4	5	6
Regular Schedule	37	29	19	30	25	20
Block Schedule	18	15	10	15	12	10

Average Course

The average course is intended for students who enter with typical mathematical and problem-solving skills. Assignments include:

- Substantial work with the skills and concepts presented in the lesson
- Applications of these skills and concepts
- Test preparation

Advanced Course

The advanced course is intended for students who enter with above-average mathematical and problem-solving skills. Assignments include:

- Substantial work with the skills and concepts presented in the lesson
- More complex skill and application exercises
- Test preparation

Block-Schedule Course

The block-schedule course is intended for schools that use a block schedule. It covers the same content as the regular schedule.

Pacing and Assignment Guide

You can adapt any lesson's assignment by incorporating material from the @HomeTutor, Test Generator, Activity Generator, Notetaking Guide, and Assessment Book with Performance Tasks.

Lesson	Average Course	Advanced Course
Lesson 1.1	**Day 1:** p. 4, Exs. 1–9 **Day 2:** p. 4, Exs. 10–17; p. 5, Exs. 1, 2	**Day 1:** p. 4, Exs. 1, 2, 5, 6, 10, 11; p. 5, Exs. 1, 2 **Day 2:** p. 5, Exs. 3–9
Lesson 1.2	**Day 1:** p. 8, Exs. 1–16; p. 10, Exs. 1–3 **Day 2:** pp. 8–9, Exs. 17–28; p. 10, Exs. 13–15 **Day 3:** p. 9, Exs. 29–36; p. 10, Exs. 22, 23	**Day 1:** p. 8, Exs. 4–6; p. 10, Exs. 1–12 **Day 2:** p. 8, Exs. 17–19; p. 10, Exs. 13–30 **Day 3:** p. 9, Ex. 29; p. 11, Exs. 31–40
Lesson 1.3	**Day 1:** p. 12, Exs. 1–6 **Day 2:** p. 15, Exs. 1–12; p. 16, Exs. 1, 2, 7, 8 **Day 3:** p. 15, Exs. 13–24; p. 16, Exs. 13, 14	**Day 1:** p. 12, Exs. 1–6 **Day 2:** p. 15, Exs. 1, 2, 7, 8; p. 16, Exs. 1–12 **Day 3:** p. 15, Exs. 13–15; p. 16, Exs. 13–22
Lesson 1.4	**Day 1:** p. 19, Exs. 1–12; p. 21, Exs. 1, 2 **Day 2:** pp. 19–20, Exs. 13–25; p. 21, Exs. 8, 9 **Day 3:** p. 20, Exs. 26–34; p. 21, Ex. 17	**Day 1:** p. 19, Exs. 1, 2; p. 21, Exs. 1–11 **Day 2:** p. 19, Exs. 10–12; p. 21, Exs. 12–21 **Day 3:** p. 20, Exs. 24, 25; p. 22, Exs. 22–31
Lesson 1.5	**Day 1:** p. 25, Exs. 1–10; p. 27, Exs. 4, 5 **Day 2:** pp. 25–26, Exs. 11–23; p. 27, Exs. 10, 11 **Day 3:** p. 26, Exs. 24–28; p. 27, Exs. 20, 21 **Day 4:** p. 29, Exs. 1, 2	**Day 1:** p. 25, Exs. 5–7; p. 27, Exs. 1–12 **Day 2:** p. 25, Exs. 17–19; pp. 27–28, Exs. 13–23 **Day 3:** p. 28, Exs. 24–30 **Day 4:** p. 29, Exs. 1, 2
Lesson 1.6	**Day 1:** p. 32, Exs. 1–6; p. 33, Exs. 1, 2 **Day 2:** p. 32, Exs. 7–11; p. 33, Ex. 3 **Day 3:** Assessment Book (pp. 1–3)	**Day 1:** p. 32, Exs. 1–3; p. 33, Exs. 1–4 **Day 2:** p. 32, Exs. 4–6; p. 33, Exs. 5–8 **Day 3:** Assessment Book (pp. 1–3)
Lesson 1.7	**Day 1:** p. 36, Exs. 1–6; p. 37, Exs. 1, 4 **Day 2:** p. 36, Exs. 7–14; p. 37, Exs. 7, 8	**Day 1:** p. 36, Exs. 1, 2; p. 37, Exs. 1–9 **Day 2:** p. 36, Exs. 4–6; p. 37, Exs. 10–18
Lesson 1.8	**Day 1:** p. 41, Exs. 1–9; p. 42, Ex. 1 **Day 2:** p. 41, Exs. 10–15; p. 42, Exs. 2, 3	**Day 1:** p. 41, Exs. 1, 2; p. 42, Exs. 1–8 **Day 2:** p. 41, Exs. 7–9; p. 42, Exs. 9–14
Lesson 1.9	**Day 1:** p. 46, Exs. 1–7; p. 47, Exs. 1, 2 **Day 2:** p. 46, Exs. 8–15; p. 47, Exs. 5–7 **Day 3:** p. 48, Exs. 1–5	**Day 1:** p. 46, Exs. 1, 2; p. 47, Exs. 1–7 **Day 2:** p. 46, Exs. 3–5; p. 47, Exs. 8–14 **Day 3:** p. 48, Exs. 1–5
Lesson 1.10	**Day 1:** p. 51, Exs. 1–9; p. 52, Exs. 1, 7 **Day 2:** p. 51, Exs. 10–17; p. 52, Exs. 9–11	**Day 1:** p. 51, Exs. 1, 7; p. 52, Exs. 1–11 **Day 2:** p. 51, Exs. 10–12; p. 52, Exs. 12–21
Lesson 1.11	**Day 1:** p. 53, Exs. 1–5 **Day 2:** p. 57, Exs. 1–12; p. 58, Exs. 1, 4 **Day 3:** p. 57, Exs. 13–19; p. 58, Exs. 7, 9	**Day 1:** p. 53, Exs. 1–5 **Day 2:** p. 57, Exs. 1–3, 9, 10; p. 58, Exs. 1–8 **Day 3:** p. 57, Exs. 13, 14; p. 58, Exs. 9–18
Lesson 1.12	**Day 1:** p. 61, Exs. 1–7; p. 62, Exs. 1, 2 **Day 2:** p. 61, Exs. 8–12; p. 62, Exs. 7, 10 **Day 3:** Assessment Book (pp. 4–6)	**Day 1:** p. 61, Exs. 1–3; p. 62, Exs. 1–6 **Day 2:** p. 61, Exs. 8, 10; p. 62, Exs. 7–12 **Day 3:** Assessment Book (pp. 4–6)
Review and Assess	**Day 1:** Review **Day 2:** Review **Day 3:** Review **Day 4:** Unit Test	**Day 1:** Review **Day 2:** Review **Day 3:** Review **Day 4:** Unit Test
Unit 1 Total—37 days		**Remaining—123 days**

Block Schedule When teaching this unit in a block schedule, you can treat each day in the pacing and assignment guide as half of a block period.

Unit 1 Mathematical Background Notes

Lesson 1.1

Students may find *drawing a diagram* to be the most useful problem solving strategy. Diagrams can help link several components of a problem.

Lessons 1.2 – 1.7

SOLVING LINEAR SYSTEMS The system of linear equations

$$S_1 \quad Ax + By = C$$
$$S_2 \quad Dx + Ey = F$$

consists of two conditional statements which may or may not be satisfied. It is important to note that the problem being posed is "S_1 *and* S_2", not "S_1 *or* S_2". The solution of "S_1 and S_2" corresponds to the intersection of two lines, whereas the solution of "S_1 or S_2" would correspond to their union.

LINEAR INEQUALITIES The graphs of linear inequalities are half-planes in the sense of Euclidean geometry, where each line L partitions the plane into half planes H_1 and H_2. Given any point P_1 interior to H_1 and a point P_2 interior to H_2, the line segment connecting P_1 and P_2 must intersect L. If L is the graph of $Ax + By = C$, then those points (x_1, y_1) satisfying $Ax_1 + By_1 < C$ belong to the interior of one half-plane, while the points (x_2, y_2) satisfying $Ax_2 + By_2 > C$ belong to the interior of the other.

LINEAR PROGRAMMING A system of linear inequalities corresponds to the intersection of several half-planes. This intersection defines a feasible region over which a linear objective function is to be optimized.

Consider the feasible region to be the polygonal floor of a building. The linear objective function is a planar (flat but sloped) roof extending over the building. At each vertex of the polygonal floor is a pillar that supports the planar roof. In this situation it is intuitively clear that the highest (and lowest) points of the roof will occur above one of these vertices.

Lessons 1.8 – 1.9

Given the rules for **matrix** addition, subtraction, and scalar multiplication, students may wonder why matrix multiplication is not defined simply by multiplying corresponding entries.

You can address this question by noting the value of being able to multiply certain matrices having different dimensions. For example, suppose a 1×3 matrix A is used to specify the unit cost of apples, pears, and oranges as 20, 35, and 15 cents, respectively. Suppose that a 3×1 matrix is used to specify the number of each kind of fruit to be purchased. Then the matrix product $A \times B$ gives the total cost of the purchase. The equation

$$A \times B = [20 \ 35 \ 15] \times \begin{bmatrix} 3 \\ 4 \\ 7 \end{bmatrix} = 60 + 140 + 105 = 305$$

corresponds to the fact that the 3 apples, 4 pears, and 7 oranges will cost $3.05.

Lessons 1.10 – 1.11

DETERMINANTS Although the mathematical theory of determinants is too elaborate to be included in a high school course, it is possible to present the student with a first exposure to this important topic.

INVERSE MATRICES This lesson exposes the student to one of the most powerful tools from linear algebra, the **inverse matrix**. It is possible to challenge students to arrive at A^{-1} for themselves by solving the four equations in four unknowns corresponding to

$$\begin{bmatrix} a & b \\ c & d \end{bmatrix} \begin{bmatrix} x & y \\ y & w \end{bmatrix} = \begin{bmatrix} 1 & 0 \\ 0 & 1 \end{bmatrix}.$$

Lesson 1.12

Graph theory is a field of mathematics dealing with the properties of linear graphs. The term **vertex-edge graph** was first used in the NCTM standards to distinguish this type of graph, which is extremely useful in solving a wide array of problems.

Teaching Unit 1

1.1 Use Problem Solving Strategies and Models (pp. 2–3)

WARM-UP EXERCISES

Solve the equation.

1. $7x + 12 = 54$ **6**

2. $236 = 20g + 16(12 - g)$ **11**

KEY CONCEPT

Verbal models can be helpful when solving real-life problems. Some problem solving strategies that can be used to write verbal models are *use a formula*, *look for a pattern*, and *draw a diagram*.

QUESTIONS TO START THE LESSON

1. What are some of the strategies that you can use to help you solve a problem? **Students may name any of the following: use a formula, look for a pattern, draw a diagram, use a verbal model, make a list, work backward, solve a simpler problem, guess, check, and revise.**

2. Describe a situation in which the strategy you chose in Question 1 would be an appropriate method for solving a problem. **Answers will vary.**

COMMON STUDENT ERROR

Students may have trouble setting up or labeling a diagram. Remind students to reread the problem after drawing the diagram to make sure that the diagram accurately reflects the situation.

EXAMPLE **You cut a piece of ribbon into 3 pieces. The second piece is 3 inches longer than the first piece, and the third piece is 4 inches longer than the first piece. Draw a diagram to illustrate the situation.**

Common Error

Correct Answer

1.2 Solve Linear Systems by Graphing (pp. 6–7)

WARM-UP EXERCISES

1. Evaluate $3x + 4y$ when $x = -5$ and $y = 2$. **–7**

2. Write the equation $x - 2y = 14$ in slope-intercept form. $y = \frac{1}{2}x - 7$

KEY CONCEPT

Systems of two linear equations can be solved graphically, and the solutions can be checked algebraically. Depending on the number of solutions, a system is classified as consistent and dependent, consistent and independent, or inconsistent.

QUESTIONS TO START THE LESSON

1. When you graph two lines in the same coordinate plane, there are three possible scenarios relating to the intersection of the lines. What are they? **no intersection (parallel lines); one point of intersection; the lines coincide**

COMMON STUDENT ERROR

Some students may check the solution in only one of the equations in the system.

EXAMPLE Solve the system. $x + y = 3$
$2x - y = 6$

Common Error

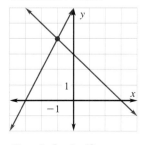

Check $(-1, 4)$:
$$x + y = 3$$
$$-4 + 7 = 3 ✓$$ ✗

Correct Answer

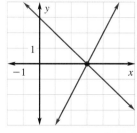

Check $(3, 0)$:
$$x + y = 3$$
$$3 + 0 = 3 ✓$$
$$2x - y = 6$$
$$2(3) - 0 = 6 ✓$$

Teaching Unit 1

1.3 Solve Linear Systems Algebraically (pp. 13–14)

WARM-UP EXERCISES

1. Solve the system by graphing. **Check graphs; (3, 1).**
$$x + y = 4$$
$$x + 3y = 6$$

KEY CONCEPT

Linear systems can be solved algebraically using either the substitution method or the elimination method. Linear systems can have one solution, no solution, or infinitely many solutions.

QUESTIONS TO START THE LESSON

1. Graph the lines $x - 2y = 12$ and $x + y = 7$ in the same coordinate plane. **Check graphs.**

2. Is it possible to tell the exact solution of the system from the graph in Question 1? Explain.
No; the lines intersect at a point with non-integer coordinates.

COMMON STUDENT ERROR

When using the elimination method, students forget to multiply each term of an equation by the constant.

EXAMPLE   **Solve the system using elimination.**
$$6x - 5y = 9$$
$$2x - 3y = 5$$

Common Error	Correct Answer
Multiply Eq. 2 by -3.	Multiply Eq. 2 by -3.
$6x - 5y = 9$	$6x - 5y = 9$
$-6x - 3y = 5$	$-6x + 9y = -15$
$-8y = 14;$	$4y = -6$
$y = -\dfrac{7}{4}$	$y = -\dfrac{3}{2}$
$6x - 5\left(-\dfrac{7}{4}\right) = 9$	$6x - 5\left(-\dfrac{3}{2}\right) = 9$
$6x + \dfrac{35}{4} = 9$	$6x + \dfrac{15}{2} = 9$
$6x = \dfrac{1}{4}; x = \dfrac{1}{24}$	$6x = \dfrac{3}{2}; x = \dfrac{1}{4}$
$\left(\dfrac{1}{24}, -\dfrac{7}{4}\right)$ ✗	$\left(\dfrac{1}{4}, -\dfrac{3}{2}\right)$

1.4 Graph Linear Inequalities in Two Variables (pp. 17–18)

WARM-UP EXERCISES

Tell whether the statement is true or false when $x = -3$ and $y = 6$.

1. $x - y > -7$ **false**   2. $x + 2y \le 15$ **true**

KEY CONCEPT

You can substitute a given ordered pair into an inequality to determine if the ordered pair is a solution. One-variable and two-variable inequalities can be graphed in a coordinate plane, and can be used to identify possible solutions.

QUESTIONS TO START THE LESSON

1. Graph $y = x$. For what four inequalities could you use this equation as a boundary line? **Check graphs; $y < x$, $y \le x$, $y > x$, $y \ge x$.**

2. Which of the inequalities in Question 1 have graphs with a solid boundary line? a dashed boundary line? What does a solid or dashed boundary line mean in terms of the solution set? **$y \le x$ and $y \ge x$; $y < x$ and $y > x$; the points on the solid line are included in the solution set, the points on the dashed line are not.**

3. Graph the inequality $y > 2x + 1$. Is the boundary line solid or dashed? How do you determine which side of the boundary line to shade? **Check graphs; dashed; if the coordinates of a test point make the inequality true, shade the side including the point. If not, shade the other side.**

COMMON STUDENT ERROR

When graphing an inequality, some students may not shade the correct half-plane.

EXAMPLE   **Graph the inequality $y > x + 2$.**

Common Error Correct Answer

1.5 Graph Systems of Linear Inequalities (pp. 23–24)

WARM-UP EXERCISES

1. Graph $y < x - 1$.　　**2.** Graph $y > |x|$.
1–2. **Check graphs.**

KEY CONCEPT

You can graph systems of two or more linear inequalities, including absolute value inequalities, to determine solutions. Systems have no solution if there is no region common to all graphs.

QUESTIONS TO START THE LESSON

1. Graph the inequality $2x + y > 9$. Choose a test point and check it in the inequality. Shade the correct region red. **Check graphs.**

2. On the same coordinate plane as above, graph the inequality $y \geq 0.5x - 2$. Which region will be included for this inequality? Shade the correct region blue. **Check graphs.**

3. Where do the common solution points lie? **in the region shaded both red and blue**

COMMON STUDENT ERROR

Students may have difficulty correctly identifying the solution set, especially when there are more than two inequalities in the system. If students do not have colored pencils, you can advise them to shade the correct regions using different sets of parallel lines.

EXAMPLE　**Graph the system of inequalities.**
$$y < -x + 3$$
$$x > 2$$
$$y \geq -2$$

Common Error　　Correct Answer

1.6 Linear Programming (pp. 30–31)

WARM-UP EXERCISES

1. Graph the system $y < 2$ and $x \leq 0$. **Check graph.**

KEY CONCEPT

Linear programming problems can be solved by graphing the constraint inequalities and using the vertices of the feasible region formed. The maximum and minimum values of the objective function each occur at a vertex of the feasible region.

QUESTIONS TO START THE LESSON

Consider the objective function $P = 2x + 3y$ and the constraints $x \geq 0$, $y \geq 0$, $x + y \leq 3$.

1. Graph the constraints in the same coordinate plane. Which integer ordered pairs adhere to the constraints? **Check graphs; (0, 0), (0, 1), (0, 2), (0, 3), (1, 0), (1, 1), (1, 2), (2, 0), (2, 1), (3, 0).**

2. Test each of the ordered pairs in the objective function. Which ordered pair maximizes the function? minimizes the function? How do these ordered pairs relate to the graph in Question 1? **(0, 3); (0, 0); They are vertices of the region.**

COMMON STUDENT ERROR

It is important that students answer the question being asked. Some students may complete the work, but incorrectly answer the question asked.

EXAMPLE　**What is the maximum value of the objective function $C = x + 2y$ for the given feasible region shown?**

Common Error
$(0, 5): C = 10$
$(1, 1): C = 3$
$(1, 6): C = 13$
The max.
value is $(1, 6)$.

Correct Answer
$(0, 5): C = 10$
$(1, 1): C = 3$
$(1, 6): C = 13$
The max.
value is 13.

Teaching Unit 1

1.7 Solve Systems of Linear Equations in Three Variables (pp. 34–35)

WARM-UP EXERCISES

1. Solve $5x + 2y = -9$ and $5x - 4y = 3$. **(−1, −2)**

KEY CONCEPT

Systems of equations in three variables can be solved using the elimination method or the substitution method. Three-variable systems have one solution, no solution, or infinitely many solutions.

QUESTIONS TO START THE LESSON

1. Draw a coordinate plane and stand a pencil up at the origin. This forms a 3-dimensional coordinate system, with the pencil as the z-axis. Where does the point lie? **Check models.**

a. $(1, 3, 0)$ **b.** $(1, 3, 1)$ **c.** $(1, 3, 2)$

COMMON STUDENT ERROR

Students may write an ordered triple not as (x, y, z), but in the order in which they solve for the variables.

EXAMPLE **Solve the system.** $x + y + z = 6$
$x + 2y - z = 10$
$-x + 3y + z = 10$

Student's Work

$$\begin{array}{r} x + y + z = 6 \\ x + 2y - z = 10 \\ \hline -y + 2z = -4 \end{array}$$

$$\begin{array}{r} x + y + z = 6 \\ -x + 3y + z = 10 \\ \hline 4y + 2z = 16 \end{array}$$

$$\begin{array}{r} -y + 2z = -4 \\ -4y - 2z = -16 \\ \hline -5y = -20 \\ y = 4 \end{array}$$

$$\begin{array}{r} -y + 2z = -4 \\ -4 + 2z = -4 \\ \hline 2z = 0 \\ z = 0 \end{array}$$

$$\begin{array}{r} x + y + z = 6 \\ x + 4 + 0 = 6 \\ \hline x = 2 \end{array}$$

Common Error
Solution: (4, 0, 2) ✗

Correct Answer
Solution: (2, 4, 0)

1.8 Perform Basic Matrix Operations (pp. 38–40)

WARM-UP EXERCISES

Identify the property of real numbers illustrated.

1. $(2 + 3) + (-1) = 2 + [3 + (-1)]$ **Associative prop.**

2. $-2(4x + 7) = -2(4x) + (-2)(7)$ **Distributive prop.**

KEY CONCEPT

Matrices are convenient tools for organizing data. If the two matrices have the same dimensions, they can be added or subtracted. Matrices can also be multiplied by a scalar.

QUESTIONS TO START THE LESSON

The table shows the average income for two summer jobs in 1995 and 2005.

	1995	2005
Lifeguard	$3840	$4800
Grass cutting	$4320	$5560

1. Organize the information into a matrix with 2 rows and 2 columns by writing the numbers in the same order in which they appear in the table. **Check matrices.**

2. What are some benefits of using a matrix instead of a table to organize the information? **A matrix allows you to perform operations using the data.**

COMMON STUDENT ERROR

Students may attempt to add matrices with different dimensions. Remind students to make sure that the matrices have the same dimensions before trying to add or subtract.

EXAMPLE **Add the matrices, if possible. If not possible, state the reason.**

$$\begin{bmatrix} 3 & -1 \\ -2 & 1 \end{bmatrix} + \begin{bmatrix} 1 \\ 4 \end{bmatrix}$$

Common Error

$$\begin{bmatrix} 3 & -1 \\ -2 & 1 \end{bmatrix} + \begin{bmatrix} 1 \\ 4 \end{bmatrix} = \begin{bmatrix} 4 & 0 \\ 2 & 5 \end{bmatrix} ✗$$

Correct Answer
Not possible; different dimensions

1.9 Multiply Matrices (pp. 43–45)

1. Multiply $-4\begin{bmatrix} 2 & -3 \\ -1 & -5 \end{bmatrix} \cdot \begin{bmatrix} -8 & 12 \\ 4 & 20 \end{bmatrix}$

KEY CONCEPT

You will find the product of matrices and perform matrix operations. Matrix multiplication can be used to solve real-life problems.

QUESTIONS TO START THE LESSON

The matrices below give the number of earrings *E* and necklaces *N* purchased by Sara and Kim, and purchase prices (in dollars) of the items.

$$\begin{array}{c} \quad E\ \ N \\ \begin{array}{c} \text{Sara} \\ \text{Kim} \end{array} \begin{bmatrix} 2 & 4 \\ 3 & 3 \end{bmatrix} \end{array} \quad \begin{array}{c} \text{Earings} \\ \text{Necklace} \end{array} \begin{bmatrix} 5 \\ 10 \end{bmatrix}$$

1. What is the total cost of Sara's purchases? **$50**

2. What is the total cost of Kim's purchases? **$45**

3. Write a matrix to represent the total costs of Sara and Kim's purchases. This matrix represents the product of the item matrix and the cost matrix. $\begin{bmatrix} 50 \\ 45 \end{bmatrix}$

COMMON STUDENT ERROR

When multiplying matrices with the same dimensions, some students may attempt to multiply corresponding entries.

EXAMPLE **Find the product:** $\begin{bmatrix} 1 & -4 \\ -3 & 2 \end{bmatrix}\begin{bmatrix} 0 & 2 \\ 1 & 5 \end{bmatrix}$

Common Error
$\begin{bmatrix} 1(0) & -4(2) \\ -3(1) & 2(5) \end{bmatrix}$ ✗

Correct Answer
$\begin{bmatrix} 1(0) - 4(1) & 1(2) - 4(5) \\ -3(0) + 2(1) & -3(2) + 2(5) \end{bmatrix}$
$= \begin{bmatrix} -4 & -18 \\ 2 & 4 \end{bmatrix}$

1.10 Evaluate Determinants and Apply Cramer's Rule (pp. 49–50)

1. Let $a = 2$, $b = -8$, $c = 3$, and $d = 5$. Find $ad - bc$.
34

KEY CONCEPT

You will evaluate the determinant of a matrix. Determinants can be used to find the area of an enclosed triangle. Cramer's rule can be used to solve linear systems and real-life problems.

QUESTIONS TO START THE LESSON

1. Explain how to find the determinant of $\begin{bmatrix} 2 & -3 \\ 4 & 5 \end{bmatrix}$.
Find the difference of the products 2(5) and 4(−3).

2. Do either of the products in Question 1 result in a negative number? Is the determinant negative? Can a determinant be negative? **yes; no; yes**

COMMON STUDENT ERROR

EXAMPLE **Use Cramer's rule to solve the system.** $\begin{aligned} y - x &= 9 \\ 2x + 3y &= 12 \end{aligned}$

Common Error
$\begin{vmatrix} 1 & -1 \\ 2 & 3 \end{vmatrix} = 3 - (-2)$
$= 5$

$x = \dfrac{\begin{vmatrix} 9 & -1 \\ 12 & 3 \end{vmatrix}}{5} = \dfrac{39}{5}$

$y = \dfrac{\begin{vmatrix} 1 & 9 \\ 2 & 12 \end{vmatrix}}{5} = -\dfrac{6}{5}$

Solution: $\left(\dfrac{39}{5}, -\dfrac{6}{5}\right)$ ✗

Correct Answer
Write in standard form:
$\begin{aligned} -x + y &= 9 \\ 2x + 3y &= 12 \end{aligned}$

$\begin{vmatrix} -1 & 1 \\ 2 & 3 \end{vmatrix} = -5$

$x = \dfrac{\begin{vmatrix} 9 & 1 \\ 12 & 3 \end{vmatrix}}{-5} = -3$

$y = \dfrac{\begin{vmatrix} -1 & 9 \\ 2 & 12 \end{vmatrix}}{-5} = 6$

Solution: $(-3, 6)$

Teaching Unit 1

1.11 Use Inverse Matrices to Solve Linear Systems (pp. 54–56)

WARM-UP EXERCISES

1. Find the product $\begin{bmatrix} 6 & -2 \\ -1 & 3 \end{bmatrix}\begin{bmatrix} 4 \\ -5 \end{bmatrix}$. $\begin{bmatrix} 34 \\ -19 \end{bmatrix}$

2. Find the determinant of $\begin{bmatrix} 12 & 6 \\ -5 & -3 \end{bmatrix}$. -6

KEY CONCEPT

A formula can be used to find the inverse of a matrix. Matrices and their inverses are used to solve matrix equations, linear systems, and multi-step problems.

QUESTIONS TO START THE LESSON

1. Explain what a multiplicative identity is. **The product of x and the multiplicative identity is x.**

2. If you multiply a matrix by the identity matrix, what result do you expect? **the original matrix**

3. Write any 2×2 matrix. Multiply the matrix by each of the matrices below. What are the results?
$\begin{bmatrix} 0 & 0 \\ 0 & 0 \end{bmatrix}$, $\begin{bmatrix} 1 & 1 \\ 1 & 1 \end{bmatrix}$, $\begin{bmatrix} 1 & 0 \\ 0 & 1 \end{bmatrix}$, $\begin{bmatrix} 0 & 1 \\ 1 & 0 \end{bmatrix}$ **Answers will vary.**

4. Which matrix is the identity matrix? Explain. $\begin{bmatrix} 1 & 0 \\ 0 & 1 \end{bmatrix}$; **the product of a 2×2 matrix and $\begin{bmatrix} 1 & 0 \\ 0 & 1 \end{bmatrix}$ is the original matrix.**

COMMON STUDENT ERROR

Students may have difficulty memorizing the formula for finding the inverse of a matrix. Remind them to multiply by $\frac{1}{\det}$, switch a and d, and change the signs of b and c.

EXAMPLE   Find the inverse of $\begin{bmatrix} 5 & 2 \\ 3 & 1 \end{bmatrix}$.

Common Error

$A^{-1} = \frac{1}{-1}\begin{bmatrix} 5 & 2 \\ 3 & 1 \end{bmatrix}$

$= \begin{bmatrix} -1 & -2 \\ -3 & -5 \end{bmatrix}$ ✗

Correct Answer

$A^{-1} = \frac{1}{-1}\begin{bmatrix} 1 & -2 \\ -3 & 5 \end{bmatrix}$

$= \begin{bmatrix} -1 & 2 \\ 3 & -5 \end{bmatrix}$

1.12 Use Vertex-Edge Graphs (pp. 59–60)

WARM-UP EXERCISES

1. Mark sells 2 large and 5 small tins of popcorn. Jacob sells 6 large and 4 small tins of popcorn. Organize the data using a matrix. **Sample answer:** $\begin{bmatrix} 2 & 5 \\ 6 & 4 \end{bmatrix}$

KEY CONCEPT

Vertex-edge graphs can be used to represent real-life situations. You can solve problems using matrices to represent vertex-edge graphs.

QUESTIONS TO START THE LESSON

1. What is the relationship between the vertex-edge graph and matrix below? **The matrix shows the number of edges between each pair of vertices.**

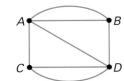

$\begin{array}{c} \\ A \\ B \\ C \\ D \end{array}\begin{array}{c} A\ B\ C\ D \\ \begin{bmatrix} 0 & 2 & 1 & 1 \\ 2 & 0 & 0 & 1 \\ 1 & 0 & 0 & 2 \\ 1 & 1 & 2 & 0 \end{bmatrix} \end{array}$

2. The matrix shown in Question 1 is symmetric about its main diagonal. Why is this true of all matrices representing vertex-edge graphs? **The entries repeat on either side of the main diagonal. The number of paths from A to B is the same as from B to A, and so on.**

COMMON STUDENT ERROR

Students may ignore multiple edges between vertices when writing a matrix for a vertex-edge graph.

EXAMPLE   Write a matrix to represent the vertex-edge graph.

Common Error

$\begin{array}{c} \\ A \\ B \\ C \end{array}\begin{array}{c} A\ B\ C \\ \begin{bmatrix} 0 & 1 & 1 \\ 1 & 0 & 1 \\ 1 & 1 & 0 \end{bmatrix} \end{array}$ ✗

Correct Answer

$\begin{array}{c} \\ A \\ B \\ C \end{array}\begin{array}{c} A\ B\ C \\ \begin{bmatrix} 0 & 1 & 3 \\ 1 & 0 & 1 \\ 3 & 1 & 0 \end{bmatrix} \end{array}$

Pacing and Assignment Guide

You can adapt any lesson's assignment by incorporating material from the @HomeTutor, Test Generator, Activity Generator, Notetaking Guide, and Assessment Book with Performance Tasks.

Lesson	Average Course	Advanced Course
Lesson 2.1	**Day 1:** p. 69, Exs. 1–7; p. 70, Exs. 1, 3 **Day 2:** p. 69, Exs. 8–16; p. 70, Exs. 5, 8, 11 **Day 3:** p. 69, Exs. 17–20; p. 70, Exs. 14, 15	**Day 1:** p. 69, Exs. 1, 4, 6; p. 70, Exs. 1–7 **Day 2:** p. 69, Exs. 8, 11, 14; p. 70, Exs. 8–13 **Day 3:** p. 69, Exs. 17, 18; p. 70, Exs. 14–18
Lesson 2.2	**Day 1:** p. 74, Exs. 1–11; p. 75, Exs. 1, 5, 8 **Day 2:** p. 74, Exs. 12–20; p. 75, Exs. 11, 14, 18	**Day 1:** p. 74, Exs. 4, 6, 9; p. 75, Exs. 1–10 **Day 2:** p. 74, Exs. 12, 15, 18; p. 75, Exs. 11–20
Lesson 2.3	**Day 1:** p. 78, Exs. 1–13; p. 79, Exs. 1, 2 **Day 2:** p. 78, Exs. 14–27; p. 79, Exs. 17, 18 **Day 3:** p. 80, Exs. 1–3	**Day 1:** p. 78, Exs. 1, 2, 7, 11; p. 79, Exs. 1–16 **Day 2:** p. 78, Exs. 14, 20; p. 79, Exs. 17–30 **Day 3:** p. 80, Exs. 1–3
Lesson 2.4	**Day 1:** p. 83, Exs. 1–12; p. 84, Exs. 1, 2 **Day 2:** p. 83, Exs. 13–21; p. 84, Exs. 13, 14 **Day 3:** Assessment Book (pp. 12–14)	**Day 1:** p. 83, Exs. 1–3; p. 84, Exs. 1–12 **Day 2:** p. 83, Exs. 10–12; p. 84, Exs. 13–22 **Day 3:** Assessment Book (pp. 12–14)
Lesson 2.5	**Day 1:** p. 87, Exs. 1–8; p. 88, Exs. 1, 2 **Day 2:** p. 87, Exs. 9–18; p. 88, Exs. 5, 9 **Day 3:** p. 87, Exs. 19–26; p. 88, Ex. 13	**Day 1:** p. 87, Exs. 1–3; p. 88, Exs. 1–6 **Day 2:** p. 87, Exs. 7–9, 13, 14; p. 88, Exs. 7–12 **Day 3:** p. 87, Exs. 19, 20; p. 88, Exs. 13–16
Lesson 2.6	**Day 1:** p. 91, Exs. 1–8; p. 92, Exs. 1, 2 **Day 2:** p. 91, Exs. 9–15; p. 92, Exs. 3, 4	**Day 1:** p. 91, Exs. 1, 2, 9, 10; p. 92, Exs. 1–6 **Day 2:** p. 91, Exs. 11, 12; p. 92, Exs. 7–13
Lesson 2.7	**Day 1:** p. 93, Exs. 1, 2 **Day 2:** p. 96, Exs. 1–10; p. 97, Exs. 1, 2 **Day 3:** p. 96, Exs. 11–17; p. 97, Exs. 9, 10 **Day 4:** p. 96, Exs. 18–23; p. 97, Exs. 19, 20	**Day 1:** p. 93, Exs. 1, 2 **Day 2:** p. 96, Exs. 1, 2, 5, 6; p. 97, Exs. 1–8 **Day 3:** p. 96, Exs. 11, 12; p. 97, Exs. 9–18 **Day 4:** p. 96, Ex. 18; p. 97, Exs. 19–25
Lesson 2.8	**Day 1:** p. 100, Exs. 1–19; p. 102, Exs. 3, 4 **Day 2:** p. 100, Exs. 20–28; p. 102, Exs. 9, 10, 17 **Day 3:** p. 101, Exs. 29–38; p. 102, Ex. 20 **Day 4:** p. 104, Exs. 1–6 **Day 5:** Assessment Book (pp. 15–17)	**Day 1:** p. 100, Exs. 2, 3, 8, 9; p. 102, Exs. 1–8 **Day 2:** p. 100, Exs. 20, 21, 26; p. 102, Exs. 9–25 **Day 3:** p. 103, Exs. 26–34 **Day 4:** p. 104, Exs. 1–6 **Day 5:** Assessment Book (pp. 15–17)
Review and Assess	**Day 1:** Review **Day 2:** Review **Day 3:** Review **Day 4:** Unit Test	**Day 1:** Review **Day 2:** Review **Day 3:** Review **Day 4:** Unit Test
	Unit 2 Total—29 days	Units 1–2 Total—66 days Remaining—94 days

Block Schedule When teaching this unit in a block schedule, you can treat each day in the pacing and assignment guide as half of a block period.

Unit 2 Mathematical Background Notes

Lessons 2.1 – 2.2

Consider the function $f(x) = a_n x^n + a_{n-1} x^{n-1} + \cdots + a_1 x + a_0$. The **degree of the polynomial** is n. For a given value of n the "end behavior" of the graph of such a function is still determined by the leading term a_n. In particular, the end behavior of the graph of $f(x)$ is the same as the end behavior of the graph of $a_n x^n$.

To obtain insight into why this is so, we can rewrite the function as

$$f(x) = a_n x^n \left(1 + \frac{a_{n-1}}{a_n} \cdot \frac{1}{x} + \frac{a_{n-2}}{a_n} \cdot \frac{1}{x^2} + \cdots + \frac{a_0}{a_n} \cdot \frac{1}{x_n} \right).$$

Except for the leading term 1, all the terms inside the parentheses become arbitrarily small in absolute value as $|x|$ becomes large. As a result, for sufficiently large values of $|x|$, the value of the expression within the parentheses will be close to 1. For such values of x, if $a_n x^n$ assumes arbitrarily large positive values, so will $f(x)$. If $a_n x^n$ assumes negative values of arbitrarily large magnitude, so will $f(x)$.

Lessons 2.3 – 2.5

FACTORING POLYNOMIALS Factoring polynomials is a logical extension of factoring quadratics. Students will factor polynomials completely using techniques learned in previous courses, plus the sum and difference of cubes, polynomial long division, synthetic division, and the factor theorem.

SOLVING POLYNOMIAL EQUATIONS Polynomial equations can be solved by first factoring and then using the zero product property.

SOLVING POLYNOMIAL INEQUALITIES This may be the first time that students have seen interval notation. Interval notation is an efficient method for writing a solution set. In this notation, there are only five symbols to know: open parentheses ( ), closed parentheses [ ], infinity ∞, negative infinity $-\infty$, and the union sign $\cup$. For simplicity, the use of the union sign has been replaced by "and" in the lesson.

Lessons 2.6 – 2.7

Consider the **rational root theorem** in a quadratic context. Let $ax^2 + bx + c = 0$, where a, b, and c are integers. If $x = \dfrac{p}{q}$ is in lowest terms, then

$$a \cdot \frac{p^2}{q^2} + b \cdot \frac{p}{q} + c = 0 \text{ Multiply by } q^2 \text{ to obtain}$$

$ap^2 + bpq + cq^2 = 0$. The sum of the first two terms is divisible by p: $ap^2 + bpq = p(ap + bq)$ and this implies that cq^2 is divisible by p as well. Because $\dfrac{p}{q}$ is in lowest terms, p and q have no common divisors other than 1. This means that when p and q are factored into primes, there is no overlap between prime factors of p and of q. As a result, all of the prime factors of p have to be "accounted for" by c: the only way cq^2 can be divisible by p is for c to be divisible by p. Therefore p is a factor of c. By an argument analogous to the one above, we can conclude that a is divisible by q. This argument carries over to equations of degree n with only minor modifications.

The **fundamental theorem of algebra** states that if $f(x)$ is a polynomial of degree n where $n > 0$, then the equation $f(x) = 0$ has at least one solution in the set of complex numbers. A corollary to the theorem states that $f(x)$ has exactly n solutions.

Lesson 2.8

For a polynomial function $f(x)$, consider the effect of multiplicity of roots on the graph of the function. Let $f(x) = q(x) \cdot (x - a)^k$, where the **multiplicity of root** a is k. For large values of k, the factor $(x - a)^k$ will be very small within 1 unit of a, which means that the graph will be flat in the interval $(a - 1, a + 1)$. If k is 1 or 2, the flatness of the graph will be limited to a small interval about a. When k is even, the factor $(x - a)^k$ is nonnegative, so the graph is tangent to the x-axis at a. When k is odd, the graph crosses the x-axis at a, even though it may be quite flat.

Teaching Unit 2

2.1 Evaluate and Graph Polynomial Functions (pp. 66–68)

WARM-UP EXERCISES

Evaluate the expression when $x = -7$.

1. $x^2 + 6x$ **7**   **2.** $3x^2 - 4x + 5$ **180**

KEY CONCEPT

Polynomial functions can be identified by the degree of the polynomial and evaluated using either direct substitution or synthetic substitution. The end behavior of the function and a table of values can be used to graph polynomial functions.

QUESTIONS TO START THE LESSON

1. What is the standard form of a linear equation? What is its degree? How many turning points does a linear function have? **$Ax + By = C$; 1; 0**

2. What is the standard form of a quadratic equation? What is its degree? How many turning points does a quadratic function have? **$ax^2 + bx + c = 0$, where $a \neq 0$; 2; 1**

3. What do you think will happen to a graph as the degree of the polynomial function increases? **The number of turning points increases.**

COMMON STUDENT ERROR

When using synthetic substitution, students may forget to write zeros for the missing terms of a polynomial.

> EXAMPLE   Use synthetic substitution to evaluate $f(x) = x^4 + 3x^2 - 5$ when $x = 2$.
>
> Common Error
>
> ```
> 2 | 1    3   -5
>   |      2   10
>     1    5    5
> ```
> $f(2) = 5$ ✗
>
> Correct Answer
>
> ```
> 2 | 1    0    3    0   -5
>   |      2    4   14   28
>     1    2    7   14   23
> ```
> $f(2) = 23$

2.2 Translate Graphs of Polynomial Functions (pp. 71–73)

WARM-UP EXERCISES

Graph the polynomial function.

1. $f(x) = -x^4 + 2$ **2.** $g(x) = x^3 - 3$
Check graphs.

KEY CONCEPT

Simple polynomial functions can be graphed as vertical and horizontal translations of parent functions.

QUESTIONS TO START THE LESSON

1. Graph $y = x^3$. **Check graphs.**

2. Use a table of values to graph the function. How does the graph compare with that of $y = x^3$?

  a. $y = (x - 2)^3$ **Graph of $y = x^3$ translated 2 units to the right.**

  b. $y = x^3 + 5$ **Graph of $y = x^3$ translated 5 units up.**

  c. $y = (x - 2)^3 + 5$ **Graph of $y = x^3$ translated 2 units to the right and 5 units up.**

  d. Make a conjecture about how h and k affect the graph of $y = (x - h)^3 + k$. **The value of h moves the graph of $y = x^3$ horizontally and the value of k moves the graph vertically.**

COMMON STUDENT ERROR

Some students may be confused about the effects of h and k on the graph of a polynomial function.

> EXAMPLE   Write an equation for a function $g(x)$ whose graph is the graph of $f(x) = x^5$ translated 4 units to the right and 3 units down.
>
> Common Error   Correct Answer
>
> $g(x) = (x + 4)^5 - 3$ ✗ $g(x) = (x - 4)^5 - 3$

Teaching Unit 2

2.3 Factor and Solve Polynomial Equations (pp. 76–77)

WARM-UP EXERCISES

Multiply the polynomials.

1. $(x + 1)(x + 5)$ $x^2 + 6x + 5$

2. $(3x - 1)(3x + 1)$ $9x^2 - 1$

3. $(x - 9)^2$ $x^2 - 18x + 81$

KEY CONCEPT

Polynomials can be factored using several techniques including factoring by finding a common monomial factor, factoring using the sum or difference of two cubes, and factoring by grouping. The zero product property can be used to solve some higher degree polynomial equations.

QUESTIONS TO START THE LESSON

1. Rewrite the equation $x(x - 2)(x + 8) = 96$ in standard form $(ax^3 + bx^2 + cx + d = 0)$.
$x^3 + 6x^2 - 16x - 96 = 0$

2. Factor the $ax^3 + bx^2$ part of your equation. What is the result? Then factor the $cx + d$ part of your equation. What is the result? What similarity do you notice? $x^3 + 6x^2 = x^2(x + 6)$; $-16x - 96 = -16(x + 6)$; **both have a factor of $(x + 6)$.**

3. Use your answer from Question 2 to write the equation from Question 1 in factored form. What three solutions do you get from the factors?
$(x + 6)(x + 4)(x - 4)$ 5 0; $-6, -4, 4$

COMMON STUDENT ERROR

Some students stop factoring before a polynomial is fully factored. Remind students to examine their answers for expressions that may be factorable.

EXAMPLE Factor $4x^3 - 4xy^2$.

Common Error	Correct Answer
$4x^3 - 4xy^2$	$4x^3 - 4xy^2$
$= 4x(x^2 - y^2)$ ✗	$= 4x(x^2 - y^2)$
	$= 4x(x + y)(x - y)$

2.4 Solve Polynomial Inequalities (pp. 81–82)

WARM-UP EXERCISES

Solve the equation.

1. $x^3 + x^2 = 2x$ $-2, 0, 1$ **2.** $x^3 + x^2 = 9x + 9$ $-3, -1, 3$

KEY CONCEPT

Polynomial inequalities can be solved algebraically or graphically. To solve a polynomial inequality algebraically, solve the corresponding equation and test a point in each resulting interval to see if it satisfies the inequality. To solve a polynomial inequality graphically, graph the corresponding polynomial function and see where the function is above and below the x-axis.

QUESTIONS TO START THE LESSON

1. Graph the polynomial function $y = 2x^3 + 9x^2 - 5x$ and identify the x-intercepts. **Check graphs; $-5, 0, \frac{1}{2}$**

2. For what values of x is the value of the function less than 0? How does your answer relate to the inequality $2x^3 + 9x^2 - 5x < 0$? $x < -5$ and $0 < x < \frac{1}{2}$; **it is the solution of the inequality.**

3. For what values of x is the value of the function greater than 0? How does your answer relate to the inequality $2x^3 + 9x^2 - 5x > 0$? $-5 < x < 0$ and $x > \frac{1}{2}$; **it is the solution of the inequality.**

COMMON STUDENT ERROR

Students may have difficulty with the use of parentheses and brackets in interval notation.

EXAMPLE The graph of the solution set of $x(x - 2)(x + 3) \geq 0$ is shown. Write the solution set using interval notation.

Common Error	Correct Answer
$(-3, 0)$ and $[2, \infty)$ ✗	$[-3, 0]$ and $[2, \infty)$

2.5 Apply the Remainder and Factor Theorems (pp. 85–86)

WARM-UP EXERCISES

1. Use synthetic substitution to evaluate
$f(x) = x^3 - x^2 + 3x - 9$ when $x = -1$. **−14**

KEY CONCEPT

Polynomial long division and synthetic division are two techniques used to divide polynomials. The factor theorem can be used to factor polynomials and find the zeros of polynomials.

QUESTIONS TO START THE LESSON

1. Use long division to divide 3105 by 12. What is the dividend? the divisor? the quotient? the remainder? **3105; 12; 258; 9**

2. How can you use multiplication to check the result of division? **The product of the quotient and divisor plus the remainder gives you the dividend.**

3. Will the method described in Question 2 work if the dividend and divisor are polynomials instead of constants? **yes**

COMMON STUDENT ERROR

Remind students that when using synthetic division, they must write the *opposite* of the constant term of the divisor.

EXAMPLE Divide $x^4 + 3x^2 - x - 3$ by $x + 2$.

Common Error

```
2 |  1   0   3   -1   -3
   |      2   4   14   26
     1   2   7   13   23
```

$x^3 + 2x^2 + 7x + 13 + \dfrac{23}{x + 2}$ ✗

Correct Answer

```
-2 |  1   0   3   -1   -3
   |     -2   4  -14   30
      1  -2   7  -15   27
```

$x^3 - 2x^2 + 7x - 15 + \dfrac{27}{x + 2}$

2.6 Find Rational Zeros (pp. 89–90)

WARM-UP EXERCISES

1. Factor $2x^2 + x - 3$. **$(2x + 3)(x - 1)$**

2. Use synthetic division to divide $x^3 + x^2 - 8x - 12$ by $(x + 2)$. **$x^2 - x - 6$**

KEY CONCEPT

The rational zero theorem is used to list the possible rational zeros of polynomial functions. Actual zeros can be found by testing the possible rational zeros using synthetic division and sketching the graph of the function to help choose values of zero to test.

QUESTIONS TO START THE LESSON

1. What are the degree and the leading coefficient of the equation $7x^2 + 20x - 3 = 0$? Factor the left side of the equation. Then identify the solutions. **$(7x - 1)(x + 3); \dfrac{1}{7}$ and −3**

2. Why are the x-intercepts of the graph of a function also called the zeros of the function? What are the zeros of the $f(x) = 7x^2 + 20x - 3$? **The x-intercepts of the graph are the x-values for which the y-values are zero; $\dfrac{1}{7}$ and −3**

COMMON STUDENT ERROR

When listing possible rational zeros, it is important to simplify fractions and eliminate duplicates.

EXAMPLE List all the values you would have to check to determine the rational zeros of $f(x) = 6x^3 - 5x^2 + 20x + 4$.

Common Error

Values to check:

$\pm\dfrac{1}{1}, \pm\dfrac{2}{1}, \pm\dfrac{4}{1}, \pm\dfrac{1}{2},$

$\pm\dfrac{2}{2}, \pm\dfrac{4}{2}, \pm\dfrac{1}{3}, \pm\dfrac{2}{3},$

$\pm\dfrac{4}{3}, \pm\dfrac{1}{6}, \pm\dfrac{2}{6}, \pm\dfrac{4}{6}$

Correct Answer

Values to check:

$\pm 1, \pm 2, \pm 4, \pm\dfrac{1}{2},$

$\pm\dfrac{1}{3}, \pm\dfrac{2}{3}, \pm\dfrac{4}{3}, \pm\dfrac{1}{6}$

Teaching Unit 2

2.7 Apply the Fundamental Theorem of Algebra (pp. 94–95)

WARM-UP EXERCISES

1. What is the degree of $f(x) = 6x^5 + 2x + 14$? **5**

2. Solve $x^2 - 4x + 7$. **$2 \pm i\sqrt{3}$**

KEY CONCEPT

The fundamental theorem of algebra can be used to determine the number of solutions of an equation. Descartes' rule of signs can be used to determine the possible number of positive, negative, and imaginary zeros of a function.

QUESTIONS TO START THE LESSON

1. If the discriminant is less than zero, how many and what type of solutions does a quadratic equation have? **two imaginary solutions**

2. What is a complex conjugate? Find the product of $\left(5 - i\sqrt{3}\right)$ and $\left(5 + i\sqrt{3}\right)$. **Complex numbers of the form $(a + bi)$ and $(a - bi)$ are complex conjugates; 28.**

COMMON STUDENT ERROR

When applying Descartes' rule of signs, students may have trouble calculating $f(-x)$. Remind students that $(-x)^n = x^n$ when n is even and $(-x)^n = -x^n$ when n is odd.

EXAMPLE Determine the possible numbers of positive real zeros and negative real zeros of the function $f(x) = x^6 - x^5 + x - 2$.

Common Error

$f(x)$: 3 sign changes in coefficients, so 3 or 1 positive real zero(s). $f(-x)$: $-x^6 + x^5 - x + 2$; 3 sign changes in coefficients, so 3 or 1 negative real zero(s). ✗

Correct Answer

$f(x)$: 3 sign changes in coefficients, so 3 or 1 positive real zero(s). $f(-x)$: $x^6 + x^5 - x + 2$; 1 sign change in coefficients, so 1 negative real zero.

2.8 Analyze Graphs of Polynomial Functions (pp. 98–99)

WARM-UP EXERCISES

1. Find the product $(x + 3)(2x + 1)$. **$2x^2 + 7x + 3$**

KEY CONCEPT

The x-intercepts of a polynomial function, a table of values, and the end behavior of the function can be used to graph the function. The turning points of a graph occur at the local minimums and local maximums of the function.

QUESTIONS TO START THE LESSON

1. A point on the graph of a polynomial function is a *turning point* if it is higher or lower than all of the nearby points on the graph. What are the turning points of the graph? **(0, 3) and (1, 1)**

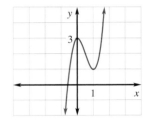

2. Use a graphing calculator to find the turning point(s) of the graph of $y = x^2 - 4x - 12$. **(2, −16)**

COMMON STUDENT ERROR

Students may erroneously believe that a polynomial function of degree n has exactly $(n - 1)$ turning points. Remind students that this is true only if a function also has n real zeros.

EXAMPLE Determine the number of turning points of the function $f(x) = x^4 - x^3 + 2x^2 + 2x - 4$.

Common Error

The degree of f is 4, so there are $4 - 1$, or 3 turning points. ✗

Correct Answer

There is 1 turning point.

Pacing and Assignment Guide

You can adapt any lesson's assignment by incorporating material from the @HomeTutor, Test Generator, Activity Generator, Notetaking Guide, and Assessment Book with Performance Tasks.

Lesson	Average Course	Advanced Course
Lesson 3.1	**Day 1:** p. 108, Exs. 1–5 **Day 2:** p. 111, Exs. 1–21; p. 112, Exs. 1, 4, 7–9 **Day 3:** p. 111, Exs. 22–36; p. 112, Exs. 25–27	**Day 1:** p. 108, Exs. 1–5 **Day 2:** p. 111, Exs. 1–3, 7–9, 13–15; p. 112, Exs. 1–15 **Day 3:** p. 111, Exs. 22–24, 32–34; p. 112, Exs. 16–36
Lesson 3.2	**Day 1:** p. 115, Exs. 1–12; p. 116, Exs. 1–3 **Day 2:** p. 115, Exs. 13–24; p. 116, Exs. 10–12 **Day 3:** p. 115, Exs. 25–35; p. 116, Exs. 20, 21 **Day 4:** p. 117, Exs. 1–4 **Day 5:** Assessment Book (pp. 23–25)	**Day 1:** p. 115, Exs. 1–3; p. 116, Exs. 1–9 **Day 2:** p. 115, Exs. 13–15; p. 116, Exs. 10–18 **Day 3:** p. 115, Exs. 25, 26; p. 116, Exs. 19–27 **Day 4:** p. 117, Exs. 1–4 **Day 5:** Assessment Book (pp. 23–25)
Lesson 3.3	**Day 1:** p. 120, Exs. 1–9; p. 121, Exs. 1, 2 **Day 2:** p. 120, Exs. 10–17; p. 121, Exs. 7, 8	**Day 1:** p. 120, Exs. 1, 2, 7, 8; p. 121, Exs. 1–10 **Day 2:** p. 120, Exs. 13, 14; p. 121, Exs. 11–20
Lesson 3.4	**Day 1:** p. 124, Exs. 1–12; p. 125, Exs. 1–3 **Day 2:** p. 124, Exs. 13–24; p. 125, Exs. 7, 8, 13, 14 **Day 3:** p. 124, Exs. 25–35; p. 125, Exs. 19, 20 **Day 4:** p. 126, Exs. 1–6 **Day 5:** Assessment Book (pp. 26–28)	**Day 1:** p. 124, Exs. 1–3; p. 125, Exs. 1–12 **Day 2:** p. 124, Exs. 19, 20; p. 125, Exs. 13–22 **Day 3:** p. 124, Exs. 25, 26; p. 125, Exs. 23–30 **Day 4:** p. 126, Exs. 1–6 **Day 5:** Assessment Book (pp. 26–28)
Review and Assess	**Day 1:** Review **Day 2:** Review **Day 3:** Review **Day 4:** Unit Test	**Day 1:** Review **Day 2:** Review **Day 3:** Review **Day 4:** Unit Test
Unit 3 Total—19 days	**Units 1–3 Total—85 days**	**Remaining—75 days**

Block Schedule When teaching this unit in a block schedule, you can treat each day in the pacing and assignment guide as half of a block period.

Unit 3 Mathematical Background Notes

Lesson 3.1

We will use the rule $a^m \cdot a^n = a^{m+n}$ as a basis for defining $a^{p/q}$, where p and q are positive integers. First consider the case of $a^{1/q}$:

$$\underbrace{a^{1/q} \cdot a^{1/q} \cdot \cdots \cdot a^{1/q}}_{q \text{ terms}} = \underbrace{a^{1/q + 1/q + \cdots + 1/q}}_{q \text{ terms}} = a^1 = a$$

Since this property also characterizes "the **q th root** of a," we are led to define $a^{1/q}$ as $\sqrt[q]{a}$.

When q is even (in the absence of complex numbers), we require that $a \geq 0$ and interpret $\sqrt[q]{a}$ as the *nonnegative q th root of a*. When q is odd, the number a has only one real q th root.

Now consider $a^{p/q}$:

$$\underbrace{a^{p/q} \cdot a^{p/q} \cdot \cdots \cdot a^{p/q}}_{q \text{ terms}} = \underbrace{a^{p/q + p/q + \cdots + p/q}}_{q \text{ terms}} = a^p$$

This makes it natural to define $a^{p/q}$ as $\sqrt[q]{a^p}$.

We are also led to

$$\underbrace{a^{1/q} \cdot a^{1/q} \cdot a^{1/q} \cdot \cdots \cdot a^{1/q}}_{p \text{ terms}} = (a^{1/q})^p = (\sqrt[q]{a})^p.$$

Fortunately, when $a \geq 0$, it is the case that $\sqrt[q]{a^p} = (\sqrt[q]{a})^p$ for all positive integers p and q.

Lesson 3.2

The commutative and associative properties of multiplication imply that for any positive integer n and real numbers a and b:

$$\underbrace{(ab)(ab) \ldots (ab)}_{n \text{ terms}} = \underbrace{(aaa \ldots)}_{n \text{ terms}}\underbrace{(bbb \ldots)}_{n \text{ terms}}$$

This shows that when n is a positive integer,

$$(ab)^n = a^n \cdot b^n.$$

On this basis students may be tempted to assume that

$$(ab)^{p/q} = a^{p/q} \cdot b^{p/q}.$$

In fact, however, the above identity may fail unless a and b are *nonnegative*. One way to emphasize this fact is to show how a failure to observe this requirement can lead to a "proof" that $-1 = 1$.

$$-1 = (-1)^{1/2}(-1)^{1/2} = [(-1)(-1)]^{1/2} = 1^{1/2} = 1$$

Lesson 3.3

Consider the problem of finding the inverse of $f(x) = a\sqrt{x - h} + k$ where $a > 0$ and $x \geq h$. Solving $y = a\sqrt{x - h} + k$ for x leads to $x = \left(\dfrac{y - k}{a}\right)^2 + h$. Interchanging the variables x and y now leads to a formula for the inverse of f, namely

$$g(x) = \left(\frac{y - k}{a}\right)^2 + h.$$

Here it is important to recall that the domain of the inverse function g is precisely the range of the original function f. Since a was assumed to be positive, the range of $f(x) = a\sqrt{x - h} + k$ is given by $x \geq h$, and this is the domain of the inverse function g given above. Failure to specify the domain of g might lead us to an inverse of $y = \pm a\sqrt{x - h} + k$ rather than the original function f.

Lesson 3.4

In the process of solving **radical equations**, a mechanistic application of algebraic rules can lead to **extraneous solutions**. For example, in solving $x = 4 + \sqrt{2x}$, a natural first step after getting the radical expression alone on one side, is to square both sides of the equation to obtain $x^2 - 8x + 16 = 2x$, then solve by factoring: $x = 2$ or $x = 8$. To see why the extraneous root $x = 2$ arises, solve the equation $x = 4 - \sqrt{2x}$, where the expressions $4 + \sqrt{2x}$ and $4 - \sqrt{2x}$ are **radical conjugates**. The same quadratic equation, $x^2 - 8x + 16 = 2x$, arises. Now $x = 2$ *is* a solution of the equation to be solved and $x = 8$ is an extraneous solution.

Teaching Unit 3

 Evaluate nth Roots and Use Rational Exponents (pp. 109–110)

WARM-UP EXERCISES

Evaluate without using a calculator.

1. $\sqrt{169}$ **13**   **2.** 3^{-3}. $\frac{1}{27}$

3. Solve $(x-4)^2 = 30$. **4 ± $\sqrt{30}$**

KEY CONCEPT

You will find the *n*th root of a real number, evaluate expressions with rational exponents, and approximate roots with a calculator.

QUESTIONS TO START THE LESSON

1. The volume of a cube with a side length of x is 64 cubic inches. Use trial and error to find a number whose cube is 64. What is the side length of the cube? **4 in.**

2. The volume of a cube with a side length of x is 43 cubic inches. Use trial and error to find a number whose cube is approximately 43. What is the approximate side length of the cube? **3.5 in.**

3. Use the $\sqrt[3]{\ }$ operation on your graphing calculator to find the side length of the cube in Question 3. Compare the result with your answer in Question 3. **3.50339806; rounds to 3.5.**

COMMON STUDENT ERROR

When evaluating expressions with rational exponents, students may mistakenly interchange the numerator and denominator of the exponent.

EXAMPLE **Evaluate the expression $64^{2/3}$.**

Common Error
$64^{2/3} = (\sqrt{64})^3$
$= 8^3$
$= 512$ ✗

Correct Answer
$64^{2/3} = (\sqrt[3]{64})^2$
$= 4^2$
$= 16$

3.2 **Apply Properties of Rational Exponents** (pp. 113–114)

WARM-UP EXERCISES

Simplify the expression.

1. $3^3 \cdot 3^4$ 3^7 **2.** $\frac{6^4}{6^{-2}}$ 6^6 **3.** $\sqrt{60}$ $2\sqrt{15}$

KEY CONCEPT

The properties of rational exponents and radicals can be used to simplify, add, and subtract expressions involving variables.

QUESTIONS TO START THE LESSON

1. How do you simplify $(m^4)^5$? What is the result? What property allows you to do this? **Multiply the exponents; m^{20}; power of a power property.**

2. Write the power $(m^{3/4})^4$ as an expression using repeated multiplication. Simplify the result. $(m^{3/4})(m^{3/4})(m^{3/4})(m^{3/4}) = m^{3/4 + 3/4 + 3/4 + 3/4} = m^3$

3. Write the power $(p^{1/2})^3$ as an expression using repeated multiplication. Simplify the result. $(p^{1/2})(p^{1/2})(p^{1/2}) = p^{1/2 + 1/2 + 1/2} = p^{3/2}$

4. Make a conjecture about the power of a power property of rational exponents. $(a^m)^n = a^{mn}$

COMMON STUDENT ERROR

When simplifying expressions involving radicals, students must multiply both the numerator and denominator of the expression by the same value.

EXAMPLE **Simplify $\sqrt[4]{\dfrac{x^7}{y^9}}$.**

Common Error
$\sqrt[4]{\dfrac{x^7}{y^9}} = \sqrt[4]{\dfrac{x^7}{y^9 \cdot y^3}}$

$= \dfrac{x\sqrt[4]{x^3}}{y^3}$ ✗

Correct Answer
$\sqrt[4]{\dfrac{x^7}{y^9}} = \sqrt[4]{\dfrac{x^7 \cdot y^3}{y^9 \cdot y^3}}$

$= \dfrac{x\sqrt[4]{x^3 y^3}}{y^3}$

Teaching Unit 3

3·3 Graph Square Root and Cube Root Functions (pp. 118–119)

WARM-UP EXERCISES

State the domain and range of the function.

1. $f(x) = 3x + 2$ **domain and range: all real numbers**

2. $g(x) = -3x^2 - 1$ **domain: all real numbers; range:** $y \leq -1$

KEY CONCEPT

The parent functions, $y = \sqrt{x}$ and $y = \sqrt[3]{x}$, can be used to graph square root and cube root functions.

QUESTIONS TO START THE LESSON

1. In the same viewing window, graph $y = x^2$ and $y = (x - 3)^2 - 2$. Compare the two graphs. **The graph of** $y = (x - 3)^2 - 2$ **is the graph of** $y = x^2$ **shifted 3 units to the right and 2 units down.**

2. In the same viewing window, graph $y = \sqrt{x}$ and $y = \sqrt{x - 3} - 2$. Compare the two graphs. **The graph of** $y = \sqrt{x - 3} - 2$ **is the graph of** $y = x^2$ **shifted 3 units to the right and 2 units down.**

3. Using what you know about quadratic functions, make a conjecture about the affect of h and k on the graph of $y = \sqrt{x - h} + k$. **h moves the graph horizontally and k moves the graph vertically.**

COMMON STUDENT ERROR

When graphing square root and cube root functions, some students may shift the parent graph horizontally in the wrong direction.

EXAMPLE **Graph** $y = \sqrt{x + 3} - 1$.

Common Error
Shift $y = \sqrt{x}$ to the right 3 units and down 1 unit.

Correct Answer
Shift $y = \sqrt{x}$ to the left 3 units and down 1 unit.

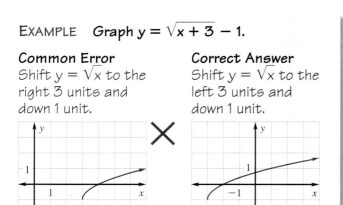

3·4 Solve Radical Equations (pp. 122–123)

WARM-UP EXERCISES

In Exercises 1 and 2, evaluate the expression.

1. $27^{4/3}$ **81**

2. $(-243)^{3/5}$ **−27**

3. Expand $(x + 2)^2$. **$x^2 + 4x + 4$**

4. Solve the equation $x^2 + 9x + 10 = x - 2$. **−2, −6**

KEY CONCEPT

To solve a radical equation, isolate the radical, raise each side of the equation to a power, and solve the resulting equation.

QUESTIONS TO START THE LESSON

In Exercises 1–4, simplify the expression.

1. $\sqrt{90}$ **$3\sqrt{10}$**

2. $\sqrt{2} \cdot \sqrt{54}$ **$6\sqrt{3}$**

3. $\sqrt{\dfrac{3x^2}{16y^2}}$ **$\dfrac{x\sqrt{3}}{4y}$**

4. $\sqrt{\dfrac{25x^3}{6y}}$ **$\dfrac{5x\sqrt{6xy}}{6y}$**

Solve the equation by completing the square.

5. $x^2 + 2x - 9 = 0$ **$-1 \pm \sqrt{10}$**

6. $x^2 - 12x + 28 = 0$ **$-6 \pm 2\sqrt{2}$**

COMMON STUDENT ERROR

Students may attempt to raise both sides of an equation to the same power before isolating the radical.

EXAMPLE **Solve** $\sqrt{4x - 7} + 2 = 5$.

Common Error

$$\sqrt{4x - 7} + 2 = 5$$
$$(\sqrt{4x - 7} + 2)^2 = 5^2$$
$$4x - 7 + 4 = 25$$
$$4x = 28$$
$$x = 7 \quad \times$$

Correct Answer

$$\sqrt{4x - 7} + 2 = 5$$
$$\sqrt{4x - 7} = 3$$
$$(\sqrt{4x - 7})^2 = 3^2$$
$$4x - 7 = 9$$
$$4x = 16$$
$$x = 4$$

Pacing and Assignment Guide

You can adapt any lesson's assignment by incorporating material from the @HomeTutor, Test Generator, Activity Generator, Notetaking Guide, and Assessment Book with Performance Tasks.

Lesson	Average Course	Advanced Course
Lesson 4.1	**Day 1:** p. 132, Exs. 1–9; p. 133, Exs. 1, 2 **Day 2:** p. 132, Exs. 10–15; p. 133, Exs. 10, 11 **Day 3:** p. 134, Exs. 1, 2	**Day 1:** p. 132, Exs. 4, 5; p. 133, Exs. 1–9 **Day 2:** p. 132, Ex. 14; p. 133, Exs. 10–15 **Day 3:** p. 134, Exs. 1, 2
Lesson 4.2	**Day 1:** p. 137, Exs. 1–9; p. 138, Exs. 1, 2 **Day 2:** p. 137, Exs. 10–14; p. 138, Exs. 3, 4 **Day 3:** p. 139, Exs. 1, 2	**Day 1:** p. 137, Exs. 1–6; p. 138, Exs. 1–6 **Day 2:** p. 137, Exs. 7, 8; p. 138, Exs. 7–13 **Day 3:** p. 139, Exs. 1, 2
Lesson 4.3	**Day 1:** p. 142, Exs. 1–14; p. 143, Exs. 1, 2, 7 **Day 2:** p. 142, Exs. 15–28; p. 143, Exs. 11, 12	**Day 1:** p. 142, Exs. 1–3; p. 143, Exs. 1–10 **Day 2:** p. 142, Exs. 13, 15, 21, 22; p. 143, Exs. 11–21
Lesson 4.4	**Day 1:** p. 144, Exs. 1–4 **Day 2:** p. 147, Exs. 1–12; p. 148, Exs. 1, 4 **Day 3:** p. 147, Exs. 13–21; p. 148, Exs. 10, 13, 14 **Day 4:** p. 147, Exs. 22–26; p. 148, Exs. 19, 20	**Day 1:** p. 144, Exs. 1–4 **Day 2:** p. 147, Exs. 1–3, 7–9; p. 148, Exs. 1–9 **Day 3:** p. 147, Exs. 13, 14, 16, 17; p. 148, Exs. 10–18 **Day 4:** p. 147, Exs. 22, 23; p. 148, Exs. 19–24
Lesson 4.5	**Day 1:** p. 153, Exs. 1, 2, 7–9; p. 154, Ex. 1, 3, 4 **Day 2:** p. 153, Exs. 3–6, 10; p. 154, Ex. 9 **Day 3:** Assessment Book (pp. 34–36)	**Day 1:** p. 153, Exs. 1, 7, 8; p. 154, Exs. 1–8 **Day 2:** p. 153, Exs. 4–6; p. 154, Exs. 9–13 **Day 3:** Assessment Book (pp. 34–36)
Lesson 4.6	**Day 1:** p. 157, Exs. 1–10; p. 158, Exs. 1, 2 **Day 2:** p. 157, Exs. 11–20; p. 158, Exs. 7, 8, 13, 14 **Day 3:** p. 157, Exs. 21–27; p. 158, Ex. 19	**Day 1:** p. 157, Exs. 1–7; p. 158, Exs. 1–6 **Day 2:** p. 157, Exs. 11–13, 17, 18; p. 158, Exs. 7–16 **Day 3:** p. 157, Exs. 21–23; p. 158, Exs. 17–22
Lesson 4.7	**Day 1:** p. 161, Exs. 1–15; p. 162, Exs. 1–3 **Day 2:** p. 161, Exs. 16–30; p. 162, Exs. 19–21 **Day 3:** p. 161, Exs. 31–41 p. 162, Ex. 33	**Day 1:** p. 161, Exs. 1–3; p. 162, Exs. 1–15 **Day 2:** p. 161, Exs. 22–24; p. 162, Exs. 16–30 **Day 3:** p. 161, Ex. 37; p. 162, Exs. 31–38
Lesson 4.8	**Day 1:** p. 167, Exs. 1–9; p. 168, Exs. 1, 2, 7 **Day 2:** p. 167, Exs. 10–22; p. 168, Exs. 10, 11, 16	**Day 1:** p. 167, Exs. 1, 2, 7; p. 168, Exs. 1–9 **Day 2:** p. 167, Exs. 10, 11, 16; p. 168, Exs. 10–21
Lesson 4.9	**Day 1:** p. 171, Exs. 1–10; p. 172, Ex. 1 **Day 2:** p. 171, Exs. 11–21; p. 172, Ex. 6 **Day 3:** Assessment Book (pp. 37–39)	**Day 1:** p. 171, Exs. 1–3, 7; p. 172, Exs. 1–5 **Day 2:** p. 171, Exs. 11–13, 17; p. 172, Exs. 6–12 **Day 3:** Assessment Book (pp. 37–39)
Review and Assess	**Day 1:** Review **Day 2:** Review **Day 3:** Review **Day 4:** Unit Test	**Day 1:** Review **Day 2:** Review **Day 3:** Review **Day 4:** Unit Test
Unit 4 Total—30 days	**Units 1–4 Total—115 days**	**Remaining—45 days**

Block Schedule When teaching this unit in a block schedule, you can treat each day in the pacing and assignment guide as half of a block period.

Unit 4 Mathematical Background Notes

Lessons 4.1 – 4.3

In earlier courses, the student has encountered functions in which the independent variable is raised to an exponent (these were referred to as "power functions"). The present unit deals with an important new class of functions, one in which the independent variable itself serves as an exponent.

Exponential functions are functions of the form $y = ab^x$, where $a \geq 0$ and b is a positive number other than 1. In Lessons 4.1 and 4.2, we take a closer look at two types of exponential functions, **exponential growth functions** and **exponential decay functions**.

The function $y = ab^x$ models exponential growth when $a > 0$ and $b > 1$, and exponential decay when $a > 0$ and $0 < b < 1$. These models are used when a real-life quantity grows or shrinks by a fixed percent at regular intervals. The amount y after t time intervals can be modeled by the equations:

$$y = a(1 + r)^t \quad \textbf{exponential growth}$$
$$y = a(1 - r)^t \quad \textbf{exponential decay}$$

where a is the initial amount and r is the percent increase or decrease.

Lesson 4.3 introduces the concept of the natural base e, one of the most important numbers in mathematics. As n approaches $+\infty$, $\left(1 + \dfrac{1}{n}\right)^n$ approaches e. A function of the form $y = ae^{rx}$ is called a **natural base exponential function**. For $a > 0$ and $r > 0$, the function is an exponential growth function, and for $a > 0$ and $r < 0$, the function is an exponential decay function.

Lessons 4.4 – 4.5

Having encountered an interesting new class of functions of the form $f(x) = b^x$, it is natural to inquire about the inverses of such functions. Taking the domain of f to be all real numbers and restricting attention to the case $b > 1$, the range of $f(x)$ consists of all *positive* real numbers.

The inverse function is called a **logarithmic function** and is written as $g(x) = \log_b x$. Its domain is the range of f, namely all positive real numbers.

Of special interest is the case $b = 10$. Here $g(x)$ is called the **common logarithm** and often written without the subscript 10. An explanation of why e, called the Euler number, is used as a base for the **natural logarithm** is better suited to a calculus class.

Lesson 4.6

While admittedly awkward, the verbal description of $\log_b x$ does provide a basis for explaining its properties. Given $\log_b u = p$ and $\log_b v = q$, our verbal rule asserts that $b^p = u$ and $b^q = v$. The laws of exponents now tell us that $uv = (b^p)(b^q) = b^{p + q}$, which can be read "the exponent to which you must raise b in order to obtain the product uv is $p + q$", and this leads to $\log_b uv = \log_b u + \log_b v$. The other properties of logarithms can be established using similar arguments.

Lessons 4.7 – 4.8

Solving exponential and logarithmic equations relies on the fact that $f(x) = b^x$ and $g(x) = \log_b x$ are inverse functions. To solve an exponential equation, take the logarithm of each side. To solve a logarithmic equation, exponentiate each side.

Lesson 4.8 relies heavily on the use of graphing calculators to solve exponential and logarithmic inequalities, but they can be solved algebraically as well. Exponential and logarithmic inequalities can be solved by solving the related equation to determine intervals, and testing a point in each interval to see in which interval(s) the inequality is satisfied.

Lesson 4.9

In previous courses, students have learned that two points determine a line. It is also true that two points determine an exponential curve and two points determine a power curve.

Teaching Unit 4

Graph Exponential Growth Functions (pp. 130–131)

WARM-UP EXERCISES

Evaluate the expression without a calculator.

1. 6^{-2} $\frac{1}{36}$

2. $32^{2/5}$ **4**

3. $-2 \cdot 9^{3/2}$ **−54**

4. State the domain and range of the function $y = -(x + 3)^2 - 2$. **domain: all real numbers, range: $y \geq -2$**

KEY CONCEPT

An exponential function has the form $y = ab^x$ where $a \neq 0$ and the base b is a positive number other than 1. If $a > 0$ and $b > 1$, then the function is an exponential growth function and b is called the growth factor. The compound interest formula is an application of the exponential growth function.

QUESTIONS TO START THE LESSON

According to legend, the inventor of the game of chess requested payment as follows: *My request is a modest one. I humbly request one grain of rice on the first square on the chess board, two grains on the second, four grains on the third, eight on the fourth, and so on.*

1. How many grains of rice are to be placed on the fifth square? the sixth square? **16, 32**

2. What is the exponential form of the number of grains of rice on each square, where $n = 1$ represents the first square? 2^{n-1}

3. A chessboard has 64 squares. How many grains of rice are to be placed on the 64th square? 2^{63}

COMMON STUDENT ERROR

When students use exponential growth models to solve problems, it is important that they do not confuse the percent increase and the growth factor.

> EXAMPLE   *The world population is growing at an average annual rate of about 1.3%. What is the growth factor?*
>
> | Common Error | Correct Answer |
> |---|---|
> | 0.013 ✗ | $1 + r = 1.013$ |

Graph Exponential Decay Functions (pp. 135–136)

WARM-UP EXERCISES

Evaluate the expression without a calculator.

1. $\left(\frac{1}{4}\right)^{-2}$ **16**

2. $-\left(\frac{5}{7}\right)^{0}$ **−1**

3. $9\left(\frac{3}{4}\right)^{-3}$ $\frac{64}{3}$

KEY CONCEPT

An exponential decay function has the form $y = ab^x$ where $a > 0$ and $0 < b < 1$. The base b of an exponential decay function is called the decay factor.

QUESTIONS TO START THE LESSON

1. What is the parent function for exponential growth functions? $y = ab^x$ where $a > 0$ and $b > 1$

2. Describe the graph of the parent function for exponential growth functions. **The graph rises from left to right, passing through the points (0, 1) and (1, b). There is a horizontal asymptote at $y = 0$.**

2. Knowing that y increases as x increases for exponential growth functions, what conjecture could you make about the value of y as x increases for exponential decay functions? **As the value of x increases, the value of y decreases.**

Teaching Unit 4

COMMON STUDENT ERROR

When writing an exponential decay model, some students may mistakenly use $y = ar^t$ instead of $y = a(1 - r)^t$ for the model.

EXAMPLE   A used car costs $10,000. The value of the car decreases by 15% each year. Write an exponential decay model for the value of the car y (in dollars) after t years.

Common Error

The initial amount is $10,000 and the percent decrease is $r = 0.15$, so $y = 10,000(0.15)^t$. ✗

Correct Answer

$y = 10,000(1 - 0.15)^t$
$= 10,000(0.85)^t$

COMMON STUDENT ERROR

Some students incorrectly believe that natural base functions are always exponential growth functions because $e > 1$. Remind students to rewrite the function so that the exponent contains only the variable x.

EXAMPLE   Is the function $f(x) = 5 \cdot e^{-2x}$ an example of exponential growth or exponential decay?

Common Error

The function is an example of exponential growth because $5 > 0$ and $e > 1$. ✗

Correct Answer

First rewrite the function with the exponent x:

$f(x) = 5 \cdot \left(\dfrac{1}{e^2}\right)^x$

Because $5 > 0$ and $0 < \dfrac{1}{e^2} < 1$, the function is an example of exponential decay.

4·3 Use Functions Involving e (pp. 140–141)

WARM-UP EXERCISES

Simplify the expression.

1. $\dfrac{20x^5y^6}{25x^4y^{-3}}$ $\dfrac{4xy^9}{5}$

2. $(-4a^2b^4)^3$ $-64a^6b^{12}$

3. $\sqrt[3]{16x^{12}y^3}$ $2x^4y\sqrt[3]{2}$

KEY CONCEPT

Natural base expressions can be simplified using properties of exponents and evaluated using a calculator. Natural base functions can be graphed as exponential growth and exponential decay functions. The formula for continuously compounded interest allows you to find account balances.

QUESTIONS TO START THE LESSON

1. The Euler number e is defined to be the number that $\left(1 + \dfrac{1}{n}\right)^n$ approaches as n approaches $+\infty$. Use a calculator to evaluate the expression for $n = 10^1$, 10^2, 10^3, 10^4, 10^5, and 10^6. Round to five decimal places. **2.59374, 2.70481, 2.71692, 2.71815, 2.71827, 2.71828**

4·4 Evaluate Logarithms and Graph Logarithmic Functions (pp. 145–146)

WARM-UP EXERCISES

Find the inverse of the function.

1. $y = 2x + 7$ $y = \dfrac{1}{2}x - \dfrac{7}{2}$

2. $y = x^3 - 1$ $y = \sqrt[3]{x + 1}$

3. An account that pays 2% annual interest compounded continuously has a balance of $5000. If no deposits are made to the account, what is the balance three years later? **$5030.09**

KEY CONCEPT

The logarithm of y with base b is denoted by $\log_b y$ and is defined as follows: $\log_b y = x$ if and only if $b^x = y$, where b and y are positive numbers with $b \neq 1$. Common logarithms have base 10 and natural logarithms have base e. Inverse properties can be used to simplify expressions and find inverses of functions.

QUESTIONS TO START THE LESSON

1. To find $\log_3 81$, you need to find how many factors of 3 you need to multiply to get 81. How many factors of 3 do you need? So this would be $\log_3 81 = \underline{\ ?\ }$. How would you write this in exponential form? **4; 4; $3^4 = 81$**

COMMON STUDENT ERROR

Because logarithms may be an unfamiliar concept, some students may have trouble evaluating a logarithmic expression. Students may become confused when trying to write the exponential form.

EXAMPLE   **Evaluate $\log_2 8$.**

Common Error	Correct Answer
Because $8^2 = 64$, $\log_2 8 = 64$.	Because $2^3 = 8$, $\log_2 8 = 3$.

COMMON STUDENT ERROR

Some students may mistakenly believe that logarithmic functions have a horizontal asymptote in addition to a vertical asymptote. This can cause students to restrict the range of a logarithmic function.

EXAMPLE   **State the domain and range of the function $y = \ln x$.**

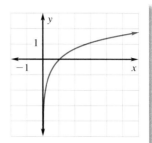

Common Error	Correct Answer
The domain is $x > 0$. The range is $y < 2$.	The domain is $x > 0$. The range is all real numbers.

4.5 Interpret Graphs of Exponential and Logarithmic Functions (pp. 149–150)

WARM-UP EXERCISES

Graph the function. Check graphs.

1. $y = \log_8 x$ **2.** $y = \log_{1/2} x$

KEY CONCEPT

An investigation of the characteristics of exponential and logarithmic functions includes looking at zeros, intervals of increase and decrease, and rate of change. The parent graph $y = \ln x$ can be used to graph translations of a natural logarithmic function.

QUESTIONS TO START THE LESSON

1. Graph the exponential function $y = 3^x$. What are the domain and range? **Check graphs; domain: all real numbers, range: $y > 0$.**

2. Graph the logarithmic function $y = \log_3 x$. What are the domain and range? How are $y = 3^x$ and $y = \log_3 x$ related? **Check graphs; domain: $x > 0$, range: all real numbers; they're inverse functions.**

4.6 Apply Properties of Logarithms (pp. 155–156)

WARM-UP EXERCISES

Evaluate the logarithm.

1. $\log_5 125$ **3**   **2.** $\log 0.0001$ **−4**

3. $\log_{16} 2$ $\frac{1}{4}$ **4.** $\log_4 0.5$ $-\frac{1}{2}$

5. $\log_{27} 9$ $\frac{2}{3}$ **6.** $\log 1000$ **3**

KEY CONCEPT

Properties of logarithms can be used to evaluate logarithms and expand logarithmic expressions. The change-of-base formula allows you to evaluate logarithms with bases other than 10 or e.

Teaching Unit 4

QUESTIONS TO START THE LESSON

The Richter scale is a logarithmic scale that measures the amount of energy released at the focus of an earthquake. For each 1 unit increase in the magnitude, the energy released increases by about 30 times.

1. An earthquake with a magnitude of 3.0 releases 30^2 times more energy than a magnitude 1.0 earthquake. How does the energy released by a magnitude 7.0 earthquake compare with that of a magnitude 1.0 earthquake? **30^6 times more**

2. Write an expression to represent how much more energy is released during an earthquake of magnitude 7.0 than one of magnitude 3.0. Simplify the expression. **$\frac{30^6}{30^2}$; $30^4 = 810{,}000$**

COMMON STUDENT ERROR

Students may make errors when condensing logarithmic expressions. Remind them that the distributive property does not hold for logarithms.

> EXAMPLE   *Condense the expression* $\ln x - \ln 9$.
>
> **Common Error**
> $\ln x - \ln 9$
> $= \ln (x - 9)$ ✗
>
> **Correct Answer**
> $\ln x - \ln 9$
> $= \ln \frac{x}{9}$

Solve Exponential and Logarithmic Equations (pp. 159–160)

WARM-UP EXERCISES

1. Write $\log_3 (3x - 6) = 2$ in exponential form.
 $3^2 = 3x - 6$

2. Write $5^x = 12$ in logarithmic form. **$\log_5 12 = x$**

KEY CONCEPT

Exponential equations can be solved by equating exponents or taking a logarithm of each side. Logarithmic equations can be solved by using the property of equality for logarithmic equations or by exponentiating each side of an equation.

QUESTIONS TO START THE LESSON

Use a graphing calculator to graph the functions defined by the expressions on both sides of the equation. Use the *intersect* feature to solve the equation.

1. $10^{2x} + 3 = 8$ **0.349**   **2.** $1.2e^{-5x} + 2.6 = 3$ **0.220**

3. $1 - 2 \ln x = 4$ **0.223**   **4.** $\log 5x + \log (x - 1) = 2$ **5**

COMMON STUDENT ERROR

Students should not reject all negative solutions for logarithmic equations. Not all negative solutions result in negative logarithms.

> EXAMPLE   *Solve* $\log (x + 7) + \log (x + 4) = 1$.
>
> **Common Error**
> $\log (x + 7)(x + 4) = 1$
> $10^{\log (x + 7)(x + 4)} = 10^1$
> $(x + 7)(x + 4) = 10$
> $x^2 + 11x + 28 = 10$
> $x^2 + 11x + 18 = 0$
> $(x + 9)(x + 2) = 0$
> $x = -9, -2$
> Negative logarithms are undefined, so there is no solution. ✗
>
> **Correct Answer**
> $\log (x + 7)(x + 4) = 1$
> $10^{\log (x + 7)(x + 4)} = 10^1$
> $(x + 7)(x + 4) = 10$
> $x^2 + 11x + 18 = 0$
> $x^2 + 11x + 18 = 0$
> $(x + 9)(x + 2) = 0$
> $x = -9, -2$
> When $x = -9$,
> $\log (-2) + \log (-5)$
> is undefined, so
> $x = -9$ is extraneous.
> When $x = -2$,
> $\log 5 + \log 2 = 1$,
> so -2 is the only solution.

Solve Exponential and Logarithmic Inequalities (pp. 163–166)

WARM-UP EXERCISES

Use a table or graph to solve the equation. Round to the nearest hundredth.

1. $6^x = 60$ **2.29**   **2.** $e^{3x} = 10$ **0.77**

3. $\log 15x = 2$ **6.67**   **4.** $\log_5 x = 2.5$ **55.90**

KEY CONCEPT

Exponential and logarithmic inequalities can be solved by graphing or using the table feature on a graphing calculator.

QUESTIONS TO START THE LESSON

1. Explain how to solve the equation $4^x = 9$ using the graphing feature on a graphing calculator. Then solve the equation. Round to the nearest hundredth. **Graph the functions defined by the expressions on both sides of the equation ($y = 4^x$ and $y = 9$) separately, and use the intersect feature to find the solution; 1.58.**

2. For what values of x is $4^x > 9$? **$x > 1.58$**

3. For what values of x is $4^x < 9$? **$0 < x < 1.58$**

COMMON STUDENT ERROR

Students must remember to use the change-of-base formula when entering logarithms into their calculators.

EXAMPLE   Solve $\log_3 x < 1.5$.

Common Error	Correct Answer
Graph $y = \log 3x$ and $y = 1.5$.	Graph $y = \log_3 x = \dfrac{\log x}{\log 3}$ and $y = 1.5$.

The graph of $y = \log_3 x$ is below the graph of $y = 1.5$ when x is between 0 and 10.54. The solution is $0 < x < 10.54$. ✗

The graph of $y = \log_3 x$ is below the graph of $y = 1.5$ when x is between 0 and 5.196. The solution is $0 < x < 5.196$.

4.9 Write and Apply Exponential and Power Functions (pp. 169–170)

WARM-UP EXERCISES

1. What is the value of y if the point $(5, y)$ is on the line $y = 1.5x + 2.3$? **9.8**

KEY CONCEPT

Exponential and power functions can be written given two points on the graph of the function. Graphing calculators can be used to find exponential and power models for data sets.

QUESTIONS TO START THE LESSON

In Exercises 1–4, use a graphing calculator to graph $y = f(x)$ and $y = \ln f(x)$ in the same viewing window. Check graphs.

1. $f(x) = 6^x$
2. $f(x) = 12^x$
3. $f(x) = \dfrac{2}{3} \cdot 2^x$
4. $f(x) = \dfrac{1}{2}\left(\dfrac{2}{3}\right)^x$

5. If a function f is an exponential function, what type of function is $y = \ln f(x)$? **linear**

COMMON STUDENT ERROR

Students may forget that for the exponential function $y = ab^x$, b must be a positive number other than 1.

EXAMPLE   Write an exponential function $y = ab^x$ whose graph passes through $(3, 27)$ and $(5, 243)$.

Common Error	Correct Answer
$27 = ab^3$ and $243 = ab^5$	$27 = ab^3$ and $243 = ab^5$
$243 = \left(\dfrac{27}{b^3}\right)b^5$	$243 = \left(\dfrac{27}{b^3}\right)b^5$
$9 = b^2$	$243 = 27b^2$
$b = 3$ or -3	$9 = b^2$ and $3 = b$
When $b = 3$, $a = 1$. When $b = -3$, $a = -1$. So, $y = 3^x$ or $y = -1(-3)^x$. ✗	Reject $b = -3$ because b must be positive. When $b = 3$, $a = 1$. So, $y = 3^x$.

Pacing and Assignment Guide

You can adapt any lesson's assignment by incorporating material from the @HomeTutor, Test Generator, Activity Generator, Notetaking Guide, and Assessment Book with Performance Tasks.

Lesson	Average Course	Advanced Course
Lesson 5.1	**Day 1:** p. 178, Exs. 1–10; p. 179, Exs. 2–4 **Day 2:** p. 178, Exs. 11–24; p. 179, Exs. 14, 15	**Day 1:** p. 178, Exs. 1–3; p. 179, Exs. 1–18 **Day 2:** p. 178, Exs. 17–19; p. 179, Exs. 19–29
Lesson 5.2	**Day 1:** p. 182, Exs. 1–13; p. 183, Exs. 1–3 **Day 2:** p. 182, Exs. 14–25; p. 183, Exs. 13, 16 **Day 3:** p. 184, Exs. 1–6	**Day 1:** p. 182, Exs. 1–3; p. 183, Exs. 1–12 **Day 2:** p. 182, Exs. 8, 14, 20–22; p. 183, Exs. 13–20 **Day 3:** p. 184, Exs. 1–6
Lesson 5.3	**Day 1:** p. 185, Exs. 1–4 **Day 2:** p. 188, Exs. 1–9; p. 189, Exs. 1, 2 **Day 3:** p. 188, Exs. 10–22; p. 189, Exs. 7, 8	**Day 1:** p. 185, Exs. 1–4 **Day 2:** p. 188, Exs. 1–6; p. 189, Exs. 1–6 **Day 3:** p. 188, Exs. 10, 16–18; p. 189, Exs. 7–15
Lesson 5.4	**Day 1:** p. 192, Exs. 1–7; p. 193, Exs. 1–3 **Day 2:** p. 192, Exs. 8–19; p. 193, Exs. 7, 9, 12 **Day 3:** Assessment Book (pp. 45–47)	**Day 1:** p. 192, Exs. 1–3, 8, 9; p. 193, Exs. 1–8 **Day 2:** p. 192, Exs. 16–18; p. 193, Exs. 9–15 **Day 3:** Assessment Book (pp. 45–47)
Lesson 5.5	**Day 1:** p. 196, Exs. 1–21; p. 198, Exs. 1, 2 **Day 2:** pp. 196–197, Exs. 22–34; p. 198, Exs. 17, 18 **Day 3:** p. 197, Exs. 35–48; p. 199, Exs. 23, 24	**Day 1:** p. 196, Exs. 1, 2, 13, 14; p. 198, Exs. 1–12 **Day 2:** p. 197, Exs. 23, 24; p. 198, Exs. 13–22 **Day 3:** p. 197, Exs. 35, 36; p. 199, Exs. 23–32
Lesson 5.6	**Day 1:** p. 202, Exs. 1–7; p. 203, Exs. 1, 2 **Day 2:** p. 202, Exs. 8–16; p. 203, Exs. 8, 9 **Day 3:** p. 202, Exs. 17–22; p. 203, Exs. 17, 18 **Day 4:** p. 204, Exs. 1–6	**Day 1:** p. 202, Exs. 1–3; p. 203, Exs. 1–7 **Day 2:** p. 202, Exs. 8–10; p. 203, Exs. 8–16 **Day 3:** p. 202, Exs. 17, 18; p. 203, Exs. 17–22 **Day 4:** p. 204, Exs. 1–6
Lesson 5.7	**Day 1:** p. 207, Exs. 1–12; p. 208, Exs. 1, 5 **Day 2:** p. 207, Exs. 13–22; p. 208, Exs. 9, 15 **Day 3:** Assessment Book (pp. 48–50)	**Day 1:** p. 207, Exs. 1, 3, 7; p. 208, Exs. 1–8 **Day 2:** p. 207, Exs. 13, 14, 17, 18; p. 208, Exs. 9–20 **Day 3:** Assessment Book (pp. 48–50)
Review and Assess	**Day 1:** Review **Day 2:** Review **Day 3:** Review **Day 4:** Unit Test	**Day 1:** Review **Day 2:** Review **Day 3:** Review **Day 4:** Unit Test
	Unit 5 Total—25 days Units 1–5 Total—140 days Remaining—20 days	

Block Schedule When teaching this unit in a block schedule, you can treat each day in the pacing and assignment guide as half of a block period.

Unit 5 Mathematical Background Notes

Lessons 5.1 – 5.4

Conic sections are described as the loci of points satisfying certain distance conditions relative to given fixed points and lines. The coordinate system then allows us to convert these conditions into equations, which in turn can be studied with algebraic techniques.

The name conic section comes from the fact that the curves are formed from the intersection of a double-napped cone and a plane.

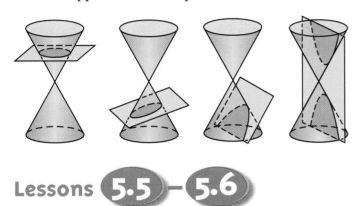

Lessons 5.5 – 5.6

From the equations for the conics in standard position, we obtain the equations of the translated curves by using the general fact that under a translation of h units horizontally and k units vertically the graph of $F(x, y) = 0$ is shifted to a curve whose equation is

$$F(x - h, y - k) = 0.$$

Applying this fact to the conics in standard position does not result in the most general equation for a conic section in the coordinate plane, since it does not take rotations of curves into account. When rotations are allowed, it can be shown that the equations of the conics are all of the form

$$(*)\ Ax^2 + Bxy + Cy^2 + Dx + Ey + F = 0,$$

for some constants $A, B, \ldots, F$. One can even determine the type of conic represented by the equation from the sign of $B^2 - 4AC$, as pointed out in Lesson 5.5.

The number of coefficients in the equation $(*)$ can be reduced to five by dividing through by a nonzero coefficient. Given five points $(x_1, y_1), \ldots, (x_5, y_5)$, and substituting x_i and y_i for x and y in the equation, gives us five linear equations in five unknowns, and this set of linear equations will generally have a unique solution. Then $(*)$ with the resulting coefficients $A, B, \ldots, F$ will be the equation of a conic section passing through all five given points. In this way we see that in general there is one and only one conic section passing through five given points. In other words, just as two points determine a straight line, so do five points determine a unique conic section.

Lesson 5.7

Let's look at the derivation of the distance formula in three dimensions. The diagram below shows the distance between points $A(x_1, y_1, z_1)$ and $B(x_2, y_2, z_2)$.

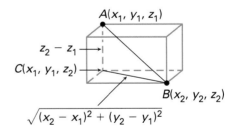

Consider the point C obtained from vertically translating point A into the same xy-plane as point B. The coordinates of C are then (x_1, y_1, z_2).

Using the distance formula for two dimensions, we get $AC = z_2 - z_1$ and $BC = \sqrt{(x_2 - x_1)^2 + (y_2 - y_1)^2}$.

By the Pythagorean theorem,
$$
\begin{aligned}
AB^2 &= BC^2 + AC^2 \\
&= \left(\sqrt{(x_2 - x_1)^2 + (y_2 - y_1)^2}\right)^2 + (z_2 - z_1)^2 \\
&= (x_2 - x_1)^2 + (y_2 - y_1)^2 + (z_2 - z_1)^2
\end{aligned}
$$

Taking the square root of both sides of the equation yields $AB = \sqrt{(x_2 - x_1)^2 + (y_2 - y_1)^2 + (z_2 - z_1)^2}$.

Teaching Unit 5

5.1 Graph and Write Equations of Parabolas (pp. 176–177)

WARM-UP EXERCISES

1. Solve $x = \frac{1}{3}y^2$ for y^2. $y^2 = 3x$

2. Solve $y = -\frac{1}{8}x^2$ for x^2. $x^2 = -8y$

3. Identify the vertex and axis of symmetry of the graph of $y = -2x^2$. **(0, 0); x = 0**

KEY CONCEPT

You will write and graph equations of parabolas in standard form. You will identify the focus, directrix, and axis of symmetry of parabolas.

QUESTIONS TO START THE LESSON

1. What is the parent function for all quadratic functions? What is the vertex of a quadratic function? Because x is squared, what effect does that have on the quadratic function? **$y = x^2$; the lowest or highest point on the function; the axis of symmetry divides the graph into mirror images.**

2. Consider the quadratic function $y = 2(x + 1)^2 - 2$. Does the parabola open up or down? What is the vertex? What is the axis of symmetry? Graph the function. How do you know this is a function? **up; (−1, −2); x = −1; check graphs; for every value of x, there is exactly one value of y.**

COMMON STUDENT ERROR

Some students will have trouble solving for p to find the focus and directrix of a parabola.

> EXAMPLE   **What is the focus of the parabola $x = 8y^2$?**
>
> | Common Error | Correct Answer |
> |---|---|
> | $x = 8y^2$ | Solve for y^2: $\frac{1}{8}x = y^2$ |
> | $4p = 8$ and $p = 2$. | $4p = \frac{1}{8}$, and $p = \frac{1}{32}$. |
> | The focus is (2, 0). ✗ | The focus is $\left(\frac{1}{32}, 0\right)$. |

5.2 Graph and Write Equations of Circles (pp. 180–181)

WARM-UP EXERCISES

Find the distance between the points.

1. (0, 0) and (6, 8) **10**   2. (0, 0) and (8, 15) **17**

Find the slope of the line perpendicular to the given line.

3. $y = 2x - 7$ **$-\frac{1}{2}$**   4. $y = -\frac{3}{4}x + 1\frac{4}{3}$

KEY CONCEPT

You will graph and write equations of circles in standard form. You will find the equation of a line tangent to a circle given the point of tangency.

QUESTIONS TO START THE LESSON

1. A dog is tied to a pole with a 10 foot leash. If the leash is taut, and the dog walks around the pole, what is the resulting shape of the path? **circle**

2. Use a graph to describe the situation. Assume the pole is at the origin, and let each block on the paper represent one foot. Use a compass to sketch the dog's path. Find the coordinates of the points on the circle that lie on the axes. How far is each point from the center? **Check graphs; (10, 0), (0, 10), (−10, 0), (0, −10); 10 ft.**

3. Estimate the coordinates of several other points on the circle. Use the distance formula to verify that the points are all 10 feet from the post. **Answers may vary.**

COMMON STUDENT ERROR

Some students may forget that the radius is squared in the standard equation of a circle.

> EXAMPLE   **Find the radius of the circle given by $x^2 + y^2 = 4$.**
>
> | Common Error | Correct Answer |
> |---|---|
> | The radius is 4. ✗ | The radius is $\sqrt{4} = 2$. |

5.3 Graph and Write Equations of Ellipses (pp. 186–187)

WARM-UP EXERCISES

Solve $a^2 + b^2 = c^2$ for the missing value.

1. $a = 12$, $b = 2$ $2\sqrt{37}$

2. $a = 3$, $c = 5$ 4

3. $b = 20$, $c = 40$ $20\sqrt{3}$

KEY CONCEPT

You will graph an equation of an ellipse in standard form and identify the vertices, co-vertices, and foci of the ellipse. You will write an equation of an ellipse given either a vertex and a co-vertex, or a vertex and a focus.

QUESTIONS TO START THE LESSON

In Exercises 1–3, you will draw an ellipse.

1. Using a piece of cardboard, decide on the location for two points representing the foci of the ellipse. Make sure you do not put the points too close to the edge of the cardboard. With your pencil point, make a small hole at each focus. **1–3. Check models.**

2. Insert a string through each focus and tie the ends together. Don't pull the string too tight. The string should be long enough that it can be pulled an inch or two away from the cardboard.

3. Use the string as a guide to sketch an ellipse. As you sketch, the tip of your pencil should be pulling the string taut.

4. Repeat steps 1–3 several times, varying both the distance between the foci and the length of the string. Use the definition of an ellipse to explain why the figures drawn in this manner are ellipses. **Check models; an ellipse is the set of all points P in a plane such that the sum of the distances between P and two fixed points is a constant. The length of the string is constant and represents the sum of the two distances.**

COMMON STUDENT ERROR

When finding the coordinates of the foci of an ellipse, some students may mistakenly use the formula $c^2 = a^2 + b^2$, instead of $c^2 = a^2 - b^2$, because of their knowledge of the Pythagorean Theorem.

EXAMPLE   Identify the foci of the ellipse given by $\dfrac{x^2}{16} + \dfrac{y^2}{49} = 1$.

Common Error	Correct Answer
$a = 7$ and $b = 4$	$a = 7$ and $b = 4$
$c^2 = a^2 + b^2$	$c^2 = a^2 - b^2$
$c^2 = 49 + 16$	$c^2 = 49 - 16$
$c^2 = 65$	$c^2 = 33$
$c = \sqrt{65}$	$c = \sqrt{33}$
The foci are at $\left(0, \sqrt{65}\right)$ and $\left(0, -\sqrt{65}\right)$. ✗	The foci are at $\left(0, \sqrt{33}\right)$ and $\left(0, -\sqrt{33}\right)$.

5.4 Graph and Write Equations of Hyperbolas (pp. 190–191)

WARM-UP EXERCISES

Identify the foci of the ellipse.

1. $\dfrac{x^2}{12} + \dfrac{y^2}{25} = 1$ $\left(0, \sqrt{13}\right)$ and $\left(0, -\sqrt{13}\right)$

2. $\dfrac{x^2}{100} + \dfrac{y^2}{96}$ $(2, 0)$ and $(-2, 0)$

3. You sail 10 miles due north from your mooring. Then you sail 5 miles due east. To the nearest tenth of a mile, how far are you from your mooring? **11.2 miles**

KEY CONCEPT

You will graph hyperbolas in standard form, and identify the vertices, foci, and asymptotes. You will write equations of hyperbolas given the foci and vertices.

Teaching Unit 5

QUESTIONS TO START THE LESSON

1. What type of graph is $y = \frac{1}{x}$? What are the two symmetric parts of the graph called? **hyperbola; branches**

2. Graph $y = \frac{1}{x-5} + 3$. What are the domain and range? What are the asymptotes? **Check graphs; domain: all real numbers except 5; range: all real numbers; the asymptotes are $x = 5$ and $y = 3$.**

3. For the graph below, what are the x-intercepts? the y-intercepts? Describe the asymptotes. **None; 1 and −1; the asymptotes are neither horizontal nor vertical, they are diagonal lines.**

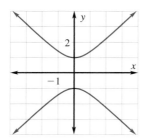

COMMON STUDENT ERROR

Some students may not know whether a hyperbola has a vertical or horizontal transverse axis. Remind them that the transverse axis is along the axis of the positive term. For example, in $\frac{x^2}{a^2} - \frac{y^2}{b^2} = 1$, the x^2 term is positive, so the graph opens along the x-axis.

EXAMPLE Graph $\frac{x^2}{16} - \frac{y^2}{4} = 1$.

Common Error   Correct Answer

 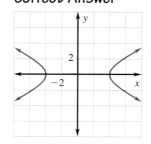

5.5 Translate and Classify Conic Sections (pp. 194–195)

WARM-UP EXERCISES

Identify the conic section.

1. $\frac{x^2}{16} + \frac{y^2}{225} = 1$ **ellipse** **2.** $\frac{x^2}{16} - \frac{y^2}{225} = 1$ **hyperbola**

KEY CONCEPT

A conic section can be classified using its equation. You will graph and write equations of translated conic sections and identify lines of symmetry.

QUESTIONS TO START THE LESSON

Identify the conic section.

1. $\frac{(x-2)^2}{9} + \frac{(y-5)^2}{25} = 1$ **ellipse**

2 $\frac{(x+1)^2}{16} - \frac{y^2}{100}$ **hyperbola**

3 $(x+1)^2 + (y+4)^2 = 49$ **circle**

4. Use a table of values to graph each equation in Questions 1−3. Then make a conjecture about how the center of the conic relates to the equation. **The center is (h, k).**

COMMON STUDENT ERROR

When completing the square for a trinomial in which a common monomial has been factored out, some students may forget to multiply by the common factor before adding the constant to both sides.

EXAMPLE Write the equation $4x^2 + 24x + y^2 = 0$ in standard form.

Common Error

$4(x^2 + 6x + ?) + y^2 = 0$
$4(x^2 + 6x + 9) + y^2 = 9$
$\frac{(x+3)^2}{2.25} + \frac{y^2}{9} = 1$ ✗

Correct Answer

$4(x^2 + 6x + ?) + y^2 = 0$
$4(x^2 + 6x + 9) + y^2 = 36$
$\frac{(x+3)^2}{9} + \frac{y^2}{36} = 1$

5.6 Solve Quadratic Systems (pp. 200–201)

WARM-UP EXERCISES

Solve the system using substitution.

1. $y = x + 4$ and $3x + 4y = 23$ **(1, 5)**

2. $x - 5y = 3$ and $3x + y = 41$ **(13, 2)**

KEY CONCEPT

Quadratic systems can be solved using graphing, substitution, or elimination.

QUESTIONS TO START THE LESSON

1. Explain the substitution method for solving a system of linear equations. Then solve the system $3x - 5y = -12$ and $2x + y = 5$ using substitution.
Solve one equation for one of the variables, substitute the expression into the other equation, and solve; (1, 3).

2. Explain the elimination method for solving a system of linear equations. Then solve the system $5x - 3y = -2$ and $-4x + 9y = 28$ using elimination.
Multiply one equation by a constant, add the resulting equation to the other equation, and solve; (2, 4).

3. Do you think that these two methods could work to solve a system of quadratic equations? **yes**

COMMON STUDENT ERROR

It is important to fully solve the problem. When finding points of intersection, students may stop when they get an answer that looks like an ordered pair.

EXAMPLE **Solve the system using substitution.**
$$x^2 + y^2 = 16, \quad x^2 = y - 4$$

Common Error
$x^2 + y^2 = 16$
$(y - 4) + y^2 = 16$
$y^2 + y - 20 = 0$
$(y + 5)(y - 4) = 0$
$y = -5, 4$
The solution is
$(-5, 4)$. ✗

Correct Answer
Solution for y as at left, but continue to solve for x. When $y = -5$, $x^2 = -9$; $y = -5$ is extraneous. When $y = 4$, $x^2 = 0$, so $x = 0$. The solution is $(0, -5)$.

5.7 Use Figures in Three-Dimensional Space (pp. 205–206)

WARM-UP EXERCISES

1. Find the distance between $(9, 1)$ and $(8, 4)$. $\sqrt{10}$

KEY CONCEPT

Many of the concepts in two-dimensional coordinate geometry can be extended to three dimensions.

QUESTIONS TO START THE LESSON

1. Consider the point $A(3, 4, 12)$ in a three-dimensional coordinate system. Use the Pythagorean theorem to find OB. **5**

2. Use the Pythagorean theorem and the lengths of $\overline{OB}$ and $\overline{AB}$ to find OA. **13**

3. Use the formula $d = \sqrt{(3 - 0)^2 + (4 - 0)^2 + (12 - 0)^2}$ to find the distance between O and A. Compare your answer to the answer in Exercise 2. **13; they are the same.**

COMMON STUDENT ERROR

Students may have trouble remembering the conventional placement of the three axes in 3-space. Remind students that the x-axis comes toward them and the z-axis goes straight up. Although it is technically not wrong to use a different placement, the conventional placement is preferred.

EXAMPLE **Graph the equation $2x + 3y + z = 6$.**

Common Error

Correct Answer

Pacing and Assignment Guide

You can adapt any lesson's assignment by incorporating material from the @HomeTutor, Test Generator, Activity Generator, Notetaking Guide, and Assessment Book with Performance Tasks.

Lesson	Average Course	Advanced Course
Lesson 6.1	**Day 1:** p. 215, Exs. 1–8; p. 216, Exs. 1, 4 **Day 2:** p. 215, Exs. 9–16; p. 216, Exs. 8, 12, 14 **Day 3:** p. 217, Exs. 1–4	**Day 1:** p. 215, Exs. 1, 3, 5; p. 216, Exs. 1–11 **Day 2:** p. 215, Exs. 9, 10, 13–15; p. 216, Exs. 12–18 **Day 3:** p. 217, Exs. 1–4
Lesson 6.2	**Day 1:** p. 218, Exs. 1, 2 **Day 2:** p. 221, Exs. 1–11; p. 222, Exs. 1, 4, 6 **Day 3:** p. 221, Exs. 12–19; p. 222, Exs. 12, 13	**Day 1:** p. 218, Exs. 1, 2 **Day 2:** p. 221, Exs. 1, 4, 6; p. 222, Exs. 1–11 **Day 3:** p. 221, Exs. 12, 13; p. 222, Exs. 12–22
Lesson 6.3	**Day 1:** p. 223, Exs. 1–3 **Day 2:** p. 226, Exs. 1–10; p. 227, Exs. 1, 2, 7 **Day 3:** p. 226, Exs. 11–17; p. 227, Exs. 11, 12 **Day 4:** Assessment Book (pp. 56–58)	**Day 1:** p. 223, Exs. 1–3 **Day 2:** p. 226, Exs. 1–3, 8–10; p. 227, Exs. 1–10 **Day 3:** p. 226, Exs. 11–13; p. 227, Exs. 11–16 **Day 4:** Assessment Book (pp. 56–58)
Lesson 6.4	**Day 1:** p. 230, Exs. 1–11; p. 231, Exs. 1, 4, 5 **Day 2:** p. 230, Exs. 12–17; p. 231, Exs. 12, 13 **Day 3:** p. 232, Exs. 1–4	**Day 1:** p. 230, Exs. 1–5; p. 231, Exs. 1–11 **Day 2:** p. 230, Exs. 12, 13; p. 231, Exs. 12–23 **Day 3:** p. 232, Exs. 1–4
Lesson 6.5	**Day 1:** p. 235, Exs. 1–3; p. 236, Ex. 1 **Day 2:** p. 235, Exs. 4–6; p. 236, Ex. 4 **Day 3:** Assessment Book (pp. 59–61)	**Day 1:** p. 235, Ex. 1; p. 236, Exs. 1–3 **Day 2:** p. 235, Ex. 4; p. 236, Exs. 4–6 **Day 3:** Assessment Book (pp. 59–61)
Review and Assess	**Day 1:** Review **Day 2:** Review **Day 3:** Review **Day 4:** Unit Test	**Day 1:** Review **Day 2:** Review **Day 3:** Review **Day 4:** Unit Test
Unit 6 Total—20 days	**Units 1–6 Total—160 days**	**Remaining—0 days**

Block Schedule When teaching this unit in a block schedule, you can treat each day in the pacing and assignment guide as half of a block period.

Unit 6 Mathematical Background Notes

Lesson 6.1

A **random variable** is a variable whose value is determined by the outcomes of a random event. There are two types of random variables, discrete and continuous. A **discrete random variable** can take on a countable number of distinct values, for example the number of times you get heads in 3 tosses of a coin. A **continuous random variable** can take on an infinite number of possible values, for example the time it takes to run a mile. A discrete random variable has an associated probability distribution while a continuous random variable has an associated probability density function.

Lesson 6.2

A **normal distribution** is determined by its mean and standard deviation. Since it is impossible to maintain tables of values for all such normal distributions, it is necessary to transform the data under study into the **standard normal distribution**, which is a normal distribution with mean 0 and standard deviation 1.

The value $z = \frac{x - \bar{x}}{\sigma}$ for a particular x-value is called the **z-score** and tells you how much a given x-value lies above or below the mean.

Lesson 6.3

In Lesson 6.1, probabilities related to a binomial distribution were calculated using the formula

$$P(k) = {}_nC_k p^k (1 - p)^{n - k}$$

However, if you need to calculate a large number of probabilities, using this formula becomes extremely tedious. In these cases, assuming that $np \geq 5$ and $n(1 - p) \geq 5$, a normal distribution may be used to approximate a binomial distribution. This is because of the central limit theorem, which states that the sum of a large number of independent observations from the same distribution has an approximate normal distribution. As the number of observations increases, the approximation becomes more and more accurate.

Lesson 6.4

Margin of error can be defined for any desired confidence level, but it is typical to use a 90%, 95%, or 99% confidence level. That means that one is, respectively, 90%, 95%, or 99% certain that the "true" percent is within a margin of error of the reported percent.

In this lesson, we define margin of error as

$$\text{margin of error} = \pm \frac{1}{\sqrt{n}}$$

where n is the sample size. This formula is a more simplistic version of the traditional formula for the margin of error at 95% confidence where

$$\text{margin of error} = \pm \frac{0.98}{\sqrt{n}}.$$

Lesson 6.5

An ideal experimental study is generally double blind, that is, neither the investigator nor those being studied know which individuals are in the experimental group and which are in the control group until all the necessary information has been gathered. Not the least reason for this is that it helps to avoid the placebo effect. Most people are familiar with this phenomena, which occurs even in non-medical situations. A person who believes he or she is receiving certain treatment may react as though it has actually been administered.

While both experimental and observational studies may produce significant statistical results, the results of experimental studies are usually considered much more convincing, because of the self-selection involved in observational studies.

Teaching Unit 6

 Construct and Interpret Binomial Distributions (pp. 212–214)

WARM-UP EXERCISES

1. The table shows the number of pets of each student in a classroom. Make a histogram of the data. **Check histograms.**

Pets	0	1	2	3	4	5
Freq.	4	7	8	5	2	1

KEY CONCEPT

A probability distribution is a function that gives the probability of each possible value of a random variable.

QUESTIONS TO START THE LESSON

A die is rolled 10 times. Each trial has two possible outcomes: success (You roll a 1 or 2), or failure: (You roll a 3, 4, 5, or 6).

1. For each trial, what is the theoretical probability of success? of failure? $\frac{1}{3}; \frac{2}{3}$

2. Working individually, roll a die 10 times. Count the successes and failures. Then summarize the class data in a table, and use the data to find the experimental probability of success and of failure. **Answers will vary.**

COMMON STUDENT ERROR

Some students incorrectly believe that the probability of half "success" and half "failure" is always the same, regardless of the number of trials.

EXAMPLE   *Compare the probabilities of getting 1 head in 2 coin flips and getting 2 heads in 4 flips.*

Common Error

When a coin is flipped, you get heads half the time; $P(1\text{ H in 2 flips}) = P(2\text{ H in 4 flips}) = 0.5$ ✗

Correct Answer

$P(1\text{ head in 2 flips}) = {}_2C_1(0.5)^1(0.5)^1 = 0.5$;
$P(2\text{ heads in 4 flips}) = {}_4C_2(0.5)^2(0.5)^2 = 0.375$

 Use Normal Distributions (pp. 219–220)

WARM-UP EXERCISES

Simplify the expression.

1. $\frac{81 - 85}{2.5}$ **−1.6**

2. $\frac{18 - 16.5}{0.5}$ **3**

3. $2(0.34) + 2(0.135) + 2(0.0235) =$ **0.997**

KEY CONCEPT

A normal distribution is a type of probability distribution that is modeled by a bell-shaped curve called a normal curve. It is symmetric about the mean. Normal distributions can be used to find probabilities.

QUESTIONS TO START THE LESSON

In Exercises 1 and 2, use the graph below of the numbers from Row 8 of Pascal's triangle.

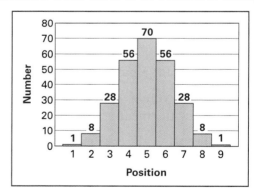

1. Draw a bell-shaped curve using the tops of the rectangles as a guide. **Check drawings.**

2. The area of each bar in the graph represents a percent of the area under the curve. The sum of the areas is a good estimate of the entire area under the curve. What is the sum of the areas? **256**

3. What percent of the area under the curve is represented by the bars in positions 4, 5, and 6? **about 71%**

COMMON STUDENT ERROR

Some students may have difficulty using the standard normal table on page 248. Remind students that they must find the z-score before using the table.

> EXAMPLE A normal distribution has mean 1.5 and standard deviation 0.25. Use the table on page 248 to find the probability that a randomly selected x-value from the distribution is less than or equal to 1.1.
>
> **Common Error**
>
> $P(x \leq 1.1)$ is in the 1 row and the 1 column. ✗
> $P(x \leq 1.1) = 0.8643$
>
> **Correct Answer**
>
> $z = \dfrac{x - \bar{x}}{\sigma} = \dfrac{1.1 - 1.5}{0.25} = -1.6.$
> $P(z \leq -1.6)$ is in the -1 row and the .6 column. $P(z \leq -1.6) = 0.0548$

QUESTIONS TO START THE LESSON

1. Complete the hypothesis: "_?_% of the students in your school have _?_." **Answers will vary.**

2. Explain how you could test your hypothesis. **Answers will vary.**

COMMON STUDENT ERROR

When using a normal approximation of a binomial distribution, some students may forget the requirement that np and $n(1 - p)$ must both be greater than or equal to 5.

> EXAMPLE A binomial distribution consists of 10 trials with a probability of success of 0.25 on each trial. Can a normal distribution be used to approximate the distribution?
>
> **Common Error**   **Correct Answer**
>
> Yes. ✗   No; $np = 10(0.25) = 2.5$, and $n(1 - p) = 10(.75) = 7.5$, so np is less than 5.

6.3 Approximate Binomial Distributions and Test Hypotheses (pp. 224–225)

WARM-UP EXERCISES

Solve the equation $\sigma = \sqrt{np(1 - p)}$ for the given values of n and p.

1. $n = 24$ and $p = 0.25$ **2.12**

2. $n = 40$ and $p = 0.72$ **2.84**

3. $n = 148$ and $p = 0.5$ **6.08**

4. $n = 350$ and $p = 0.22$ **7.75**

5. Three of 25 students in your class are left-handed. What percent of students in your class are left-handed? **12%**

KEY CONCEPT

A binomial distribution consists of n trials with probability p of success on each trial. If $np \geq 5$ and $n(1 - p) \geq 5$, then the binomial distribution can be approximated by a normal distribution with mean np and standard deviation $\sqrt{np(1 - p)}$. Also, you will test a hypothesis about a statistical measure for a population.

6.4 Select and Draw Conclusions from Samples (pp. 228–229)

WARM-UP EXERCISES

1. Evaluate $\dfrac{1}{\sqrt{205}}$. **0.070**

2. Solve $0.035 = \dfrac{1}{\sqrt{n}}$. **about 816**

3. The mean score on an exam was 80. You scored within 8 points of the mean. If $x = 80 \pm 8$ represents your possible score x on the exam, what is the range of your score? **$72 \leq x \leq 88$**

KEY CONCEPT

Samples can be classified as self-selected, systematic, convenience, or random. Samples can be biased or unbiased. The margin of error gives a limit on how much the responses of the sample would differ from the responses of the population.

Teaching Unit 6

QUESTIONS TO START THE LESSON

1. Have you seen surveys stating facts similar to "44% of the voters approve of the president's performance" or "72% of parents think video games have become too violent?" Did you ever wonder how they decided which voters or parents to question? **Answers may vary.**

2. *How can the way a survey group is selected influence the results of a survey?* Consider the survey question "Do you think teachers should assign homework every night?" If only teachers were surveyed, how might this affect the survey? What if only students were questioned? **Teachers are more likely to want homework assigned every night than students.**

3. *How can the number of people surveyed affect the results?* Which would result in a more useful survey about the quality of a school's cafeteria food—a survey of 10 students or a survey of 100 students? Why? **The survey of 100 students is more useful because the larger the sample, the more accurate the results.**

COMMON STUDENT ERROR

When using the margin of error formula, students must be careful not to confuse a percent used in the problem with the margin of error.

EXAMPLE In a survey, 15% of students in your school said they planned to attend the senior prom. The margin of error for the survey is ±10%. How many seniors were surveyed?

Common Error	Correct Answer
$0.15 = \pm \dfrac{1}{\sqrt{n}}$	$\pm 0.1 = \pm \dfrac{1}{\sqrt{n}}$
$(0.15)^2 = \left(\pm \dfrac{1}{\sqrt{n}} \right)^2$	$(\pm 0.1)^2 = \left(\pm \dfrac{1}{\sqrt{n}} \right)^2$
$0.0225 = \dfrac{1}{n}$	$0.01 = \dfrac{1}{n}$
$n = \dfrac{1}{0.0225}$	$n = \dfrac{1}{0.01}$
$n = 44$ ✗	$n = 100$

WARM-UP EXERCISES

1. At a candidates' night, a speaker asks all those who vote regularly to raise their hands. Do you think the number of hands raised accurately reflects the number of regular voters in the group? Why or why not? *Sample answer:* **No; those who don't vote regularly may not want to admit it.**

KEY CONCEPT

A study usually consists of two groups, an experimental group that will undergo some procedure or treatment, and a control group that will not. There should be as few differences as possible between the control group and the experimental group, other than the procedure or treatment they undergo.

QUESTIONS TO START THE LESSON

1. A public safety agency wants to study how driver education programs affect teens' driving habits. They identify all teens in one town who got their licenses in a given month and plan to investigate their safety records over a one-year period. How should they choose the experimental group? the control group? **The experimental group should be teens who passed a driver education course; the control group should be teens who did not.**

COMMON STUDENT ERROR

Students may not recognize flaws in an experiment.

EXAMPLE An investigator studies two groups of students, bus riders and walkers, and observes that when allowed to choose their own lunch times, bused students choose earlier lunch times. The investigator concludes that walking delays hunger. Is the study flawed?

Common Error	Correct Answer
No. ✗	Yes; bused students may eat breakfast earlier and get hungry earlier.

Professional Articles Contents

The following pages include information about the *Georgia High School Mathematics 3* program and explain how it reflects current research in mathematics instruction.

Providing Universal Access

Diverse Students

In most classrooms, students present a variety of achievement levels, skills, and needs. The goal for all students is the same: We want them to develop sufficient computational, procedural, and problem solving skills to provide a solid foundation for further study of mathematics. However, all students do not arrive at these competencies at the same time or in the same way.

Georgia High School Mathematics 3 is organized so that much of the differentiation for special needs students is built into the program. Activities provide students with models for conceptual understanding of the mathematical reasoning behind key concepts. Ample practice is provided, and mathematical reasoning and problem solving exercises are included throughout the unit.

Setting the Right Tone

There are three key strategies recommended for teachers as they adapt any program to students' needs.

- Use frequent assessment as a way to determine what each student does or does not know, and use that assessment as the basis for planning.

- Plan modifications of curriculum and instruction ahead of time so that you are ready to differentiate as the need arises.

- Use a variety of grouping strategies to facilitate learning. A combination of whole class instruction and temporary groupings of students, with groups organized around students' needs, will facilitate management of the variety of achievement levels and learning needs in the classroom.

Assessment, planning, and flexible grouping are essential to ensuring that your students have the optimal chance for success. In addition to these three key strategies, general guidelines for establishing a classroom designed to meet students' needs are:

1. Establish an atmosphere where students feel comfortable asking questions and are rewarded for asking about things they don't understand.

2. Maintain the same goals for all students. Allow additional time and practice for students who need it, and provide challenging alternatives for those who are ready to move more quickly.

3. Clearly identify the skill, concept, or standards you are working on and measure progress towards those ends.

4. Have students show their work. It is much easier for teachers to understand where a student gets confused if they have evidence of the student's thought process.

5. Try small modifications in curriculum and instruction before more drastic ones.

6. Don't persist with a strategy that isn't working. Try something else.

7. Encourage effort and persistence, and celebrate successes with your students.

Varying Curriculum and Instruction

1. *Time* Most students whose achievement is below grade level will need more time. Students who are not fluent in English will need more time. Perhaps the day can be extended through study hall, regular homework assignments, tutoring, or Saturday, summer, or "off track" catch-up sessions.

2. *Presentation* Instructing in a variety of ways and taking a single concept and explaining verbally and visually with concrete and abstract examples provide students multiple opportunities for understanding.

3. *Task Parameters* Multi-step problems can be especially difficult for students. These types of problems are just combinations of simpler problems and can be broken down into simpler steps, with additional help and practice at each step. Confusing elements can be minimized and extraneous material eliminated.

Three Basic Student Groups

Grade Level Group	Underachieving Group	Intensive Needs Group
Students achieving at grade level may have minor, occasional difficulties but they can be assisted to maintain their progress with varied instruction, extra practice, and individual or group assistance on an as-needed basis.	These learners are not achieving at expected grade level but can, with a program that provides targeted assistance. Systematic differentiation such as preteaching, reteaching, and additional instructional time should be planned.	Intensive students are those whose performance is two or more years below grade level. These students will probably already be eligible for special education services and require an intervention program.
SUGGESTED PLAN	**SUGGESTED PLAN**	**SUGGESTED PLAN**
1. Assess what these students already know.	1. Assess what these students already know.	1. Assess what these students already know.
2. Progress through *Georgia High School Mathematics 3* at the recommended pace and sequence using varied instruction.	2. Provide additional scaffolding.	2. Determine if these students have an IEP.
3. On an ad hoc basis, review or provide additional practice as needed.	3. Focus on the key concepts and present material systematically.	3. Refer students for special education testing or child study team discussion; enlist the help of specialists.
	4. Vary the kinds of instruction so that students have several opportunities to understand.	4. Carefully consider each student's most appropriate placement in mathematics.
	5. Provide additional practice homework.	

For Students Who Have Trouble Paying Attention

Students who have a hard time staying focused need to be taught strategies for organizing their work and keeping track of where they are.

1. Present the work in smaller chunks over smaller time periods and then gradually increase expectations.

2. Use cumulative review and practice. Have students periodically review what they learned in previous units and provide additional practice if they have forgotten.

3. Make it more obvious what the student should focus on. For example, use the test generator to put only four problems on each page.

4. Help students develop simple strategies for bringing work to and from class.

5. Allow movement and schedule breaks.

6. Minimize distractions by seating students who are easily distracted near the teacher and away from hallway noise.

7. Graphic organizers such as Venn diagrams, tree diagrams, lists, outlines, tables, and charts can all provide structures for organizing and remembering information.

8. Establish routines. Students who know their routine find it easier to work independently.

For Students Who Have Trouble Understanding the Concepts

Several strategies can help students make steady progress in mathematics. These include:

1. Focus on key mathematical concepts.

2. Review key concepts and skills from earlier lessons, chapters, or years.

3. Preteach key concepts and vocabulary.

4. Anticipate problem areas.

5. Provide scaffolding (guided practice) for students who need extra help.

6. Think out loud to show hidden steps.

7. Provide a sample problem to which students can return when they get stuck.

8. Break problems into simpler components.

9. Explicitly teach students a variety of problem solving strategies and help them select one that fits the situation.

10. Present concepts in a variety of ways: visually, verbally, concretely, abstractly, etc.

11. Encourage students to draw a picture or use a visual aid, such as a number line, graph, or diagram.

12. Provide sufficient practice.

Maximizing Success for English Learners

English learners in your classroom may be at, behind, or ahead of grade expectations in mathematics. You can maximize success for English learners by assessing each student's reading achievement to form a basis for program planning. The tables below summarize the attributes of two types of English learners—those with low reading achievement and those with high reading achievement—and how you can help accommodate their needs.

High Reading Achievement

Who is the student?
- Student may have been designated as an English learner because oral skills lag behind reading skills.
- Student may not test well in mathematics.
- Most students can make rapid progress in mathematics; a few may have learning difficulties that require the help of a specialist.

What to do?
- Assess mathematics achievement in a variety of ways.
- Concentrate on developing oral fluency.
- Focus on vocabulary specific to mathematics.
- Use a student's reading ability to improve his or her math scores.

Low Reading Achievement

Who is the student?
- Student may be new to the class, school, or country.
- Student may have had inadequate schooling.
- Student may have moved a lot.
- Student may be unmotivated or have test anxiety.
- Low reading achievement may be depressing mathematics scores.
- Student may have gaps and holes in knowledge.
- Student may need special education assistance.

What to do?
- Examine cumulative folder for other testing, notes, etc.
- Ask questions about language use and prior schooling.
- Delay any testing for a week or two. Help student feel comfortable in the class during that period of time.
- Administer mathematics achievement test and reading test, in an individual setting.
- Assess this student at weekly intervals and monitor classroom work to determine if progress is being made.

Suggestions for Mathematics Teachers of English Learners

1. *Allocate additional time for mathematics.* Many students will be translating from English to their primary language and back again. When you ask questions, allow extra time for students to respond. Reading mathematics textbooks and understanding what is asked for in a word problem will be slower.

2. *Use students' background knowledge.* Some English learners will have developed substantial background in mathematics; others will have very little. Find out what students know and then build on more.

3. *Reduce the amount and sophistication of the English language used.* This may be done by reordering the lessons in each chapter to begin with key vocabulary, followed by problems with a minimum of written English, followed by at least one word problem each day. Choose word problems that don't rely on assumed background knowledge. Keep your questions direct and simple. Speak more slowly, avoid idioms and slang, be precise and concise, and use short sentences and simple vocabulary. Using hand gestures and pictures as well as words aids communication.

4. *Develop predictable routines.* Introduce one concept per day. Keeping the focus simple will aid students in understanding the point of the lesson.

5. *Use different methods for getting a point across.* Presenting concepts verbally and visually, with concrete examples and in abstract mathematical symbols, and using pictures, graphs, diagrams, and charts will enhance a student's chance of understanding at least one of the presentations. As you introduce a new word, rule, or property, write it down.

6. *Provide opportunities for English learners to interact with their English-speaking peers.* Students who are learning a language need to hear native speakers using the language, and they need opportunities to use their new mathematics vocabulary in their speech and in their writing.

7. *Allow English learners to demonstrate what they know in a variety of ways.* When students first learn a language, they generally understand the spoken language before they can produce it themselves. Allow students to point, nod, gesture, draw a picture, or work math problems without words as they learn English.

8. *Extend mathematics instructional time* through homework, an extra class period, summer school, or tutoring. Many of the suggestions for English learners can be carried out in collaboration with language arts teachers or other specialists, and are well-suited for discussion in a language arts class, English as a second language class, or in a tutorial.

Differentiating Instruction

All students, whether they are struggling, average, or advanced learners, have opportunities to make continuing progress in developing the skills they need to become successful adults. To develop these skills, students need to participate in courses that are based on challenging curriculum standards and assessment objectives.

The *Georgia High School Mathematics 3* program provides you with helpful materials for differentiating instruction to reach all students, for assessing student progress throughout the course, and for diagnosing student understanding in order to provide appropriate prescription and remediation. The tables below show some of the ways in which this program helps you differentiate for the diverse classroom.

Planning and Motivating the Lesson	
Feature	**Description**
Student Edition: Investigating Math Activities	Pre-lesson activities where students explore concepts and discover mathematical results
Teacher's Edition: Pacing and Assignment Guides	Schedules for teaching the lessons of each unit, along with homework assignments for every lesson
Teacher's Edition: Warm-up Exercises	Exercises that review skills needed for the upcoming lessons
Teacher's Edition: Questions to Start the Lesson	Questions that motivate the concepts being taught in the lesson
Activity Generator	Software that offers leveled activities for most lessons and teaching commentary to guide students from the concrete to the abstract

Teaching the Lesson

Feature	Description
Student Edition: Guided Practice	Problems for each example that help you monitor how well students are grasping concepts and skills as you present the lesson
Student Edition: Leveled Exercise Sets	Exercise sets for each lesson are divided into two difficulty levels (Exercise Set A and Exercise Set B)
Student Edition: Problem Solving Workshops	Features that present alternative methods for solving an example from the previous lesson or show a stepped-out solution for an example from the previous lesson
Notetaking Guide	A workbook that gives students a framework for recording the key concepts of every lesson; also available on transparencies
@HomeTutor	Software that provides animated examples and instruction, self-scoring exercises, and customized student progress reports

Reviewing and Assessing

Feature	Description
Student Edition: Unit Tests	Tests at the end of every unit; a Performance Task for the unit is included in the Unit Test
Georgia Assessment Book with Performance Tasks for Mathematics 3	Provides practice for future testing situations when students will be asked to meet the Georgia Performance Standards
Georgia Test Preparation and Practice for Mathematics 3	Contains a diagnostic test, a practice worksheet for every Georgia Performance standard, and a practice test
Test Generator	Software that creates customized, editable test and practice worksheets based on topics you select
McDougal Littell Assessment System	Innovative standards-based assessment software the helps you test, score, report, and reteach

Research-Based Solutions

The *Georgia High School Mathematics 3* program reflects current research in education. The Student Edition, Teacher's Edition, Notetaking Guide, and other ancillary materials provide opportunities for teachers and students to experience a number of different learning strategies both in school and at home.

One group of instructional strategies used in this program are the instructional strategies presented in *Classroom Instruction that Works**, a publication from the Association for Supervision and Curriculum Development. The nine strategies discussed in that publication are summarized below, along with a description of the strategy's use in the *Georgia High School Mathematics 3* program.

1. *Identifying Similarities and Differences*

   This strategy includes comparing and classifying and suggests representing comparisons in graphic or symbolic form.

   Mathematics 3 examples include Multiple Representations exercises throughout the units in the Student Edition.

2. *Summarizing and Notetaking*

   This strategy includes deciding when to delete, substitute, or keep information if writing a summary and using a variety of notetaking formats—e.g., outlines, webbing, or a combination technique—and suggests encouraging students to use notes as a study guide for tests.

   Mathematics 3 examples include the entire *Georgia Notetaking Guide*.

3. *Reinforcing Effort and Providing Recognition*

   This strategy includes making the connection between effort and achievement clear to students and providing recognition for attainment of specific goals to stimulate motivation.

   Mathematics 3 examples include Guided Practice exercises in the Student Edition, Questions to Start the Lesson in the Teacher's Edition, and Checkpoint exercises in the *Georgia Notetaking Guide*.

4. *Homework and Practice*

   This strategy includes making the purpose of homework assignments clear to students and focusing practice assignments on specific elements of a complex skill.

   Mathematics 3 examples include leveled exercise sets (Exercise Set A and Exercise Set B) in each lesson in the Student Edition and the Practice exercises in each lesson in the *Georgia Notetaking Guide*.

*Marzano, Robert J., Debra J. Pickering, and Jane E. Pollack, *Classroom Instruction that Works: Research-Based Strategies for Increasing Student Achievement* and its accompanying handbook. Alexandria, Virginia: Association for Supervision and Curriculum Development, 2001.

5. *Nonlinguistic Presentations*

This strategy includes creating nonlinguistic presentations—including creating graphic organizers, making physical models, generating mental pictures, drawing pictures and pictographs, and engaging in cooperative learning.

Mathematics 3 examples include Multiple Representations exercises and Investigating Math Activities in the Student Edition and activities from the Activity Generator.

6. *Cooperative Learning*

This strategy includes a description of the five defining elements of cooperative learning—positive interdependence, face-to-face interaction, individual and group accountability, interpersonal and group skills, and group processing—and gives suggestions for grouping techniques.

Mathematics 3 examples include Investigating Math Activities in the Student Edition and activities from the Activity Generator.

7. *Setting Objectives and Providing Feedback*

This strategy includes using instructional goals to narrow what students focus on and suggests providing feedback that is specific to a criterion and encouraging students to personalize their teacher's goals and to provide some of their own feedback.

Mathematics 3 examples include the Goal statement and the appropriate Georgia Performance Standards given at the beginning of every lesson in the Student Edition and the Goal statements given at the beginning of every lesson in the Georgia Notetaking Guide.

8. *Generating and Testing Hypotheses*

This strategy includes using a variety of structured tasks to guide students through generating and testing hypotheses, using induction or deduction, and suggests asking students to clearly explain their hypotheses and their conclusions to help deepen their understanding

Mathematics 3 examples include the Draw Conclusions exercises in the Investigating Math Activities in the Student Edition.

9. *Cues, Questions, and Advance Organizers*

This strategy includes asking questions or giving explicit cues before a learning experience to provide students with a preview of what they are about to experience; using verbal and graphic advance organizers, or having students skim information before reading as an advance organizer.

Mathematics 3 examples include the Questions given at the beginning of the Investigating Math Activities and Technology Activities in the Student Edition and pre-reading lesson elements such as the Vocabulary box and Example heads throughout the book.

McDougal Littell

GEORGIA HIGH SCHOOL MATHEMATICS 3

McDougal Littell
A DIVISION OF HOUGHTON MIFFLIN COMPANY
Evanston, Illinois • Boston • Dallas

Copyright © 2008 McDougal Littell, a division of Houghton Mifflin Company.

All rights reserved.

Warning: No part of this work may be reproduced or transmitted in any form or by any means, electronic or mechanical, including photocopying and recording, or by any information storage or retrieval system without the prior written permission of McDougal Littell unless such copying is expressly permitted by federal copyright law. Address inquiries to Supervisor, Rights and Permissions, McDougal Littell, P.O. Box 1667, Evanston, IL 60204.

ISBN-10: 0-618-92008-0
ISBN-13: 978-0-618-92008-2   123456789—DRV—11 10 09 08 07

Internet Web Site: http://www.mcdougallittell.com

About This Book

McDougal Littell Georgia High School Mathematics 3

The Georgia High School Mathematics 3 book covers all of the Georgia Performance Standards for Mathematics 3. Its content has been organized into a convenient sequence that corresponds to the strands of the Georgia Performance Standards. Georgia standards that correlate to the content of each lesson are given at point of use in the Student Edition and Teacher's Edition of *Georgia High School Mathematics 3.*

At the front of this book, you will find a complete listing of all the Georgia Performance Standards for Mathematics 3, along with a correlation of these standards to appropriate lessons in *Georgia High School Mathematics 3.*

Advisers and Reviewers

Curriculum Advisers and Reviewers

Michele Borror Long
Mathematics Teacher
LaGrange High School
LaGrange, GA

Sandye Ashley
Mathematics Teacher
Rome Middle School
Rome, GA

Georgia Panel

Ernest Adams
Mathematics Teacher,
   Department Chair
Northview High School
Duluth, GA

Salvatore Angelica
Mathematics Teacher
Luella High School
Locust Grove, GA

Sandra Campagnone
Mathematics Teacher
Pebblebrook High School
Mableton, GA

Mack Graham
Mathematics Teacher
Benjamin E. Mays High School
Atlanta, GA

Debra Hodge
Mathematics Teacher
Dunwoody High School
Dunwoody, GA

Carletta Malcom
Mathematics Teacher,
   Department Chair
Cedar Grove High School
Ellenwood, GA

Yvonne Pringle
Mathematics Teacher,
   Department Chair
North Atlanta High School
Atlanta, GA

Maria Travitz
Mathematics Teacher
Kennesaw Mountain High School
Kennesaw, GA

Melissa Walker
Mathematics Teacher,
   Department Chair
Martin Luther King, Jr. High School
Lithonia, GA

Contents

Student Resources

Use the English–Spanish Glossary to see definitions in English and Spanish, as well as examples illustrating vocabulary.

Look up items in the alphabetical Index to find where a particular math topic is covered in the book.

Use the Selected Answers to check your work.

Correlation to Standards

Correlation of *McDougal Littell Georgia High School Mathematics 3* to the Georgia Performance Standards for Mathematics 3

ALGEBRA

Students will investigate exponential, logarithmic and polynomial functions of degree higher than 2. Students will understand matrices and use them to solve problems.

Georgia Performance Standard		Lesson/Activity
MM3A1	Students will analyze graphs of polynomial functions of higher degree.	
MM3A1a	Graph simple polynomial functions as translations of the function $f(x) = ax^n$.	Lesson 2.2
MM3A1b	Understand the effects of the following on the graph of a polynomial function: degree, lead coefficient, and multiplicity of real zeros.	Lesson 2.1, Investigating Math Activity 2.7, Lesson 2.8
MM3A1c	Determine whether a polynomial function has symmetry and whether it is even, odd, or neither.	Lesson 2.1, Lesson 2.2
MM3A1d	Investigate and explain characteristics of polynomial functions, including domain and range, intercepts, zeros, relative and absolute extrema, intervals of increase and decrease, and end behavior.	Lesson 2.1, Lesson 2.2, Investigating Math Activity 2.7, Lesson 2.8, Technology Activity 2.8
MM3A2	Students will explore logarithmic functions as inverses of exponential functions.	
MM3A2a	Define and understand properties of nth roots.	Lesson 3.1, Investigating Math Activity 3.1
MM3A2b	Extend properties of exponents to include rational exponents.	Lesson 3.1, Lesson 3.2, Problem Solving Workshop 3.2
MM3A2c	Define logarithmic functions as inverses of exponential functions.	Lesson 4.4, Investigating Math Activity 4.4
MM3A2d	Understand and use properties of logarithms by extending laws of exponents.	Lesson 4.6
MM3A2e	Investigate and explain characteristics of exponential and logarithmic functions including domain and range, asymptotes, zeros, intercepts, intervals of increase and decrease, and rate of change.	Lesson 4.1, Lesson 4.2, Lesson 4.3, Lesson 4.4, Lesson 4.5
MM3A2f	Graph functions as transformations of $f(x) = a^x$, $f(x) = \log_a x$, $f(x) = e^x$, $f(x) = \ln x$.	Lesson 4.1, Lesson 4.2, Lesson 4.3, Lesson 4.4, Lesson 4.5

Georgia Performance Standard		Lesson/Activity
MM3A2g	Explore real phenomena related to exponential and logarithmic functions including half-life and doubling time.	Lesson 4.1, Problem Solving Workshop 4.1, Lesson 4.2, Technology Activity 4.2, Lesson 4.3, Lesson 4.6, Lesson 4.9
MM3A3	Students will solve a variety of equations and inequalities.	
MM3A3a	Find real and complex roots of higher degree polynomial equations using the factor theorem, remainder theorem, rational root theorem, and fundamental theorem of algebra, incorporating complex and radical conjugates.	Lesson 2.5, Lesson 2.6, Lesson 2.7, Investigating Math Activity 2.7
MM3A3b	Solve polynomial, exponential, and logarithmic equations analytically, graphically, and using appropriate technology.	Lesson 2.3, Problem Solving Workshop 2.3, Lesson 4.7
MM3A3c	Solve polynomial, exponential, and logarithmic inequalities analytically, graphically, and using appropriate technology. Represent solution sets of inequalities using interval notation.	Lesson 2.4, Lesson 4.8
MM3A3d	Solve a variety of types of equations by appropriate means choosing among mental calculation, pencil and paper, or appropriate technology.	Lesson 2.3, Problem Solving Workshop 2.3, Lesson 2.5, Lesson 2.6, Lesson 2.7, Lesson 3.1, Lesson 3.3, Lesson 3.4, Technology Activity 3.4, Problem Solving Workshop 4.1, Lesson 4.3, Lesson 4.7
MM3A4	Students will perform basic operations with matrices.	
MM3A4a	Add, subtract, multiply, and invert matrices, when possible, choosing appropriate methods including technology.	Lesson 1.8, Lesson 1.9, Technology Activity 1.9, Investigating Math Activity 1.11
MM3A4b	Find the inverses of two-by-two matrices using pencil and paper, and find inverses of larger matrices using technology.	Lesson 1.11, Investigating Math Activity 1.11
MM3A4c	Examine the properties of matrices, contrasting them with properties of real numbers.	Lesson 1.8, Lesson 1.9
MM3A5	Students will use matrices to formulate and solve problems.	
MM3A5a	Represent a system of linear equations as a matrix equation.	Lesson 1.11
MM3A5b	Solve matrix equations using inverse matrices.	Lesson 1.11
MM3A5c	Represent and solve realistic problems using systems of linear equations.	Lesson 1.2, Lesson 1.3, Investigating Math Activity 1.3, Lesson 1.7, Lesson 1.10

Georgia Performance Standard		Lesson/Activity
MM3A6	Students will solve linear programming problems in two variables.	
MM3A6a	Solve systems of inequalities in two variables, showing the solutions graphically.	Lesson 1.4, Lesson 1.5, Problem Solving Workshop 1.5
MM3A6b	Represent and solve realistic problems using linear programming.	Lesson 1.6
MM3A7	Students will understand and apply matrix representations of vertex-edge graphs.	
MM3A7a	Use graphs to represent realistic situations.	Lesson 1.12
MM3A7b	Use matrices to represent graphs, and solve problems that can be represented by graphs.	Lesson 1.12

GEOMETRY

Students will understand and use the analytic geometry of conic sections and of planes and spheres in space.

MM3G1	Students will investigate the relationships between lines and circles.	
MM3G1a	Find equations of circles.	Lesson 5.2, Problem Solving Workshop 5.2
MM3G1b	Graph a circle given an equation in general form.	Lesson 5.2
MM3G1c	Find the equation of a tangent line to a circle at a given point.	Lesson 5.2
MM3G1d	Solve a system of equations involving a circle and a line.	Lesson 5.6, Technology Activity 5.6
MM3G1e	Solve a system of equations involving two circles.	Lesson 5.6
MM3G2	Students will recognize, analyze, and graph the equations of the conic sections (parabolas, circles, ellipses, and hyperbolas).	
MM3G2a	Convert equations of conics by completing the square.	Lesson 5.5
MM3G2b	Graph conic sections, identifying fundamental characteristics.	Lesson 5.1, Lesson 5.3, Investigating Math Activity 5.3, Lesson 5.4, Lesson 5.5
MM3G2c	Write equations of conic sections given appropriate information.	Lesson 5.1, Lesson 5.3, Lesson 5.4, Lesson 5.5
MM3G3	Students will investigate planes and spheres.	
MM3G3a	Plot the point (x, y, z) and understand it as a vertex of a rectangular prism.	Lesson 5.7
MM3G3b	Apply the distance formula in 3-space.	Lesson 5.7

Georgia Performance Standard		Lesson/Activity
MM3G3c	Recognize and understand equations of planes and spheres.	Lesson 5.7

DATA ANALYSIS AND PROBABILITY

Students will use a normal distribution to calculate probabilities. They will organize, represent, investigate, interpret, and make inferences using data from both observational studies and experiments.

MM3D1	Students will create probability histograms of discrete random variables, using both experimental and theoretical probabilities.	Lesson 6.1, Technology Activity 6.1
MM3D2	**Students will solve problems involving probabilities by interpreting a normal distribution as a probability histogram for a continuous random variable (z-scores are used for a general normal distribution).**	
MM3D2a	Determine intervals about the mean that include a given percent of data.	Lesson 6.2, Investigating Math Activity 6.2
MM3D2b	Determine the probability that a given value falls within a specified interval.	Lesson 6.2, Lesson 6.3
MM3D2c	Estimate how many items in a population fall within a specified interval.	Lesson 6.2, Lesson 6.3
MM3D3	Students will understand the differences between experimental and observational studies by posing questions and collecting, analyzing, and interpreting data.	Lesson 6.3, Investigating Math Activity 6.3, Lesson 6.4, Problem Solving Workshop 6.4, Lesson 6.5

UNIT 1
Algebra: Linear Systems, Matrices, and Vertex-Edge Graphs

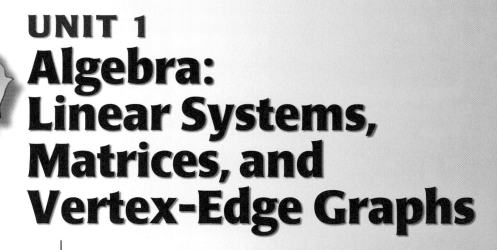

Use Problem Solving Strategies and Models

Georgia Performance Standards: MM3P1d, MM3P3a

Goal Solve problems using verbal models.

Vocabulary

When solving real-life problems, write an equation called a **verbal model** in words before you write the equation in mathematical symbols.

Example 1   Use a formula

A rectangular corral has an area of 3500 square meters. If the length of the corral is 75 meters, what is the width of the corral?

Solution

You can use the formula for the area of a rectangle as a verbal model.

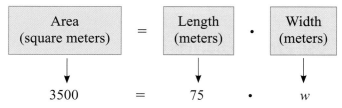

An equation for this situation is $3500 = 75w$. Solve for w.

$3500 = 75w$ Write equation.

$46.7 \approx w$ Divide each side by 75.

The width of the corral is about 46.7 meters.

Guided Practice for Example 1

1. The perimeter of a rectangular city park is 1260 yards. The width of the park is 290 yards. What is the length of the park? **340 yd**

2. A boat travels at a speed of 32 miles per hour. How long will it take the boat to travel 144 miles? **4.5 h**

Example 2   Look for a pattern

Look for a pattern in the table. Then write an equation that represents the table.

x	0	1	2	3
y	0	6	12	18

Solution

The x-values increase by 1 and the y-values increase by 6. You can use this pattern to write the equation $y = 6x$.

Guided Practice for Example 2

Look for a pattern in the table. Then write an equation that represents the table.

3.

x	0	1	2	3
y	0	−3	−6	−9

$y = -3x$

4.

x	0	1	2	3
y	1	8	15	22

$y = 7x + 1$

Example 3   **Draw a diagram**

Rock Pond You are designing a square rock pond surrounded by a brick sidewalk of uniform width. The pond has a side length of 32 feet. The side length of the outside square is 40 feet. Draw a diagram to find the width of the sidewalk.

Solution

Begin by drawing and labeling a diagram, as shown below.

From the diagram, you can write and solve an equation to find w.

$w + 32 + w = 40$	Write equation.
$2w + 32 = 40$	Combine like terms.
$2w = 8$	Subtract 6 from each side.
$w = 4$	Divide each side by 2.

The width of the sidewalk is 4 feet.

Guided Practice for Example 3

5. **Fabric** A piece of fabric is 50 inches long. You cut the fabric into two pieces. The first piece is x inches long. The second piece is 16 inches longer than the first piece. Draw and label a diagram of the fabric. Then write and solve an equation to find x. **See Additional Answers beginning on page AA1.**

6. **Construction** You want to create an open rectangular box from a square piece of cardboard. The cardboard is 24 inches by 24 inches and you will cut 3 inch squares from each corner. Draw a diagram to find the length of the box. **See Additional Answers beginning on page AA1.**

Exercise Set A

MM3P1d Monitor and reflect on the process of mathematical problem solving.

MM3P3a Organize and consolidate their mathematical thinking through communication.

Use the formula $d = rt$ for distance traveled to solve for the missing variable.

1. $d = \underline{\quad?\quad}$, $r = 45$ mi/h, $t = 7$ h **315 mi**

2. $d = 420$ mi, $r = 70$ mi/h, $t = \underline{\quad?\quad}$ **6 h**

3. $d = 504$ mi, $r = \underline{\quad?\quad}$, $t = 8$ h **63 mi/h**

4. $d = 577.5$ mi, $r = 55$ mi/h, $t = \underline{\quad?\quad}$ **10.5 h**

Use the formula $A = bh$ for the area of a parallelogram to solve for the missing variable.

5. $A = \underline{\quad?\quad}$, $b = 9$ ft, $h = 6$ ft **54 ft²**

6. $A = 62$ in.², $b = \underline{\quad?\quad}$, $h = 4$ in. **15.5 in.**

7. $A = 195$ m², $b = 15$ m, $h = \underline{\quad?\quad}$ **13 m**

8. $A = \underline{\quad?\quad}$, $b = 26$ cm, $h = 17$ cm **442 cm²**

9. **Error Analysis** *Describe* and correct the error in writing an equation.
In the table the inputs increase by 5. An equation that represents the table is $y = 2x + 9$.

x	0	5	10	15
y	9	19	29	39

An equation that represents the table is $y = 9 + 10x$.

Look for a pattern in the table. Then write an equation that represents the table.

10.

x	0	1	2	3
y	9	17	25	33

$y = 8x + 9$

11.

x	0	1	2	3
y	34	37	40	43

$y = 3x + 34$

12.

x	0	1	2	3
y	79	74	69	64

$y = 79 - 5x$

13.

x	0	1	2	3
y	58	47	36	25

$y = 58 - 11x$

14. **Windsurfing** The highest speed reached by a windsurfer is about 56.04 miles per hour. How far could a windsurfer travel in 1.5 hours at this speed? **84.06 mi**

15. **Shopping** You buy a pair of jeans for $29.99. T-shirts are on sale for $8.95 each. You have $80 to spend for clothes. How many T-shirts can you purchase? **5**

16. **Travel** You and a friend take turns driving on a 530 mile trip. Your friend drives for 4.5 hours at an average speed of 60 miles per hour. What must your average speed be for the remainder of the trip if you want to reach your hotel in 4 more hours? **65 mi/h**

17. **Remodeling** A five gallon bucket of polyurethane can seal 3200 square feet of floor space. If you need to cover 9000 square feet, how many buckets of polyurethane must be purchased in order to cover it? **3**

| MM3P1d | Monitor and reflect on the process of mathematical problem solving. |
| MM3P3a | Organize and consolidate their mathematical thinking through communication. |

Look for a pattern in the table. Then write an equation that represents the table.

1.

x	0	1	2	3
y	22	28	34	40

$y = 6x + 22$

2.

x	0	4	8	12
y	60	52	44	36

$y = -2x + 60$

3. Multiple Representations Your cell phone plan costs $52 per month plus $.10 per text message. You receive a bill for $69.20.

  a. Making a Table Copy and complete the table below. Use the table to estimate how many text messages you sent. *Sample answer:* **175 text messages**

Text messages	0	50	100	150	200
Monthly bill	$52	?	?	?	?
		$57	$62	$67	$72

  b. Writing a Model Write an equation for the situation. Solve it to find exactly how many text messages you sent. **69.2 = 0.1x + 52; 172 text messages**

  c. Comparing Answers Is your estimate from part (a) compatible with the exact answer from part (b)? *Explain.* **Sample answer: Yes; the estimate in part (a) was comparable to the exact answer in part (b).**

4. Commission A salesman earns a base salary of $12,000 per year. The salesman also receives a 7% commission on his sales. If his total sales exceed $500,000 for the year, a bonus of $5000 is paid in December. Last year the salesman reported an income of $56,921 to the IRS. What were his total sales? **$570,300**

5. Wood Shop You have a piece of wood that is 84 inches long. You cut the wood into three pieces. The second piece is 8 inches longer than the first piece. The third piece is 16 inches longer than the second piece. Draw a diagram and then write and solve an equation to find the lengths of the three pieces.

See Additional Answers beginning on page AA1.

6. Painting You and a group of friends volunteer to help paint a house. You need to paint 4 rooms in 8 hours. If each person can paint one room in 10 hours, how many people will it take to paint all of the rooms on time? **5**

7. Art Gallery The owner of an art gallery wants to hang five paintings on a wall so that the spaces between the paintings are the same. The owner also wants the spaces at the left and right of the group of paintings to be twice the space between any two adjacent paintings. The wall is 24 feet wide and the paintings are 2 feet wide. Draw a diagram and then write and solve an equation to find how to position the paintings. **See Additional Answers beginning on page AA1.**

UNIT 1

Solve Linear Systems by Graphing

Georgia Performance Standards: MM3A5c

Goal Solve systems of linear equations.

Vocabulary

A **system of two linear equations** in two variables x and y, also called a linear system, consists of two equations that can be written in the following form:
$Ax + By = C$ and $Dx + Ey = F.$

A **solution of a system** of linear equations in two variables is an ordered pair (x, y) that satisfies each equation.

A system that has at least one solution is **consistent.**

If a system has no solution, the system is **inconsistent.** The graph of this system is a pair of parallel lines.

A consistent system that has exactly one solution is **independent.**

A consistent system that has infinitely many solutions is **dependent.** The graph of this system is a pair of lines that coincide.

Example 1 Solve a system graphically

Graph the linear system and estimate the solution. Then check the solution algebraically.

$y + 3x = 5$ **Equation 1**

$y - 2x = -5$ **Equation 2**

Solution

Begin by graphing both equations, as shown at the right. From the graph, the lines appear to intersect at $(2, -1)$. The solution can be checked algebraically:

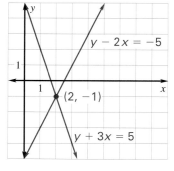

Equation 1	**Equation 2**
$y + 3x = 5$	$y - 2x = -5$
$(-1) + 3(2) \overset{?}{=} 5$	$-1 - 2(2) \overset{?}{=} -5$
$-1 + 6 \overset{?}{=} 5$	$-1 - 4 \overset{?}{=} -5$
$5 = 5 ✓$	$-5 = -5 ✓$

The solution is $(2, -1)$.

Guided Practice for Example 1

Graph the linear system and estimate the solution. Then check the solution algebraically. **1–3. See Additional Answers beginning on page AA1.**

1. $y = 4x - 1$
$y = 3x$

2. $3x + y = 7$
$y = 2x - 3$

3. $2x + 3y = 5$
$3x - 4y = -1$

Georgia Performance Standards

MM3A5c   Represent and solve realistic problems using systems of linear equations.

Example 2   **Classify a system of two linear equations**

Classify each system as *consistent and independent, consistent and dependent,* or *inconsistent.*

a. $10x - 2y = 14$ Equation 1
        $5x - y = 7$ Equation 2

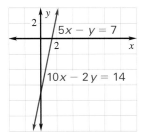

The graphs of the equations are the same line. The system is consistent and dependent.

b. $3x + 2y = 2$ Equation 1
        $3x + 2y = 4$ Equation 2

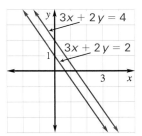

The graphs of the equations are parallel lines. The system is inconsistent.

Example 3   **Write and use a linear system**

Resort Costs   Resort A charges $70 per night, plus a one-time surcharge of $5. Resort B charges $65 per night, plus a one-time surcharge of $20. After how many nights will the total cost of the two options be the same?

Let x represent the number of nights at the resort.
Let y represent the total cost of the stay at the resort.

$y = 70x + 5$ Equation 1 (Resort A)

$y = 65x + 20$ Equation 2 (Resort B)

To solve the system, graph the equations. The lines appear to intersect at (3, 215). So, after 3 nights the total cost of the two options is the same.

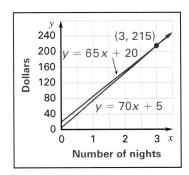

Guided Practice for Examples 2 and 3

Solve the system. Then classify the system as *consistent and independent, consistent and dependent,* or *inconsistent.*

4. $y = -2x$ $(-1, 2)$;
        $y = x + 3$ consistent and independent

5. $y - 3x = 2$ no solutions;
        $y - 3x = 3$ inconsistent

6. $x + y = 6$ infinitely many solutions;
        $-2x - 2y = -12$ consistent and dependent

7.   **What If?** In Example 3, suppose Resort A charges $70 per night, plus a one-time surcharge of $10 and Resort B charges $60 per night, plus a one-time surcharge of $30. After how many nights will the total cost of the two options be the same? **two nights**

MM3A5c Represent and solve realistic problems using systems of linear equations.

Match the linear system with its graph. Then classify the system as *consistent and independent*, *consistent and dependent*, or *inconsistent*.

1. $3x - 2y = 2$
$-2x + y = -2$
C; consistent and independent

2. $4x - y = 3$
$-8x + 2y = -6$
A; consistent and dependent

3. $x + 3y = 2$
$-3x - 9y = 18$
B; inconsistent

A.

B.

C.

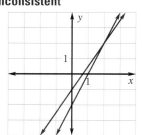

Graph the linear system and estimate the solution. Then check the solution algebraically. 4–15. See Additional Answers beginning on page AA1.

4. $2x + 3y = 8$
$-x + y = -4$

5. $3x + 5y = -4$
$2x - y = -7$

6. $x - 2y = 4$
$4x + 2y = 6$

7. $3x + y = 3$
$-2x + y = 3$

8. $5x - 2y = -1$
$x - 3y = 5$

9. $x - 2y = -5$
$-2x + 6y = 18$

10. $3x + 3y = 3$
$x + 2y = 0$

11. $2x - 4y = 2$
$-2x + 3y = 0$

12. $5x - 3y = -17$
$4x + 5y = 16$

13. $4x - y = -6$
$3x + 7y = 11$

14. $5x - 3y = 3$
$-x - y = -7$

15. $6x + y = -26$
$-4x - 7y = -8$

16. **Error Analysis** A student used the check shown to conclude that $(1, -2)$ is a solution of this system:

$5x - y = 7$
$x + 4y = -5$

Describe and correct the student's error.
See Additional Answers beginning on page AA1.

$5x - y = 7$
$5(1) - (-2) \stackrel{?}{=} 7$
$7 = 7$

So, $(1, -2)$ is a solution of the system.

Solve the system. Then classify the system as *consistent and independent*, *consistent and dependent*, or *inconsistent*.

17. $y = -1$
$5x + y = 9$
$(2, -1)$; consistent and independent

18. $4x - y = 10$
$x - 4y = -5$
$(3, 2)$; consistent and independent

19. $y = 5x + 3$
$y = 5x - 3$
no solution; inconsistent

Exercise Set A (continued)

20–28. See Additional Answers beginning on page AA1.

20. $y = 2x - 1$

$-8x + 4y = -4$

21. $-20x + 16y = -24$

$5x - 4y = 6$

22. $4x - 5y = -9$

$3x - 5y = -13$

23. $3x + 7y = 9$

$2x + 9y = 6$

24. $4x + 5y = 4$

$6x + 9y = 12$

25. $8x + 9y = 7$

$5x - 2y = 12$

26. $x - 2y = 5$

$2x - 4y = 10$

27. $5x + y = 16$

$-3x + y = 0$

28. $2x + \frac{1}{2}y = 4$

$12x - 6y = -12$

29. Work Schedule You worked 18 hours last week and earned a total of $124 before taxes. Your job as a lifeguard pays $8 per hour, and your job as a cashier pays $6 per hour. How many hours did you work at each job? **lifeguard: 8 h, cashier: 10 h**

30. Law Enforcement During one calendar year, a state trooper issued a total of 385 citations for warnings and speeding tickets. Of these, there were 31 more warnings than speeding tickets. How many warnings and how many speeding tickets were issued? **warnings: 208, speeding tickets: 177**

31. Concert A vendor sold 200 tickets for an upcoming rock concert. Floor seats were $36 and stadium seats were $28. The vendor sold $6080 in tickets. How many $36 and $28 tickets did the vendor sell? **60 tickets at $36; 140 tickets at $28**

32. Multiple Representations The price of refrigerator A is $800, and the price of refrigerator B is $1300. The cost of electricity needed to operate the refrigerators is $50 per year for refrigerator A and $40 per year for refrigerator B.
See Additional Answers beginning on page AA1.

   a. Writing Equations Write an equation for the cost of owning refrigerator A and an equation for the cost of owning refrigerator B.

   b. Graphing Equations Graph the equations from part (a). After how many years are the total costs of owning the refrigerators equal?

   c. Checking Reasonableness Is your solution from part (b) reasonable in this situation? *Explain.*

In Exercises 33–36, use the following information.

Break-Even Analysis You purchase a music store for $115,000. The estimated monthly revenue is $5500 and expected monthly costs are $3200.

33. Let R represent the revenue during the first t months. Write a linear model for R. **$R = 5500t$**

34. Let C represent the costs during the first t months including the purchase price. Write a linear model for C. **$C = 3200t + 115{,}000$**

35. Graph the linear models for revenue and cost on the same coordinate plane.
See Additional Answers beginning on page AA1.

36. How many months will it take until revenue and costs are equal (at the "break-even point")? **50**

Graph the linear system and estimate the solution. Then check the solution algebraically. 1–12. See Additional Answers beginning on page AA1.

1. $x + 2y = 7$
$3x + y = 6$

2. $2x + 3y = 1$
$2x - y = 5$

3. $4x - 3y = 8$
$4x + 2y = -12$

4. $-3x - y = 1$
$x + y = 3$

5. $6x - 3y = 3$
$2x + 3y = 1$

6. $2x + 3y = 3$
$-x + 6y = -4$

7. $4x + 4y = 3$
$-2x + 5y = 2$

8. $3x - 4y = -5$
$-6x - 4y = 1$

9. $9x - 2y = 0$
$3x + 4y = 7$

10. $y = 3x + 2$
$15x - 5y = -10$

11. $x - 7y = 4$
$-3x + 21y = -12$

12. $2x + 9y = 4$
$-6x - 3y = -4$

Solve the system. Then classify the system as *consistent and independent*, *consistent and dependent*, or *inconsistent*. 13–21. See Additional Answers beginning on page AA1.

13. $3x - 4y = 5$
$2x + y = 7$

14. $-2x + 6y = -2$
$-3x + 2y = 4$

15. $5x + 2y = -3$
$3x + y = -1$

16. $4x + 3y = -1$
$-2x - 3y = -4$

17. $8x + 4y = -4$
$x - 2y = 6$

18. $x - 5y = -5$
$3x - 15y = 9$

19. $3x + 4y = 8$
$-6x - 8y = -16$

20. $\frac{3}{2}x - y = 1$
$\frac{2}{3}x - y = \frac{3}{4}$

21. $2x + y = -5$
$\frac{1}{2}x - y = -3$

22. Write a system of equations that has no solutions. ***Sample answer:*** $x + y = 2$
$x + y = 5$

23. Write a system of equations that has infinitely many solutions. ***Sample answer:*** $x + y = 2$
$2x + 2y = 4$

24. Write a system of equations that has exactly one solution. ***Sample answer:*** $x + y = 2$
$2x + y = 5$

Graph the system and estimate the solution(s). Then check the solution(s) algebraically. 25–30. See Additional Answers beginning on page AA1.

25. $y = |x + 1|$
$y = x$

26. $y = |x - 4|$
$y = x$

27. $y = |x - 1|$
$y = -x + 2$

28. $y = |x + 1|$
$y = x - 2$

29. $y = |x| - 5$
$y = 5$

30. $y = |x| + 3$
$y = 3$

Exercise Set B (continued)

In Exercises 31 and 32, use the following information.

Test Questions A math test is to have 20 questions. The test format uses multiple choice worth 4 points each and problem solving questions worth 6 points each. The test has a total of 100 points.

31. Write a system of equations to determine how many of each type of question are used. $x + y = 20$
$4x + 6y = 100$

32. Solve the system. **10 multiple choice questions, 10 problem solving questions**

33. Multiple Representations The price of washer A is $756, and the price of washer B is $1424. The cost needed to operate the washers is $90.25 per year for washer A and $48.50 per year for washer B. **See Additional Answers beginning on page AA1.**

    a. Writing Equations Write an equation for the cost of owning washer A and an equation for the cost of owning washer B.

    b. Graphing Equations Graph the equations from part (a). Estimate the number of years before the total costs of owning the washers are equal. Use a graphing calculator to check your estimate.

    c. Checking Reasonableness Is your solution from part (b) reasonable in this situation? *Explain.*

In Exercises 34–36, use the following information.

Buying a Computer Store 1 is advertising that all desktop computers are 20% off for a limited time. Store 2 is advertising a $250 rebate on all desktop computers. Assume that the lowest priced desktop computer is $700.

34. Let x represent the original price and y represent the sale price. Write a system of equations that describes the prices of the computers in both stores. $y = 0.8x$
$y = x - 250$

35. Graph the system. **See Additional Answers beginning on page AA1.**

36. Under what circumstances does Store 1 have a better deal than Store 2?
Store 1 has the better deal when the regular price is greater than $1250.

In Exercises 37–40, use the following information.

Business Investing A business invests $10,000 in equipment to produce a product. Each unit of the product costs $.75 to produce and is sold for $1.25.

37. Let R represent the revenue obtained by selling x units. Write a linear model for R. $R = 1.25x$

38. Let C represent the total cost of producing x units. Write a linear model for C. $C = 0.75x + 10,000$

39. Graph the linear models for revenue and total cost on the same coordinate plane.
See Additional Answers beginning on page AA1.

40. How many units must be sold before the revenue and costs are equal (at the "break-even point")? **20,000 units**

Investigating Math Activity

Systems with Many or No Solutions

Use before Lesson 1.3

Materials	graphing calculator

Question

How can you determine whether a system of linear equations has no solution or an infinite number of solutions without solving or graphing the system?

Explore

Determine whether the system has many or no solutions.

Graph the system of linear equations. Use the graph to determine whether the system has no solutions or an infinite number of solutions.

$x + 2y = 6$
$3x + 6y = 3$

STEP 1 Enter the equations in slope-intercept form.

STEP 2 Graph the equations in a standard viewing window.

STEP 3 The graph shows that the number of solutions is zero.

Draw Conclusions

In Exercises 1–3, graph the system of linear equations. Use the graph to determine whether the system has no solutions or an infinite number of solutions. 1–3. See Additional Answers beginning on page AA1.

1. $5x - 2y = 9$
   $20x - 8y = -28$

2. $x - 4y = 10$
   $2x - 8y = 20$

3. $8x - 6y = 10$
   $-12x + 9y = -15$

4. What types of lines were graphed in the Explore and Exercise 1? In each system, how do the coefficients of x compare? the coefficients of y? the constants?
   See Additional Answers beginning on page AA1.

5. What types of lines were graphed in Exercise 2 and Exercise 3? In each system, how do the coefficients of x compare? the coefficients of y? the constants?
   See Additional Answers beginning on page AA1.

6. **Reasoning** Based on your results, make a conjecture about the relationship between the equations in a system and whether it has no solutions or an infinite number of solutions. **See Additional Answers beginning on page AA1.**

Solve Linear Systems Algebraically

Georgia Performance Standards: MM3A5c

Goal Solve linear systems algebraically.

Vocabulary

To use the **substitution method,** Step 1 is to *solve* one of the equations for one of its variables. Step 2 is to *substitute* the expression from Step 1 into the other equation and solve for the other variable. Step 3 is to *substitute* the value from Step 2 into the revised equation from Step 1 and solve.

To use the **elimination method,** Step 1 is to *multiply* one or both of the equations by a constant to obtain coefficients that differ only in sign for one of the variables. Step 2 is to *add* the revised equations from Step 1 and solve for the remaining variable. Step 3 is to *substitute* the value obtained in Step 2 into either of the original equations and solve for the other variable.

Example 1   Use the substitution method

Solve the system using the substitution method.

$6x + 3y = 12$ **Equation 1**

$3x + y = 5$ **Equation 2**

Solution

STEP 1 **Solve** Equation 2 for y.

$$y = 5 - 3x$$

STEP 2 **Substitute** the expression for y into Equation 1 and solve for x.

$6x + 3(5 - 3x) = 12$ Substitute $5 - 3x$ for y.

$x = 1$ Solve for x.

STEP 3 **Substitute** the value of x into the revised equation from Step 1 and solve for y.

$y = 5 - 3(1)$ Substitute 1 for x.

$y = 2$ Solve for y.

The solution is $(1, 2)$.

Guided Practice for Example 1

Solve the system using the substitution method.

1. $2x + y = 4$ **(2, 0)**
  $3x - 5y = 6$

2. $3x + 6y = 3$ **(3, −1)**
  $x - 2y = 5$

3. $2x - y = 6$ **(4, 2)**
  $-3x + 2y = -8$

Georgia Performance Standards

MM3A5c Represent and solve realistic problems using systems of linear equations.

Example 2 **Use the elimination method**

School T-Shirts Your school sells short sleeve T-shirts that cost the school $5 each and are sold for $8 each. Long sleeve T-shirts cost the school $7 each and are sold for $13 each. The school spends a total of $2450 on T-shirts and sells all of them for $4325. How many of each type of T-shirt are sold?

STEP 1 **Write** a system of equations. Let x represent the number of short sleeve T-shirts and let y represent the number of long sleeve T-shirts.

$5x + 7y = 2450$ Equation 1: Total cost for all T-shirts

$8x + 13y = 4325$ Equation 2: Total revenue from all T-shirts sold

STEP 2 **Multiply** Equation 1 by -8 and Equation 2 by 5 so that the coefficients of x differ only in sign. Then add the revised equations and solve for y.

$5x + 7y = 2450$ $\times\ -8$ $-40x - 56y = -19{,}600$

$8x + 13y = 4325$ $\times\ 5$ $40x + 65y = 21{,}625$

$9y = 2025$ $y = 225$

STEP 3 **Substitute** the value of y into one of the original equations and solve for x.

$5x + 7(225) = 2450$ Substitute 225 for y in Equation 1.

$x = 175$ Simplify and solve for x.

The school sold 175 short sleeve T-shirts and 225 long sleeve T-shirts.

Example 3 **Solve linear systems with many or no solutions**

a. Solve: $9x - 3y = 6$
       $3x - y = 2$

b. Solve: $x - 2y = 5$
       $4x - 8y = 3$

a. $y = 3x - 2$ Solve second equation for y.

$9x - 3(3x - 2) = 6$ Substitute $3x - 2$ for y in first equation.

$6 = 6$ Simplify.

Because the equation $6 = 6$ is always true, there are infinitely many solutions.

b. $-4x + 8y = -20$ Multiply first equation by -4.

$4x - 8y = 3$ Add the second equation.

$0 = -17$

Because the equation $0 = -17$ is never true, there is no solution.

Guided Practice for Examples 2 and 3

Solve the linear system by any algebraic method.

4. $7x + 2y = -5$
$3x - 4y = -7$
$(-1, 1)$

5. $2x - 3y = 3$
$4x - 5y = 9$
$(6, 3)$

6. $3x - y = 5$
$6x - 2y = 10$
infinitely many solutions

7. $x - 2y = 5$
$4x - 8y = -3$
no solutions

LESSON 1.3 **Exercise Set A**

MM3A5c   Represent and solve realistic problems using systems of linear equations.

Solve the system using the substitution method.

1. $x + 2y = 6$ **(2, 2)**
$3x - 2y = 2$

2. $x + 3y = 3$ **(3, 0)**
$2x - 4y = 6$

3. $4x + y = 7$ **(2, −1)**
$2x + 5y = -1$

4. $2x - 3y = 3$ $\left(\frac{9}{4}, \frac{1}{2}\right)$
$-2x + y = -4$

5. $3x + 2y = -2$ $\left(\frac{2}{3}, -2\right)$
$6x - y = 6$

6. $8x + 2y = 2$ **(−1, 5)**
$x + 3y = 14$

Solve the system using the elimination method.

7. $-3x + 3y = 3$ **(2, 3)**
$3x + y = 9$

8. $5x - y = -9$ **(−1, 4)**
$2x + y = 2$

9. $-5x + 12y = 20$ **(−16, −5)**
$x - 2y = -6$

10. $4x - 2y = -2$ $\left(\frac{1}{2}, 2\right)$
$6x + y = 5$

11. $3x + 2y = 1$ $\left(-\frac{4}{5}, \frac{17}{10}\right)$
$4x + 6y = 7$

12. $7x - 3y = 6$ **(0, −2)**
$-2x + 5y = -10$

Solve the system using any algebraic method.

13. $5x + 7y = -2$ **(1, −1)**
$2x - 7y = 9$

14. $x + 3y = 1$ **(−2, 1)**
$3x + 7y = 1$

15. $4x + 6y = 8$ **no solution**
$2x + 3y = 3$

16. $8x - 5y = -17$ $\left(-\frac{13}{2}, -7\right)$
$-2x + y = 6$

17. $3x - 8y = 0$ **(16, 6)**
$-2x + 5y = -2$

18. $4x - 6y = 2$ $\left(\frac{2}{7}, -\frac{1}{7}\right)$
$5x + 3y = 1$

19. $2x - 5y = 3$ **infinitely many solutions**
$-4x + 10y = -6$

20. $8x + 3y = 10$ $\left(\frac{23}{13}, -\frac{18}{13}\right)$
$-6x + y = -12$

21. $\frac{5}{4}x + y = -\frac{9}{2}$ **(6, −12)**
$x + \frac{3}{2}y = -12$

22. Business A nut wholesaler sells a mix of peanuts and cashews. The wholesaler charges $2.65 per pound for peanuts and $4.90 per pound for cashews. The mix is to sell for $3.28 per pound. How many pounds of peanuts and how many pounds of cashews should be used to make 125 pounds of the mix? **90 pounds of peanuts, 35 pounds of cashews**

23. Hair Salon A hair salon receives a shipment of 84 bottles of hair conditioner to use and sell to customers. The two types of conditioners received are type A, which is used for regular hair, and type B, which is used for dry hair. Type A costs $6.50 per bottle and type B costs $8.25 per bottle. The hair salon's invoice for the conditioner is $588. How many of each type of conditioner are in the shipment? **60 of type A, 24 of type B**

24. Birthday Gift You and your sister decide to combine your weekly overtime earnings to buy a birthday gift for your mother. Your overtime rate is $18 per hour and your sister's overtime rate is $24 per hour. The total amount earned for the gift was $288. If you worked two more hours of overtime than your sister, how many overtime hours did each of you work? **you: 8 h, your sister: 6 h**

UNIT 1

MM3A5c   Represent and solve realistic problems using systems of linear equations.

Solve the system using the substitution method.

1. $2x + 4y = -4$ **(4, −3)**
$x - 2y = 10$

2. $2x + y = -3$ **(−6, 9)**
$-6x - 4y = 0$

3. $4x + y = -1$ **infinitely many solutions**
$8x + 2y = -2$

4. $6x - 3y = 12$ **infinitely many solutions**
$-2x + y = -4$

5. $x + 2y = 11$ **(−3, 7)**
$4x + 3y = 9$

6. $\frac{1}{5}x + 2y = \frac{4}{3}$ $\left(\frac{5}{3}, \frac{1}{2}\right)$
$x + \frac{2}{3}y = 2$

Solve the system using the elimination method.

7. $2x + 4y = -10$ **(3, −4)**
$-3x - 2y = -1$

8. $6x + 12y = -7$ **no solution**
$x + 2y = 2$

9. $5x + 4y = -3$ **(1, −2)**
$3x - 7y = 17$

10. $-2x + \frac{5}{3}y = -5$ **(5, 3)**
$3x - \frac{7}{2}y = \frac{9}{2}$

11. $\frac{1}{2}x + 3y = 9$ **(6, 2)**
$\frac{1}{3}x + y = 4$

12. $\frac{4}{3}x + 6y = -1$ $\left(\frac{3}{4}, -\frac{1}{3}\right)$
$4x - 4y = \frac{13}{3}$

Solve the system using any algebraic method.

13. $0.25x + 0.5y = 7.5$ **(10, 10)**
$0.4x + 0.5y = 9$

14. $0.5x - 0.3y = 1.3$ **(5, 4)**
$-1.4x + 1.2y = -2.2$

15. $2x - 3y = 1$ $\left(\frac{17}{7}, \frac{9}{7}\right)$
$x + 2y = 5$

16. $3x - \frac{5}{3}y = 5$ **no solution**
$-\frac{3}{5}x + \frac{1}{3}y = -5$

17. $0.3x - 0.2y = 1.4$ $\left(\frac{14}{3}, 0\right)$
$0.12x - 0.8y = 0.56$

18. $3.3x - 1.5y = 5.22$ **(2.4, 1.8)**
$1.1x + 2.6y = 7.32$

19. **Aviation** Flying with the wind, a plane flew 600 miles in 3 hours. Flying against the wind, the plane could fly only 300 miles in the same amount of time. Find the speed of the plane in calm air and the speed of the wind. **plane: 150 mi/h, wind: 50 mi/h**

20. **Business** For a recent job, an electrician earned $50 per hour, and the electrician's apprentice earned $20 per hour. The electrician worked 6 hours more than the apprentice, and together they earned a total of $650. How much money did each person earn? **apprentice: $100, electrician: $550**

21. **DVD Cable** In order to connect your DVD player to your TV set, you need a cable with a special adapter at both ends. An 8 foot cable costs $24.50 and a 4 foot cable costs $15.50. The total cost is the sum of the cost of the adapters and the cost of the cable itself. What would you expect to pay for a 6 foot cable? **$20.00**

22. **Challenge** Find a and b so that $(-2, -1)$ is the unique solution to the system below.
$ax + by = -7$ **a = 2, b = 3**
$-ax + 2by = -2$

UNIT 1

Graph Linear Inequalities in Two Variables

Georgia Performance Standards: MM3A6a

Goal Graph linear inequalities in two variables.

Vocabulary

A **linear inequality in two variables** can be written in one of four forms: $Ax + By < C$, $Ax + By \leq C$, $Ax + By > C$, $Ax + By \geq C$.

An ordered pair (x, y) is a **solution of a linear inequality** in two variables if the inequality is true when the values of x and y are substituted into the inequality.

The **graph of a linear inequality** in two variables is the set of all points in a coordinate plane that represent solutions of the inequality.

A line divides the plane into two **half-planes.**

Example 1 **Solution of a linear inequality in two variables**

Tell whether the ordered pairs (5, −1) and (−2, 6) are solutions of the inequality 2x + 3y > 9.

Ordered Pair	Substitute	Conclusion
$(5, -1)$	$2(5) + 3(-1) = 7 \not> 9$	$(5, -1)$ is not a solution.
$(-2, 6)$	$2(-2) + 3(6) = 14 > 9$	$(-2, 6)$ is a solution.

Guided Practice for Example 1

Tell whether the given ordered pairs are solutions of the inequality.

1. $4x - y \leq 2$; (2, 4), (1, −3) **(2, 4) is *not* a solution; (1, −3) is *not* a solution.**

2. $\frac{3}{2}x + 5y \geq 15$; (−2, 4), (0, −3) **(−2, 4) is a solution; (0, −3) is *not* a solution.**

Example 2 **Graph linear inequalities in one or two variables**

a. Graph $y \geq 1$ in a coordinate plane.

Graph the boundary line $y = 1$. Use a solid line because the inequality symbol is $\geq$. Because $(0, 2)$ is a solution, shade the half-plane that contains $(0, 2)$.

b. Graph $2x + y < -3$.

Graph the boundary line $2x + y = -3$. Use a dashed line because the inequality symbol is $<$. Because $(0, 0)$ is *not* a solution, shade the half-plane that does *not* contain $(0, 0)$.

Georgia Performance Standards

MM3A6a   Solve systems of inequalities in two variables, showing the solutions graphically.

Guided Practice for Example 2

Graph the inequality in a coordinate plane. 3–5. See Additional Answers beginning on page AA1.

3. $x < -1$

4. $y \leq 3x$

5. $x + 4y < 8$

Example 3   **Solve a multi-step problem**

The perimeter of a rectangle is to be more than 16 inches. Write an inequality describing the possible dimensions of the rectangle. Then graph the inequality and identify three solutions.

STEP 1 **Write** an inequality. An inequality is $2x + 2y > 16$.

STEP 2 **Graph** the inequality. First graph the boundary line $2x + 2y = 16$. Use a dashed line because the inequality symbol is >. Because $(0, 0)$ is *not* a solution, shade the half-plane that does *not* contain $(0, 0)$. Because x and y cannot be negative, shade only points in Quadrant I.

STEP 3 **Identify** solutions on the graph. Three solutions of the inequality are $(1, 8)$, $(2, 10)$, and $(4, 7)$.

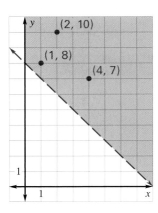

Example 4   **Graph an absolute value inequality**

Graph $y \leq |x| + 1$.

STEP 1 **Graph** the equation of the boundary, $y = |x| + 1$. Use a solid line because the inequality is $\leq$.

STEP 2 **Test** the point $(0, 0)$. Because $(0, 0)$ is a solution of the inequality, shade the portion of the coordinate plane outside the absolute value graph.

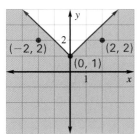

Guided Practice for Examples 3 and 4

6. Rework Example 3 if the perimeter of the rectangle is to be no less than 20 centimeters. See Additional Answers beginning on page AA1.

Graph the inequality. 7–9. See Additional Answers beginning on page AA1.

7. $y \leq 3|x|$

8. $y > -|x| + 3$

9. $y \geq |x + 2| - 1$

MM3A6a   Solve systems of inequalities in two variables, showing the solutions graphically.

Tell whether the given ordered pairs are solutions of the inequality.

1. $x - y < 4$; $(5, 4)$, $(-1, -4)$ **yes; yes**

2. $2x + 3y \leq -3$; $(0, -1)$, $(-3, 2)$ **yes; no**

3. $4x - 2y > 5$; $(5, 8)$, $(-1, -4)$ **no; no**

4. $8y - 2x \geq 15$; $(1, 2)$, $(3, 3)$ **no; yes**

5. $2y < 5x + 10$; $(-2, -1)$, $(-1, 2)$ **yes; yes**

6. $10x \geq 14 - 8y$; $(2, 4)$, $(4, -3)$ **yes; yes**

Match the inequality with its graph.

7. $3x - 2y \geq -4$ **B**

8. $3x - 2y \leq -4$ **C**

9. $3x - 2y > -4$ **A**

A.

B.

C.
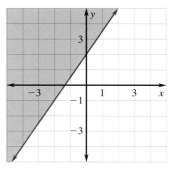

Graph the inequality in a coordinate plane. **10–21. See Additional Answers beginning on page AA1.**

10. $x > 2$

11. $x \leq -1$

12. $2x \leq 8$

13. $y \geq -2$

14. $y < 3$

15. $\frac{1}{4}y \leq 1$

16. $y < 2x - 1$

17. $y \geq \frac{1}{2}x + 2$

18. $3x + y > -3$

19. $x + 3y \leq 6$

20. $x - 3y > -3$

21. $-6x - 2y \leq 4$

Error Analysis *Describe* and correct the error in graphing the inequality.
22 and 23. See Additional Answers beginning on page AA1.

22. $y < x + 3$

23. $y \geq -3x - 4$

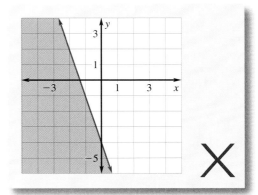

Exercise Set A (continued)

Write an inequality represented by the graph.

24. $x < 4$

25. 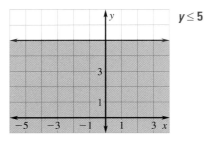 $y \le 5$

Graph the inequality in a coordinate plane. 26–28. See Additional Answers beginning on page AA1.

26. $y > |x - 3|$ 27. $y \le |x| + 4$ 28. $y \ge |x + 2| - 1$

In Exercises 29 and 30, use the following information.

Summer Job You offer to mow your neighbors' lawns for $20 or to wash their cars for $10. Your goal is to earn at least $1500 this summer.

29. Write and graph an inequality that represents the possible number of lawns you would have to mow x and cars you would have to wash y in order to reach your goal.
    See Additional Answers beginning on page AA1.

30. What ordered pair represents mowing 50 lawns and washing 65 cars? Is this ordered pair a solution of the inequality? **(50, 65); yes**

In Exercises 31–33, use the following information.

Music Lessons Your parents have budgeted $550 for you to take music lessons on the piano for $25 and on the saxophone for $20.

31. Write and graph an inequality that represents the possible number of piano lessons x and saxophone lessons y you can take this summer.
    See Additional Answers beginning on page AA1.

32. Is it possible to take 12 piano lessons and 15 saxophone lessons this summer? **no**

33. If you take 14 piano lessons, what is the maximum number of saxophone lessons you can take? **10**

34. **Vacation** On a two week vacation, you and your brother can rent one canoe for $12 per day or rent two mountain bikes for $15 each per day. Together, you have $140 to spend.
    See Additional Answers beginning on page AA1.

    a. Write and graph an inequality describing the possible numbers of days you and your brother can canoe or bicycle together.

    b. Give three solutions of the inequality from part (a).

    c. You decide that on one day you will canoe alone and your brother will bicycle alone. Repeat parts (a) and (b) using this new condition.

LESSON 1.4 **Exercise Set B**

 MM3A6a Solve systems of inequalities in two variables, showing the solutions graphically.

Tell whether the given ordered pairs are solutions of the inequality
$-1.5y - 3x > 4$.

1. $(-1.5, -1)$ **yes**
2. $(-2.5, 2)$ **yes**
3. $(-3, -4)$ **yes**
4. $(3.5, -2.5)$ **no**

Match the inequality with its graph.

5. $y > |x + 4| - 3$ **C**
6. $y < |x + 4| - 3$ **B**
7. $y \geq |x + 4| - 3$ **A**

A. **B.** **C.**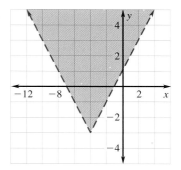

Graph the inequality in a coordinate plane. 8–19. See Additional Answers beginning on page AA1.

8. $x + 2 < 6$
9. $y - 2 \geq -1$
10. $2x + y \leq 0$
11. $5x - 2y \leq 3$
12. $-7x + 4y < 2$
13. $3x - 6y > -12$
14. $-x - 3y \geq -8$
15. $4x - 5y \leq -7$
16. $-6x + 8y < 4$
17. $y \geq 3|x - 2| + 1$
18. $y > -\frac{1}{2}|x + 1| + \frac{3}{2}$
19. $3 - 2y \geq 6|x - 3| - 3$

Error Analysis *Describe* **and correct the error in graphing the inequality.**
20 and 21. See Additional Answers beginning on page AA1.

20. $y > 2|x - 3| - 2$
21. $y \leq \frac{1}{2}|x + 1| + 4$

 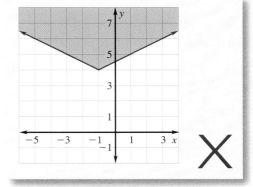

Exercise Set B (continued)

Write an inequality represented by the graph.

22. 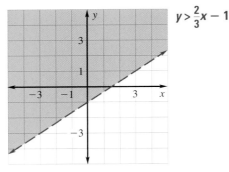 $y > \frac{2}{3}x - 1$

23. 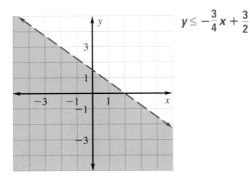 $y \le -\frac{3}{4}x + \frac{3}{2}$

24. 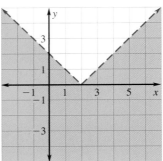 $y < |x - 2|$

25. 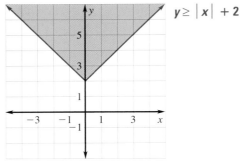 $y \ge |x| + 2$

In Exercises 26–28, use the following information.

Test Scores A chemistry exam included multiple choice questions that were worth 3 points each and fill-in-the-blank questions that were worth 2 points each. The highest score in the class was 88 out of a possible 100 points.

26. Write an inequality that represents the number of x multiple choice and y fill-in-the-blank questions that could have been answered correctly by any student in the class. **$3x + 2y \le 88$**

27. Graph the inequality. **See Additional Answers beginning on page AA1.**

28. Is it possible that someone in the class answered 13 multiple choice questions and 25 fill-in-the-blank questions correctly? **no**

In Exercises 29–31, use the following information.

Music Lessons The high school music teacher offers piano lessons to students for a flat fee of $10 plus $5 per hour.

29. Write an equation that represents the cost c of lessons as a function of time t offered by the high school music teacher. **$c = 5t + 10$**

30. Write and graph an inequality that represents the amount a competitor must charge if the competitor always wants to charge less than the music teacher.
See Additional Answers beginning on page AA1.

31. Is it possible for a competitor to offer a lower flat fee but a higher hourly rate and always charge less than the music teacher? *Explain.* **no; The initial cost will be less but as the hours increase the cost will eventually surpass the music teacher's cost due to the higher hourly rate.**

Graph Systems of Linear Inequalities

Georgia Performance Standards: MM3A6a

Goal Graph systems of linear inequalities.

Vocabulary

The following is an example of a **system of linear inequalities** in two variables:
$x + y \leq 6$ and $2x - y > 6$.

A **solution of a system of inequalities** is an ordered pair that is a solution of each inequality in the system.

The **graph of a system of inequalities** is the graph of all solutions of the system.

Example 1 Graph a system of two inequalities

Graph the system of inequalities.

$y < x + 2$ **Inequality 1**

$y \geq -2x$ **Inequality 2**

Solution

STEP 1 **Graph** each inequality in the system. Use red for $y < x + 2$ and blue for $y \geq -2x$.

STEP 2 **Identify** the region that is common to both graphs. It is the region that is shaded purple.

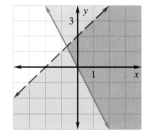

Example 2 Graph a system with no solution

Graph the system of inequalities.

$y > x + 2$ **Inequality 1**

$y \leq x + 1$ **Inequality 2**

Solution

STEP 1 **Graph** each inequality in the system. Use red for $y > x + 2$ and blue for $y \leq x + 1$.

STEP 2 **Identify** the region that is common to both graphs. There is no common region shaded by both inequalities. So, the system has no solution.

Example 3 **Graph a system with an absolute value inequality**

Graph the system of inequalities.

$y \geq 0$ **Inequality 1**

$y < |x - 1|$ **Inequality 2**

STEP 1 **Graph** each inequality in the system.
Use red for $y \geq 0$ and blue for $y < |x - 1|$.

STEP 2 **Identify** the region that is common to both graphs. It is the region that is shaded purple.

Guided Practice for Examples 1, 2, and 3

Graph the system of inequalities. 1–9. See Additional Answers beginning on page AA1.

1. $y > 1$
$y \leq 3$

2. $x < 3$
$y < 4$

3. $y \leq -x - 1$
$y \leq \frac{1}{2}x - 1$

4. $y \geq 2$
$y < -2$

5. $y > -x$
$y < -x - 2$

6. $y \geq x + 1$
$y \leq x - 1$

7. $y < |x|$
$y \geq 0$

8. $y \leq -|x| + 2$
$y \geq 0$

9. $y \geq |x - 1|$
$y < 2$

Example 4 **Graph a system of three or more inequalities**

Graph the system of inequalities.

$y \leq -x + 2$ **Inequality 1**

$x \geq 1$ **Inequality 2**

$y > -2$ **Inequality 3**

Graph each inequality in the system. Then identify the region that is common to all the graphs. The solution of the system is the region that is shaded.

Guided Practice for Example 4

Graph the system of inequalities. 10–12. See Additional Answers beginning on page AA1.

10. $x \geq 0$
$y \geq 0$
$y < x$

11. $x \geq -2$
$y \leq 0$
$y \geq x$

12. $x \geq 0$
$y > x$
$y < 2$

Exercise Set A

MM3A6a   Solve systems of inequalities in two variables, showing the solutions graphically.

Match the system of inequalities with its graph.

1. $x + y > 1$ **B**
$-2x + 3y \geq -6$

2. $x + y < 1$ **C**
$-2x + 3y < -6$

3. $x + y \leq 1$ **A**
$-2x + 3y > -6$

A.

B.

C.
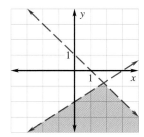

4. Error Analysis *Describe* and correct the error in graphing the system of inequalities.

$$y \geq -4$$
$$y \leq 2x - 2$$

See Additional Answers beginning on page AA1.

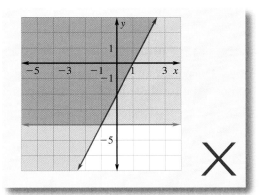

Graph the system of inequalities. 5–19. See Additional Answers beginning on page AA1.

5. $x > -1$
$y > -1$

6. $x \geq -2$
$y < 1$

7. $y \leq 3$
$y > 1$

8. $x + y \geq 0$
$-x + y \geq 0$

9. $y > -2x$
$2x - y > 1$

10. $2x + y < 5$
$y > 2|x - 1|$

11. $x + 2y < 2$
$3x + y \leq 3$

12. $y > 2x - 3$
$x > -1$
$y < 3$

13. $y \leq |x| + 4$
$x < 2$
$y \geq 2$

14. $y < \frac{1}{2}x + 3$
$y \geq -2x - 3$
$x \leq 3$

15. $x + y > -2$
$-x + y > -2$
$y \geq 0$

16. $y \leq -\frac{1}{3}x + 2$
$y > 3x - 3$
$x > -1$

17. $x + 2y \leq 8$
$x + 4y \geq 8$
$x \geq 0$

18. $x + 2y \leq 10$
$2x + y \leq 8$
$2x - 5y < 20$

19. $x + 2y \leq 5$
$2x - 4y \leq -10$
$3x + 6y > -12$

Exercise Set A *(continued)*

Write a system of two linear inequalities that has the ordered pair as a solution. 20–23. Answers will vary.

20. $(2, -3)$

21. $(-1, -6)$

22. $(-4, 0)$

23. $(0, -5)$

24. The diagram at the right shows the graph of a system of two inequalities. Write a system of inequalities that represents the graph. $y \geq |x - 1| + 1$
$y < 4$

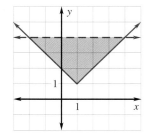

In Exercises 25 and 26, use the following information.

Distance During a family trip, you share the driving with your dad. At most, you are allowed to drive for three hours. While driving, your maximum speed is 55 miles per hour.

25. Write a system of inequalities describing the possible number of hours t and distance d you may have driven. $t \leq 3$
$d \leq 55t$

26. Is it possible for you to have driven 160 miles? **yes**

27. **Summer Jobs** You can work at most 24 hours next week. You need to earn at least $100 to cover your weekly expenses. Your babsitting job pays $7 per hour and your job at the grocery store pays $6.50 per hour. **See Additional Answers beginning on page AA1.**

    a. Write a system of inequalities to describe the situation.

    b. Graph the system you wrote in part (a).

    c. Give three possible solutions for the number of hours you can work at each job.

28. **Multiple Representations** The homecoming committee must consist of 9 to 12 representatives from the junior and senior classes. The committee must include at least 4 juniors and at least 4 seniors. Let x be the number of juniors and y be the number of seniors. **See Additional Answers beginning on page AA1.**

    a. **Writing a System** Write a system of inequalities to describe the situation.

    b. **Graphing a System** Graph the system you wrote in part (a).

    c. **Finding Solutions** Give two possible solutions for the numbers of juniors and seniors on the homecoming committee.

Exercise Set B

MM3A6a Solve systems of inequalities in two variables, showing the solutions graphically.

Match the system of inequalities with its graph.

1. $x \le 3$ **C**
$y \ge -2$
$y < x$
$3x + 2y \le 8$

2. $x \le 3$ **A**
$y \ge -2$
$y > x$
$3x + 2y \ge 8$

3. $x \le 3$ **B**
$y \le -2$
$y < x$
$3x + 2y \le 8$

A.

B.

C.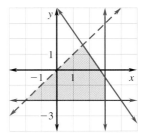

Graph the system of inequalities. 4–15. See Additional Answers beginning on page AA1.

4. $x - y > -1$
$2x + y < -1$

5. $y \le -3x$
$x + 4y < 8$

6. $3x + 4y \ge -10$
$2x - 3y > -6$

7. $2x + y \le 3$
$y \ge |x| + 1$

8. $y > -2|x + 1| - 2$
$2x - y < 4$

9. $x + y < 1$
$y > \frac{1}{2}|x - 2| - 3$

10. $-x + y < 4$
$x + 3y > -9$
$x > -3$

11. $2x + y < 3$
$x - y > -1$
$x + 2y \ge 0$

12. $3x + 6y > 4$
$3x - 4y > 4$
$x - y < 5$

13. $-2x + y < 3$
$x + y > 1$
$y \le 0$
$y > -2$

14. $-2x + 4y < 8$
$2x + 4y > -8$
$-4x + y \ge 0$
$x \ge -2$

15. $3x + 2y \le 6$
$-3x + 2y \le 6$
$3x + 2y \ge -6$
$-3x + 2y \ge -6$

Write a system of four linear inequalities that has the ordered pair as a solution. 16–19. Answers will vary.

16. $(2, -1)$

17. $(-2, -4)$

18. $(-3, 0)$

19. $(6, 7)$

Write a system of linear inequalities for the shaded region. 20–22. See Additional Answers beginning on page AA1.

20.

21.

22.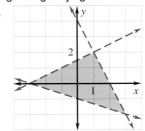

UNIT 1

Exercise Set B (continued)

23. Visual Thinking Write a system of linear inequalities whose graph is a pentagon and its interior. **Answers will vary**.

24. **Arena Seating** For an upcoming event, a 2500 seat arena is selling tickets for $25 and $15. At least 1000 tickets must be priced at $15 and total sales need to exceed $10,000 to make a profit. Let x represent the number of tickets priced at $25 and y represent the number of tickets priced at $15. Write a system of inequalities that shows the possible combinations of ticket sales in order to make a profit.

$x + y \leq 2500$
$25x + 15y > 10,000$
$y \geq 1000$
$x \geq 0$

25. **Softball** In softball, the strike zone is a rectangle the width of home plate that extends from the batter's knees to a point halfway between the shoulders and the top of the uniform pants. The width of home plate is 17 inches. Suppose a batter's knees are 18 inches above the ground and the point halfway between her shoulder and the top of her pants is 40 inches above the ground. Write and graph a system of inequalities that represents the strike zone. **See Additional Answers beginning on page AA1**.

26. Multiple Representations Near the end of summer, a department store has a summer clothes sale to make room for winter attire. The sale allows customers to save 20% to 50% on all clothing items regularly priced at $15 or more.
See Additional Answers beginning on page AA1.
  a. **Writing a System** Write a system of inequalities with x as the regular price and y as the sale price.
  b. **Graphing a System** Graph the system of inequalities.
  c. **Describing Solutions** Give the range of possible sale prices for an item regularly priced at $45.

27. **Heart Rate** A person's theoretical maximum heart rate (in heartbeats per minute) is $200 - x$ where x is the person's age in years ($20 \leq x \leq 65$). When a person exercises, it is recommended that the person strive for a heart rate that is at least 50% of the maximum and at most 75% of the maximum. **See Additional Answers beginning on page AA1**.

  a. Write a system of linear inequalities that describes the given information.

  b. Graph the system you wrote in part (a).

  c. A 36-year-old person has a heart rate of 145 heartbeats per minute when exercising. Is the person's heart rate in the recommended range? *Explain*.

28. Challenge You and a friend are trying to guess the number of peanuts in a jar. You both agree that the jar contains at least 500 peanuts. You guess that there are x peanuts, and your friend guesses that there are y peanuts. The actual number of peanuts in the jar is 1000. Write and graph a system of inequalities describing the values of x and y for which your guess is closer than your friend's guess to the actual number of peanuts. **See Additional Answers beginning on page AA1**.

Georgia Performance Standards

MM3A6a Solve systems of inequalities in two variables, showing the solutions graphically.

LESSON 1.5

Problem Solving Workshop

Problem A furniture store is having a sale. All chairs that have a regular price of $50 to $250 are on sale for 15% to 75% off. Write a system of linear inequalities for the regular chair prices and possible sale prices. Graph the system of inequalities. Find the range of possible sale prices for a chair that is regularly priced at $160.

STEP 1 Read and Understand

What do you know? The regular prices of chairs and the sale percentages

What do you want to find out? The possible sale prices for a chair that is regularly priced at $160

STEP 2 Make a Plan Use what you know to write and graph a system of linear inequalities.

STEP 3 Solve the Problem Let x be the regular chair price and y be the sale price. From the information, you can write the following four inequalities.

$x \geq 50$	Regular price must be at least $50.
$x \leq 250$	Regular price can be at most $250.
$y \geq 0.25x$	Sale price is at least $(100 - 75)\% = 25\%$ of regular price.
$y \leq 0.85x$	Sale price is at most $(100 - 15)\% = 85\%$ of regular price.

Graph each inequality in the system. The region that is common to all is shaded.

Identify the sale prices for $160 chairs. From the graph, when $x = 160$, the value of y is between 40 and 136, inclusive.

Therefore, chairs regularly priced at $160 sell for between $40 and $136, inclusive, during the sale.

STEP 4 Look Back Use the inequalities to find the range of y values when $x = 160$. So, $y \geq 0.25(160) = 40$ and $y \leq 0.85(160) = 136$. The value of y is between 40 and 136, inclusive. The answer is correct.

Practice See Additional Answers beginning on page AA1.

1. **Shopping** All MP3 players at an electronics store that have a regular price of $100 to $330 are on sale for 10% to 35% off. Write a system of linear inequalities for the regular MP3 player prices and possible sale prices. Graph the system of inequalities. Use the graph to estimate the range of possible sale prices for an MP3 player that is regularly priced at $200.

2. **Garden** You are designing a rectangular garden that is to be enclosed by a fence no longer than 500 feet. The length of the garden must be greater than 50 feet and the width of the garden must be greater than 25 feet. Write a system of linear inequalities for the dimensions of the garden. Graph the system of inequalities. Find the range of possible widths for a length of 120 feet.

Linear Programming

Georgia Performance Standards: MM3A6b

Goal Solve linear programming problems.

Vocabulary

Linear programming is a process of maximizing or minimizing a linear *objective function*. The **objective function** gives a quantity that is to be maximized (or minimized), and is subject to **constraints** that are linear inequalities.

If all the constraints in a linear programming problem are graphed, the intersection of the graph is called the **feasible region.** If this region is bounded, then the objective function has a maximum value and a minimum value on the region. Moreover, the maximum and minimum values each occur at a vertex of the feasible region.

Example 1   Use linear programming to maximize profit

Crafts Toy wagons are made to sell at a craft fair. It takes 4 hours to make a small wagon and 6 hours to make a large wagon. The owner of the craft booth will make a profit of $12 for a small wagon and $20 for a large wagon. The craft booth owner has no more than 60 hours available to make wagons and wants to have at least 6 small wagons to sell. How many of each size should be made to maximize profit?

Solution

Let x represent the number of small wagons made and let y represent the number of large wagons made. The total profit P is given by the equation $P = 12x + 20y$.

STEP 1 **Graph** a system of constraints.

$x \geq 6$	Make at least 6 small wagons.
$y \geq 0$	Number of large wagons cannot be negative.
$4x + 6y \leq 60$	No more than 60 hours available to work.

STEP 2 **Evaluate** the profit function $P = 12x + 20y$ at each vertex of the feasible region.

At $(6, 0)$: $P = 12(6) + 20(0) = 72$

At $(6, 6)$: $P = 12(6) + 20(6) = 192$ ◄—— **Maximum**

At $(15, 0)$: $P = 12(15) + 20(0) = 180$

The owner can maximize profit by making 6 small wagons and 6 large wagons.

Guided Practice for Example 1

1. Rework Example 1 if the owner of the craft booth has no more than 40 hours available to make wagons and wants to have at least 4 small wagons to sell.
   4 small wagons, 4 large wagons

Example 2 Solve a linear programming problem

Find the minimum value and the maximum value of the objective function $C = 3x + 2y$ subject to the following constraints.

$$x \geq 0$$

$$y \geq 0$$

$$x + 3y \leq 15$$

$$4x + y \leq 16$$

Solution

STEP 1 **Graph** the system of constraints. Find the coordinates of the vertices of the feasible region by solving systems of two linear equations. The solution of the system

$$x + 3y = 15$$

$$4x + y = 16$$

gives the vertex $(3, 4)$. The other three vertices are $(0, 0)$, $(4, 0)$, and $(0, 5)$.

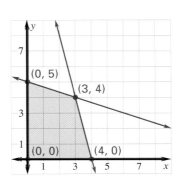

STEP 2 **Evaluate** the function $C = 3x + 2y$ at each vertex.

At $(0, 0)$: $C = 3(0) + 2(0) = 0$ ◄——— **Minimum**

At $(4, 0)$: $C = 3(4) + 2(0) = 12$

At $(3, 4)$: $C = 3(3) + 2(4) = 17$ ◄——— **Maximum**

At $(0, 5)$: $C = 3(0) + 2(5) = 10$

The minimum value of C is 0. It occurs when $x = 0$ and $y = 0$.

The maximum value of C is 17. It occurs when $x = 3$ and $y = 4$.

Guided Practice for Example 2

Find the minimum and maximum values of the objective function subject to the given constraints.

2. Objective function:
$C = 4x + 3y$ **0; 32**

Constraints:

$x \geq 0$

$y \geq 0$

$x + y \leq 8$

3. Objective function:
$C = 7x + 5y$ **14; 44**

Constraints:

$x \geq 2$

$y \geq 0$

$2x + y \leq 10$

4. Objective function:
$C = 2x + 8y$ **0; 56**

Constraints:

$x \geq 0$

$y \geq 0$

$x + 2y \leq 14$

$6x + y \leq 18$

LESSON 1.6

Exercise Set A

MM3A6b Represent and solve realistic problems using linear programming.

Find the minimum and maximum values of the objective function for the given feasible region.

1. $C = x + 2y$ **1; 16**

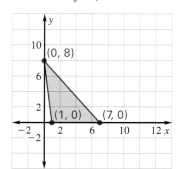

2. $C = 6x - 4y$ **−64; 56**

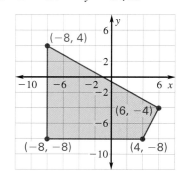

3. $C = 5x + 7y$ **270; 920**

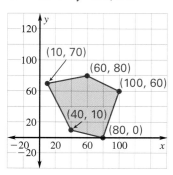

Find the minimum and maximum values of the objective function subject to the given constraints.

4. Objective function: **0; 24**

$C = 3x + 4y$

Constraints:

$x \geq 0$

$y \geq 0$

$x + y \leq 6$

5. Objective function: **10; 50**

$C = 2x + 5y$

Constraints:

$x \leq 5$

$y \geq 4$

$-2x + 5y \leq 30$

6. Objective function: **13; 41**

$C = 7x + 3y$

Constraints:

$x \geq 1$

$y \geq 2$

$6x + 4y \leq 38$

7. Objective function: **24; 72**

$C = 4x + 6y$

Constraints:

$x \geq 0$

$y \leq 8$

$-2x + 3y \geq 12$

8. Objective function: **0; 40**

$C = 8x + 7y$

Constraints:

$x \geq 0$

$y \geq 0$

$4x + 4y \leq 20$

$x + 2y \leq 8$

9. Objective function: **9; 27**

$C = 3x + 5y$

Constraints:

$x \geq 0$

$2x + 3y \geq 6$

$3x - y \leq 9$

$x + 4y \leq 16$

10. Craft Fair Piñatas are made to sell at a craft fair. It takes 2 hours to make a mini piñata and 3 hours to make a regular-sized piñata. The owner of the craft booth will make a profit of $14 for each mini piñata sold and $22 for each regular-sized piñata sold. If the craft booth owner has no more than 40 hours available to make piñatas and wants to have at least 16 piñatas to sell, how many of each size piñata should be made to maximize profit? **8 mini piñatas, 8 regular-sized piñatas**

11. Manufacturing A company manufactures inkjet printers and laser printers. The company can make a total of 60 printers per day, and it has 120 labor-hours per day available. It takes 1 labor-hour to make an inkjet printer and 3 labor-hours to make a laser printer. The profit is $45 per inkjet printer and $65 per laser printer. How many of each type of printer should the company make to maximize its daily profit? **30 inkjet printers, 30 laser printers**

LESSON 1.6

Exercise Set B

MM3A6b   Represent and solve realistic problems using linear programming.

Find the minimum and maximum values of the objective function subject to the given constraints.

1. Objective function: 46; 100

$C = 6x + 7y$

Constraints:

$x \geq 3$

$y \geq 4$

$2x + 6y \leq 48$

2. Objective function: 0; 32

$C = 8x + 3y$

Constraints:

$x \geq 0$

$y \geq 0$

$x + \frac{1}{2}y \leq 4$

3. Objective function: 0; 38

$C = 5x + 2y$

Constraints:

$x \geq 0$

$y \geq 0$

$4x - y \leq 20$

$x + 2y \leq 14$

4. Objective function: 8000; 21,000

$C = 20x + 30y$

Constraints:

$x \geq 0$

$y \geq 0$

$7x + 8y \leq 5600$

$7x + 8y \geq 2800$

5. Objective function: 0; no maximum

$C = 3x + y$

Constraints:

$x \geq 0$

$y \geq -3$

$y \geq -x$

$x - 4y \geq -20$

6. Objective function: 0; 40

$C = x + 2y$

Constraints:

$x \geq 0$

$y \geq 0$

$2x + 3y \leq 60$

$2x + y \leq 28$

$4x + y \leq 48$

7. **Error Analysis** *Describe* and correct the error in finding the minimum and maximum values of the objective function $C = 2x + 5y$ subject to the following constraints.

$x \geq 2$

$y \geq 2$

$x + y \leq 16$

$3x + y \leq 32$

$-\frac{1}{2}x + y \geq \frac{1}{2}$

See Additional Answers beginning on page AA1.

The minimum value of C is 14. It occurs when $x = 2$ and $y = 2$. The maximum value of C is 56. It occurs when $x = 8$ and $y = 8$.

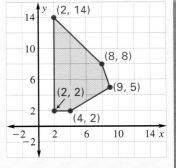

8. **Manufacturing** A bicycle company produces two models of bicycles. The table below shows the number of hours it takes for assembling, painting, and packaging each model. The total times available are 4000 hours for assembling, 4800 hours for painting, and 1500 hours for packaging. The profits are \$55 for model A and \$60 for model B. How many of each model of bicycle should the company make to maximize profit? What is the maximum profit? **Model A: 750, Model B: 1000; \$101,250**

	Assembling	Painting	Packaging
Hours, Model A	2	4	1
Hours, Model B	2.5	1	0.75

Solve Systems of Linear Equations in Three Variables

Georgia Performance Standards: MM3A5c

Goal Solve systems of equations in three variables.

Vocabulary

A **linear equation in three variables** x, y, and z is an equation of the form $ax + by + cz = d$ where a, b, and c are not all zero.

An example of a **system of three linear equations** in three variables is:

$x + 2y + z = 3$ Equation 1
$2x + y + z = 4$ Equation 2
$x - y - z = 2$ Equation 3

A **solution of a system with three variables** is an **ordered triple** (x, y, z) whose coordinates make each equation true.

Example 1   **Use the elimination method**

Solve the system. $2x + 3y - z = 13$ **Equation 1**
$3x + y - 3z = 11$ **Equation 2**
$x - y + z = 3$ **Equation 3**

STEP 1 **Rewrite** the system as a linear system in *two* variables.

$\begin{array}{ll} 2x + 3y - z = 13 & \text{Add 3 times Equation 3} \\ \underline{3x - 3y + 3z = 9} & \text{to Equation 1.} \\ 5x + 2z = 22 & \text{New Equation 1} \end{array}$

$\begin{array}{ll} 3x + y - 3z = 11 & \text{Add Equations 2 and 3.} \\ \underline{x - y + z = 3} & \\ 4x - 2z = 14 & \text{New Equation 2} \end{array}$

STEP 2 **Solve** the new linear system for both of its variables.

$\begin{array}{ll} 5x + 2z = 22 & \text{Add new Equation 1 and new Equation 2.} \\ \underline{4x - 2z = 14} & \\ 9x = 36 & \\ x = 4 & \text{Solve for } x. \\ z = 1 & \text{Substitute into new Equation 1 or 2 to find } z. \end{array}$

STEP 3 **Substitute** $x = 4$ and $z = 1$ into an original equation and solve for y.

$\begin{array}{ll} x - y + z = 3 & \text{Write original Equation 3.} \\ 4 - y + 1 = 3 & \text{Substitute 4 for } x \text{ and 1 for } z. \\ y = 2 & \text{Solve for } y. \end{array}$

Because $x = 4$, $y = 2$, and $z = 1$, the solution is the ordered triple $(4, 2, 1)$.

Georgia Performance Standards

MM3A5c   Represent and solve realistic problems using systems of linear equations.

| **Example 2** | **Solve a three-variable system with no solution** |

Solve the system.

$$2x - 2y + 2z = 9 \qquad \text{Equation 1}$$
$$x - y + z = 5 \qquad \text{Equation 2}$$
$$3x + y + 2z = 4 \qquad \text{Equation 3}$$

When you multiply Equation 2 by -2 and add the result to Equation 1, you obtain a false equation.

$$\begin{array}{ll} 2x - 2y + 2z = 9 & \text{Add } -2 \text{ times Equation 2 to Equation 1.} \\ \underline{-2x + 2y - 2z = -10} & \\ 0 = -1 & \text{New Equation 1} \end{array}$$

Because you obtain a false equation, the original system has no solution.

| **Example 3** | **Solve a three-variable system with many solutions** |

Solve the system.

$$x + y + z = 3 \qquad \text{Equation 1}$$
$$x + y - z = 3 \qquad \text{Equation 2}$$
$$3x + 3y + z = 9 \qquad \text{Equation 3}$$

STEP 1 Rewrite the system as a linear system in *two* variables.

$$\begin{array}{ll} x + y + z = 3 & \text{Add Equation 1 to Equation 2.} \\ \underline{x + y - z = 3} & \\ 2x + 2y = 6 & \text{New Equation 1} \\ \\ x + y - z = 3 & \text{Add Equation 2 to Equation 3.} \\ \underline{3x + 3y + z = 9} & \\ 4x + 4y = 12 & \text{New Equation 2} \end{array}$$

STEP 2 Solve the new linear system for both of its variables.

$$\begin{array}{ll} -4x - 4y = -12 & \text{Add } -2 \text{ times new Equation 1} \\ \underline{4x + 4y = 12} & \text{and new Equation 2.} \\ 0 = 0 & \end{array}$$

Because you obtain the identity $0 = 0$, the system has infinitely many solutions.

STEP 3 Describe the solution. Divide new Equation 1 by 2 to get $x + y = 3$, or $y = -x + 3$. Substituting this into the original Equation 1 produces $z = 0$. Any ordered triple of the form $(x, -x + 3, 0)$ is a solution of the system.

Guided Practice for Examples 1, 2, and 3

Solve the system.

1. $2x + y + z = 5$
    $x - y + 2z = 4$
    $x + y + z = 4$
    (1, 1, 2)

2. $x + 2y + z = 7$
    $x - y + z = 4$
    $3x + 6y + 3z = 9$
    no solution

3. $x + y + z = 2$
    $x + y - z = 2$
    $2x + 2y + z = 4$
    $(x, -x + 2, 0)$

UNIT 1

Exercise Set A

MM3A5c Represent and solve realistic problems using systems of linear equations.

Tell whether the given ordered triple is a solution of the system.

1. $(2, 1, 3)$ no

$2x - y + 5z = 16$

$x - 3y + 2z = 5$

$x + 2y + z = 7$

2. $(5, -2, 2)$ no

$2x - y + z = 5$

$x + 2y - z = -1$

$-2x + y - 3z = -15$

3. $(3, 3, 4)$ no

$x + 2y - 2z = 1$

$7x - 4y + z = 11$

$2x - 3y + 2z = 5$

Solve the system using any algebraic method.

4. $x + y - 5z = -5$

$y - 2z = 14$ $(-43, -2, -8)$

$4y - 2z = 8$

5. $x - y + z = 5$ $(2, 1, 4)$

$2y + 3z = 14$

$-3y + 2z = 5$

6. $-3x + y - z = -2$ $(-1, 0, 5)$

$2x - y - 2z = -12$

$4x + 2y + z = 1$

7. $x - 2y + z = -1$ $(3, 1, -2)$

$x + 2y - z = 7$

$x + y + z = 2$

8. $x - 2y + 4z = -19$ $(1, 6, -2)$

$2x + y - 3z = 14$

$3x + y + 2z = 5$

9. $x - 2y - 3z = -7$ $(5, -3, 6)$

$4x + 5y - 2z = -7$

$-2x + y + z = -7$

10. $8x - 2y + z = -6$ $(-2, -3, 4)$

$-x + 3y - 2z = -15$

$3x - y + 4z = 13$

11. $2x + 2y + z = -5$

$2x + y + 3z = 7$

$-4x - 2y - 6z = -14$

$\left(-\dfrac{5}{2}z + \dfrac{19}{2}, 2z - 12, z\right)$

12. $3x - 4y - 4z = 8$ $\left(2, \dfrac{1}{2}, -1\right)$

$4x + 2y - 2z = 11$

$-5x + 8y + 3z = -9$

13. **Harvest Yields** A farmer makes three deliveries to the feed mill during one harvest. The harvest produced 2885 bushels of corn, 1335 bushels of wheat, and 1230 bushels of soybeans. Use the table to write and solve a system of equations to find the total number of bushels in each delivery.

Crop	First Delivery	Second Delivery	Third Delivery
Corn	50%	75%	40%
Wheat	30%	10%	30%
Soybeans	20%	15%	30%

$0.5x + 0.75y + 0.4z = 2885$
$0.3x + 0.1y + 0.3z = 1335$
$0.2x + 0.15y + 0.3z = 1230$;
1st delivery: 1800,
2nd delivery: 1500,
3rd delivery: 2150

14. **Harvest Earnings** The feed mill pays a farmer $6930.00 for the first delivery, $5475.00 for the second delivery, and $8879.50 for the third delivery. The table shows the number of bushels included in each delivery. Use the table to write and solve a system of equations to find the price per bushel that the farmer received for each crop.

Delivery	Corn	Wheat	Soybeans
First Delivery	900	540	360
Second Delivery	1125	150	225
Third Delivery	860	645	645

$900x + 540y + 360z = 6930$
$1125x + 150y + 225z = 5475$
$860x + 645y + 645z = 8879.5$;
corn: $3.20, wheat: $3.50,
soybean: $6.00

Exercise Set B

MM3A5c Represent and solve realistic problems using systems of linear equations.

Solve the system using the elimination method.

1. $x + 2y + 2z = -2$ **(2, 1, -3)**
$2x - y + 3z = -6$
$x - 3y + 2z = -7$

2. $-3x + y - 3z = -13$
$2x - y + z = 8$ **(1, -4, 2)**
$4x + 2y + 3z = 2$

3. $2x + 4y - 4z = 6$ $\left(\frac{4}{13}z, \frac{11}{13}z, z\right)$
$x + 2y - 2z = 1$
$5x - 3y + z = 5$

Solve the system using the substitution method.

4. $2x + 2y - z = 9$ **(4, -2, -5)**
$3x - y + 3z = -1$
$x - 2y + z = 3$

5. $x - 3y - z = -1$ $\left(\frac{1}{2}, 1, -\frac{3}{2}\right)$
$2x + 2y + 2z = 0$
$3x + y + 3z = -2$

6. $4x - 2y + 3z = 19$ $\left(3, -\frac{1}{2}, 2\right)$
$x + 4y - 2z = -3$
$2x + 6y + z = 5$

Solve the system using any algebraic method.

7. $2x + 5y - 4z = -3$ $\left(\frac{3}{2}, -2, -1\right)$
$4x + 2y - 2z = 4$
$2x - 8y - 2z = 21$

8. $2x + 2y - z = -1$ $\left(\frac{1}{3}, -\frac{2}{3}, \frac{1}{3}\right)$
$-2x + 2y + 3z = -1$
$3x - y + 4z = 3$

9. $3x - y - 2z = 6$ **(7, -21, 18)**
$2x + 3y + 3z = 5$
$4x + 2y + z = 4$

10. $x + 2y - z = 4$ **(-z, z + 2, z)**
$3x - y + 4z = -2$
$6x + 5y + z = 10$

11. $x - 2y + z = \frac{7}{6}$ $\left(\frac{4}{3}, -\frac{1}{4}, -\frac{2}{3}\right)$
$2x + y - 3z = \frac{53}{12}$
$3x + 3y + 2z = \frac{23}{12}$

12. $x - 2y + 3z = 8$
$4x - 2y - 2z = -6$
$-2x + y + z = 3$
$\left(\frac{5}{3}z - \frac{14}{3}, \frac{7}{3}z - \frac{19}{3}, z\right)$

13. $w + x - 2y + z = 1$ **(1, 1, 1, 1)**
$2w - x + 3y - 2z = 2$
$w + 3x - y + 4z = 7$
$3w + x - y + 2z = 5$

14. $w + x + 2y + z = 2$
$2w + 2x + y + 3z = 0$
$2w - 4x - 2y - z = 7$
$-w + 2x + y - z = -2$
(2, -1, 1, -1)

15. $-w + 3x - y - 4z = 6$
$2w + 4x + 2y - z = 6$
$w - x + y + 3z = -4$
$3w - x + 3y + z = 4$
(2 - y, 0, y, -2)

In Exercises 16–18, use the following information.

Polynomial Curve Fitting You can use a system of equations to find a polynomial of degree n whose graph passes through $(n + 1)$ points. Consider a polynomial of degree 2, $y = ax^2 + bx + c$. Suppose $(1, -2)$, $(-2, 7)$, and $(-5, -2)$ lie on the graph. Using the point $(1, -2)$, the following equation can be derived:

$$y = ax^2 + bx + c$$
$$-2 = a(1)^2 + b(1) + c$$
$$-2 = a + b + c$$

The equation $a + b + c = -2$ becomes the first equation in the system.

16. Write the equations in the system that correspond to the points $(-2, 7)$ and $(-5, -2)$.
$4a - 2b + c = 7; 25a - 5b + c = -2$

17. Write a system of equations for the coefficients of a polynomial of degree 2 whose graph passes through $(1, -2)$, $(-2, 7)$, and $(-5, -2)$. Solve the system.
$a + b + c = -2, 4a - 2b + c = 7, 25a - 5b + c = -2; a = -1, b = -4, c = 3$

18. Write the polynomial. $y = -x^2 - 4x + 3$

Perform Basic Matrix Operations

Georgia Performance Standards: MM3A4a, MM3A4c

Goal Perform operations with matrices.

Vocabulary

A **matrix** is a rectangular arrangement of numbers in rows and columns. The **dimensions** of a matrix with m rows and n columns are $m \times n$. The numbers in a matrix are its **elements. Equal matrices** have the same dimensions and the elements in corresponding positions are equal.

To add or subtract two matrices, simply add or subtract elements in corresponding positions. You can add or subtract matrices only if they have the same dimensions.

In matrix algebra, a real number is often called a **scalar.** To perform **scalar multiplication,** you multiply each element in the matrix by the scalar.

Properties of Matrix Operations

Many of the properties you have used with real numbers can be applied to matrices. In the properties below, let A, B, and C be matrices with the same dimensions, and let k be a scalar.

Associative Property of Addition	$(A + B) + C = A + (B + C)$
Commutative Property of Addition	$A + B = B + A$
Distributive Property of Addition	$k(A + B) = kA + kB$
Distributive Property of Subtraction	$k(A - B) = kA - kB$

Example 1 Add and subtract matrices

Perform the indicated operation, if possible.

a. $\begin{bmatrix} -9 & 0 \\ -1 & 5 \end{bmatrix} + \begin{bmatrix} 1 & 7 \\ 10 & -2 \end{bmatrix} = \begin{bmatrix} -9 + 1 & 0 + 7 \\ -1 + 10 & 5 + (-2) \end{bmatrix} = \begin{bmatrix} -8 & 7 \\ 9 & 3 \end{bmatrix}$

b. $\begin{bmatrix} -8 & -5 \\ 7 & 9 \end{bmatrix} - \begin{bmatrix} 1 & 2 \\ 8 & -2 \end{bmatrix} = \begin{bmatrix} -8 - 1 & -5 - 2 \\ 7 - 8 & 9 - (-2) \end{bmatrix} = \begin{bmatrix} -9 & -7 \\ -1 & 11 \end{bmatrix}$

Guided Practice for Example 1

1. $\begin{bmatrix} 3 & -4 \\ 0 & 6 \end{bmatrix} + \begin{bmatrix} -7 & 5 \\ 10 & -2 \end{bmatrix} \begin{bmatrix} -4 & 1 \\ 10 & 4 \end{bmatrix}$

2. $\begin{bmatrix} -6 & -4 \\ 3 & 7 \end{bmatrix} - \begin{bmatrix} -1 & 3 \\ -5 & -4 \end{bmatrix} \begin{bmatrix} -5 & -7 \\ 8 & 11 \end{bmatrix}$

3. $\begin{bmatrix} 2 & -1 & 3 \\ 8 & -9 & 6 \end{bmatrix} + \begin{bmatrix} -3 & 1 & -2 \\ 4 & 6 & 7 \end{bmatrix} \begin{bmatrix} -1 & 0 & 1 \\ 12 & -3 & 13 \end{bmatrix}$

4. $\begin{bmatrix} 0 & -5 & 8 \\ 3 & -3 & 6 \\ 4 & 7 & -2 \end{bmatrix} - \begin{bmatrix} -4 & 1 & -1 \\ 9 & -5 & 3 \\ 5 & 8 & 1 \end{bmatrix} \begin{bmatrix} 4 & -6 & 9 \\ -6 & 2 & 3 \\ -1 & -1 & -3 \end{bmatrix}$

Georgia Performance Standards

MM3A4a   Add, subtract, multiply, and invert matrices, when possible, choosing appropriate methods, including technology.

MM3A4c   Examine the properties of matrices, contrasting them with properties of real numbers. ☑

Example 2   **Multiply a matrix by a scalar**

Perform the indicated operation, if possible.

$$-3\begin{bmatrix} 0 & 3 \\ -2 & 5 \\ 1 & 4 \end{bmatrix} = \begin{bmatrix} -3(0) & -3(3) \\ -3(-2) & -3(5) \\ -3(1) & -3(4) \end{bmatrix} = \begin{bmatrix} 0 & -9 \\ 6 & -15 \\ -3 & -12 \end{bmatrix}$$

Guided Practice for Example 2

Perform the indicated operation, if possible.

5. $2\begin{bmatrix} -3 & 0 \\ -2 & 1 \end{bmatrix}$ $\begin{bmatrix} -6 & 0 \\ -4 & 2 \end{bmatrix}$

6. $4\begin{bmatrix} 1 & -7 \\ -3 & 0 \\ -1 & 2 \end{bmatrix}$ $\begin{bmatrix} 4 & -28 \\ -12 & 0 \\ -4 & 8 \end{bmatrix}$

7. $-3\begin{bmatrix} 5 & 4 & -2 \\ 0 & 3 & 1 \end{bmatrix}$ $\begin{bmatrix} -15 & -12 & 6 \\ 0 & -9 & -3 \end{bmatrix}$

Example 3   **Solve a multi-step problem**

Gardening Last year you planted 12 geraniums, 36 begonias, and 20 petunias. This year you planted 10 geraniums, 40 begonias, and 32 petunias. Organize the data using two matrices. Write and interpret a matrix that gives the average number of flowers for the two year period.

Solution

STEP 1 **Organize** the data using two 3×1 matrices, as shown.

	Last year (A)	This year (B)
Geraniums	$\begin{bmatrix} 12 \\ 36 \\ 20 \end{bmatrix}$	$\begin{bmatrix} 10 \\ 40 \\ 32 \end{bmatrix}$
Begonias		
Petunias		

STEP 2 **Write** a matrix for the average number of flowers by multiplying the sum of A and B by $\frac{1}{2}$. You can use the distributive property to rewrite the expression as shown.

$$\frac{1}{2}(A + B) = \frac{1}{2}A + \frac{1}{2}B = \frac{1}{2}\begin{bmatrix} 12 \\ 36 \\ 20 \end{bmatrix} + \frac{1}{2}\begin{bmatrix} 10 \\ 40 \\ 32 \end{bmatrix}$$

$$= \begin{bmatrix} 6 \\ 18 \\ 10 \end{bmatrix} + \begin{bmatrix} 5 \\ 20 \\ 16 \end{bmatrix} = \begin{bmatrix} 11 \\ 38 \\ 26 \end{bmatrix}$$

STEP 3 **Interpret** the matrix from Step 2. You planted an average of 11 geraniums, 38 begonias, and 26 petunias over the last two years.

UNIT 1

Guided Practice for Example 3

8. In Example 3, find $A - B$ and explain what information this matrix gives.
The difference of the two matrices represents the change in the number of flowers.
$$\begin{bmatrix} 2 \\ -4 \\ -12 \end{bmatrix}$$

9. **Bakery** A local bakery keeps track of their sales as shown below.

Last Month Store 1: 620 rolls, 240 cakes, and 38 pies

Store 2: 510 rolls, 190 cakes, and 30 pies

This Month Store 1: 860 rolls, 270 cakes, and 54 pies

Store 2: 780 rolls, 230 cakes, and 46 pies

Organize the data using two matrices. Write and interpret a matrix that gives the average number of bakery items sold per store over the two month period. **Store 1 averaged 740 rolls, 255 cakes, and 46 pies for the two-month period. Store 2 averaged 645 rolls, 210 cakes, and 38 pies for the two-month period.**
$$\begin{bmatrix} 740 & 645 \\ 255 & 210 \\ 46 & 38 \end{bmatrix}$$

Example 4 **Solve a matrix equation**

Solve the matrix equation for x and y.

$$3\left(\begin{bmatrix} 5x & -2 \\ 6 & -4 \end{bmatrix} + \begin{bmatrix} 3 & 7 \\ -5 & -y \end{bmatrix}\right) = \begin{bmatrix} -36 & 15 \\ 3 & -27 \end{bmatrix}$$

Solution

Simplify the left side of the equation.

$$3\left(\begin{bmatrix} 5x & -2 \\ 6 & -4 \end{bmatrix} + \begin{bmatrix} 3 & 7 \\ -5 & -y \end{bmatrix}\right) = \begin{bmatrix} -36 & 15 \\ 3 & -27 \end{bmatrix}$$ Write original equation.

$$3\begin{bmatrix} 5x + 3 & 5 \\ 1 & -4 - y \end{bmatrix} = \begin{bmatrix} -36 & 15 \\ 3 & -27 \end{bmatrix}$$ Add matrices inside parentheses.

$$\begin{bmatrix} 15x + 9 & 15 \\ 3 & -12 - 3y \end{bmatrix} = \begin{bmatrix} -36 & 15 \\ 3 & -27 \end{bmatrix}$$ Perform scalar multiplication.

Equate corresponding elements and solve the two resulting equations.

$$15x + 9 = -36 \qquad\qquad -12 - 3y = -27$$
$$x = -3 \qquad\qquad\qquad y = 5$$

The solution is $x = -3$ and $y = 5$.

Guided Practice for Example 4

Solve the matrix equation for x and y.

10. $\begin{bmatrix} 10 & -3y \\ 6 & 13 \end{bmatrix} = \begin{bmatrix} 10 & -15 \\ 6x & 13 \end{bmatrix}$ $x = 1, y = 5$

11. $\begin{bmatrix} 12 & 3 \\ 6y & 5 \end{bmatrix} = \begin{bmatrix} -4x & 3 \\ 24 & 5 \end{bmatrix}$ $x = -3, y = 4$

12. Solve $-2\left(\begin{bmatrix} -3x & -1 \\ 4 & y \end{bmatrix} + \begin{bmatrix} 9 & -4 \\ -6 & 3 \end{bmatrix}\right) = \begin{bmatrix} 6 & 10 \\ 4 & -20 \end{bmatrix}$ for x and y. $x = 4, y = 7$

Exercise Set A

MM3A4a Add, subtract, multiply, and invert matrices, when possible, choosing appropriate methods, including technology.

MM3A4c Examine the properties of matrices, contrasting them with properties of real numbers.

Perform the indicated operation, if possible. If not possible, state the reason.
1–6. See Additional Answers beginning on page AA1.

1. $\begin{bmatrix} 2 & 1 \\ 6 & 4 \end{bmatrix} - \begin{bmatrix} -2 & 1 \\ -4 & 0 \end{bmatrix}$

2. $\begin{bmatrix} 5 & 2 \\ -1 & 4 \\ -3 & 6 \end{bmatrix} + \begin{bmatrix} -2 & 4 \\ 6 & -2 \\ 7 & -5 \end{bmatrix}$

3. $\begin{bmatrix} 6 & 4 & 3 \\ 1 & -3 & 2 \\ 8 & 7 & 1 \end{bmatrix} - \begin{bmatrix} 4 & 5 & -4 \\ 5 & 1 & 0 \\ 6 & 4 & 7 \end{bmatrix}$

4. $\begin{bmatrix} -4 & 2 & 3 \end{bmatrix} + \begin{bmatrix} -2 \\ 0 \\ -1 \end{bmatrix}$

5. $\begin{bmatrix} 10 & -5 & 7 \\ 2 & -12 & 0 \\ 8 & -4 & 6 \end{bmatrix} + \begin{bmatrix} -7 & 14 & 6 \\ 0 & 12 & -4 \\ 2 & 7 & 3 \end{bmatrix}$

6. $\begin{bmatrix} 10 & -7 & 14 \\ -5 & -10 & 0 \\ 9 & -3 & -7 \end{bmatrix} - \begin{bmatrix} -1 & -3 & 8 \\ -12 & 0 & 6 \\ 10 & -5 & 5 \end{bmatrix}$

Perform the indicated operation. 7–9. See Additional Answers beginning on page AA1.

7. $-3\begin{bmatrix} 4 & 2 \\ 3 & 2 \end{bmatrix}$

8. $-2\begin{bmatrix} 3 & 0 & -1 \\ 0.5 & -6 & 4 \\ 7 & -1.25 & 9 \end{bmatrix}$

9. $-4\begin{bmatrix} 4 & 1 \\ -5 & 0 \\ 1 & -3 \end{bmatrix}$

Solve the matrix equation for x and y.

10. $\begin{bmatrix} -2x & 6 \\ 3y & 9 \end{bmatrix} = \begin{bmatrix} -8 & 6 \\ -12 & 9 \end{bmatrix}$ *x* = 4, *y* = −4

11. $\begin{bmatrix} 4 & 5x \\ -2 & 5 \end{bmatrix} + \begin{bmatrix} -11 & 2 \\ 6 & 5 \end{bmatrix} = \begin{bmatrix} y & 12 \\ 4 & 10 \end{bmatrix}$
   x = 2, *y* = −7

In Exercises 12–15, use the following information.

Book Prices The matrices below show the number of books sold and the average price (in dollars) for the years 2002, 2003, and 2004.

	2002 (D) Sold	Price	**2003 (E)** Sold	Price	**2004 (F)** Sold	Price
Book A	125,000	52.00	110,000	55.50	90,000	47.50
Book B	85,000	83.50	95,000	85.50	100,000	89.00
Book C	190,000	45.60	210,000	56.25	225,000	75.25

12. You purchased book A in 2002, book C in 2003, and book B in 2004. How much did you spend on these three books? **$197.25**

13. How many more (or less) volumes of book B were sold in 2004 than in 2002? **15,000 more**

14. How much more (or less) is the price of book A in 2004 than in 2002? **$4.50 less**

15. In 2005, would you expect book C sales to be *more* or *less* than 100,000? **more**

Exercise Set B

MM3A4a Add, subtract, multiply, and invert matrices, when possible, choosing appropriate methods, including technology.

MM3A4c Examine the properties of matrices, contrasting them with properties of real numbers.

Perform the indicated operation, if possible. If not possible, state the reason.

1–10. See Additional Answers beginning on page AA1.

1. $\begin{bmatrix} 3 & 4 \\ -1 & 8 \end{bmatrix} - \begin{bmatrix} -2 & 6 \\ -5 & 0 \end{bmatrix}$

2. $\begin{bmatrix} 3 & 8 \\ 2 & 0 \\ -4 & 4 \end{bmatrix} + 3\begin{bmatrix} 4 & 3 \\ 1 & -2 \\ 2 & 6 \end{bmatrix}$

3. $-2\begin{bmatrix} 2 & 1 \\ 0 & -3 \end{bmatrix} - 6\begin{bmatrix} 0 & 3 \\ -1 & 4 \end{bmatrix}$

4. $\begin{bmatrix} 4 & 0 & 9 \\ 1 & -2 & 0 \\ 8 & 7 & 11 \end{bmatrix} - \begin{bmatrix} 0 & -2 \\ 2 & 0 \\ 5 & 7 \end{bmatrix}$

5. $3\left(\begin{bmatrix} 2 \\ -1 \end{bmatrix} + 2\begin{bmatrix} 0 \\ 2 \end{bmatrix} \right) - \begin{bmatrix} 5 \\ 8 \end{bmatrix}$

6. $\frac{1}{2}\begin{bmatrix} 1 & 2 \\ -2 & 3 \end{bmatrix} + \begin{bmatrix} 9 \\ 5 \end{bmatrix}$

7. $\frac{1}{3}\begin{bmatrix} -1 & 3 & 0 \\ 4 & -6 & 12 \\ 7 & 5 & -3 \end{bmatrix} + \begin{bmatrix} 2 & -1 & 2 \\ 0 & 5 & -2 \\ 4 & 7 & 3 \end{bmatrix}$

8. $\frac{1}{2}\left(\begin{bmatrix} 3 & -1 \\ 4 & 5 \end{bmatrix} + \begin{bmatrix} 5 & -3 \\ 0 & 7 \end{bmatrix} \right) - \begin{bmatrix} 4 & 2 \\ 1 & 0 \end{bmatrix}$

9. $6\left(\frac{2}{3}\begin{bmatrix} 2 & 3 \\ 6 & -5 \\ -1 & 0 \end{bmatrix} + \frac{1}{2}\begin{bmatrix} -4 & 2 \\ 3 & 0 \\ 1 & -8 \end{bmatrix} \right)$

10. $\begin{bmatrix} 1 & 3 \\ 4 & 0 \end{bmatrix} - \frac{3}{2}\left(\begin{bmatrix} 4 & -1 \\ 5 & 8 \end{bmatrix} + \frac{1}{2}\begin{bmatrix} 6 & 3 \\ 0 & -1 \end{bmatrix} \right)$

Solve the matrix equation for x and y.

11. $2\begin{bmatrix} 2x & 0 \\ 3 & -3y \end{bmatrix} = \begin{bmatrix} -12 & 0 \\ 6y & -6y \end{bmatrix}$ x = −3, y = 1

12. $3\begin{bmatrix} 3 & -2x \\ 2 & 4 \\ -y & 2 \end{bmatrix} - \begin{bmatrix} 2 & -2x \\ 0 & 5 \\ -2y & -2 \end{bmatrix} = \begin{bmatrix} 7 & 8 \\ 6 & 7 \\ 0 & 8 \end{bmatrix}$ x = −2, y = 0

13. Sun Block With the growing health concerns about sun exposure and skin protection, it is very important to wear sun block when outdoors. Two department stores had the following sales of the most popular sun block.

Store A: x in May, $2x$ in June, $3x - 150$ in July

Store B: y in May, $1.5y + 220$ in June, $3y - 60$ in July

$\begin{array}{c} \text{Store A} \\ \text{Store B} \end{array}\begin{bmatrix} x & 2x & 3x - 150 \\ y & 1.5y + 220 & 3y - 60 \end{bmatrix}$

Write a matrix that represents the sun block sales for the given months.

14. Medical Insurance A company offers medical, vision, and dental insurance to its employees. The annual employee costs for this year and next year are shown in the following matrices. Use the matrices to write a matrix that shows the *monthly* changes from this year to next year. Round to the nearest penny.

	This Year		Next Year			
	Single	Family	Single	Family		
Medical	725.52	2243.64	780.36	2352.28	4.57	9.05
Vision	29.76	220.08	35.24	236.12	0.46	1.34
Dental	57.36	198.36	46.78	172.88	−0.88	−2.12

Multiply Matrices

Georgia Performance Standards: MM3A4a, MM3A4c

Goal Multiply matrices.

Vocabulary

The product of two matrices A and B is defined provided the number of columns in A is equal to the number of rows in B. If A is an $m \times n$ matrix and B is an $n \times p$ matrix, then the product AB is an $m \times p$ matrix.

When multiplying matrices, to find the element in the ith row and jth column of the product matrix AB, multiply each element in the ith row of A by the corresponding element in the jth column of B, then add the products, as shown below.

$$
\overset{A}{\begin{bmatrix} a & b \\ c & d \end{bmatrix}} \overset{B}{\begin{bmatrix} e & f \\ g & h \end{bmatrix}} = \overset{AB}{\begin{bmatrix} ae + bg & af + bh \\ ce + dg & cf + dh \end{bmatrix}}
$$

Properties of Matrix Operations

To evaluate expressions involving matrices, use the properties below. Let A, B, and C be matrices and let k be a scalar.

Associative Property of Matrix Multiplication $A(BC) = (AB)C$

Left Distributive Property $A(B + C) = AB + AC$

Right Distributive Property $(A + B)C = AC + BC$

Associative Property of Scalar Multiplication $k(AB) = (kA)B = A(kB)$

It is important to note that, in general, matrix multiplication is *not* commutative. So, the product BA is usually not the same as the product AB.

Example 1   Describe matrix products

State whether the product _AB_ is defined. If so, give the dimensions of _AB_.

a. $A: 5 \times 3, B: 3 \times 2$

b. $A: 2 \times 3, B: 2 \times 4$

Solution

a. Because A is a **5 × 3** matrix and B is a **3 × 2** matrix, the product AB is defined and is a **5 × 2** matrix.

b. Because the number of columns in A (three) does not equal the number of rows in B (two), the product AB is not defined.

Guided Practice for Example 1

State whether the product _AB_ is defined. If so, give the dimensions of _AB_.

1. $A: 4 \times 2, B: 2 \times 2$ **defined; 4 × 2**

2. $A: 5 \times 2, B: 5 \times 2$ **not defined**

Georgia Performance Standards

MM3A4a   Add, subtract, multiply, and invert matrices, when possible, choosing appropriate methods, including technology. ☑

MM3A4c   Examine the properties of matrices, contrasting them with properties of real numbers. ☑

UNIT 1

Example 2   **Find the product of two matrices**

Find AB if $A = \begin{bmatrix} 3 & 6 \\ 7 & -1 \end{bmatrix}$ and $B = \begin{bmatrix} 4 & 2 \\ -3 & 8 \end{bmatrix}$.

Because the number of columns in A (two) equals the number of rows in B (two), the product AB is defined and is a 2×2 matrix.

STEP 1 **Multiply** the numbers in the first row of A by the numbers in the first column of B, add the products, and put the result in the first row, first column of AB.

$$\begin{bmatrix} 3 & 6 \\ 7 & -1 \end{bmatrix}\begin{bmatrix} 4 & 2 \\ -3 & 8 \end{bmatrix} = \begin{bmatrix} 3(4) + 6(-3) & \\ & \end{bmatrix}$$

STEP 2 **Multiply** the numbers in the first row of A by the numbers in the second column of B, add the products, and put the result in the first row, second column of AB.

$$\begin{bmatrix} 3 & 6 \\ 7 & -1 \end{bmatrix}\begin{bmatrix} 4 & 2 \\ -3 & 8 \end{bmatrix} = \begin{bmatrix} 3(4) + 6(-3) & 3(2) + 6(8) \\ & \end{bmatrix}$$

STEP 3 **Multiply** the numbers in the second row of A by the numbers in the first column of B, add the products, and put the result in the second row, first column of AB.

$$\begin{bmatrix} 3 & 6 \\ 7 & -1 \end{bmatrix}\begin{bmatrix} 4 & 2 \\ -3 & 8 \end{bmatrix} = \begin{bmatrix} 3(4) + 6(-3) & 3(2) + 6(8) \\ 7(4) + (-1)(-3) & \end{bmatrix}$$

STEP 4 **Multiply** the numbers in the second row of A by the numbers in the second column of B, add the products, and put the result in the second row, second column of AB.

$$\begin{bmatrix} 3 & 6 \\ 7 & -1 \end{bmatrix}\begin{bmatrix} 4 & 2 \\ -3 & 8 \end{bmatrix} = \begin{bmatrix} 3(4) + 6(-3) & 3(2) + 6(8) \\ 7(4) + (-1)(-3) & 7(2) + (-1)(8) \end{bmatrix}$$

STEP 5 **Simplify** the product matrix.

$$\begin{bmatrix} 3(4) + 6(-3) & 3(2) + 6(8) \\ 7(4) + (-1)(-3) & 7(2) + (-1)(8) \end{bmatrix} = \begin{bmatrix} -6 & 54 \\ 31 & 6 \end{bmatrix}$$

Guided Practice for Example 2

Find the product. If it is not defined, state the reason.

3. $\begin{bmatrix} 4 \\ -2 \end{bmatrix}\begin{bmatrix} 1 & 3 \end{bmatrix}$

$\begin{bmatrix} 4 & 12 \\ -2 & -6 \end{bmatrix}$

4. $\begin{bmatrix} 2 & 3 \\ 4 & 7 \end{bmatrix}\begin{bmatrix} -5 & -2 \\ 1 & 6 \end{bmatrix}$

$\begin{bmatrix} -7 & 14 \\ -13 & 34 \end{bmatrix}$

5. $\begin{bmatrix} 1 & -3 \\ 5 & 8 \end{bmatrix}\begin{bmatrix} -9 & 7 \\ -2 & -4 \end{bmatrix}$

$\begin{bmatrix} -3 & 19 \\ -61 & 3 \end{bmatrix}$

Example 3 **Use matrix operations**

Using the given matrices, evaluate the expression $B(A + C)$.

$$A = \begin{bmatrix} 2 & -1 \\ -6 & 4 \end{bmatrix}, \quad B = \begin{bmatrix} 4 & 2 \\ 1 & -5 \end{bmatrix}, \quad C = \begin{bmatrix} 0 & -3 \\ 4 & 5 \end{bmatrix}$$

$$B(A + C) = \begin{bmatrix} 4 & 2 \\ 1 & -5 \end{bmatrix} \left(\begin{bmatrix} 2 & -1 \\ -6 & 4 \end{bmatrix} + \begin{bmatrix} 0 & -3 \\ 4 & 5 \end{bmatrix} \right)$$

$$= \begin{bmatrix} 4 & 2 \\ 1 & -5 \end{bmatrix} \cdot \begin{bmatrix} 2 & -4 \\ -2 & 9 \end{bmatrix} = \begin{bmatrix} 4 & 2 \\ 12 & -49 \end{bmatrix}$$

Guided Practice for Example 3

Using the given matrices, evaluate the expression.

$$A = \begin{bmatrix} -2 & 6 \\ 1 & 3 \end{bmatrix}, \quad B = \begin{bmatrix} 0 & 2 \\ 4 & -5 \end{bmatrix}, \quad C = \begin{bmatrix} 5 & -1 \\ -2 & 0 \end{bmatrix}$$

6. $AB + C$ $\begin{bmatrix} 29 & -35 \\ 10 & -13 \end{bmatrix}$ **7.** $2AB$ $\begin{bmatrix} 48 & -68 \\ 24 & -26 \end{bmatrix}$ **8.** $A(B + C)$ $\begin{bmatrix} 2 & -32 \\ 11 & -14 \end{bmatrix}$

Example 4 **Use matrices to calculate total cost**

School Supplies You and a friend are purchasing school supplies. You buy 4 binders and 1 notepad. Your friend buys 2 binders and 3 notepads. Each binder costs $3.50 and each notepad costs $2. Write a supplies matrix and a cost per item matrix. Then use matrix multiplication to write a total cost matrix.

Solution

	Supplies	
	Binders	Notepads
You	4	1
Friend	2	3

	Cost
	Dollars
Binders	3.5
Notepads	2

The total cost can be found by multiplying the 2×2 supplies matrix by the 2×1 cost per item matrix. The product is a 2×1 total cost matrix.

$$\begin{bmatrix} 4 & 1 \\ 2 & 3 \end{bmatrix} \cdot \begin{bmatrix} 3.5 \\ 2 \end{bmatrix} = \begin{bmatrix} 16 \\ 13 \end{bmatrix}$$

The total cost of the school supplies is the sum of the rows of the total cost matrix, or $29.

Guided Practice for Example 4

9. Rework Example 3 if a binder costs $3 and a notepad costs $2.50. **$28**

LESSON 1.9

Exercise Set A

MM3A4a Add, subtract, multiply, and invert matrices, when possible, choosing appropriate methods, including technology.

MM3A4c Examine the properties of matrices, contrasting them with properties of real numbers.

State the dimensions of each matrix and determine whether the product AB is defined. If so, give the dimensions of AB.

1. $A = \begin{bmatrix} 2 & 1 \\ 5 & 0 \\ 1 & 2 \end{bmatrix}$, $B = \begin{bmatrix} 2 & 1 & 5 \end{bmatrix}$ *A:* 3 × 2; *B:* 1 × 3; *not* defined

2. $A = \begin{bmatrix} 2 & -3 & 4 \\ -2 & 1 & 0 \end{bmatrix}$, $B = \begin{bmatrix} 1 & 2 & 0 \\ 5 & 4 & 3 \\ -4 & 2 & -5 \end{bmatrix}$ *A:* 2 × 3; *B:* 3 × 3; defined; 2 × 3

Find the product. If it is not defined, state the reason.

3. $\begin{bmatrix} 3 & 2 \end{bmatrix} \begin{bmatrix} 1 \\ 4 \end{bmatrix}$ $\begin{bmatrix} 11 \end{bmatrix}$

4. $\begin{bmatrix} 1 & -1 \\ 2 & 1 \end{bmatrix} \begin{bmatrix} 2 & -2 \\ 1 & 2 \end{bmatrix}$ $\begin{bmatrix} 1 & -4 \\ 5 & -2 \end{bmatrix}$

5. $\begin{bmatrix} 2 \\ -1 \\ 3 \end{bmatrix} \begin{bmatrix} -1 & 3 \end{bmatrix}$ $\begin{bmatrix} -2 & 6 \\ 1 & -3 \\ -3 & 9 \end{bmatrix}$

6. $\begin{bmatrix} 3 & 5 \\ -2 & 4 \end{bmatrix} \begin{bmatrix} 2 & -1 \\ 4 & 0 \end{bmatrix}$ $\begin{bmatrix} 26 & -3 \\ 12 & 2 \end{bmatrix}$

7. $\begin{bmatrix} 5 & 1 & 0 \\ -2 & 3 & 1 \\ 0 & 2 & 4 \end{bmatrix} \begin{bmatrix} -1 & 2 & -3 \\ 0 & 5 & 4 \\ 2 & -1 & 2 \end{bmatrix}$ $\begin{bmatrix} -5 & 15 & -11 \\ 4 & 10 & 20 \\ 8 & 6 & 16 \end{bmatrix}$

8. $\begin{bmatrix} 2 \\ 1 \end{bmatrix} \begin{bmatrix} 1 & 2 & 4 \\ -2 & 3 & 1 \end{bmatrix}$ The matrices cannot be multiplied because the number of columns in $\begin{bmatrix} 2 \\ 1 \end{bmatrix}$ does not equal the number of rows in $\begin{bmatrix} 1 & 2 & 4 \\ -2 & 3 & 1 \end{bmatrix}$.

9. $\begin{bmatrix} -1 & 6 & 2 & 4 \end{bmatrix} \begin{bmatrix} 1 \\ -1 \\ 4 \\ 0 \end{bmatrix}$ $\begin{bmatrix} 1 \end{bmatrix}$

10. $\begin{bmatrix} 2 & -3 \\ 4 & -2 \\ 0 & -1 \end{bmatrix} \begin{bmatrix} 2 & 1 & -1 \\ 5 & 3 & 2 \end{bmatrix}$ $\begin{bmatrix} -11 & -7 & -8 \\ -2 & -2 & -8 \\ -5 & -3 & -2 \end{bmatrix}$

11. $\begin{bmatrix} 0 & 1 & 0 \\ 2 & 3 & -1 \\ -2 & 4 & 0 \\ 5 & 0 & -2 \end{bmatrix} \begin{bmatrix} 2 \\ -3 \\ 1 \end{bmatrix}$ $\begin{bmatrix} -3 \\ -6 \\ -16 \\ 8 \end{bmatrix}$

Using the given matrices, evaluate the expression.

$A = \begin{bmatrix} 2 & -1 \\ 3 & 2 \end{bmatrix}$, $B = \begin{bmatrix} 1 & 0 \\ 3 & -2 \end{bmatrix}$, $C = \begin{bmatrix} 3 & -2 \\ -1 & 4 \end{bmatrix}$

12. $-2BC$ **12.** $\begin{bmatrix} -6 & 4 \\ -22 & 28 \end{bmatrix}$

13. $AC - AB$ **13.** $\begin{bmatrix} 8 & -10 \\ -2 & 6 \end{bmatrix}$

14. $BA + BC$ **14.** $\begin{bmatrix} 5 & -3 \\ 11 & -21 \end{bmatrix}$

15. Football Tickets to the football game cost \$2.50 for students, \$5.00 for adults, and \$4.00 for senior citizens. Attendance for the first game of the postseason was 120 students, 185 adults, and 34 senior citizens. Attendance for the second game of the postseason was 150 students, 210 adults, and 50 senior citizens. Use matrix multiplication to find the revenue from ticket sales for each game.   Game 1 $\begin{bmatrix} \$1361 \\ \$1625 \end{bmatrix}$ Game 2

Exercise Set B

MM3A4a Add, subtract, multiply, and invert matrices, when possible, choosing appropriate methods, including technology.

MM3A4c Examine the properties of matrices, contrasting them with properties of real numbers.

Find the product. If it is not defined, state the reason. 1–4. See Additional Answers beginning on page AA1.

1. $\begin{bmatrix} -4 & 2 \\ -1 & 0 \\ 3 & 1 \end{bmatrix} \begin{bmatrix} 2 & 1 \\ 3 & 5 \end{bmatrix}$

2. $\begin{bmatrix} 3 & -1 & 0 \\ 2 & 5 & -4 \end{bmatrix} \begin{bmatrix} 1 & 0 \\ 0 & 1 \end{bmatrix}$

3. $\begin{bmatrix} 5 & 0 & -2 \\ 1 & 6 & 0 \\ -2 & 3 & 1 \end{bmatrix} \begin{bmatrix} 1 & 0 \\ -3 & 2 \\ 2 & -1 \end{bmatrix}$

4. $\begin{bmatrix} -2 \\ -1 \\ 3 \\ 4 \end{bmatrix} \begin{bmatrix} 2 & 3 & -1 \end{bmatrix}$

Using the given matrices, evaluate the expression. 5–10. See Additional Answers beginning on page AA1.

$$A = \begin{bmatrix} 2 & -1 \\ 1 & 3 \end{bmatrix}, B = \begin{bmatrix} 2 & 3 \\ 0 & -2 \end{bmatrix}, C = \begin{bmatrix} 4 & -1 \\ 1 & 2 \\ 3 & -2 \end{bmatrix}, D = \begin{bmatrix} 1 & 0 & -2 \\ 4 & 1 & 6 \\ 2 & -1 & 2 \end{bmatrix}, E = \begin{bmatrix} -3 & 0 & 1 \\ 2 & 5 & -3 \\ -1 & 0 & 2 \end{bmatrix}$$

5. $-AB$

6. $\frac{1}{2}CB$

7. $CA - CB$

8. DC

9. CAB

10. $EC(A + B)$

Solve for x and y.

11. $\begin{bmatrix} 1 & 2 & -1 \\ 3 & -2 & 1 \\ 0 & 2 & 4 \end{bmatrix} \begin{bmatrix} x \\ 2 \\ -1 \end{bmatrix} = \begin{bmatrix} 8 \\ y \\ 0 \end{bmatrix}$ $x = 3, y = 4$

12. $\begin{bmatrix} 3 & 2 & -1 \\ -2 & 0 & 2 \end{bmatrix} \begin{bmatrix} 2 & x \\ -1 & 4 \\ 3 & y \end{bmatrix} = \begin{bmatrix} 1 & 0 \\ 2 & 4 \end{bmatrix}$ $x = -3, y = -1$

13. Geometry Matrix B contains the coordinates of the vertices of the triangle shown in the graph. Calculate AB and determine what effect the multiplication of matrix A has on the graph.

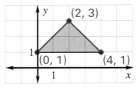

$$A = \begin{bmatrix} -1 & 0 \\ 0 & -1 \end{bmatrix} \qquad B = \begin{bmatrix} 0 & 2 & 4 \\ 1 & 3 & 1 \end{bmatrix} \quad AB = \begin{bmatrix} 0 & -2 & -4 \\ -1 & -3 & -1 \end{bmatrix}; \text{ reflection through the origin}$$

14. Mayor Election Candidate A and candidate B are running for mayor of a small town. After attending a debate, some citizens change their minds about the candidate for whom they will vote. Let $m = 25\%$ be the percent of citizens that switch from candidate A to candidate B. Let $n = 16\%$ be the percent of citizens that switch from candidate B to candidate A. Before the debate, candidate A was expected to win the election 1200 votes to 950 votes. After the debate, how many votes will candidate A and candidate B receive? Use the transition matrix T to help answer the question.

candidate A: 1052; candidate B: 1098

$$T = \begin{bmatrix} 1 - m & n \\ m & 1 - n \end{bmatrix}$$

Georgia Performance Standards

MM3A4a Add, subtract, multiply, and invert matrices, when possible, choosing appropriate methods, including technology.

Technology Activity

Matrix Operations

Use after Lesson 1.9

Question

How can you use a graphing calculator to perform matrix operations?

Example

Use a graphing calculator to perform operations with matrices.

Using matrices A and B below, find $A + B$ and $2A + 3B$.

$$A = \begin{bmatrix} 7 & -2 & 1 \\ 4 & -8 & 9 \end{bmatrix} \qquad B = \begin{bmatrix} -1 & 3 & -4 \\ 0 & 6 & 12 \end{bmatrix}$$

STEP 1
Enter Matrix A
Enter the dimensions and elements of matrix A.

STEP 2
Enter Matrix B
Enter the dimensions and elements of matrix B.

STEP 3
Perform calculations
From the home screen, calculate $A + B$ and $2A - 3B$.

Practice

Use a graphing calculator to perform the indicated operation(s).

1–4. See Additional Answers beginning on page AA1.

1. $\begin{bmatrix} -7 & 2 \\ 4 & 8 \end{bmatrix} + \begin{bmatrix} 10 & -6 \\ 5 & -8 \end{bmatrix}$

2. $3.5\begin{bmatrix} 11.6 & 7.8 & -4.2 \\ -0.6 & 5.4 & -2.1 \end{bmatrix}$

3. $\begin{bmatrix} 4 & 9 & 14 \\ -5 & -13 & -10 \\ 8 & 11 & 7 \end{bmatrix} + \begin{bmatrix} -8 & 10 & 0 \\ -7 & 12 & 3 \\ -1 & -9 & -5 \end{bmatrix}$

4. $2\begin{bmatrix} 5 & -2 \\ 7 & -5 \\ -3 & -1 \end{bmatrix} - 4\begin{bmatrix} 4 & 1 \\ -9 & 0 \\ -2 & 15 \end{bmatrix}$

5. Book Sales The matrices below show book sales (in thousands of dollars) at a chain of bookstores for August and September. The book formats are hardcover and paperback. The categories of books are romance (R), mystery (M), science fiction (S), and children's (C). Use a graphing calculator to find the total sales of each format and category for August and September.

Total Sales

	R	M	S	C
Hardcover	44	38	42	21
Paperback	72	46	25	57

August

	R	M	S	C
Hardcover	20	18	23	12
Paperback	34	21	15	30

September

	R	M	S	C
Hardcover	24	20	19	9
Paperback	38	25	10	27

UNIT 1

Evaluate Determinants and Apply Cramer's Rule

Georgia Performance Standards: MM3A5c

Goal Evaluate determinants of matrices.

Vocabulary

Associated with each square matrix ($n \times n$) is a real number called its **determinant**. The determinant of a matrix A is denoted by det A or by $|A|$.

Determinant of a 2 × 2 Matrix

$$\det \begin{bmatrix} a & b \\ c & d \end{bmatrix} = \begin{vmatrix} a & b \\ c & d \end{vmatrix} = ad - cb$$

The determinant of a 2 × 2 matrix is the difference of the products of the elements on the diagonals.

Determinant of a 3 × 3 Matrix

Repeat the first two columns to the right of the determinant. Then **subtract** the sum of the **red products** from the sum of the **blue products**.

$$\det \begin{bmatrix} a & b & c \\ d & e & f \\ g & h & i \end{bmatrix} = \begin{vmatrix} a & b & c \\ d & e & f \\ g & h & i \end{vmatrix} \begin{matrix} a & b \\ d & e \\ g & h \end{matrix} = (aei + bfg + cdh) - (gec + hfa + idb)$$

The **coefficient matrix** of the linear system $ax + by = e$ and $cx + dy = f$ is $\begin{bmatrix} a & b \\ c & d \end{bmatrix}$.

Cramer's rule is another method for solving linear systems.

Cramer's rule for a 2 × 2 System: Let A be the coefficient matrix of the linear system $ax + by = e$ and $cx + dy = f$. If det $A \neq 0$, then the system has exactly one solution.

The solution is $x = \dfrac{\begin{vmatrix} e & b \\ f & d \end{vmatrix}}{\det A}$ and $y = \dfrac{\begin{vmatrix} a & e \\ c & f \end{vmatrix}}{\det A}$.

Cramer's rule for a 3 × 3 System: Let A be the coefficient matrix of the linear system $ax + by + cz = j$, $dx + ey + fz = k$ and $gx + hy + iz = \ell$. If det $A \neq 0$, then the system has exactly one solution.

The solution is $x = \dfrac{\begin{vmatrix} j & b & c \\ k & e & f \\ \ell & h & i \end{vmatrix}}{\det A}$, $y = \dfrac{\begin{vmatrix} a & j & c \\ d & k & f \\ g & \ell & i \end{vmatrix}}{\det A}$, and $z = \dfrac{\begin{vmatrix} a & b & j \\ d & e & k \\ g & h & \ell \end{vmatrix}}{\det A}$.

Example 1 Evaluate determinants

a. $\det \begin{bmatrix} 8 & -2 \\ 4 & 7 \end{bmatrix} = \begin{vmatrix} 8 & -2 \\ 4 & 7 \end{vmatrix} = 8(7) - 4(-2) = 56 + 8 = 64$

b. $\det \begin{bmatrix} 3 & 0 & 1 \\ -3 & 4 & 2 \\ -2 & 1 & -1 \end{bmatrix} = \begin{vmatrix} 3 & 0 & 1 \\ -3 & 4 & 2 \\ -2 & 1 & -1 \end{vmatrix} \begin{matrix} 3 & 0 \\ -3 & 4 \\ -2 & 1 \end{matrix}$

$= [(-12) + 0 + (-3)] - (-8 + 6 + 0) = -15 - (-2) = -13$

Georgia Performance Standards

MM3A5c Represent and solve realistic problems using systems of linear equations.

Example 2   Use Cramer's rule for a 2 × 2 system

Use Cramer's rule to solve the linear system: $7x + 5y = 16$

$4x - 2y = 14$

STEP 1 **Evaluate** the determinant of the coefficient matrix.

$$\begin{vmatrix} 7 & 5 \\ 4 & -2 \end{vmatrix} = -14 - 20 = -34$$

STEP 2 **Apply** Cramer's rule because the determinant is not zero.

$$x = \frac{\begin{vmatrix} 16 & 5 \\ 14 & -2 \end{vmatrix}}{-34} = \frac{-32 - 70}{-34} = 3 \qquad y = \frac{\begin{vmatrix} 7 & 16 \\ 4 & 14 \end{vmatrix}}{-34} = \frac{98 - 64}{-34} = -1$$

The solution is $(3, -1)$.

Example 3   Solve a multi-step problem

Pricing Two bottles of water and 1 bottle of juice sell for $2.55. Two bottles of juice and 1 bottle of milk sell for $2.45. One bottle of water, 1 bottle of juice, and 1 bottle of milk sell for $2.30. Use a linear system and Cramer's rule to find the prices of the water, juice, and milk.

STEP 1 **Write** a linear system using $w, j,$ and m to represent the various number of bottles.

$2w + j = 2.55$

$2j + m = 2.45$

$w + j + m = 2.30$

STEP 2 **Evaluate** the determinant of the coefficient matrix.

$$\begin{vmatrix} 2 & 1 & 0 \\ 0 & 2 & 1 \\ 1 & 1 & 1 \end{vmatrix}\begin{matrix} 2 & 0 \\ 0 & 2 \\ 1 & 1 \end{matrix} = 4 + 1 + 0 - (0 + 2 + 0) = 3$$

STEP 3 **Apply** Cramer's rule because the determinant is not zero.

$$w = \frac{\begin{vmatrix} 2.55 & 1 & 0 \\ 2.45 & 2 & 1 \\ 2.30 & 1 & 1 \end{vmatrix}}{3} = 0.80 \quad j = \frac{\begin{vmatrix} 2 & 2.55 & 0 \\ 0 & 2.45 & 1 \\ 1 & 2.30 & 1 \end{vmatrix}}{3} = 0.95 \quad m = \frac{\begin{vmatrix} 2 & 1 & 2.55 \\ 0 & 2 & 2.45 \\ 1 & 1 & 2.30 \end{vmatrix}}{3} = 0.55$$

The price of water is $.80, the price of juice is $.95, and the price of milk is $.55.

Guided Practice for Examples 1, 2, and 3

1. Evaluate $\begin{vmatrix} -6 & 2 \\ 4 & -3 \end{vmatrix}$. **10**

2. Evaluate $\begin{vmatrix} 4 & 1 & 5 \\ -2 & 0 & 1 \\ 3 & 2 & -1 \end{vmatrix}$. **−27**

Use Cramer's rule to solve the linear system.

3. $2x + y = 11$ **(3, 5)**
$-3x + 2y = 1$

4. $4x - 5y = 6$ **(4, 2)**
$7x - 12y = 4$

5. $-6x + 4y + z = 32$ **(−1, 6, 2)**
$5x + 2y + 3z = 13$
$x - y + z = -5$

UNIT 1

Exercise Set A

MM3A5c Represent and solve realistic problems using systems of linear equations.

Evaluate the determinant of the matrix.

1. $\begin{bmatrix} 5 & -2 \\ 4 & -4 \end{bmatrix}$ -12

2. $\begin{bmatrix} 3 & -5 \\ -2 & -3 \end{bmatrix}$ -19

3. $\begin{bmatrix} \frac{1}{2} & \frac{2}{3} \\ 6 & 5 \end{bmatrix}$ $-\frac{3}{2}$

4. $\begin{bmatrix} 5 & -1 & 3 \\ 4 & 0 & 2 \\ 1 & -2 & -5 \end{bmatrix}$ -26

5. $\begin{bmatrix} 3 & 2 & 9 \\ 0 & 1 & -4 \\ 5 & -1 & 2 \end{bmatrix}$ -91

6. $\begin{bmatrix} 1 & 15 & 2 \\ 0 & 1 & 3 \\ 2 & 12 & 2 \end{bmatrix}$ 52

In Exercises 7–9, use the formula below to find the area of a triangle with vertices (x_1, y_1), (x_2, y_2), and (x_3, y_3). The symbol $\pm$ indicates that the appropriate sign should be chosen to yield a positive value.

$$\text{Area} = \pm\frac{1}{2}\begin{vmatrix} x_1 & y_1 & 1 \\ x_2 & y_2 & 1 \\ x_3 & y_3 & 1 \end{vmatrix}$$

7. 6

8. 5.5

9. 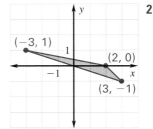 2

Use Cramer's rule to solve the linear system.

10. $x - 5y = -1$ $(4, 1)$
$-2x + 5y = -3$

11. $x + 2y = 1$ $(-5, 3)$
$-3x - 7y = -6$

12. $2x + 6y = 12$ $(6, 0)$
$-x + 7y = -6$

13. $2x + 2y + z = 2$ $(1, -1, 2)$
$-x + 3y + z = -2$
$3x + 2z = 7$

14. $2x - 5y + 2z = 2$ $(3, 0, -2)$
$-3x + y - 6z = 3$
$x + y + z = 1$

15. $3x + 2y + 3z = -1$ $\left(\frac{1}{2}, \frac{1}{4}, -1\right)$
$2x - 8y + 2z = -3$
$x + 6y + 4z = -2$

In Exercises 16 and 17, use the following information.

Gasoline You fill up your car with 15 gallons of premium gasoline and fill up a 5 gallon gas can with regular gasoline for various appliances around the house. You pay the cashier $42. The price of regular gasoline y is 20 cents less per gallon than the price of premium gasoline x.

16. Write a system of linear equations that models the price per gallon for regular and premium gasoline. $15x + 5y = 42$
$x - y = 0.2$

17. Use Cramer's rule to find the price per gallon of regular and premium gasoline.
Premium: $2.15, Regular $1.95

Exercise Set B

MM3A5c Represent and solve realistic problems using systems of linear equations.

Evaluate the determinant of the matrix.

1. $\begin{bmatrix} 3 & 5 \\ -2 & 4 \end{bmatrix}$ **22**

2. $\begin{bmatrix} 4 & -2 \\ 3 & 2 \end{bmatrix}$ **14**

3. $\begin{bmatrix} 2 & 0 & -1 \\ 3 & 2 & 1 \\ 1 & 4 & 2 \end{bmatrix}$ **−10**

4. $\begin{bmatrix} 2 & 0 & 0 \\ 0 & -5 & 0 \\ 0 & 0 & -2 \end{bmatrix}$ **20**

5. $\begin{bmatrix} 6 & 1 & -2 \\ 4 & -2 & 0 \\ -2 & 4 & 3 \end{bmatrix}$ **−72**

6. $\begin{bmatrix} 7 & -2 & 6 \\ 3 & -1 & 5 \\ -6 & 2 & 4 \end{bmatrix}$ **−14**

Use the formula on the previous page to find the area of the triangle with the given vertices.

7. $A(0, -4), B\left(-3, \frac{1}{2}\right), C(2, -1)$ **9**

8. $A\left(\frac{1}{2}, 3\right), B(-3, -1), C\left(3, \frac{1}{2}\right)$ **$9\frac{3}{8}$**

Use Cramer's rule to solve the linear system.

9. $3x - 3y = -6$ **(4, 6)**
$4x + y = 22$

10. $2x + 3y = 0$ **(−3, 2)**
$5x + 7y = -1$

11. $4x + 3y = 4$ **(7, −8)**
$-2x - 3y = 10$

12. $3x + 6y + z = 3$ **(3, −2, 6)**
$x + 3y + z = 3$
$3x + y - 2z = -5$

13. $x - 3y + 2z = 2$ $\left(-\frac{61}{8}, \frac{3}{8}, \frac{43}{8}\right)$
$5x + 2y + 9z = 11$
$3x - y + 6z = 9$

14. $4x + 3y + z = 3$ **(1, −1, 2)**
$3x + 5y + 2z = 2$
$2x + 2y + 2z = 4$

15. $x + 2y + z = 8$ **(−7, 3, 9)**
$-2x + 2y - 2z = 2$
$3x + 4y + z = 0$

16. $x - 3y + 2z = -6$ $\left(\frac{2}{3}, 2, -\frac{1}{3}\right)$
$-3x + y - 6z = 2$
$9x + y + 3z = 7$

17. $2x - 2y + 3z = -1$ **(−3, −4, −1)**
$6x - 7y + 5z = 5$
$5x + 2y - 7z = -16$

In Exercises 18 and 19, use the following information.

Electoral College In the 1976 presidential election, 538 electoral votes were cast. Of these, x went to Jimmy Carter, y went to Gerald Ford, and z went to Ronald Reagan. The value of x is 57 more than y. The value of y is 239 more than z.

18. Write a system of linear equations that models the electoral votes cast in the 1976 presidential election.

$x + y + z = 538$
$x - y = 57$
$y - z = 239$

19. Use Cramer's rule to find the values of x, y, and z. **(297, 240, 1)**

20. **Determinant Relationships** Let $A = \begin{bmatrix} 2 & 3 \\ 4 & 1 \end{bmatrix}$ and $B = \begin{bmatrix} 5 & 6 \\ 7 & 8 \end{bmatrix}$. How is det AB related to det A and det B? How is det AB related to det BA? **det AB = (det A)(det B); det AB = det BA**

21. **Challenge** Let $A = \begin{bmatrix} a & b \\ c & d \end{bmatrix}$ and $B = \begin{bmatrix} w & x \\ y & z \end{bmatrix}$. Show that the det AB = (det A)(det B).

Find AB. Then det $AB = (ad - bc)(wz - xy)$.
Find det A and det B. Then (det A)(det B) = $(ad - bc)(wz - xy)$.

Georgia Performance Standards

MM3A4a   Add, subtract, multiply, and invert matrices, when possible, choosing appropriate methods, including technology.

MM3A4b   Find the inverses of two-by-two matrices using pencil and paper, and find inverses of larger matrices using technology.

Investigating Math Activity

Inverse Matrices

Use before Lesson 1.11

Question

How can you determine whether or not two matrices are inverses of each other?

Explore

Multiply matrices.

Use the matrices below to calculate AB, BA, CD, and DC.

$$A = \begin{bmatrix} 2 & 3 \\ 1 & 2 \end{bmatrix} \qquad B = \begin{bmatrix} 2 & -3 \\ -1 & 2 \end{bmatrix} \qquad AB = \begin{bmatrix} 1 & 0 \\ 0 & 1 \end{bmatrix}, BA = \begin{bmatrix} 1 & 0 \\ 0 & 1 \end{bmatrix},$$

$$C = \begin{bmatrix} 0 & -1 & 2 \\ 1 & 1 & -1 \\ 2 & 0 & 3 \end{bmatrix} \qquad D = \begin{bmatrix} 3 & 3 & -1 \\ -5 & -4 & 2 \\ -2 & -2 & 1 \end{bmatrix} \quad CD = \begin{bmatrix} 1 & 0 & 0 \\ 0 & 1 & 0 \\ 0 & 0 & 1 \end{bmatrix}, DC = \begin{bmatrix} 1 & 0 & 0 \\ 0 & 1 & 0 \\ 0 & 0 & 1 \end{bmatrix}$$

Draw Conclusions

1.   *Compare* the products AB and BA. **They are the same. They are both 2 × 2 matrices with 1's on the main diagonal and 0's elsewhere.**
2.   *Compare* the products CD and DC. **They are the same. They are both 3 × 3 matrices with 1's on the main diagonal and 0's elsewhere.**
3.   Reasoning Based on your observations, make a conjecture about the products of inverse matrices. **Two matrices are inverses of each other if their product (in both orders) is a matrix with the same dimensions with 1's on the main diagonal and 0's elsewhere.**
4.   Test your conjecture using matrices E and F, which are inverses of each other. Revise your answer to Exercise 3 if necessary.

$$E = \begin{bmatrix} -3 & -2 \\ 8 & 5 \end{bmatrix} \qquad F = \begin{bmatrix} 5 & 2 \\ -8 & -3 \end{bmatrix} \quad EF = \begin{bmatrix} 1 & 0 \\ 0 & 1 \end{bmatrix}; FE = \begin{bmatrix} 1 & 0 \\ 0 & 1 \end{bmatrix}$$

5.   Reasoning Based on your observations, what is the inverse of the matrix $\begin{bmatrix} -5 & -3 \\ 3 & 2 \end{bmatrix}$? **D**

   A. $\begin{bmatrix} -2 & 3 \\ 3 & 5 \end{bmatrix}$ **B.** $\begin{bmatrix} -2 & 3 \\ -3 & 5 \end{bmatrix}$ **C.** $\begin{bmatrix} 2 & -3 \\ 3 & 5 \end{bmatrix}$ **D.** $\begin{bmatrix} -2 & -3 \\ 3 & 5 \end{bmatrix}$

Use Inverse Matrices to Solve Linear Systems

Georgia Performance Standards: MM3A4b, MM3A5a, MM3A5b

Goal Solve linear systems using inverse matrices.

Vocabulary

The $n \times n$ **identity matrix** is a matrix with 1's on the main diagonal and 0's elsewhere. If A is any $n \times n$ matrix and I is the $n \times n$ identity matrix, then $AI = A$ and $IA = A$.

2 × 2 Identity Matrix

$$I = \begin{bmatrix} 1 & 0 \\ 0 & 1 \end{bmatrix}$$

3 × 3 Identity Matrix

$$I = \begin{bmatrix} 1 & 0 & 0 \\ 0 & 1 & 0 \\ 0 & 0 & 1 \end{bmatrix}$$

Two $n \times n$ matrices A and B are **inverses** of each other if their product (in both orders) is the $n \times n$ identity matrix. That is, $AB = I$ and $BA = I$. An $n \times n$ matrix A has an inverse if and only if det $A \neq 0$. the symbol for the inverse of A is A^{-1}.

Inverse of 2 × 2 Matrix: The inverse of the matrix

$$A = \begin{bmatrix} a & b \\ c & d \end{bmatrix} \text{ is } A^{-1} = \frac{1}{|A|}\begin{bmatrix} d & -b \\ -c & a \end{bmatrix} = \frac{1}{ad - cb}\begin{bmatrix} d & -b \\ -c & a \end{bmatrix} \text{ provided } ad - cb \neq 0.$$

The inverse of a 3×3 matrix is difficult to compute by hand. In this case, a graphing calculator can be used to find the inverse matrix.

In the matrix equation $AX = B$, matrix A is the coefficient matrix, X is **the matrix of variables,** and B is the **matrix of constants.**

Example 1 **Find the inverse of a 2 × 2 matrix**

Find the inverse of $A = \begin{bmatrix} 4 & 7 \\ 3 & 5 \end{bmatrix}$.

Solution

$$A^{-1} = \frac{1}{20 - 21}\begin{bmatrix} 5 & -7 \\ -3 & 4 \end{bmatrix}$$

$$= -1\begin{bmatrix} 5 & -7 \\ -3 & 4 \end{bmatrix}$$

$$= \begin{bmatrix} -5 & 7 \\ 3 & -4 \end{bmatrix}$$

Guided Practice for Example 1

Find the inverse of the matrix.

1. $\begin{bmatrix} 2 & 1 \\ 7 & 3 \end{bmatrix}$ $\begin{bmatrix} -3 & 1 \\ 7 & -2 \end{bmatrix}$ **2.** $\begin{bmatrix} -4 & 4 \\ -5 & 6 \end{bmatrix}$ $\begin{bmatrix} -\frac{3}{2} & 1 \\ -\frac{5}{4} & 1 \end{bmatrix}$ **3.** $\begin{bmatrix} -3 & -8 \\ -2 & -1 \end{bmatrix}$ $\begin{bmatrix} \frac{1}{13} & -\frac{8}{13} \\ -\frac{2}{13} & \frac{3}{13} \end{bmatrix}$

Example 2   Solve a matrix equation

Solve the matrix equation $AX = B$ for the 2×2 matrix X.

$$\overbrace{\begin{bmatrix} 1 & 1 \\ 6 & 7 \end{bmatrix}}^{A} X = \overbrace{\begin{bmatrix} 2 & 3 \\ 1 & 4 \end{bmatrix}}^{B}$$

Begin by finding the inverse of A.

$$A^{-1} = \frac{1}{7-6}\begin{bmatrix} 7 & -1 \\ -6 & 1 \end{bmatrix} = \begin{bmatrix} 7 & -1 \\ -6 & 1 \end{bmatrix}$$

To solve the equation for X, multiply both sides of the equation by A^{-1} on the left.

$$\begin{bmatrix} 7 & -1 \\ -6 & 1 \end{bmatrix}\begin{bmatrix} 1 & 1 \\ 6 & 7 \end{bmatrix}X = \begin{bmatrix} 7 & -1 \\ -6 & 1 \end{bmatrix}\begin{bmatrix} 2 & 3 \\ 1 & 4 \end{bmatrix} \qquad A^{-1}AX = A^{-1}B$$

$$\begin{bmatrix} 1 & 0 \\ 0 & 1 \end{bmatrix}X = \begin{bmatrix} 13 & 17 \\ -11 & -14 \end{bmatrix} \qquad IX = A^{-1}B$$

$$X = \begin{bmatrix} 13 & 17 \\ -11 & -14 \end{bmatrix} \qquad X = A^{-1}B$$

Guided Practice for Example 2

Solve the matrix equation. 4–6. See Additional Answers beginning on page AA1.

4. $\begin{bmatrix} 1 & 1 \\ 2 & 3 \end{bmatrix}X = \begin{bmatrix} 6 & 4 \\ 2 & 8 \end{bmatrix}$ **5.** $\begin{bmatrix} 1 & 1 \\ 3 & 4 \end{bmatrix}X = \begin{bmatrix} 1 & 2 \\ 1 & 3 \end{bmatrix}$ **6.** $\begin{bmatrix} 9 & 4 \\ 2 & 1 \end{bmatrix}X = \begin{bmatrix} 0 & -1 \\ 3 & 2 \end{bmatrix}$

Example 3   Find the inverse of a 3 × 3 matrix

Use a graphing calculator to find the inverse of A. Then use the calculator to verify the result. $A = \begin{bmatrix} 4 & 0 & -1 \\ 6 & -2 & 0 \\ 3 & 1 & -4 \end{bmatrix}$

Enter matrix A into a graphing calculator and calculate A^{-1}.
Then compute AA^{-1} and $A^{-1}A$ to verify that you obtain the 3×3 identity matrix.

Example 4   **Solve a linear system**

Use an inverse matrix to
solve the linear system.
$$3x + 2y = 1 \qquad \textbf{Equation 1}$$
$$4x + y = -2 \qquad \textbf{Equation 2}$$

STEP 1 **Write** the linear system as a matrix equation $AX = B$.

$$\begin{bmatrix} 3 & 2 \\ 4 & 1 \end{bmatrix} \begin{bmatrix} x \\ y \end{bmatrix} = \begin{bmatrix} 1 \\ -2 \end{bmatrix}$$

STEP 2 **Find** the inverse of matrix A.

$$A^{-1} = \frac{1}{3-8} \begin{bmatrix} 1 & -2 \\ -4 & 3 \end{bmatrix} = \begin{bmatrix} -0.2 & 0.4 \\ 0.8 & -0.6 \end{bmatrix}$$

STEP 3 **Multiply** the matrix of constants by A^{-1} on the left.

$$X = A^{-1}B = \begin{bmatrix} -0.2 & 0.4 \\ 0.8 & -0.6 \end{bmatrix} \begin{bmatrix} 1 \\ -2 \end{bmatrix} = \begin{bmatrix} -1 \\ 2 \end{bmatrix} = \begin{bmatrix} x \\ y \end{bmatrix}$$

The solution of the system is $(-1, 2)$.

Example 5   **Solve a multi-step problem**

Gift Shop A gift shop sells three beach packages. Package A that includes 2 towels, 1 tube of sunscreen, and 1 beach chair costs $21. Package B that includes 3 towels and 2 beach chairs costs $31. Package C that includes 1 tube of sunscreen and 2 beach chairs costs $19. Find the cost of each package item.

STEP 1 **Write** a system of equations. Let t be
the cost of a towel, s be the cost of
the tube of sunscreen, and c be the
cost of a beach chair.

$$2t + s + c = 21 \qquad \text{Package A}$$
$$3t + 2c = 31 \qquad \text{Package B}$$
$$s + 2c = 19 \qquad \text{Package C}$$

STEP 2 **Rewrite** the system as a matrix equation
and solve $X = A^{-1}B$ with a graphing
calculator.

$$\begin{bmatrix} 2 & 1 & 1 \\ 3 & 0 & 2 \\ 0 & 1 & 2 \end{bmatrix} \cdot \begin{bmatrix} t \\ s \\ c \end{bmatrix} = \begin{bmatrix} 21 \\ 31 \\ 19 \end{bmatrix}$$

A towel costs $5, sunscreen costs $3, and a chair costs $8.

Guided Practice for Examples 3, 4, and 5

7. Use a graphing calculator to find the inverse of $A = \begin{bmatrix} 1 & 1 & 2 \\ 2 & 4 & -3 \\ 3 & 6 & -5 \end{bmatrix}$. $\begin{bmatrix} 2 & -17 & 11 \\ -1 & 11 & -7 \\ 0 & 3 & -2 \end{bmatrix}$

Use an inverse matrix to solve the linear system.

8. $2x - y = -4$ **(3, 10)**
   $x + y = 13$

9. $3x - y = 1$ **(1, 2)**
   $-x + 2y = 3$

10. $2x + y = -1$ **(−1, 1)**
    $3x - y = -4$

11. Rework Example 5 with cost of Package A = $23, cost of Package B = $36, and cost of Package C = $20. $t = 6, s = 2, c = 9$

MM3A4b   Find the inverses of two-by-two matrices using pencil and paper, and find inverses of larger matrices using technology.

MM3A5a   Represent a system of linear equations as a matrix equation.

MM3A5b   Solve matrix equations using inverse matrices.

Find the inverse of the matrix, if it exists.

1. $\begin{bmatrix} 4 & 7 \\ 1 & 2 \end{bmatrix}$ $\begin{bmatrix} 2 & -7 \\ -1 & 4 \end{bmatrix}$

2. $\begin{bmatrix} 3 & 2 \\ 4 & 2 \end{bmatrix}$ $\begin{bmatrix} -1 & 1 \\ 2 & -\frac{3}{2} \end{bmatrix}$

3. $\begin{bmatrix} 4 & -2 \\ 3 & 1 \end{bmatrix}$ $\begin{bmatrix} \frac{1}{10} & -\frac{1}{5} \\ -\frac{3}{10} & \frac{2}{5} \end{bmatrix}$

4. $\begin{bmatrix} 7 & 14 \\ 3 & 6 \end{bmatrix}$ no inverse

5. $\begin{bmatrix} -4 & -2 \\ 5 & 2 \end{bmatrix}$ $\begin{bmatrix} 1 & 1 \\ -\frac{5}{2} & -2 \end{bmatrix}$

6. $\begin{bmatrix} 3 & -3 \\ -3 & -2 \end{bmatrix}$ $\begin{bmatrix} \frac{2}{15} & -\frac{1}{5} \\ -\frac{1}{5} & -\frac{1}{5} \end{bmatrix}$

Use a graphing calculator to find the inverse of the matrix.

7. $\begin{bmatrix} 1 & 3 & 5 \\ 0 & 3 & 5 \\ 0 & 0 & 5 \end{bmatrix}$ $\begin{bmatrix} 1 & -1 & 0 \\ 0 & \frac{1}{3} & -\frac{1}{3} \\ 0 & 0 & \frac{1}{5} \end{bmatrix}$

8. $\begin{bmatrix} 0 & 1 & 0 \\ 2 & 1 & -2 \\ 0 & 2 & 2 \end{bmatrix}$ $\begin{bmatrix} -\frac{3}{2} & \frac{1}{2} & \frac{1}{2} \\ 1 & 0 & 0 \\ -1 & 0 & \frac{1}{2} \end{bmatrix}$

Solve the matrix equation.

9. $\begin{bmatrix} 2 & 1 \\ 3 & 2 \end{bmatrix} X = \begin{bmatrix} 5 & 1 \\ 2 & 1 \end{bmatrix}$ $\begin{bmatrix} 8 & 1 \\ -11 & -1 \end{bmatrix}$

10. $\begin{bmatrix} 4 & 3 \\ 2 & 2 \end{bmatrix} X = \begin{bmatrix} -2 & 3 \\ -1 & 2 \end{bmatrix}$ $\begin{bmatrix} -\frac{1}{2} & 0 \\ 0 & 1 \end{bmatrix}$

11. $\begin{bmatrix} 3 & 1 \\ 6 & 3 \end{bmatrix} X = \begin{bmatrix} 1 & 4 & -2 \\ 6 & 0 & -3 \end{bmatrix}$ $\begin{bmatrix} -1 & 4 & -1 \\ 4 & -8 & 1 \end{bmatrix}$

12. $\begin{bmatrix} 6 & 2 \\ 5 & 1 \end{bmatrix} X = \begin{bmatrix} 9 & 12 & 6 \\ -4 & 3 & 8 \end{bmatrix}$

Use an inverse matrix to solve the linear system.

13. $3x - 2y = 2$ **(2, 2)**
$2x - y = 2$

14. $5x + 3y = 4$ **(−4, 8)**
$2x + 2y = 8$

$\begin{bmatrix} -\frac{17}{4} & -\frac{3}{2} & \frac{5}{2} \\ \frac{69}{4} & \frac{21}{2} & -\frac{9}{2} \end{bmatrix}$

15. $3x + y + 2z = 9$ **(1, −2, 4)**
$-2x + 2y + 3z = 6$
$2x - y + z = 8$

16. $3x + 3y + 3z = -12$ **(−3, 5, −6)**
$5x + 2y + 2z = -17$
$2x - 4y - z = -20$

17. Multiple Representations During the 2004–2005 NBA season, Shaquille O'Neal scored 1669 points while making 1011 shots. Shaq's points were a combination of 3-point field goals, 2-point field goals, and 1-point free throws. He made 305 more 2-point field goals than free throws. **See Additional Answers beginning on page AA1.**

a. Writing a System Write a system of equations for the number of shots made during the season.

b. Writing a Matrix Equation Write the system of equations from part (a) as a matrix equation $AX = B$.

c. Solving a System Use an inverse matrix to solve the system of equations. How many of each type of shot did Shaq make during the season?

UNIT 1

Exercise Set B

MM3A4b Find the inverses of two-by-two matrices using pencil and paper, and find inverses of larger matrices using technology.

MM3A5a Represent a system of linear equations as a matrix equation.

MM3A5b Solve matrix equations using inverse matrices.

Find the inverse of the matrix, if it exists.

1. $\begin{bmatrix} 3 & 6 \\ 2 & 4 \end{bmatrix}$ no inverse

2. $\begin{bmatrix} -2 & 6 \\ 4 & -10 \end{bmatrix}$ $\begin{bmatrix} \frac{5}{2} & \frac{3}{2} \\ 1 & \frac{1}{2} \end{bmatrix}$

3. $\begin{bmatrix} 3 & 7 \\ -1 & 2 \end{bmatrix}$ $\begin{bmatrix} \frac{2}{13} & -\frac{7}{13} \\ \frac{1}{13} & \frac{3}{13} \end{bmatrix}$

Use a graphing calculator to find the inverse of the matrix, if it exists.

4–6. See Additional Answers beginning on page AA1.

4. $\begin{bmatrix} 3 & 2 & 2 \\ 1 & 2 & 0 \\ 4 & -4 & 1 \end{bmatrix}$

5. $\begin{bmatrix} -2 & -1 & 4 \\ 2 & -4 & 0 \\ 0 & 1 & 1 \end{bmatrix}$

6. $\begin{bmatrix} 2 & 4 & 2 \\ 3 & 1 & 0 \\ 0 & 5 & 1 \end{bmatrix}$

Solve the matrix equation.

7. $\begin{bmatrix} -2 & 6 \\ -3 & 8 \end{bmatrix} X - \begin{bmatrix} -3 & 4 & 2 \\ 5 & -6 & 0 \end{bmatrix} = \begin{bmatrix} 9 & 2 & -7 \\ -3 & 4 & 8 \end{bmatrix}$ $\begin{bmatrix} 18 & 30 & -44 \\ 7 & 11 & -\frac{31}{2} \end{bmatrix}$

8. $\begin{bmatrix} 3 & 0 & -2 \\ 0 & 2 & 0 \\ 4 & -1 & 4 \end{bmatrix} X + \begin{bmatrix} 5 \\ -2 \\ 4 \end{bmatrix} = \begin{bmatrix} 7 \\ 12 \\ -9 \end{bmatrix}$ $\begin{bmatrix} -0.2 \\ 7 \\ -1.3 \end{bmatrix}$

Use an inverse matrix to solve the linear system.

9. $4x + 5y = 7$ $(-7, 7)$
$-2x - y = 7$

10. $2x + 2y = 12$ $(4, 2)$
$3x - 3y = 6$

11. $-4x + 7y = -9$ $\left(\frac{1}{2}, -1\right)$
$2x - y = 2$

12. $2x + 3y + 4z = 7$ $(-3, -1, 4)$
$-x + 5y + 2z = 6$
$-3x + 6y = 3$

13. $3x + y - 2z = 3$ $(6, -7, 4)$
$-2x + 2y + 3z = -14$
$5x - y - 3z = 25$

14. $4x - 3y + 4z = -5$ $\left(-\frac{3}{2}, \frac{1}{3}, \frac{1}{2}\right)$
$-2x + 3y + 2z = 5$
$8x - 6y + 14z = -7$

15. **Inverse Properties** Let $A = \begin{bmatrix} 3 & 2 \\ 4 & 3 \end{bmatrix}$. How is A related to $(A^{-1})^{-1}$? $A = (A^{-1})^{-1}$

16. **Multiple Representations** An accountant for a company is creating part of the fiscal budget for next year. She has $500,000 to allocate between salaries, insurance, and general expenses. Based on previous financial statements, she expects to spend eight times as much on salaries x as on insurance y. Also, general expenses z historically cost 20% of the amount spent on salaries and insurance combined.
   See Additional Answers beginning on page AA1.
   a. **Writing a System** Write a system of equations for the amount allocated to each category.
   b. **Writing a Matrix Equation** Write the system of equations from part (a) as a matrix equation $AX = B$.
   c. **Solving a System** Use an inverse matrix to solve the system of equations. How much is allocated to each category?

Use Vertex-Edge Graphs

Georgia Performance Standards: MM3A7a, MM3A7b

Goal Use vertex-edge graphs to represent real-life situations.

Vocabulary

A **vertex-edge graph** is a collection of points and line segments connecting some (possibly empty) subset of the points.

An **edge of a vertex-edge graph** is a line segment connecting the vertices of a graph. A **vertex of a vertex-edge graph** is a point that is either the endpoint of an edge or not part of an edge.

Example 1   Use a vertex-edge graph to represent a situation

Transportation An airline serves four cities: Bedford, Columbia, Dunwich, and Exton. There are flights between Bedford and Columbia, Bedford and Dunwich, and Columbia and Exton. Draw a vertex-edge graph to represent this situation.

Solution

STEP 1 **Represent** the cities using points. Let the points B represent Bedford, C represent Columbia, D represent Dunwich, and E represent Exton.

STEP 2 **Draw** the edges for the graph. Two vertices are connected by an edge if there are flights between the corresponding cities. Draw edges connecting B and C, B and D, and C and E.

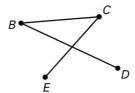

Guided Practice for Example 1

1. **Transportation** An airline serves five cities: Lowell, Montour, Newman, Peoria, and Orlando. There are flights between Lowell and Montour, Lowell and Orlando, Montour and Orlando, Newman and Orlando, and Newman and Peoria. Draw a vertex-edge graph to represent this situation.
   See Additional Answers beginning on page AA1.

Georgia Performance Standards

MM3A7a   Use graphs to represent realistic situations.   ☑

MM3A7b   Use matrices to represent graphs, and solve problems ☑
that can be represented by graphs.

Example 2 Use a matrix to represent a vertex-edge graph

Use a matrix _A_ to represent the vertex-edge graph from Example 1.

Because there are four cities, the dimensions of the matrix A are 4×4. Label the rows and columns of A with the letters of the vertices that represent each city, as shown below. If there is a flight from a city in the ith row to a city in the jth column, the element in row i, column j should be 1. If there is no flight between two cities, then enter a 0 in the appropriate position of the matrix.

$$A = \begin{array}{c} \\ B \\ C \\ D \\ E \end{array} \begin{array}{cccc} B & C & D & E \\ \left[\begin{array}{cccc} 0 & 1 & 1 & 0 \\ 1 & 0 & 0 & 1 \\ 1 & 0 & 0 & 0 \\ 0 & 1 & 0 & 0 \end{array} \right] \end{array}$$

Example 3 Use a matrix representing a vertex-edge graph

Use the matrix you found in Example 2 to calculate A^2. What does A^2 represent?

Solution

Enter matrix A into a graphing calculator and calculate A^2.

The matrix A^2 gives the number of ways you can fly from one city to another using exactly two flights. For instance, to find the number of two-flight trips from Columbia to Dunwich, locate the element in row C, column D. Because the element is 1, you can conclude that there is exactly 1 way you can fly from Columbia to Dunwich using exactly two flights.

$$A^2 = \begin{array}{c} \\ B \\ C \\ D \\ E \end{array} \begin{array}{cccc} B & C & D & E \\ \left[\begin{array}{cccc} 2 & 0 & 0 & 1 \\ 0 & 2 & 1 & 0 \\ 0 & 1 & 1 & 0 \\ 1 & 0 & 0 & 1 \end{array} \right] \end{array}$$ ← row C, column D

Guided Practice for Examples 2 and 3

2. Use the information from Examples 2 and 3 and a graphing calculator to calculate A^3. What does this matrix represent?

3. Why is there a 0 in the first row, first column of A but a 2 in the first row, first column of A^2?

2 and 3. See Additional
Answers beginning on
page AA1.

UNIT 1

LESSON
1.12

**Exercise
Set A**

MM3A7a   Use graphs to represent realistic situations.

MM3A7b   Use matrices to represent graphs, and solve
problems that can be represented by graphs.

**In Exercises 1–3, determine the number of vertices and edges in the
vertex-edge graph.**

1.

5 vertices; 7 edges

2.

6 vertices; 9 edges

3.

5 vertices; 8 edges

In Exercises 4–6, determine whether the statement is *true* or *false*.

You want to buy four types of fish for your new aquarium. Some fish
can live together in the same tank while others cannot. The vertex-edge
graph at the right represents four types of fish: gouramis (*G*), tetras (*T*),
black mollies (*B*), and angelfish (*A*). An edge connecting two vertices
indicates that those two types of fish can live together.

4.   All four types of fish can live in the same tank. **false**

5.   Angelfish can live in the same tank with black mollies. **false**

6.   Gouramis can share a tank with any of the other fish. **true**

7. *Sample answer:* 2 tanks: one tank
with gouramis, tetras, and black
mollies; another tank with just
angelfish; 2 tanks: one tank with
gouramis and angelfish; another
tank with tetras and black mollies

7.   Use the information above to give two examples of the number of tanks you could
use to house all the fish. State the type(s) of fish living in each tank.

**In Exercises 8 and 9, each vertex of the vertex-edge graph represents a
city. An edge connecting two vertices indicates the cities are connected
by a highway. Write a matrix that represents the vertex-edge graph.**

8.

$$\begin{array}{c} \\ J \\ K \\ L \\ M \end{array} \begin{array}{c} \begin{array}{cccc} J & K & L & M \end{array} \\ \begin{bmatrix} 0 & 2 & 2 & 1 \\ 2 & 0 & 0 & 1 \\ 2 & 0 & 0 & 1 \\ 1 & 1 & 1 & 0 \end{bmatrix} \end{array}$$

9.

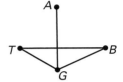

$$\begin{array}{c} \\ C \\ D \\ E \\ F \\ G \end{array} \begin{array}{c} \begin{array}{ccccc} C & D & E & F & G \end{array} \\ \begin{bmatrix} 0 & 1 & 0 & 0 & 0 \\ 1 & 0 & 0 & 1 & 2 \\ 0 & 0 & 0 & 2 & 0 \\ 0 & 1 & 2 & 0 & 1 \\ 0 & 2 & 0 & 1 & 0 \end{bmatrix} \end{array}$$

**In Exercises 10–12, draw a vertex-edge graph to represent the portion of
the United States. Let each state be represented by a vertex, then draw an
edge between two vertices if the states share a border.** 10–12. See Additional Answers
beginning on page AA1.

10.

11.

12.

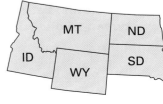

UNIT 1

LESSON
1.12

**Exercise
Set B**

MM3A7a   Use graphs to represent realistic situations.

MM3A7b   Use matrices to represent graphs, and solve
problems that can be represented by graphs.

In Exercises 1–4, determine whether the statement is *true* or *false*.

You are mixing different solutions in a chemistry lab. Some solutions
can be mixed together while others cannot. The vertex-edge graph at
the right represents five types of solutions. An edge connecting two
vertices indicates that those two solutions can be mixed together.

1. All the solutions can be mixed together. **false**

2. Solution F can be mixed with any other solution. **false**

3. Solution H can be mixed with any other solution. **true**

4. Solution K can be mixed with exactly three other solutions. **true**

**In Exercises 5 and 6, use the vertex-edge graph that
shows a portion of the city or town where you live.
The distances given are in miles.**

5. You are going from home to your cousin's house.
What is the shortest route and its distance?

6. You are at home. You need to go to your friend's house
and stop at school. What is the shortest distance including
your return home? **18 mi**

5. The shortest route is to the pizza shop, to your friend's
house, then to your cousin's house, a distance of 7 miles.

**In Exercises 7–9, each vertex of the vertex-edge graph
represents a town. An edge connecting two vertices
indicates the towns are connected by a road. Write a
matrix that represents the vertex-edge graph.**

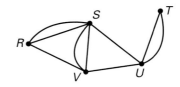

7 and 8. See Additional Answers beginning on page AA1.
7. Write a matrix M that represents the vertex-edge graph.

8. Use a graphing calculator to calculate M^2.

9. Use the matrix from Exercise 8 to find the number of ways
you can travel between the two given towns using 2 roads.

   a. Town R to Town V **4**　　**b.** Town T to Town S **2**

   c. Town V to Town S **3**　　**d.** Town S back to Town S **9**

**In Exercises 10–12, draw a vertex-edge graph to represent the portion of
the United States. Let each state be represented by a vertex, then draw an
edge between two vertices if the states share a border.**

10–12. See Additional
Answers beginning on
page AA1.

10.

11.

12.

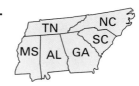

TEST | for Unit 1

1. Look for a pattern in the table shown. Then write an equation that represents the table. $y = 11x + 25$

x	0	1	2	3
y	25	36	47	58

Solve the system using any method.

2. $3x + 5y = -1$ (−2, 1)
   $2x - y = -5$

3. $x - 2y = 6$ no solution
   $5x - 10y = 3$

4. $-4x + 3y = 19$ (−1, 5)
   $6x + y = -1$

Graph the inequality. 5–7. See Additional Answers beginning on page AA1.

5. $\frac{1}{3}y \le 2$

6. $6x - 3y > -12$

7. $y \ge |x + 3| - 4$

Graph the system of inequalities. 8–10. See Additional Answers beginning on page AA1.

8. $y \ge |x - 3|$
   $y < 4$

9. $y > 2x - 5$
   $x \ge -1$
   $y \le 3$

10. $x - y < 4$
    $3x - y > -1$
    $6x + 2y \le 3$

11. Find the minimum and maximum values of the objective function $C = 3x + 5y$ subject to the constraints $x \ge 0$, $y \ge 0$, $-3x + 6y \le 18$, and $x + y \le 6$. **0; 26**

Solve the system using any algebraic method.

12. $x + y - 2z = -6$ (1, −1, 3)
    $y - 3z = -10$
    $5y - 2z = -11$

13. $-2x + y - z = 6$
    $3x - y + z = -7$
    $6x + y - z = -2$ (−1, z + 4, z)

14. $x - y + z = 8$ no solution
    $3x - 3y + 3z = 1$
    $4x + y + 5z = 3$

Using the given matrices, evaluate the expression. 15–18. See Additional Answers beginning on page AA1.

$$A = \begin{bmatrix} -1 & 3 \\ -4 & 5 \end{bmatrix}, B = \begin{bmatrix} 0 & 2 \\ 3 & -4 \end{bmatrix}, C = \begin{bmatrix} -7 & -2 \\ 0 & -3 \end{bmatrix}, D = \begin{bmatrix} 3 & -1 & 2 \\ 4 & -2 & 0 \\ 0 & -3 & -4 \end{bmatrix}, E = \begin{bmatrix} 2 & 5 & -3 \\ 7 & 2 & -6 \\ 1 & -5 & -1 \end{bmatrix}$$

15. $A + 2B$

16. $4D - E$

17. $A(B + C)$

18. $2AC + 3AB$

Evaluate the determinant of the matrix.

19. $\begin{bmatrix} -5 & -7 \\ -4 & 6 \end{bmatrix}$ −58

20. $\begin{bmatrix} 10 & 9 \\ -8 & 3 \end{bmatrix}$ 102

21. $\begin{bmatrix} 3 & 0 & 2 \\ -4 & 6 & 4 \\ 5 & -1 & 1 \end{bmatrix}$ −22

Use Cramer's rule to solve the linear system.

22. $x - 4y = 10$ (−2, −3)
    $-2x + 5y = -11$

23. $3x + 7y = 5$ (4, −1)
    $x - 2y = 6$

24. $2x + 3y + 2z = 3$ (−2, 3, −1)
    $x - 7y + 3z = -26$
    $x + 5y + 4z = 9$

25. Find the inverse, if it exists, of the matrices (a) $\begin{bmatrix} -3 & 7 \\ 2 & -5 \end{bmatrix}$ and (b) $\begin{bmatrix} -4 & -3 \\ -8 & -6 \end{bmatrix}$.

a. $\begin{bmatrix} -5 & -7 \\ -2 & -3 \end{bmatrix}$
b. no inverse

26. Shipping A shipment of machine parts was trucked from Georgia to Kentucky in 11 hours. The trip covered about 649 miles. What was the average speed of the truck? **59 mi/h**

27. School A student advisory board at your school must consist of 7 to 10 representatives from junior and senior classes. The board must include at least 3 juniors and 3 seniors. Write and graph a system of inequalities to describe the situation. Then give two solutions for the numbers of juniors and seniors on the board. **See Additional Answers beginning on page AA1.**

28. Craft Fair You are decorating jewelry boxes to sell at a fair. It takes you 3 hours to decorate a small jewelry box and 4 hours to decorate a large jewelry box. You make a profit of $12 for a small jewelry box and $18 for a large jewelry box. If you have no more than 36 hours available and want at least 10 jewelry boxes to sell, how many of each size should you decorate to maximize your profit? **4 small jewelry boxes, 6 large jewelry boxes**

29. Shopping Before taxes, two pairs of jeans and a T-shirt cost $59.48. Two T-shirts and a pair of sandals cost $33.00. One pair of jeans, one T-shirt, and one pair of sandals cost $48.49. Use a linear system and Cramer's rule to find the prices of a pair of jeans, a T-shirt, and a pair of sandals. **pair of jeans: $24.99; T-shirt: $9.50; pair of sandals: $14**

30. Geography Draw a vertex-edge graph to represent the counties shown in the map: Mitchell (M), Colquitt (C), Decatur (D), Grady (G), Thomas (T), and Brooks (B). Let each county be represented by a vertex, then draw an edge between two vertices if the counties share a border. **See Additional Answers beginning on page AA1.**

Performance Task

Inventory **See Additional Answers beginning on page AA1.**

A company manufactures three models of MP3 players: music only (M), music/photo (MP), and music/photo/video (MPV). The MP3 players are shipped to two warehouses. The number of units shipped to each warehouse this month and last month are given in matrices A and B.

	This month (A)			Last month (B)			Price (C)	
	M	MP	MPV	M	MP	MPV		
Warehouse 1	12,000	14,000	8000	15,000	18,000	10,000	M	$99.99
Warehouse 2	10,000	12,000	6000	14,000	16,000	9000	MP	$179.99
							MPV	$249.99

a. Write a matrix M that gives the total number of each type of MP3 player shipped to the two warehouses for the two months.

b. Calculate $\frac{1}{2}M$. What does this matrix represent?

c. The prices of the models are given in matrix C. Use your result from part (a) and a graphing calculator to write a matrix that gives the total value of the MP3 players shipped to each warehouse in the last two months.

d. In one week, an electronics store sells 64 MP3 players for a total of $9339.36. There were twice as many music-only MP3 players sold than music/photo MP3 players. Write a system of equations to represent this situation. How many of each type of MP3 player were sold at the store?

UNIT 2
Algebra: Polynomial Functions

Evaluate and Graph Polynomial Functions

Georgia Performance Standards: MM3A1b, MM3A1c, MM3A1d

Goal Evaluate and graph other polynomial functions.

Vocabulary

A **polynomial** is a monomial or a sum of monomials. A **polynomial function** is a function of the form $f(x) = a_n x^n + a_{n-1} x^{n-1} + \cdots + a_1 x + a_0$ where $a^n \neq 0$, the exponents are all whole numbers, and the coefficients are all real numbers.

The **degree of a polynomial function** is the exponent in the term where the variable is raised to the greatest power.

The **leading coefficient** is the coefficient in the term of a polynomial function that has the greatest exponent.

A polynomial function is in **standard form** if its terms are written in descending order of exponents from left to right.

Synthetic substitution is another way to evaluate a polynomial function, involving fewer operations than direct substitution.

The **end behavior** of a polynomial function's graph is the behavior of the graph as x approaches positive infinity $(+\infty)$ or negative infinity $(-\infty)$.

If the degree of a polynomial function is odd and the leading coefficient is positive, then $f(x) \to +\infty$ as $x \to +\infty$ and $f(x) \to -\infty$ as $x \to -\infty$.

If the degree of a polynomial function is odd and the leading coefficient is negative, then $f(x) \to -\infty$ as $x \to +\infty$ and $f(x) \to +\infty$ as $x \to -\infty$.

If the degree of a polynomial function is even and the leading coefficient is positive, then $f(x) \to +\infty$ as $x \to +\infty$ and $f(x) \to +\infty$ as $x \to -\infty$.

If the degree of a polynomial function is even and the leading coefficient is negative, then $f(x) \to -\infty$ as $x \to +\infty$ and $f(x) \to -\infty$ as $x \to -\infty$.

A function f is **even** if $f(-x) = f(x)$. The graph of an even function is symmetric with respect to the y-axis. A function f is **odd** if $f(-x) = -f(x)$. The graph of an odd function is symmetric with respect to the origin.

Example 1   Identify polynomial functions

Decide whether the function is a polynomial function. If so, write it in standard form and state its degree and leading coefficient.

a. $g(x) = -5x + 6x^{-2}$ 　　　　**b.** $t(x) = -\sqrt{5}x + 2$

Solution

a. The function $g(x)$ is not a polynomial function because the term $6x^{-2}$ has an exponent that is not a whole number.

b. The function $t(x)$ is a polynomial function written in standard form. It has degree 1 and a leading coefficient of $-\sqrt{5}$.

Example 2 Evaluate a polynomial function

Use (a) direct substitution and (b) synthetic substitution to evaluate $g(x) = -4x^3 + 3x^2 - 7$ when $x = -2$.

Solution

a. $g(x) = -4x^3 + 3x^2 - 7$ Write original function.

$g(-2) = -4(-2)^3 + 3(-2)^2 - 7$ Substitute -2 for x.

$= 37$ Simplify.

b.

STEP 1 Write the coefficients of $g(x)$ in order of descending exponents. Write the x-value at which $g(x)$ is being evaluated to the left.

$$-2 \,\big|\, \begin{array}{cccc} -4 & 3 & 0 & -7 \end{array}$$

STEP 2 Bring down the leading coefficient. Multiply the leading coefficient by the x-value. Write the product under the second coefficient. Add.

$$-2 \,\big|\, \begin{array}{cccc} -4 & 3 & 0 & -7 \\ & 8 & & \\ \hline -4 & 11 & & \end{array}$$

STEP 3 Multiply the previous sum by the x-value. Write the product under the third coefficient. Add. Repeat for all the remaining coefficients. The final sum is the value of $g(x)$ at the given x-value.

$$-2 \,\big|\, \begin{array}{cccc} -4 & 3 & 0 & -7 \\ & 8 & -22 & 44 \\ \hline -4 & 11 & -22 & 37 \end{array}$$

Synthetic substitution gives $g(x) = 37$, which matches the result in part (a).

Guided Practice for Examples 1 and 2

1–4. See Additional Answers beginning on page AA1.

Decide whether the function is a polynomial function. If so, write it in standard form and state its degree and leading coefficient.

1. $g(x) = ix + 7$ **2.** $s(x) = 2x^2 + x^{-1}$ **3.** $d(x) = 3\pi x^2$

4. Evaluate $g(x) = -4x^2 + 6$ when $x = 3$ using direct substitution. Check with synthetic substitution.

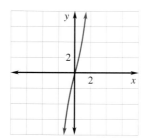

Example 3   Describe end behavior

Describe the end behavior of the graph. Then describe the degree and leading coefficient of the polynomial function.

Solution

From the graph, $f(x) \to -\infty$ as $x \to -\infty$ and $f(x) \to +\infty$ as $x \to +\infty$. The degree is odd and the leading coefficient is positive.

Example 4   Graph and analyze a polynomial function

Graph and analyze the function $f(x) = -2x^4 + 4x^2 - 2$.

a. Graph the function.

b. Find the domain and range of the function.

c. Describe the degree and leading coefficient of the function.

d. Decide whether the function is *even, odd,* or *neither.* Describe any symmetries in the graph.

e. Identify where the function increases and decreases.

Solution

a. Make a table of values and plot the corresponding points. Connect the points with a smooth curve.

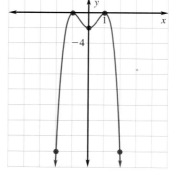

x	−2	−1	0	1	2
y	−18	0	−2	0	−18

b. The domain is all real numbers and the range is $y \le 0$.

c. The degree is even and the leading coefficient is negative.

d. The function is even because
$$f(-x) = -2(-x)^4 + 4(-x)^2 - 2 = -2x^4 + 4x^2 - 2 = f(x).$$
The graph of the function is symmetric with respect to the y-axis.

e. The function increases for $x < -1$ and $0 < x < 1$. The function decreases for $-1 < x < 0$ and $x > 1$.

Guided Practice for Examples 3 and 4

Describe the end behavior of the graph of the polynomial function by completing these statements: $f(x) \to$ _?_ as $x \to -\infty$ and $f(x) \to$ _?_ as $x \to +\infty$. 5–7. See Additional Answers beginning on page AA1.

5. $f(x) = x^4 - 2x^2 + 1$

6. $f(x) = x^3 - 7x - 6$

7. Graph and analyze the function $f(x) = x^3 - x^2 - 2x$.

Exercise Set A

MM3A1b Understand the effects of the following on the graph of a polynomial function: degree, lead coefficient, and multiplicity of real zeros.

MM3A1c Determine whether a polynomial function has symmetry and whether it is even, odd, or neither.

MM3A1d Investigate and explain characteristics of polynomial functions, including domain and range, intercepts, zeros, relative and absolute extrema, intervals of increase and decrease, and end behavior.

Decide whether the function is a polynomial function. If it is, write the function in standard form and state the degree and leading coefficient.

1. $f(x) = 7 - 2x$
yes; $f(x) = -2x + 7$; 1; −2

2. $g(x) = 2x - x^3 + 8$
yes; $g(x) = -x^3 + 2x + 8$; 3; −1

3. $h(x) = x^4 - x^{-3}$ no

Use direct substitution to evaluate the polynomial function for the given value of x.

4. $f(x) = 6x^4 - x^3 + 3x^2 - 5x + 9; x = -1$ 24

5. $g(x) = 7x - x^4 + 1; x = -4$ −283

Use synthetic substitution to evaluate the polynomial function for the given value of x.

6. $f(x) = 7x^4 - 3x^3 + x^2 + 5x - 9; x = 2$ 93

7. $g(x) = x^3 - 8x + 6; x = -3$ 3

***Describe* the end behavior of the graph of the polynomial function by completing these statements: $f(x) \to$ __?__ as $x \to -\infty$ and $f(x) \to$ __?__ as $x \to +\infty$.**

8. $f(x) = -5x^3$
$+\infty, -\infty$

9. $f(x) = 2x^5 - 7x^2 - 4x$
$-\infty, +\infty$

10. $f(x) = -12x^6 - 2x + 5$
$-\infty, -\infty$

Decide whether the function is *even, odd*, or *neither. Describe* any symmetries in the graph. 11–13. See Additional Answers beginning on page AA1.

11. $f(x) = x^2 - 3$

12. $g(x) = x^3 - 5x$

13. $f(x) = -2x^5 + 8x$

Graph the polynomial function. 14–16. See Additional Answers beginning on page AA1.

14. $f(x) = -x^3 - 2$

15. $g(x) = x^4 + 2x$

16. $h(x) = -x^4 + 2x^3 - 5x + 1$

For the polynomial function, (a) graph the function, (b) find the domain and range, (c) describe the degree and leading coefficient, (d) describe any symmetry, and (e) identify where the function increases and decreases.

17. $f(x) = -x^3$

18. $f(x) = x^4 + 1$

19. $f(x) = 3(x^3 - 13x + 12)$

17–19. See Additional Answers beginning on page AA1.

20. Multiple Representations The retail space in shopping centers in the United States from 1986 to 2003 can be modeled by $S = -0.0388t^4 + 1.723t^3 - 28t^2 + 309t + 3481$ where S is the amount of retail space (in millions of square feet) and t is the number of years since 1986.

a–c. See Additional Answers beginning on page AA1.

a. Graphing a Function Graph the function on the domain $0 \le t \le 17$.

b. Using a Graph Use the graph to estimate the first year that the amount of retail space was greater than 5 billion square feet.

c. Predicting a Value Use the model to predict the amount of retail space in the year 2010. Is it appropriate to use the model to make this prediction? *Explain.*

UNIT 2

MM3A1b Understand the effects of the following on the graph of a polynomial function: degree, lead coefficient, and multiplicity of real zeros.

MM3A1c Determine whether a polynomial function has symmetry and whether it is even, odd, or neither.

MM3A1d Investigate and explain characteristics of polynomial functions, including domain and range, intercepts, zeros, relative and absolute extrema, intervals of increase and decrease, and end behavior.

Decide whether the function is a polynomial function. If it is, write the function in standard form and state the degree and leading coefficient.

1. $f(x) = x^3\sqrt{5} + 7 - 2x^2$
  yes; $f(x) = x^3\sqrt{5}; -2x^2 + 7; 3; \sqrt{5}$

2. $g(x) = \pi - 4x^2 + 2x^{-1}$
  no

Use direct substitution to evaluate the polynomial function for the given value of x. Then check your answer using synthetic substitution.

3. $f(x) = 2x^5 - 3x^4 + x^3 - 6x + 20; x = 2$ 32

4. $g(x) = -8x^3 + 5x^2 + 14; x = -3$ 275

Describe **the end behavior of the graph of the polynomial function by completing these statements:** $f(x) \to$ __?__ **as** $x \to -\infty$ **and** $f(x) \to$ __?__ **as** $x \to +\infty$.

5. $f(x) = -x^7 + 10x$
  $+\infty, -\infty$

6. $f(x) = 0.6x^3 - 2x^2 + 27$
  $-\infty, +\infty$

7. $f(x) = x^{102} + 4x^{99}$
  $+\infty, +\infty$

Decide whether the function is *even, odd, or neither. Describe* **any symmetries in the graph.** 8–10. See Additional Answers beginning on page AA1.

8. $f(x) = -x^4 + 3$

9. $g(x) = 2x^3 + 6x$

10. $f(x) = x^6 - x^4 - 2$

Graph the polynomial function. 11–13. See Additional Answers beginning on page AA1.

11. $f(x) = 0.5 - 2x^4$

12. $g(x) = -2x^7 - 4$

13. $h(x) = x^3\sqrt{2} - 2x + 3$

For the polynomial function, (a) graph the function, (b) find the domain and range, (c) describe the degree and leading coefficient, (d) describe any symmetry, and (e) identify where the function increases and decreases.

14. $f(x) = -x^4 + 6x^2$

15. $f(x) = 2x^4 - 4x^2 + 8$

16. $f(x) = -x^3 + 3x^2 - 2x + 5$

14–16. See Additional Answers beginning on page AA1.

17. Critical Thinking Give an example of a polynomial function f such that
$f(x) \to -\infty$ as $x \to -\infty$ and $f(x) \to -\infty$ as $x \to +\infty$. *Sample answer:* $f(x) = -x^4 + 2x^3$

18. **Child Development** The average heights B and G (in inches) for boys and girls ages 2 to 20, respectively, can be modeled by the functions $B = -0.001t^4 + 0.04t^3 - 0.57t^2 + 5.7t + 25$ and $G = 0.000007t^4 - 0.00276t^3 - 0.012t^2 + 3.1t + 27$ where t is the age (in years).

  a. According to the models, what is the difference in average height between 16-year-old boys and girls?

  b. Sketch the graphs of the two models in the same coordinate plane.

  See Additional Answers beginning on page AA1.

  c. During an annual physical, a doctor measures a 14-year-old to be 60 inches tall. Is the 14-year-old more likely to be male or female? *Explain.*

Translate Graphs of Polynomial Functions

Georgia Performance Standards: MM3A1a, MM3A1c, MM3A1d

Goal Graph translations of polynomial functions.

Example 1 **Translate a polynomial function vertically**

Graph $g(x) = x^4 + 5$. Compare the graph with the graph of $f(x) = x^4$.

STEP 1 **Make** a table of values and plot the corresponding points.

x	−2	−1	0	1	2
y	21	6	0	6	21

STEP 2 **Connect** the points with a smooth curve and check the end behavior. The degree is even and the leading coefficient is positive. So, $g(x) \to +\infty$ as $x \to -\infty$ and $g(x) \to +\infty$ as $x \to +\infty$.

STEP 3 **Compare** with $f(x) = x^4$. The graph of $g(x) = x^4 + 5$ is the graph of $f(x) = x^4$ translated up 5 units. The domains of f and g are all real numbers. The range of f is $y \geq 0$ and the range of g is $y \geq 5$. The function f has x- and y-intercepts of 0 and g has a y-intercept of 5. Notice that both f and g are symmetric with respect to the y-axis and are even functions because $f(-x) = (-x)^4 = f(x)$ and $g(-x) = (-x)^4 + 5 = g(x)$.

Example 2 **Translate a polynomial function vertically**

Graph $g(x) = x^4 - 2$. Compare the graph with the graph of $f(x) = x^4$.

STEP 1 **Make** a table of values and plot the corresponding points.

x	−2	−1	0	1	2
y	14	−1	−2	−1	14

STEP 2 **Connect** the points with a smooth curve and check the end behavior. The degree is even and the leading coefficient is positive. So, $g(x) \to +\infty$ as $x \to -\infty$ and $g(x) \to +\infty$ as $x \to +\infty$.

STEP 3 **Compare** with $f(x) = x^4$. The graph of $g(x) = x^4 - 2$ is the graph of $f(x) = x^4$ translated down 2 units. The domains of f and g are all real numbers. The range of f is $y \geq 0$ and the range of g is $y \geq -2$. The function f has x- and y-intercepts of 0 and g has x-intercepts of about -1.1 and 1.1, and a y-intercept of -2. Notice that both f and g are symmetric with respect to the y-axis and are even functions because $f(-x) = (-x)^4 = f(x)$ and $g(-x) = (-x)^4 - 2 = g(x)$.

Georgia Performance Standards

MM3A1a Graph simple polynomial functions as translations of the function $f(x) = ax^n$. ☑

MM3A1c Determine whether a polynomial function has symmetry and whether it is even, odd, or neither. ☑

MM3A1d Investigate and explain characteristics of polynomial functions, including domain and range, intercepts, zeros, relative and absolute extrema, intervals of increase and decrease, and end behavior. ☑

Guided Practice for Examples 1 and 2

Graph the function $g(x)$. *Compare* the graph with the graph of $f(x)$. 1–4. See Additional Answers beginning on page AA1.

1. $g(x) = x^3 + 1, f(x) = x^3$

2. $g(x) = x^3 - 4, f(x) = x^3$

3. $g(x) = x^4 - 3, f(x) = x^4$

4. $g(x) = x^4 + 2, f(x) = x^4$

Example 3 **Translate a polynomial function horizontally**

Graph $g(x) = 2(x - 2)^3$. Compare the graph with the graph of $f(x) = 2x^3$.

Solution

STEP 1 **Make** a table of values and plot the corresponding points.

x	−1	0	1	2	3
y	−54	−16	−2	0	2

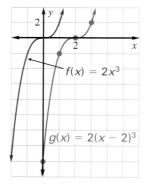

$f(x) = 2x^3$

$g(x) = 2(x - 2)^3$

STEP 2 **Connect** the points with a smooth curve and check the end behavior. The degree is odd and the leading coefficient is positive. So, $g(x) \to -\infty$ as $x \to -\infty$ and $g(x) \to +\infty$ as $x \to +\infty$.

STEP 3 **Compare** with $f(x) = 2x^3$. The graph of $g(x) = 2(x - 2)^3$ is the graph of $f(x) = 2x^3$ translated to the right 2 units. The domains and ranges of both functions are all real numbers. The function f has x- and y-intercepts of 0 and g has an x-intercept of 2 and a y-intercept of -16. Notice that f is symmetric with respect to the origin and is an odd function because $f(-x) = 2(-x)^3 = -f(x)$. Notice that g is neither even nor odd because $g(-x) = 2(-x - 2)^3$, which is not equal to $-g(x)$ or $g(x)$.

Guided Practice for Example 3

Graph the function g(x). *Compare* the graph with the graph of f(x). 5–8. See Additional Answers beginning on page AA1.

5. $g(x) = (x - 1)^3, f(x) = x^3$

6. $g(x) = (x + 4)^4, f(x) = x^4$

7. $g(x) = 3(x - 3)^4, f(x) = 3x^4$

8. $g(x) = \frac{1}{2}(x + 2)^3, f(x) = \frac{1}{2}x^3$

Example 4 Translate a polynomial function

Graph $g(x) = -\frac{1}{2}(x + 1)^4 - 3$. Compare the graph with the graph of $f(x) = -\frac{1}{2}x^4$.

Solution

STEP 1 **Make** a table of values and plot the corresponding points.

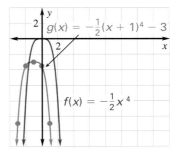

x	−3	−2	−1	0	1
y	−11	−3.5	−3	−3.5	−11

STEP 2 **Connect** the points with a smooth curve and check the end behavior. The degree is even and the leading coefficient is negative. So, $g(x) \to -\infty$ as $x \to -\infty$ and $g(x) \to -\infty$ as $x \to +\infty$.

STEP 3 **Compare** with $f(x) = -\frac{1}{2}x^4$. The graph of $g(x) = -\frac{1}{2}(x + 1)^4 - 3$ is the graph of $f(x) = -\frac{1}{2}x^4$ translated to the left 1 unit and down 3 units. The domains of f and g are all real numbers. The range of f is $y \le 0$ and the range of g is $y \le -3$. The function f has x- and y-intercepts of 0 and g has a y-intercept of -3.5. Notice that f is symmetric with respect to the y-axis and is an even function because $f(-x) = -\frac{1}{2}(-x)^4 = f(x)$. Notice that g is neither even nor odd because $g(-x) = -\frac{1}{2}(-x + 1)^4 - 3$, which is not equal to $-g(x)$ or $g(x)$.

Guided Practice for Example 4

Graph the function g(x). *Compare* the graph with the graph of f(x). 9–12. See Additional Answers beginning on page AA1.

9. $g(x) = (x + 4)^3 - 2, f(x) = x^3$

10. $g(x) = -\frac{3}{2}(x - 1)^3 + 3, f(x) = -\frac{3}{2}x^3$

11. $g(x) = -(x - 2)^4 + 1, f(x) = -x^4$

12. $g(x) = \frac{2}{3}(x + 2)^4 - 2, f(x) = \frac{2}{3}x^4$

MM3A1a	Graph simple polynomial functions as translations of the function $f(x) = ax^n$.
MM3A1c	Determine whether a polynomial function has symmetry and whether it is even, odd, or neither.
MM3A1d	Investigate and explain characteristics of polynomial functions, including domain and range, intercepts, zeros, relative and absolute extrema, intervals of increase and decrease, and end behavior.

Match the function with its graph.

1. $y = x^3 + 4$ **C**

2. $y = (x + 4)^3$ **A**

3. $y = -x^3 + 4$ **B**

A.

B.

C.
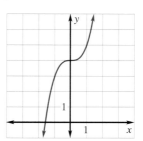

***Explain* how the graphs of *f* and *g* are related.**

4. $f(x) = -x^3$, $g(x) = -(x - 8)^3$ The graph of *g* is the graph of *f* translated to the right 8 units.

5. $f(x) = 2x^4$, $g(x) = 2x^4 - 6$ The graph of *g* is the graph of *f* translated down 6 units.

Graph the function. *Compare* the graph with the graph of $f(x) = x^3$.

6. $g(x) = x^3 - 1$

7. $g(x) = x^3 + 2$

8. $g(x) = (x - 4)^3$

6–8. See Additional Answers beginning on page AA1.

Graph the function. *Compare* the graph with the graph of $f(x) = -2x^3$.

9. $g(x) = -2x^3 + 3$

10. $g(x) = -2(x - 1)^3$

11. $g(x) = -2(x + 2)^3 + 4$

9–11. See Additional Answers beginning on page AA1.

Graph the function. *Compare* the graph with the graph of $f(x) = x^4$.

12. $g(x) = (x + 1)^4$

13. $g(x) = x^4 - 5$

14. $g(x) = (x - 3)^4$

12–14. See Additional Answers beginning on page AA1.

Graph the function. *Compare* the graph with the graph of $f(x) = \frac{1}{3}x^4$.

15–17. See Additional Answers beginning on page AA1.

15. $g(x) = \frac{1}{3}x^4 - 2$

16. $g(x) = \frac{1}{3}(x + 3)^4$

17. $g(x) = \frac{1}{3}(x - 1)^4 + 1$

Write an equation for the function that is described by the given characteristics.

18. The shape of $f(x) = x^3$, but moved 7 units down. $y = x^3 - 7$

19. The shape of $f(x) = x^4$, but moved 5 units to the left. $y = (x + 5)^4$

20. **Geometry** The volume of a cube with side length x feet is given by $V_1 = x^3$. The volume of a cube with side length $(x + 2)$ feet is given by $V_2 = (x + 2)^3$.
See Additional Answers beginning on page AA1.

   a. Graph V_1 and V_2. *Explain* how the graphs are related.

   b. Find the volume of each cube when $x = 6$.

Exercise Set B

MM3A1a	Graph simple polynomial functions as translations of the function $f(x) = ax^n$.
MM3A1c	Determine whether a polynomial function has symmetry and whether it is even, odd, or neither.
MM3A1d	Investigate and explain characteristics of polynomial functions, including domain and range, intercepts, zeros, relative and absolute extrema, intervals of increase and decrease, and end behavior.

***Explain* how the graphs of *f* and *g* are related.**

1. $f(x) = x^3, g(x) = x^3 - 7$

2. $f(x) = x^4, g(x) = (x + 6)^4$

3. $f(x) = \frac{1}{4}x^3, g(x) = \frac{1}{4}(x + 3)^3 - 1$

4. $f(x) = -4x^4, g(x) = -4(x - 1)^4 + 0.5$

1–4. See Additional Answers beginning on page AA1.

Graph the function. *Compare* the graph with the graph of $f(x) = -x^3$.

5. $g(x) = -x^3 + 4$

6. $g(x) = -(x + 2)^3$

7. $g(x) = -(x - 5)^3 + 1$

5–7. See Additional Answers beginning on page AA1.

Graph the function. *Compare* the graph with the graph of $f(x) = \frac{3}{2}x^3$.

8–10. See Additional Answers beginning on page AA1.

8. $g(x) = \frac{3}{2}x^3 - 2$

9. $g(x) = \frac{3}{2}(x - 4)^3$

10. $g(x) = \frac{3}{2}(x + 1)^3 - 3$

Graph the function. *Compare* the graph with the graph of $f(x) = x^4$.

11. $g(x) = (x - 3)^4$

12. $g(x) = x^4 + 4$

13. $g(x) = (x + 3)^4 - 5$

11–13. See Additional Answers beginning on page AA1.

Graph the function. *Compare* the graph with the graph of $f(x) = 0.5x^4$.

14. $g(x) = 0.5x^4 + 1$

15. $g(x) = 0.5(x - 6)^4$

16. $g(x) = 0.5(x - 2)^4 + 3$

14–16. See Additional Answers beginning on page AA1.

17. Error Analysis A student tried to explain how the graphs of $f(x) = -2x^3$ and $g(x) = -2(x - 5)^3 + 4$ are related. *Describe* and correct the error.

> The graph of $g(x) = -2(x - 5)^3 + 4$ is the graph of $f(x) = -2x^3$ translated left 5 units and down 4 units.

See Additional Answers beginning on page AA1.

Write an equation for the function that is described by the given characteristics.

18. The shape of $f(x) = -x^3$, but moved 4 units to the right and 6 units down. $y = -(x - 4)^3 - 6$

19. The shape of $f(x) = 3x^4$, but moved 7 units to the left and 1 unit up. $y = 3(x + 7)^4 + 1$

20. Multiple Representations The volume of a ball with radius r inches is given by $V_1 = \frac{4}{3}\pi r^3$. The radius of a second ball is 1 inch greater than the radius of the first ball.

   a. Writing a Function Write a function that represents the volume V_2 of the second ball.

   b. Graphing Functions Graph V_1 and V_2.

   c. Analyzing Graphs *Explain* how the graphs are related.

   d. Calculating a Value Find the volume of each ball when $r = 4.5$ inches.

   See Additional Answers beginning on page AA1.

Factor and Solve Polynomial Equations

Georgia Performance Standards: MM3A3b, MM3A3d

Goal Factor and solve polynomial equations.

Vocabulary

A factorable polynomial with integer coefficients is **factored completely** if it is written as a product of unfactorable polynomials with integer coefficients. To factor the sum of two cubes, use the pattern $a^3 + b^3 = (a + b)(a^2 - ab + b^2)$. To factor the difference of two cubes, use the pattern $a^3 - b^3 = (a - b)(a^2 + ab + b^2)$.

For some polynomials you can **factor by grouping** pairs of terms that have a common monomial factor.

An expression of the form $au^2 + bu + c$, where u is any expression in x, is said to be in **quadratic form**.

Example 1   **Factor the sum or difference of two cubes**

Factor the polynomial completely.

a. $4x^4 - 108x = 4x(x^3 - 27)$	Factor common monomial.
$= 4x(x - 3)(x^2 + 3x + 9)$	Difference of two cubes
b. $2b^3 + 16a^3 = 2(b^3 + 8a^3)$	Factor common monomial.
$= 2(b + 2a)(b^2 - 2ab + 4a^2)$	Sum of two cubes

Example 2   **Factor by grouping**

Factor the polynomial $x^3 + 2x^2 - x - 2$ completely.

$x^3 + 2x^2 - x - 2 = x^2(x + 2) - 1(x + 2)$	Factor by grouping.
$= (x^2 - 1)(x + 2)$	Distributive property
$= (x + 1)(x - 1)(x + 2)$	Difference of two squares

Example 3   **Factor polynomials in quadratic form**

Factor completely: (a) $3x^8 + 18x^5 + 24x^2$ and (b) $81g^4 - 256$.

a. $3x^8 + 18x^5 + 24x^2 = 3x^2(x^6 + 6x^3 + 8)$	Factor common monomial.
$= 3x^2(x^3 + 2)(x^3 + 4)$	Factor trinomial in quadratic form.
b. $81g^4 - 256 = (9g^2)^2 - (16)^2$	Write as difference of two squares.
$= (9g^2 + 16)(9g^2 - 16)$	Difference of two squares
$= (9g^2 + 16)(3g + 4)(3g - 4)$	Difference of two squares

Example 4 **Find real-number solutions**

Find the real-number solutions of the equation $x^4 - 7x^2 = -12$.

$x^4 - 7x^2 + 12 = 0$	Write in standard form.
$(x^2 - 4)(x^2 - 3) = 0$	Factor trinomial.
$(x + 2)(x - 2)(x^2 - 3) = 0$	Difference of two squares
$x = -2, x = 2, x = \sqrt{3}, \text{ or } x = -\sqrt{3}$	Zero product property

Example 5 **Solve a polynomial equation**

Box Dimensions The dimensions (in inches) of a jewelry box
are: length $4x$, width $(x - 1)$, and height $(x - 2)$. If the volume
of the box is 24 cubic inches, find the dimensions of the box.

Solution

Volume (cubic inches)	=	Length (inches)	·	Width (inches)	·	Height (inches)
↓		↓		↓		↓
24	=	$4x$	·	$(x - 1)$	·	$(x - 2)$

$24 = (4x)(x - 1)(x - 2)$	Write equation.
$0 = 4x^3 - 12x^2 + 8x - 24$	Write in standard form.
$0 = 4x^2(x - 3) + 8(x - 3)$	Factor by grouping.
$0 = (4x^2 + 8)(x - 3)$	Distributive property

The only real solution is $x = 3$. The jewelry box is 12 in. long, 2 in. wide, and 1 in. high.

Guided Practice for Examples 1, 2, 3, 4, and 5

Factor the polynomial completely. 1–6. See Additional Answers beginning on page AA1.

1. $7x^5 - 56x^2$
2. $128y^6 + 2$
3. $x^3 - 3x^2 - 4x + 12$
4. $y^3 + 7y^2 - 9y - 63$
5. $3b^6 + 6b^4 + 3b^2$
6. $z^8 - 16$

Find the real-number solutions of the equation.

7. $x^4 - 3x^2 + 2 = 0$
   $\pm1, \pm\sqrt{2}$
8. $x^5 - 8x^3 = -12x$
   $0, \pm\sqrt{6}, \pm\sqrt{2}$
9. $x^5 - 12x^3 = -27x$
   $0, \pm\sqrt{3}, \pm3$

10. The dimensions (in inches) of a jewelry box are: length $2x$, width $(x - 1)$, and
    height $(x - 3)$. If the volume of the box is 24 cubic inches, find the dimensions
    of the box. 8 in. by 3 in. by 1 in.

MM3A3b   Solve polynomial, exponential, and logarithmic equations analytically, graphically, and using appropriate technology.

MM3A3d   Solve a variety of types of equations by appropriate means choosing among mental calculation, pencil and paper, or appropriate technology.

Factor the sum or difference of cubes.

1. $x^3 + 125$ $(x + 5)(x^2 - 5x + 25)$

2. $y^3 - 8$ $(y - 2)(y^2 + 2y + 4)$

3. $64n^3 - 27$ $(4n - 3)(16n^2 + 12n + 9)$

4. $27g^3 + 343$ $(3g + 7)(9g^2 - 21g + 49)$

5. $w^3 + 27$ $(w + 3)(w^2 - 3w + 9)$

6. $8v^3 - 125$ $(2v - 5)(4v^2 + 10v + 25)$

Factor the polynomial by grouping.

7. $r^3 - 3r^2 + 6r - 18$ $(r^2 + 6)(r - 3)$

8. $x^3 + 6x^2 + 7x + 42$ $(x^2 + 7)(x + 6)$

9. $c^3 + 4c^2 - 9c - 36$ $(c + 3)(c - 3)(c + 4)$

10. $9m^3 + 18m^2 - 4m - 8$ $(3m + 2)(3m - 2)(m + 2)$

Factor the polynomial in quadratic form.

11. $x^4 - 36$
    $(x^2 - 6)(x^2 + 6)$

12. $x^4 + x^2 - 20$
    $(x + 2)(x - 2)(x^2 + 5)$

13. $6y^6 - 5y^3 - 4$
    $(2y^3 + 1)(3y^3 - 4)$

Factor the polynomial completely.

14. $x^6 - 4$ $(x^3 + 2)(x^3 - 2)$

15. $d^4 - 7d^2 + 10$ $(d^2 - 5)(d^2 - 2)$

16. $24q^3 - 81$ $3(2q - 3)(4q^2 + 6q + 9)$

17. $a^6 + 7a^3 + 6$ $(a^3 + 6)(a + 1)(a^2 - a + 1)$

18. $-4x^4 + 26x^2 - 30$ $-2(2x^2 - 3)(x^2 - 5)$

19. $2b^4 + 14b^3 - 16b - 112$
    $2(b + 7)(b - 2)(b^2 + 2b + 4)$

Find the real-number solutions of the equation.

20. $n^4 = -6n^3$ $-6, 0$

21. $4k^3 = 9k^2$ $0, \frac{9}{4}$

22. $x^3 + 2x^2 - 25x - 50 = 0$ $-5, -2, 5$

23. $6w^3 + 30w^2 - 18w - 90 = 0$ $-5, -\sqrt{3}, \sqrt{3}$

24. $y^4 + 45 = 14y^2$ $-3, -\sqrt{5}, \sqrt{5}, 3$

25. $3r^5 + 15r^3 - 18r = 0$ $-1, 0, 1$

26. **Error Analysis** *Describe* and correct the error in finding all real-number solutions.
    The factor $2x$ was not set equal to 0.
    $2x^3 - 50x = 0$
    $2x(x^2 - 25) = 0$
    $x = 0$ or $x = -5$ or $x = 5$

$$2x^3 - 50x = 0$$
$$2x(x^2 - 25) = 0$$
$$x^2 - 25 = 0$$
$$x = -5 \text{ or } x = 5$$
✗

27. **City Park** You are designing a marble planter for a city park. You want the length of the planter to be six times the height and the width to be three times the height. The sides should be one foot thick. Because the planter will be on the sidewalk, it does not need a bottom. What should the outer dimensions of the planter be if it is to hold 4 cubic feet of dirt? **6 ft by 3 ft by 1 ft**

Exercise Set B

MM3A3b Solve polynomial, exponential, and logarithmic equations analytically, graphically, and using appropriate technology.

MM3A3d Solve a variety of types of equations by appropriate means choosing among mental calculation, pencil and paper, or appropriate technology.

Factor the polynomial completely using any method.

1. $x^3 - 512$ $(x - 8)(x^2 + 8x + 64)$

2. $2a^3 + 432$ $2(a + 6)(a^2 - 6a + 36)$

3. $7h^3 + 448$ $7(h + 4)(h^2 - 4h + 16)$

4. $-3c^3 + 24$ $-3(c - 2)(c^2 + 2c + 4)$

5. $12x^3 - 6x^2 + 2x - 1$ $(6x^2 + 1)(2x - 1)$

6. $3k^4 + 27k^3 - 7k - 63$ $(3k^3 - 7)(k + 9)$

7. $3n^3 - 10n^2 - 48n + 160$ $(n + 4)(n - 4)(3n - 10)$

8. $x^6 + x^5 - x^4 - x^3$ $x^3(x + 1)^2(x - 1)$

9. $y^4 - 81$ $(y^2 + 9)(y + 3)(y - 3)$

10. $2z^4 - 1250$ $2(z^2 + 25)(z + 5)(z - 5)$

11. $6a^4 + 13a^2 - 5$ $(3a^2 - 1)(2a^2 + 5)$

12. $6b^4 - 17b^2 - 28$ $(6b^2 + 7)(b + 2)(b - 2)$

13. $r^5 + r^3 - r^2 - 1$ $(r - 1)(r^2 + r + 1)(r^2 + 1)$

14. $-4w^8 - 8w^6 + 4w^4 + 8w^2$ $-4w^2(w^2 + 2)(w^2 + 1)(w + 1)(w - 1)$

15. $a^6b^3 + 125$ $(a^2b + 5)(a^4b^2 - 5a^2b + 25)$

16. $2ac^2 - 5bc^2 - 2ad^2 + 5bd^2$ $(c - d)(c + d)(2a - 5b)$

Find the real-number solutions of the equation.

17. $x^3 + 1000 = 0$ -10

18. $27g^3 - 8 = 0$ $\frac{2}{3}$

19. $6v^3 = 384$ 4

20. $p^3 + 4p^2 - 9p = 36$ $-4, -3, 3$

21. $125q^4 - 27 = 125q^3 - 27q$ $-\frac{3}{5}, 1$

22. $s^4 - 11s^2 + 28 = 0$ $-\sqrt{7}, -2, 2, \sqrt{7}$

23. $162y^4 = 2$ $-\frac{1}{3}, \frac{1}{3}$

24. $m^6 - 64 = 0$ $-2, 2$

25. $3z^{11} - 3z^5 = 0$ $-1, 0, 1$

26. $16h^5 - 25h^3 + 9h = 0$ $-1, -\frac{3}{4}, 0, \frac{3}{4}, 1$

27. $12n^7 + 2n^5 = 30n^3$ $-\frac{\sqrt{6}}{2}, 0, \frac{\sqrt{6}}{2}$

28. $6r^7 + 6r^5 = 9r^6 + 9r^4$ $0, \frac{3}{2}$

29. **Critical Thinking** Write a polynomial that can be factored using grouping and the sum of cubes. Show the complete factorization of your polynomial.
Sample answer: $x^4 + 5x^3 + x + 5$; $(x + 5)(x + 1)(x^2 - x + 1)$

30. **Theater** A stage crew is assembling a three-level semi-circular platform on a stage for a performance. The platform has the dimensions shown in the diagram and a total volume of 756π cubic feet.

    a. What is the volume, in terms of x, of each of the three levels of the platform? $V_1 = 18\pi x^2$, $V_2 = 8\pi x^3$, $V_3 = 2\pi x^3$,

    b. Use what you know about the total volume to write an equation involving x. $28\pi x^3 = 756\pi$

    c. Solve the equation from part (b). $x = 3$

    d. Use your solution from part (c) to calculate the dimensions (radius and height) of each of the levels of the platform. level 1: 18 ft, 3 ft; level 2: 12 ft, 3 ft; level 3: 6 ft, 3 ft

2x
2x
2x
x
x
x

Georgia Performance Standards

MM3A3b Solve polynomial, exponential, and logarithmic equations analytically, graphically, and using appropriate technology. ☑

MM3A3d Solve a variety of types of equations by appropriate means choosing among mental calculation, pencil and paper, or appropriate technology. ☑

LESSON 2.3

Problem Solving Workshop

Problem In Example 5 on page 77, you solved a polynomial equation by factoring. You can also solve a polynomial equation *using a graph*. The dimensions (in inches) of a jewelry box are: length $4x$, width $(x - 1)$, and height $(x - 2)$. If the volume of the box is 24 cubic inches, find the dimensions of the box.

STEP 1 Write a function for the volume of the jewelry box. The volume of a rectangular prism is length • width • height. So, the volume y of the jewelry box is given by this function: $y = 4x(x - 1)(x - 2)$.

STEP 2 Graph the equations $y = 24$ and $y = 4x(x - 1)(x - 2)$. Choose a viewing window that shows the intersection of the graphs.

STEP 3 Identify the coordinates of the intersection point. On a graphing calculator, you use the *intersect* feature. The intersection point is (3, 24).

The volume of the jewelry box is 24 cubic inches when x is 3. So, the dimensions of the jewelry box should be as follows:

Length = 4(3) = 12 inches, width = 3 − 1 = 2 inches, height = 3 − 2 = 1 inch

Practice

1. **What If?** Suppose the volume of the jewelry box is 240 cubic inches. Find the dimensions of the jewelry box using a graph.
   length: 20 in., width: 4 in., height: 3 in.

2. **Packaging** A factory needs a box that has a volume of 1485 cubic inches. The width should be 2 inches less than the height, and the length should be 4 inches greater than the height. Find the dimensions of the box using a graph.
   length: 15 in., width: 9 in., height: 11 in.

3. **Population** From 1980 to 2005, the population P (in thousands) of Columbus, Georgia can be modeled by the function

   $$P(x) = -0.0018x^3 + 0.039x^2 + 0.79x + 169$$

   where x is the number of years since 1980. In what year was the population of Columbus, Georgia about 179 thousand? Solve the problem using a graph. **1990**

Solve Polynomial Inequalities

Georgia Performance Standards: MM3A3c

Goal Solve polynomial inequalities.

Vocabulary

A **polynomial inequality** in one variable can be written as one of the following:

$$a_n x^n + a_{n-1} x^{n-1} + \cdots + a_1 x + a_0 < 0, \qquad a_n x^n + a_{n-1} x^{n-1} + \cdots + a_1 x + a_0 > 0,$$

$$a_n x^n + a_{n-1} x^{n-1} + \cdots + a_1 x + a_0 \leq 0, \qquad a_n x^n + a_{n-1} x^{n-1} + \cdots + a_1 x + a_0 \geq 0$$

where $a_n \neq 0$.

Inequalities can be used to describe subsets of real numbers called **intervals.** In the bounded intervals below, the real numbers a and b are the endpoints of each interval.

Inequality	$a \leq x \leq b$	$a < x < b$	$a \leq x < b$	$a < x \leq b$
Notation	$[a, b]$	(a, b)	$[a, b)$	$(a, b]$

Unbounded intervals are also written in this notation.

Inequality	$x \geq a$	$x > a$	$x \leq b$	$x < b$
Notation	$[a, +\infty)$	$(a, +\infty)$	$(-\infty, b]$	$(-\infty, b)$

Example 1 **Solve a polynomial inequality algebraically**

Solve $x^3 - 3x^2 > 10x$ algebraically.

First, write and solve the equation obtained by replacing $>$ with $=$.

$x^3 - 3x^2 = 10x$	Write equation that corresponds to original inequality.
$x^3 - 3x^2 - 10x = 0$	Write in standard form. $\frac{1}{2}$
$x(x - 5)(x + 2) = 0$	Factor.
$x = 0, x = 5,$ or $x = -2$	Zero product property

The numbers 0, 5, and -2 are the critical x-values of the inequality $x^3 - 3x^2 > 10x$. Plot 0, 5, and -2 on a number line, using open dots because the values do not satisfy the inequality. The critical x-values partition the number line into four intervals. Test an x-value in each interval to see if it satisfies the inequality.

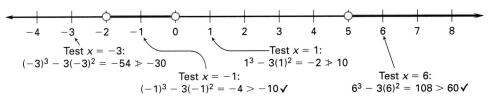

Test $x = -3$:
$(-3)^3 - 3(-3)^2 = -54 \not> -30$

Test $x = -1$:
$(-1)^3 - 3(-1)^2 = -4 > -10$ ✓

Test $x = 1$:
$1^3 - 3(1)^2 = -2 \not> 10$

Test $x = 6$:
$6^3 - 3(6)^2 = 108 > 60$ ✓

The solution set consists of all real numbers in the intervals $(-2, 0)$ and $(5, \infty)$.

Guided Practice for Example 1

Solve the inequality algebraically. **1–3. See Additional Answers beginning on page AA1.**

1. $x^3 - 4x \geq 0$ **2.** $-3x^3 + 10x^2 \leq -8x$ **3.** $x^3 - 3x^2 - x + 3 < 0$

Georgia Performance Standards

MM3A3c   Solve polynomial, exponential, and logarithmic inequalities analytically, graphically, and using appropriate technology. Represent solution sets of inequalities using interval notation.

Example 2   Solve a polynomial inequality by graphing

Solve $2x^3 + x^2 - 6x \leq 0$ by graphing.

The solution consists of the x-values for which the graph of $y = 2x^3 + x^2 - 6x$ lies on or below the x-axis. Find the graph's x-intercepts by letting $y = 0$ and solve for x.

$2x^3 + x^2 - 6x = 0$ Set y equal to 0.

$x(2x - 3)(x + 2) = 0$ Factor.

$x = 0, x = \dfrac{3}{2},$ or $x = -2$ Zero product property

Graph the polynomial and plot the x-intercepts $0, \dfrac{3}{2},$ and -2. The graph lies on or below the x-axis to the left of (and including) $x = -2$ and between (and including) $x = 0$ and $x = \dfrac{3}{2}$.

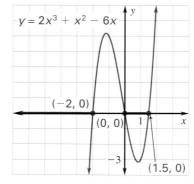

The solution set consists of all real numbers in the intervals $(-\infty, -2]$ and $\left[0, \dfrac{3}{2}\right]$.

Example 3   Use a polynomial inequality as a model

Cruise Ships The number C of North American cruise ships can be modeled by $C(x) = -0.067x^3 + 0.37x^2 + 9.0x + 131$, $0 \leq x \leq 8$ where x is the number of years since 1997. For what years was the number of cruise ships greater than 175?

Solution

You want to find the values of x for which:

$$C(x) > 175$$

$$-0.067x^3 + 0.37x^2 + 9.0x + 131 > 175$$

$$-0.067x^3 + 0.37x^2 + 9.0x - 44 > 0$$

Graph $y = -0.067x^3 + 0.37x^2 + 9.0x - 44$ on the domain $0 \leq x \leq 8$. The graph's x-intercept is about 4.8. The graph lies above the x-axis when $4.8 < x \leq 8$.

There were more than 175 cruise ships in the years 2002–2005.

Guided Practice for Examples 2 and 3

Solve the inequality using a graph.

4. $x^3 - 5x^2 + 4x \geq 0$
[0, 1] and [4, ∞)

5. $2x^3 + 8x^2 < -6x$
(−∞, −3) and (−1, 0)

6. $x^4 - 8x^2 - 9 \leq 0$
[−3, 3]

7. Use the information in Example 3 to determine in what years there were at least 155 cruise ships. **2000–2005**

UNIT 2

Solve the inequality algebraically.

1. $x^3 + x^2 - 20x < 0$
$(-\infty, 5)$ and $(0, 4)$

2. $x^3 - 9x \geq 0$
$[-3, 0]$ and $[3, \infty)$

3. $x^4 - 16 > 0$
$(-\infty, -2)$ and $(2, \infty)$

4. $x^3 - 5x^2 \leq 24x$
$(-\infty, -3]$ and $[0, 8]$

5. $2x^4 - 7x^2 > 4$
$(-\infty, -2)$ and $(2, \infty)$

6. $x^4 + x^2 < 2$
$(-1, 1)$

7. $x^3 - x^2 - 16x + 16 \geq 0$
$[-4, 1]$ and $[4, \infty)$

8. $x^4(x - 3) \leq 0$
$[-\infty, 3]$

9. $2x^3 - 3x^2 - 32x > -48$
$\left(-4, \dfrac{3}{2}\right)$, and $(4, \infty)$

Solve the inequality using a graph.

10. $x^3 + x^2 - 4x - 4 > 0$

11. $x^4 - 11x^2 + 18 \leq 0$

12. $3x^4 - 1 \leq 11$

13. $x^5 - 36x > 0$

14. $3x^3 - 6x^2 - 2x \leq 7x$

15. $-6x^3 + 19x^2 \geq 10x$

16. $x^4 - 14 < 0$

17. $-\dfrac{1}{2}x^3 + 4x^2 \geq 1$

18. $x^3 - 0.2x^2 - 3.16x + 1.4 < 0$

10–18. See Additional Answers beginning on page AA1.

19. **Error Analysis** *Describe* and correct the error in solving the inequality $x^3 - 4x^2 + 3x > 0$ by graphing.

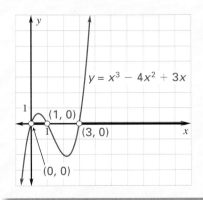

$y = x^3 - 4x^2 + 3x$
(1, 0)
(3, 0)
(0, 0)

The solution set is all real numbers in the intervals $[0, 1]$ and $[3, \infty)$.

The open dots on the graph mean that the values do not satisfy the inequality. The solution set is $(0, 1)$ and $(3, \infty)$.

✗

20. **Picnic Cooler** A rectangular picnic cooler has length 3 inches more than its width and height 6 inches more than its width. If the volume of the cooler is more than 648 cubic inches, what are the possible widths of the cooler? **The width is greater than 6 inches.**

21. **Investment** P dollars, invested at interest rate r compounded annually, increases to an amount A where

$$A = P(1 + r)^3$$

in 3 years. An investment of $1000 is to increase to an amount greater than $1200 in 3 years.

a. Write an inequality that represents the situation. **$1000(1 + r)^3 > 1200$**

b. Use a graph to solve the inequality and interpret your answer.
The interest rate must be greater than 6.3%.

MM3A3c   Solve polynomial, exponential, and logarithmic inequalities analytically, graphically, and using appropriate technology. Represent solution sets of inequalities using interval notation.

Solve the inequality algebraically. 1–6. See Additional Answers beginning on page AA1.

1. $x^3 - 4x^2 - 20x + 48 > 0$

2. $x^4 + 4x^3 - 12x^2 \le 0$

3. $4x^4 + 4 \le 17x^2$

4. $x^3 - 2x < 0$

5. $2x^3 + 3x^2 - 18x > 27$

6. $x^4 + x^3 - 2x^2 \ge 2x$

Solve the inequality using a graph.

7. $x^3 - 5x^2 - 22x + 56 > 0$
   $(-4, 2)$ and $(7, \infty)$

8. $x^4 - 8x^2 + 15 \le 0$
   $[-2.2, -1.7]$ and $[1.7, 2.2]$

9. $2x^3 + x^2 - 5x - 2 \le 0$
   $(-\infty, -1.6]$ and $[-0.4, 1.5]$

10. $\frac{1}{4}x^4 - 4x < -3$
    $(0.8, 2.2)$

11. $1.2x^3 + 3.07x^2 - x > 3.71$
    $(-2.4, -1.3)$ and $(1, \infty)$

12. $-0.3x^3 + 15.2x^2 \ge -2.3x$
    $(-\infty, -0.15]$ and $[0, 50.8]$

Solve the inequality using any method.

13. $x^3 + 4x^2 - 8x > 96$ $(4, \infty)$

14. $(x^2 - 4)(x - 1)^2 \le 0$ $[-2, 2]$

15. $2x^3 - 11x^2 + 3x \ge 54$ $[6, \infty)$

16. $(x + 4)^2(x - 4)(x - 3) < 0$
    $(3, 4)$

17. $11x^3 - 11x^2 - x + 1 \le 0$
    $(-\infty, -0.3]$ and $[0.3, 1]$

18. $1.8x^4 - x^3 + 3.2x > 0.5$
    $(-\infty, -1.1)$ and $(0.16, \infty)$

19. **Critical Thinking** *Describe* how the solution of the inequality $x^3 + 7x^2 - x - 7 < 0$ changes if $<$ is replaced with $\le$. **If $<$ is replaced with $\le$, then the solution set changes from $(-\infty, -7)$ and $(-1, 1)$ to $(-\infty, -7]$ and $[-1, 1]$.**

20. **Critical Thinking** Write a polynomial inequality in one variable that has a solution set consisting of the intervals $(0, 3)$ and $(6, \infty)$. *Sample answer: $x^3 - 9x^2 + 18x > 0$*

21. **Packaging** An open box is to be made from a square piece of material, 36 centimeters on a side, by cutting equal squares with sides of length x from the corners and folding up the sides as shown in the figure. If the volume of the box is to be greater than 2700 cubic centimeters, what are the possible heights of the box? **The height of the box is greater than 3 inches and less than 9.6 inches.**

22. **Multiple Representations** The numbers $M(x)$ of morning newspapers and $E(x)$ of evening newspapers in the United States can be modeled by

    $M(x) = -0.035x^3 + 0.31x^2 + 20.5x + 555, 0 \le x \le 15$ See Additional Answers beginning on page AA1.

    $E(x) = 0.035x^3 + 0.35x^2 - 42.1x + 1083, 0 \le x \le 15$

    where x is the number of years since 1990.

    a. **Writing an Inequality** Write an inequality that you can use to find the years for which $M(x)$ is less than $E(x)$.

    b. **Finding a Solution** Use a table to find the solution of the inequality from part (a). Your table should contain x-values from 0 to 15. Interpret your answer.

    c. **Checking a Solution** Check the solution you found in part (b) by using a graphing calculator to solve the inequality $M(x) < E(x)$ graphically.

Apply the Remainder and Factor Theorems

Georgia Performance Standards: MM3A3a, MM3A3d

Goal Use theorems to factor polynomials.

Vocabulary

Polynomial long division can be used to divide a polynomial $f(x)$ by a divisor polynomial $d(x)$, producing a quotient polynomial $q(x)$ and a remainder polynomial $r(x)$.

Synthetic division can be used to divide any polynomial by a divisor of the form $x - k$.

Remainder Theorem: If a polynomial $f(x)$ is divided by $x - k$, then the remainder is $r = f(k)$.

Factor Theorem: A polynomial $f(x)$ has a factor $x - k$, if and only if $f(k) = 0$.

Example 1 **Use polynomial long division**

Divide $f(x) = x^3 + 2$ by $x + 1$ using long division.

Solution

$$
\begin{array}{r}
x^2 - x + 1 \\
x + 1\overline{)x^3 + 0x^2 + 0x + 2}
\end{array}
$$

$\underline{x^3 + x^2}$	Multiply divisor by $x^3/x = x^2$.
$-x^2 + 0x$	Subtract.
$\underline{-x^2 - x}$	Multiply divisor by $-x^2/x = -x$.
$x + 2$	Subtract.
$\underline{x + 1}$	Multiply divisor by $x/x = 1$.
1	Subtract.

$$\frac{x^3 + 2}{x + 1} = x^2 - x + 1 + \frac{1}{x + 1}$$

Example 2 **Use synthetic division**

Divide $f(x) = x^3 + 2$ by $x + 1$ using synthetic division.

Write $x + 1$ in the form $x - k$: $x + 1 = x - (-1)$. So, write -1 to the left of the coefficients of $f(x)$, as shown.

$$
\begin{array}{r|rrrr}
-1 & 1 & 0 & 0 & 2 \\
& & -1 & 1 & -1 \\
\hline
& 1 & -1 & 1 & 1
\end{array}
$$

coefficients of quotient $\longrightarrow$ 1 -1 1   1 $\longleftarrow$ remainder

So, $\dfrac{x^3 + 2}{x + 1} = x^2 - x + 1 + \dfrac{1}{x + 1}$, which is the same result as in Example 1.

Guided Practice for Examples 1 and 2

Divide using polynomial long division.

1. $(2x^4 + 2x^3 + x^2 - x - 1) \div (x + 1)$

   $2x^3 + x - 2 + \dfrac{1}{x+1}$

2. $(x^3 + 3x^2 - x - 3) \div (x^2 - 1)$

   $x + 3$

Divide using synthetic division.

3. $(x^4 + 2x^3 - 5x^2 + 3x - 1) \div (x - 1)$

   $x^3 + 3x^2 - 2x + 1$

4. $(-x^4 + 4x^2 + 5x + 5) \div (x + 2)$

   $-x^3 + 2x^2 + 5 - \dfrac{5}{x+2}$

Example 3   Factor a polynomial

Factor $f(x) = x^3 - 4x^2 + x + 6$ completely given that $x - 3$ is a factor.

Because $x - 3$ is a factor of $f(x)$, you know that $f(3) = 0$. Use synthetic division to find the other factors.

Use the result to write $f(x)$ as a product of two factors and then factor completely.

$$\begin{array}{r|rrrr} 3 & 1 & -4 & 1 & 6 \\ & & 3 & -3 & -6 \\ \hline & 1 & -1 & -2 & 0 \end{array}$$

$f(x) = x^3 - 4x^2 + x + 6 = (x - 3)(x^2 - x - 2) = (x - 3)(x - 2)(x + 1)$

Guided Practice for Example 3

Factor the polynomial completely given that $x - 3$ is a factor.

5. $x^3 - 3x^2 - x + 3$

   $(x - 3)(x + 1)(x - 1)$

6. $x^3 - 2x^2 - 5x + 6$

   $(x - 3)(x - 1)(x + 2)$

7. $x^3 - 6x^2 + 11x - 6$

   $(x - 3)(x - 1)(x - 2)$

Example 4   Finding zeros of functions

Find the other zeros of $f(x) = x^3 + 2x^2 - x - 2$ given that $f(-1) = 0$.

Because $f(-1) = 0$, $x + 1$ is a factor of f. Use synthetic division to find the other factors.

Use the result to write $f(x)$ as a product of two factors and then factor completely.

$$\begin{array}{r|rrrr} -1 & 1 & 2 & -1 & -2 \\ & & -1 & -1 & 2 \\ \hline & 1 & 1 & -2 & 0 \end{array}$$

$f(x) = x^3 + 2x^2 - x - 2 = (x + 1)(x^2 + x - 2) = (x + 1)(x + 2)(x - 1)$

The zeros are -1, -2, and 1.

Guided Practice for Example 4

A polynomial f and one zero of f are given. Find the other zeros of f.

8. $f(x) = x^3 - 3x^2 + 4; 2$ $-1, 2$

9. $f(x) = x^3 - x^2 - 4x + 4; -2$ $1, 2$

Exercise Set A

MM3A3a Find real and complex roots of higher degree polynomial equations using the factor theorem, remainder theorem, rational root theorem, and fundamental theorem of algebra, incorporating complex and radical conjugates.

MM3A3d Solve a variety of types of equations by appropriate means choosing among mental calculation, pencil and paper, or appropriate technology.

Divide using polynomial long division.

1. $(x^2 + 5x - 14) \div (x - 2)$ $x + 7$

2. $(x^2 - 2x - 48) \div (x + 5)$ $x - 7 - \dfrac{13}{x + 5}$

3. $(x^3 + x + 30) \div (x + 3)$ $x^2 - 3x + 10$

4. $(6x^2 - 5x + 9) \div (2x - 1)$ $3x - 1 + \dfrac{8}{2x - 1}$

5. $(8x^3 + 5x^2 - 12x + 10) \div (x^2 - 3)$
$$8x + 5 + \dfrac{12x + 25}{x^2 - 3}$$

6. $(5x^4 + 2x^3 - 9x + 12) \div (x^2 - 3x + 4)$
$$5x^2 + 17x + 31 + \dfrac{16x - 112}{x^2 - 3x + 4}$$

Divide using synthetic division.

7. $(x^2 + 7x + 12) \div (x + 4)$

8. $(x^3 - 3x^2 + 8x - 5) \div (x - 1)$

9. $(x^4 - 7x^2 + 9x - 10) \div (x - 2)$

10. $(2x^4 - x^3 + 4) \div (x + 1)$

11. $(2x^4 - 11x^3 + 15x^2 + 6x - 18) \div (x - 3)$

12. $(x^4 - 6x^3 - 40x + 33) \div (x - 7)$

7–12. See Additional Answers beginning on page AA1.

A polynomial *f* and a factor of *f* are given. Factor *f* completely.

13. $f(x) = x^3 - 3x^2 - 16x - 12; x - 6$
$(x - 6)(x + 1)(x + 2)$

14. $f(x) = x^3 - 12x^2 + 12x + 80; x - 10$
$(x - 10)(x - 4)(x + 2)$

15. $f(x) = x^3 - 18x^2 + 95x - 126; x - 9$
$(x - 9)(x - 2)(x - 7)$

16. $f(x) = x^3 - x^2 - 21x + 45; x + 5$
$(x + 5)(x - 3)^2$

17. $f(x) = 4x^3 - 4x^2 - 9x + 9; x - 1$
$(x - 1)(2x + 3)(2x - 3)$

18. $f(x) = 3x^3 - 16x^2 - 103x + 36; x + 4$
$(x + 4)(3x - 1)(x - 9)$

A polynomial *f* and one zero of *f* are given. Find the other zeros of *f*.

19. $f(x) = x^3 + 2x^2 - 20x + 24; -6$ 2

20. $f(x) = x^3 + 11x^2 - 150x - 1512; -14$ $-9, 12$

21. $f(x) = 2x^3 + 3x^2 - 39x - 20; 4$ $-5, -\dfrac{1}{2}$

22. $f(x) = 15x^3 - 119x^2 - 10x + 16; 8$ $-\dfrac{2}{5}, \dfrac{1}{3}$

23. $f(x) = x^3 - 3x^2 - 45x + 175; -7$ 5

24. $f(x) = x^3 - 9x^2 - 5x + 45; 9$ $-\sqrt{5}, \sqrt{5}$

25. **Geometry** The volume of the box shown at the right is given by $V = 2x^3 - 11x^2 + 10x + 8$. Find an expression for the missing dimension.
$x - 2$

$2x + 1$

$x - 4$

?

26. **Fuel Consumption** From 1995 to 2002, the total fuel consumption T (in billions of gallons) by cars in the United States and the U.S. population P (in millions) can be modeled by

$$T = -0.003x^3 - 0.02x^2 + 1.3x + 68 \text{ and } P = 3x + 267$$

where x is the number of years since 1995. Write a function for the average amount of fuel consumed by each person from 1995 to 2002. **See Additional Answers beginning on page AA1.**

UNIT 2

Exercise Set B

MM3A3a Find real and complex roots of higher degree polynomial equations using the factor theorem, remainder theorem, rational root theorem, and fundamental theorem of algebra, incorporating complex and radical conjugates.

MM3A3d Solve a variety of types of equations by appropriate means choosing among mental calculation, pencil and paper, or appropriate technology.

Divide using polynomial long division. 1–4. See Additional Answers beginning on page AA1.

1. $(4x^3 - 2x^2 + 6x - 1) \div (2x + 3)$

2. $(5x^4 + 8x - 9) \div (x^2 - 4)$

3. $(2x^4 + 2x^3 - 10x - 9) \div (x^3 + x^2 - 5)$

4. $(8x^4 + 2x^2 - 12x + 9) \div (x^2 + x - 3)$

Divide using synthetic division. 5–8. See Additional Answers beginning on page AA1.

5. $(x^4 + 5x^3 - 2x^2 - 4x + 4) \div (x + 3)$

6. $(3x^4 - x^2 + 6x) \div (x - 3)$

7. $(4x + 2x^3 + 7x^2 - 1) \div (x + 1)$

8. $(2x^3 + 3x^5 + 1 - 5x) \div (x - 1)$

A polynomial f and a factor of f are given. Factor f completely.

9. $f(x) = x^3 + 9x^2 - 37x - 165; x - 5$ **(x − 5)(x + 3)(x + 11)**

10. $f(x) = 4x^3 + 8x^2 - 25x - 50; x + 2$ **(x + 2)(2x + 5)(2x − 5)**

11. $f(x) = 4x^4 + 26x^3 - 8x^2 + 39x - 21; x + 7$ **(x + 7)(2x − 1)(2x² + 3)**

12. $f(x) = 6x^5 - 38x^4 + 12x^3 - 15x^2 + 95x - 30; x - 6$ **(x − 6)(3x − 1)(2x³ − 5)**

A polynomial f and one zero of f are given. Find the other zeros of f.
13 and 14. See Additional Answers beginning on page AA1.

13. $f(x) = 2x^3 + 11x^2 + 9x + 2; -\dfrac{1}{2}$

14. $f(x) = x^3 + x^2 + 2x + 24; -3$

15. Consider the polynomial function $f(x) = x^3 + 3x^2 - 36x + 32$.

   a. Given that $f(4) = 0$, find the other zeros of f. **1, −8**

   b. Based on your results from part (a), what are the factors of the polynomial $x^3 + 3x^2 - 36x + 32$? **x − 4, x − 1, x + 8**

   c. What are the solutions of the polynomial equation $x^3 + 3x^2 - 36x + 32 = 0$?
      x = 4, x = 1, x = −8

16. **Company Profit** The price p (in dollars) that a television manufacturer is able to charge for a television is given by $p = 300 - 8x^2$ where x is the number (in millions) of televisions produced. It costs the company $175 to make a television.

   a. Write an expression for the company's total revenue in terms of x. **300x − 8x³**

   b. Write a function for the company's profit P as a function of x. **P = 125x − 8x³**

   c. Currently, the company produces 2.5 million televisions and makes a profit of $187,500,000. Write and solve an equation to find a lesser number of televisions that the company could produce and still yield the same profit. **−8x³ + 125x − 187.5 = 0; about 2.06 million televisions**

   d. Do all of the solutions in part (c) make sense in this situation? *Explain.*
      No. −4.56 is a solution of the equation that does not make sense because the company cannot produce a negative number of televisions.

Find Rational Zeros

Georgia Performance Standards: MM3A3a, MM3A3d

Goal Find all real zeros of a polynomial function.

Example 1 **Find zeros when the leading coefficient is 1**

Find all real zeros of $f(x) = x^3 - 7x^2 + 14x - 8$.

The rational root theorem states if $a_n x^n + \cdots + a_1 x + a_0$ has integer coefficients,

then every rational zero of f has the form $\dfrac{p}{q} = \dfrac{\text{factor of constant term } a_0}{\text{factor of leading coefficient } a_n}$.

STEP 1 **List** the possible rational zeros. The leading coefficient is 1 and the constant term is -8. The possible rational zeros are: $x = \pm 1, \pm 2, \pm 4, \pm 8$

STEP 2 **Test** these zeros using synthetic division. Test $x = 4$:

$$
\begin{array}{r|rrrr}
4 & 1 & -7 & 14 & -8 \\
  &   & 4 & -12 & 8 \\
\hline
  & 1 & -3 & 2 & 0
\end{array}
$$

$\leftarrow$ 4 is a zero.

Because 4 is a zero of f, write $f(x) = (x - 4)(x^2 - 3x + 2)$.

STEP 3 **Factor** the trinomial and use the factor theorem.

$$f(x) = (x - 4)(x^2 - 3x + 2) = (x - 4)(x - 2)(x - 1)$$

The zeros are 1, 2, and 4.

Example 2 **Find zeros when the leading coefficient is not 1**

Find all real zeros of $f(x) = 3x^3 - 17x^2 + 18x + 8$.

STEP 1 **List** the possible rational zeros of f: $x = \pm 1, \pm 2, \pm 4, \pm 8, \pm \dfrac{1}{3}, \pm \dfrac{2}{3}, \pm \dfrac{4}{3}, \pm \dfrac{8}{3}$

STEP 2 **Choose** a reasonable value to check using the graph of the function.

STEP 3 **Check** $x = -\dfrac{1}{3}$:

$$
\begin{array}{r|rrrr}
-\frac{1}{3} & 3 & -17 & 18 & 8 \\
  &   & -1 & 6 & -8 \\
\hline
  & 3 & -18 & 24 & 0
\end{array}
$$

$\leftarrow$ $-\dfrac{1}{3}$ is a zero.

STEP 4 **Factor** out a binomial using the result of synthetic division.

$$
\begin{aligned}
f(x) &= \left(x + \tfrac{1}{3}\right)(3x^2 - 18x + 24) \\
&= \left(x + \tfrac{1}{3}\right)(3)(x^2 - 6x + 8) \\
&= (3x + 1)(x - 2)(x - 4)
\end{aligned}
$$

The real zeros of f are $-\dfrac{1}{3}$, 2, and 4.

UNIT 2

Guided Practice for Examples 1 and 2

Find all real zeros of the function.

1. $f(x) = x^3 + x^2 - 4x - 4$ $-2, -1, 2$

2. $f(x) = x^3 + 2x^2 - 11x - 12$ $-4, -1, 3$

3. $f(x) = 2x^3 - 5x^2 + x + 2$ $-\dfrac{1}{2}, 1, 2$

4. $g(x) = x^3 - 3x^2 - x + 3$ $-1, 1, 3$

5. $g(x) = x^3 - 2x^2 - 5x + 6$ $-2, 1, 3$

6. $g(x) = x^3 - 6x^2 + 11x - 6$ $1, 2, 3$

Example 3   **Solve a multi-step problem**

Desk Organizer The length of a rectangular desk organizer is 4 inches greater than the width. The height is $\dfrac{1}{3}$ of the width and the volume is 21 cubic inches. What are the dimensions of the organizer?

STEP 1 **Write** an equation for the volume of the organizer.

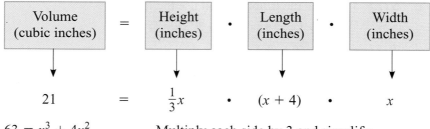

Volume (cubic inches)	=	Height (inches)	·	Length (inches)	·	Width (inches)
21	=	$\dfrac{1}{3}x$	·	$(x + 4)$	·	x

$63 = x^3 + 4x^2$ Multiply each side by 3 and simplify.

$0 = x^3 + 4x^2 - 63$ Subtract 63 from each side.

STEP 2 **List** the possible rational solutions: $\pm 1, \pm 3, \pm 7, \pm 9, \pm 21, \pm 63$

STEP 3 **Test** the possible rational solutions. Only positive x-values make sense.

$$
\begin{array}{r|rrrr}
3 & 1 & 4 & 0 & -63 \\
  &   & 3 & 21 & 63 \\
\hline
  & 1 & 7 & 21 & 0
\end{array}
$$
  ← 3 is a solution.

STEP 4 **Check** for other solutions. The other solutions are imaginary numbers and can be discarded.

The width is 3 inches, the length is $3 + 4 = 7$ inches, and the height is $\dfrac{1}{3}(3) = 1$ inch.

Guided Practice for Example 3

7. A pyramid has a square base with sides of length x, a height of $x - 2$, and a volume of 3. Write a polynomial equation to model the situation. List the possible rational solutions of the equation, and then find the dimensions of the pyramid.
See Additional Answers beginning on page AA1.

UNIT 2

LESSON 2.6 **Exercise Set A**

MM3A3a Find real and complex roots of higher degree polynomial equations using the factor theorem, remainder theorem, rational root theorem, and fundamental theorem of algebra, incorporating complex and radical conjugates.

MM3A3d Solve a variety of types of equations by appropriate means choosing among mental calculation, pencil and paper, or appropriate technology.

List the possible rational zeros of the function using the rational root theorem. 1–4. See Additional Answers beginning on page AA1.

1. $f(x) = x^4 - 6x^3 + 8x^2 - 21$

2. $h(x) = 2x^3 + 7x^2 - 7x + 30$

3. $h(x) = 5x^4 + 12x^3 - 16x^2 + 10$

4. $g(x) = 9x^5 + 3x^3 + 7x - 4$

Find all real zeros of the function.

5. $f(x) = x^3 - 3x^2 - 6x + 8$ **−2, 1, 4**

6. $g(x) = x^3 + 4x^2 - x - 4$ **−4, −1, 1**

7. $f(x) = x^3 + 72 - 5x^2 - 18x$ **−4, 3, 6**

8. $f(x) = x^3 + x^2 - 2x - 2$ **$-\sqrt{2}, -1, \sqrt{2}$**

Use the graph to shorten the list of possible rational zeros of the function. Then find all real zeros of the function.

9. $f(x) = 4x^3 - 8x^2 - 15x + 9$ $-\dfrac{3}{2}, \dfrac{1}{2}, 3$

10. $f(x) = 2x^3 - 5x^2 - 4x + 10$ $-\sqrt{2}, \sqrt{2}, \dfrac{5}{2}$

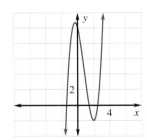

Find all real zeros of the function.

11. $g(x) = 2x^3 + 4x^2 - 2x - 4$ **−2, −1, 1**

12. $f(x) = 2x^3 - 5x^2 - 14x + 8$ $-2, \dfrac{1}{2}, 4$

13. $h(x) = 2x^4 + 5x^3 - 5x^2 - 5x + 3$
$-3, -1, \dfrac{1}{2}, 1$

14. $f(x) = 2x^4 + 3x^3 - 6x^2 - 6x + 4$
$-2, -\sqrt{2}, \sqrt{2}, \dfrac{1}{2}$

15. **Mail** From 1995 to 2003, the amount of mail M (in billions of pieces) handled by the U.S. Postal Service can be modeled by $M = 0.05(t^4 - 18t^3 + 89t^2 - 32t + 3680)$ where t is the number of years since 1995. In which year were there about 204,000,000,000 pieces of mail handled?

a. Write a polynomial equation that can be used to answer the question. $t^4 - 18t^3 + 89t^2 - 32t - 400$

b. List the possible whole-number solutions of the equation in part (a) that are less than or equal to 8. **1, 2, 4, 5, 8**

c. Use synthetic division to determine which of the possible solutions in part (b) is an actual solution. Then answer the question in the problem statement. **4; 1999**

d. Use a graphing calculator to graph and identify any additional real solutions of the equation that are reasonable. **about 6.4 or 2001**

UNIT 2

Exercise Set B

MM3A3a Find real and complex roots of higher degree polynomial equations using the factor theorem, remainder theorem, rational root theorem, and fundamental theorem of algebra, incorporating complex and radical conjugates.

MM3A3d Solve a variety of types of equations by appropriate means choosing among mental calculation, pencil and paper, or appropriate technology.

Find all real zeros of the function.

1. $f(x) = x^3 - 4x^2 - 7x + 10$ $\;-2, 1, 5$

2. $g(x) = x^5 - x^4 - 7x^3 + 11x^2 - 8x + 12$ $\;-3, 2$

3. $h(x) = x^4 + 4x^3 + x^2 - 8x - 6$ $\;-3, -\sqrt{2}, -1, \sqrt{2}$

4. $g(x) = x^3 + 2x^2 - 34x + 7$ $\;-7, \dfrac{5 - \sqrt{21}}{2}, \dfrac{5 + \sqrt{21}}{2}$

5. $f(x) = x^4 + 4x^3 - 14x^2 - 20x - 3$ $\;-3 - 2\sqrt{2}, -1, -3 + 2\sqrt{2}, 3$

6. $h(x) = x^5 + 15x^4 + 72x^3 + 80x^2 - 225x - 375$ $\;-5, -\sqrt{3}, \sqrt{3}$

7. $h(x) = 24x^4 - 26x^3 - 45x^2 - x + 6$ $\;-\dfrac{3}{4}, -\dfrac{1}{2}, \dfrac{1}{3}, 2$

8. $f(x) = 8x^3 + 28x^2 + 14x - 15$ $\;-\dfrac{5}{2}, -\dfrac{3}{2}, \dfrac{1}{2}$

9. $f(x) = 18x^5 + 51x^4 - 60x + 75 - 34x^3 - 178x^2$ $\;-\sqrt{3}, -\dfrac{5}{3}, \dfrac{1}{2}, \sqrt{3}$

10. $g(x) = 6x^5 - 116x^3 - x^4 - 53x^2 + 24 + 50x$ $\;-4, 2 - \sqrt{7}, -\dfrac{1}{2}, \dfrac{2}{3}, 2 + \sqrt{7}$

11. Write a polynomial function f that has a leading coefficient of 6 and has 12 possible rational zeros according to the rational root theorem. ***Sample answer:*** $f(x) = 6x^3 - 7x^2 + 10x + 2$

12. *Critical Thinking* Consider the function $f(x) = 2x^4 + 5x^3 - 21x^2 - 36x$.
   a. *Explain* why the rational root theorem cannot be directly applied to this function. **The function f has no constant term.**
   b. Factor out the common monomial factor of f. $\;x(2x^3 + 5x^2 - 21x - 36)$
   c. Apply the rational root theorem to find all the real zeros of f. $\;-4, -\dfrac{3}{2}, 0, 3$
   d. Find all the real zeros of $f(x) = 3x^5 - x^4 - 6x^3 + 2x^2$. $\;-\sqrt{2}, 0, \dfrac{1}{3}, \sqrt{2}$

13. *Critical Thinking* Consider the functions
   $f(x) = x^3 + 2x^2 - 19x - 20,\; g(x) = -x^3 - 2x^2 + 19x + 20,$
   $h(x) = 2x^3 + 4x^2 - 38x - 40,\;$ and $j(x) = 4x^3 + 8x^2 - 76x - 80.$
   a. Use the rational root theorem to find all of the real zeros of each function. **for each function: $-5, -1, 4$**
   b. Note that $g(x) = -f(x),\; h(x) = 2f(x),$ and $j(x) = 4f(x)$. What can you conclude about the zeros of $f(x)$ and $af(x)$? **The zeros of $f(x)$ are also the zeros of $af(x)$.**
   c. *Explain* why the rational root theorem cannot be directly applied to
   $$f(x) = \frac{4}{3}x^3 + 3x^2 - \frac{10}{3}x - 1.$$ **To apply the rational zero theorem, the coefficients must be integers.**
   d. Use the conclusion from part (b) to find the real zeros of the function in part (c).
   $\;-3, -\dfrac{1}{4}, 1$

Georgia Performance Standards

MM3A1b Understand the effects of the following on the graph of a polynomial function: degree, lead coefficient, and multiplicity of real zeros.

MM3A1d Investigate and explain characteristics of polynomial functions, including domain and range, intercepts, zeros, relative and absolute extrema, intervals of increase and decrease, and end behavior.

MM3A3a Find real and complex roots of higher degree polynomial equations using the factor theorem, remainder theorem, rational root theorem, and fundamental theorem of algebra, incorporating complex and radical conjugates.

Investigating Math Activity
Zeros of a Polynomial Function

Use before Lesson 2.7

Materials graphing calculator

Question

How many zeros can a polynomial function have?

Explore

Find the zeros of a function.

Graph the function $y = x^2 + 2x - 8$ on a graphing calculator and determine the number of zeros of the function.

STEP 1 Enter the function in the equation editor window.

STEP 2 Set the screen to a standard viewing window.

STEP 3 Use the graph to determine the number of zeros.

STEP 4 Look at the function and determine its degree.

Draw Conclusions

1. Determine the number of zeros and the degree of each function.

   a. $y = x^2 + 2x - 8$ **2, 2**

   b. $y = x^3 + 5x^2 + 4x - 3$ **3, 3**

   c. $y = x^4 + 6x^3 - 3x^2 - 8x + 1$ **4, 4**

2. **Reasoning** What relationship do you notice between the degree of a function and the number of zeros of the function? **They are the same.**

Apply the Fundamental Theorem of Algebra

Georgia Performance Standards: MM3A3a, MM3A3d

Goal Classify the zeros of polynomial functions.

Vocabulary

When a factor of a polynomial appears more than once, you can count its solution more than once. The repeated factor produces a **repeated solution.**

The Fundamental Theorem of Algebra: If $f(x)$ is a polynomial of degree n where $n > 0$, then the equation $f(x) = 0$ has at least one solution in the set of complex numbers.

Corollary to the Fundamental Theorem of Algebra: If $f(x)$ is a polynomial of degree n where $n > 0$, then the equation $f(x) = 0$ has exactly n solutions provided each solution repeated twice is counted as 2 solutions, each solution repeated three times is counted as 3 solutions, and so on.

Complex Conjugates Theorem: If f is a polynomial function with real coefficients, and $a + bi$ is an imaginary zero of f, then $a - bi$ is also a zero of f.

Irrational Conjugates Theorem: Suppose f is a polynomial function with rational coefficients, and a and b are rational numbers such that $\sqrt{b}$ is irrational. If $a + \sqrt{b}$ is a zero of f, then $a - \sqrt{b}$ is also a zero of f.

Descartes' Rule of Signs: Let $f(x) = a_n x^n + a_{n-1} x^{n-1} + \cdots + a_2 x^2 + a_1 x + a_0$ be a polynomial function with real coefficients. The number of *positive real zeros* of f is equal to the number of changes in sign of the coefficients of $f(x)$ or is less than this by an even number. The number of *negative real zeros* of f is equal to the number of changes in sign of the coefficients of $f(-x)$ or is less than this by an even number.

Example 1 Find the zeros of a polynomial function

Find all zeros of $f(x) = x^5 - x^4 - 7x^3 + 11x^2 + 16x - 20$.

Solution

STEP 1 **Find** the rational zeros of f. The possible rational zeros are: $x = \pm 1, \pm 2, \pm 4, \pm 5, \pm 10,$ and ± 20. Using synthetic division you find that -2 is a zero repeated twice and 1 is also a zero.

STEP 2 **Write** $f(x)$ in factored form. Dividing f by its known factors $x + 2$, $x + 2$, and $x - 1$ gives a quotient of $x^2 - 4x + 5$.
So, $f(x) = (x - 1)(x + 2)^2(x^2 - 4x + 5)$.

STEP 3 **Find** the complex zeros of f. Use the quadratic formula to factor the trinomial into linear factors.
$$f(x) = (x - 1)(x + 2)^2[x - (2 + i)][x - (2 - i)]$$

The zeros are $-2, -2, 1, 2 + i,$ and $2 - i$.

Georgia Performance Standards

MM3A3a   Find real and complex roots of higher degree polynomial equations using the factor theorem, remainder theorem, rational root theorem, and fundamental theorem of algebra, incorporating complex and radical conjugates.

MM3A3d   Solve a variety of types of equations by appropriate means choosing among mental calculation, pencil and paper, or appropriate technology.

Example 2   Use zeros to write a polynomial function

Write a polynomial function of least degree that has rational coefficients, a leading coefficient of 1, and 4 and $1 + \sqrt{2}$ as zeros.

By the irrational conjugates theorem, $1 - \sqrt{2}$ is a zero. Use the zeros and the factor theorem to write $f(x)$ as a product of three factors.

$f(x) = (x - 4)[x - (1 + \sqrt{2})][x - (1 - \sqrt{2})]$ Write $f(x)$ in factored form.

$\quad = (x - 4)[(x - 1) - \sqrt{2}][(x - 1) + \sqrt{2}]$ Regroup terms.

$\quad = (x - 4)[(x - 1)^2 - (\sqrt{2})^2]$ Multiply.

$\quad = (x - 4)(x^2 - 2x - 1)$ Simplify.

$\quad = x^3 - 6x^2 + 7x + 4$ Write in standard form.

Example 3   Solve a polynomial equation

Determine the possible numbers of positive real zeros, negative real zeros, and imaginary zeros for $f(x) = x^4 + 2x^3 - x^2 + 3x + 5$.

The coefficients of $f(x) = x^4 + 2x^3 - x^2 + 3x + 5$ have 2 sign changes, so f has 2 or 0 positive real zero(s).

$f(-x) = (-x)^4 + 2(-x)^3 - (-x)^2 + 3(-x) + 5 = x^4 - 2x^3 - x^2 - 3x + 5$

The coefficients in $f(-x)$ have 2 sign changes, so f has 2 or 0 negative real zero(s).

The function has a total of 4 zeros, so the possible combinations are 2 positive real zeros and 2 negative real zeros, 2 positive real zeros and 2 imaginary zeros, 2 negative real zeros and 2 imaginary zeros, or 4 imaginary zeros.

Guided Practice for Examples 1, 2, and 3

Find all zeros of the function.

1. $f(x) = x^3 - 2x^2 + 3x - 2$ $1, \dfrac{1 \pm i\sqrt{7}}{2}$ **2.** $f(x) = x^4 - 4x^3 + 5x^2 - 2x - 12$
                                                             $-1, 3, 1 \pm i\sqrt{3}$

Write a polynomial function f of least degree that has rational coefficients, a leading coefficient of 1, and the given zeros.

3. $-2, -1, 1$ **4.** $i, 4$ **5.** $i, 2 - \sqrt{3}$

$\quad x^3 + 2x^2 - x - 2$ $x^3 - 4x^2 + x - 4$ $x^4 - 4x^3 + 2x^2 - 4x + 1$

Determine the possible numbers of positive real zeros, negative real zeros, and imaginary zeros for the function. 6 and 7. See Additional Answers beginning on page AA1.

6. $g(x) = x^3 + x^2 - 3x - 7$ **7.** $h(x) = x^4 - 3x^3 + 4x - 2$

MM3A3a Find real and complex roots of higher degree polynomial equations using the factor theorem, remainder theorem, rational root theorem, and fundamental theorem of algebra, incorporating complex and radical conjugates.

MM3A3d Solve a variety of types of equations by appropriate means choosing among mental calculation, pencil and paper, or appropriate technology.

Identify the number of solutions or zeros.

1. $f(x) = 5x^3 - 6x^2 + 2x - 3$ **3**

2. $g(s) = 8s^6 - 3s^4 - 11s^3 - 2s^2 + 4$ **6**

3. $-3y^7 + 5y^5 - 12y + 2 = 6$ **7**

4. $4 - 7x = x^2 - 3x^5$ **5**

Find all the zeros of the polynomial function.

5. $h(x) = x^3 - 3x^2 - x + 3$ **−1, 1, 3**

6. $f(x) = x^4 - 4x^3 - 20x^2 + 48x$ **−4, 0, 2, 6**

7. $g(x) = x^3 + 5x^2 + x + 5$ **−5, −i, i**

8. $g(x) = x^4 - 9x^3 + 23x^2 - 81x + 126$
   2, 7, −3i, 3i

9. $f(x) = x^3 - x^2 - 11x + 3$ **−3, 2 + √3, 2 − √3**

10. $h(x) = 2x^4 + x^3 + x^2 + x - 1$ **−1, $\frac{1}{2}$, −i, i**

Write a polynomial function f of least degree that has rational coefficients, a leading coefficient of 1, and the given zeros.

11. $-7, -4$
    $f(x) = x^2 + 11x + 28$

12. $1, 2, 5$
    $f(x) = x^3 - 8x^2 + 17x - 10$

13. $-3, 0, 1$
    $f(x) = x^3 + 2x^2 - 3x$

14. $4, i, -i$
    $f(x) = x^3 - 4x^2 + x - 4$

15. $-5, 0, -2i, 2i$
    $f(x) = x^4 + 5x^3 + 4x^2 + 20x$

16. $8, 2 + i$
    $f(x) = x^3 - 12x^2 + 37x - 40$

17. **Error Analysis** *Describe* and correct the error in writing a polynomial function with rational coefficients and zeros 3 and $2 + i$.

    See Additional Answers beginning on page AA1.

    $$f(x) = (x - 3)[x - (2 + i)]$$
    $$= x(x - 2 - i) - 3(x - 2 - i)$$
    $$= x^2 - 2x - ix - 3x + 6 + 3i$$
    $$= x^2 - (5 + i)x + (6 + 3i)$$

    ✗

Use a graphing calculator to graph the function. Then use the *zero* (or *root*) feature to approximate the real zeros of the function.

18. $g(x) = x^3 - x^2 - 5x + 3$
    −2.09, 0.57, 2.51

19. $h(x) = 2x^3 - x^2 - 3x - 1$
    −0.62, −0.50, 1.62

20. $f(x) = x^4 - 2x - 1$
    −0.47, 1.40

21. $g(x) = x^4 - x^3 - 20x^2 + 10x + 27$
    −4.09, −0.98, 1.47, 4.60

22. **Sporting Goods** For 1998 through 2005, the sales S (in billions of dollars) of sporting goods can be modeled by $S = 0.007t^3 + 0.1t^2 + 1.4t + 70$ where t is the number of years since 1998. In which year were sales about $78 billion? **2002**

23. **Grocery Store Revenue** For the 25 years that a grocery store has been open, its annual revenue R (in millions of dollars) can be modeled by

    $$R = \frac{1}{10,000}(-t^4 + 12t^3 - 77t^2 + 600t + 13,650)$$

    where t is the number of years since the opening of the store. In what year(s) was the revenue about $1.5 million? **3 and 9 years after opening**

MM3A3a Find real and complex roots of higher degree polynomial equations using the factor theorem, remainder theorem, rational root theorem, and fundamental theorem of algebra, incorporating complex and radical conjugates.

MM3A3d Solve a variety of types of equations by appropriate means choosing among mental calculation, pencil and paper, or appropriate technology.

Find all the zeros of the polynomial function. 1–8. See Additional Answers beginning on page AA1.

1. $f(x) = x^4 + 4x^3 - 6x^2 - 36x - 27$

2. $h(x) = x^4 - 4x^3 + 4x - 1$

3. $g(x) = 2x^5 - 4x^4 - 2x^3 + 28x^2$

4. $g(x) = 2x^4 - x^3 - 42x^2 + 16x + 160$

5. $h(x) = 2x^4 - 7x^3 - 27x^2 + 63x + 81$

6. $f(x) = x^3 + 2x^2 + 4x - 7$

7. $g(x) = x^4 + 2x^3 + 2x - 1$
(*Hint:* $-i$ is a zero.)

8. $h(x) = x^4 - 2x^3 + 14x^2 + 6x - 51$
(*Hint:* $1 + 4i$ is a zero.)

Write a polynomial function f of least degree that has rational coefficients, a leading coefficient of 2, and the given zeros. 9–14. See Additional Answers beginning on page AA1.

9. $-4, 0, 2, 4$

10. $2i, -2i, 5i, -5i$

11. $-5, \sqrt{3}$

12. $0, 3 + 4i$

13. $1, 2, 4 + \sqrt{2}$

14. $0, 3, i, 5 - 2i$

Determine the possible numbers of positive real zeros, negative real zeros, and imaginary zeros for the function.

15. $h(x) = x^3 - 4x^2 + 5x + 9$
2 or 0; 1; 2 or 0

16. $g(x) = x^4 + 3x^2 - 10x + 16$
2 or 0; 0; 4, 2, or 0

17. $f(x) = x^5 - 6x^4 - 3x^3 + 7x^2 - 8x + 1$
4, 2, or 0; 1; 4, 2, or 0

18. $g(x) = x^{10} - x^8 + x^6 - x^4 + x^2 - 1$
5, 3, or 1; 5, 3, or 1; 8, 6, 4, 2, or 0

Use a graphing calculator to graph the function. Then use the *zero* (or *root*) feature to approximate the real zeros of the function.

19. $g(x) = x^4 + 3x^2 - 2$
−0.75, 0.75

20. $h(x) = x^5 + 12x^3 - 4x^2 + 16x + 25$
−0.86

21. $f(x) = -x^6 + 4x^5 - 2x^2 + 9$
−1.06, 3.98

22. $g(x) = 3x^6 + 5x^5 - 30x^4 - 37x^3 - 25x^2$
−3.65, 3.11

23. Critical Thinking The graph of a polynomial of degree 5 has four distinct *x*-intercepts. What can be said about one of its zeros? Sketch a graph of this situation. See Additional Answers beginning on page AA1.

24. Critical Thinking Find a counterexample to disprove the following statement.

The polynomial function of least degree with integer coefficients and zeros at
$x = -4$, $x = 2$, and $x = 5$ is unique.
Sample answer: $f(x) = x^3 - 3x^2 - 18x + 40$ and $g(x) = 2x^3 - 6x^2 - 36x + 80$

25. **College Tuition** For 1998 through 2005, the enrollment E and cost of tuition T (in dollars) can be modeled by See Additional Answers beginning on page AA1.

$E = -29.881t^2 + 190t + 4935$ and $T = 10.543t^3 - 118.83t^2 + 921t + 9979$

where t is the number of years since 1998.

a. Write a model that represents the total tuition R brought in by the college in a given year.

b. In which year did the college take in $62,638,000 in tuition?

UNIT 2

Analyze Graphs of Polynomial Functions

Georgia Performance Standards: MM3A1b, MM3A1d

Goal Use intercepts to graph polynomial functions.

Vocabulary

The graph of a polynomial function of degree n has *at most* $n - 1$ turning points.

The y-coordinate of a turning point is a **local maximum** of the function if the point is higher than all nearby points. The y-coordinate of a turning point is a **local minimum** of the function if the point is lower than all nearby points.

The **multiplicity of a root** is the number of times a given polynomial equation has a value as a root. For the polynomial equation $f(x) = 0$, k is a repeated solution, or a root with a multiplicity greater than 1, if and only if the factor $x - k$ has an exponent greater than 1 when $f(x)$ is factored completely. If the exponent is odd, the graph of f crosses the x-axis at the zero. If the exponent is even, the graph of f touches the x-axis at the zero.

Example 1   Use *x*-intercepts to graph a polynomial function

Graph the function $f(x) = 0.2(x - 3)^2(x + 1)^2$.

STEP 1 **Plot** the x-intercepts, $(-1, 0)$ and $(3, 0)$.

STEP 2 **Plot** points between and beyond the x-intercepts.

x	−2	0	1	2	4
y	5	1.8	3.2	1.8	5

STEP 3 **Determine** end behavior and multiplicity. Because f has four factors of the form $x - k$ and a constant factor of 0.2, it is a quartic function with a positive leading coefficient. So, $f(x) \to +\infty$ as $x \to -\infty$ and $f(x) \to +\infty$ as $x \to +\infty$. The zeros -1 and 3 are both repeated twice. So, the graph of f touches the x-axis at $(-1, 0)$ and $(3, 0)$.

STEP 4 **Draw** the graph so that it passes through the plotted points and has the appropriate end behavior.

Example 2   Find turning points

Graph the function $h(x) = -x^4 - 2x^3 + 3x^2 + 4x - 4$. Identify the *x*-intercepts and the points where the local maximums and local minimums occur.

Use a graphing calculator to graph the function. The graph of h has two x-intercepts and three turning points. Use the calculator's *zero*, *minimum*, and *maximum* features to approximate the coordinates of the points. The x-intercepts are $x = -2$ and $x = 1$. The function has a local minimum at $(-0.5, -5.0625)$. The function has local maximums at $(-2, 0)$ and $(1, 0)$.

Georgia Performance Standards

MM3A1b Understand the effects of the following on the graph ☑
of a polynomial function: degree, lead coefficient,
and multiplicity of real zeros.

MM3A1d Investigate and explain characteristics of polynomial ☑
functions, including domain and range, intercepts,
zeros, relative and absolute extrema, intervals of
increase and decrease, and end behavior.

Example 3   **Maximize a polynomial model**

Metal Box You are making an open rectangular box out of a 4-inch
by 12-inch piece of metal. The box will be formed by making the
cuts shown in the diagram and folding up the sides so that the flaps
are square. You want the box to have the greatest volume possible.

12 in.

4 in.

- How long should you make the cuts?
- What is the maximum volume?
- What will be the dimensions of the finished box?

Solution

Write a verbal model for the volume. Then write a function.

Volume (cubic inches)	=	Length (inches)	·	Width (inches)	·	Height (inches)

$$V = (12 - 2x) \cdot (4 - 2x) \cdot x$$
$$= (48 - 32x + 4x^2)x \qquad \text{Use FOIL method.}$$
$$= 4x^3 - 32x^2 + 48x \qquad \text{Write in standard form.}$$

To find the maximum volume, graph the volume
function on a graphing calculator using $0 < x < 2$
from the physical restrictions on the size of the flaps.
From the graph, you can see that the maximum is
about 20.2 and occurs when $x \approx 0.9$.

Maximum
X=0.90283354 Y=20.1961

The maximum volume is about 20.2 cubic inches.
The dimensions of the box are about 10.2 inches, by
2.2 inches by 0.9 inch.

Guided Practice for Examples 1, 2 and 3

**Graph the function. Identify the *x*-intercepts and the points where the
local maximums and local minimums occur.** 1 and 2. See Additional Answers
beginning on page AA1.

1. $f(x) = \frac{1}{2}x^3 - 6x - 8$

2. $f(x) = x^3 + 5x^2 + 7x + 3$

3. In Example 3, how do the answers change if the piece of metal is 6 inches by
12 inches? **The dimensions of the finished box are about 9.4 in. by 3.4 in. by 1.3 in.
The maximum volume is about 41.6 in.³**

UNIT 2

Exercise Set A

MM3A1b Understand the effects of the following on the graph of a polynomial function: degree, lead coefficient, and multiplicity of real zeros.

MM3A1d Investigate and explain characteristics of polynomial functions, including domain and range, intercepts, zeros, relative and absolute extrema, intervals of increase and decrease, and end behavior.

1. **Error Analysis** *Describe* and correct the error in the following statement. **The error is in calling −6 a factor. The correct statement is If −6 is a solution of the polynomial equation f(x) = 0, then (x + 6) is a factor of f(x).**

If −6 is a solution of the polynomial equation $f(x) = 0$, then −6 is a factor of $f(x)$.

For the given degree *n* of a polynomial function, determine the maximum number of turns in the graph of the function.

2. $n = 3$ **2**   3. $n = 5$ **4**   4. $n = 2$ **1**   5. $n = 4$ **3**

Determine the *x*-intercepts of the function.

6. $g(x) = (x + 3)(x - 2)(x - 5)$ **−3, 2, 5**   7. $h(x) = (x + 4)(x - 6)(x - 8)$ **−4, 6, 8**

8. $f(x) = (x + 3)^2(x - 2)$ **−3, 2**   9. $f(x) = (x + 5)(x + 1)(x - 7)$ **−5, −1, 7**

10. $g(x) = (x + 6)^3(x + 2)$ **−6, −2**   11. $h(x) = (x - 8)^5$ **8**

Find all the real zeros of the function. Then determine the multiplicity of each zero and the exact number of turning points of the graph.

12. $f(x) = x^2(x + 1)$ 13. $g(x) = (x + 2)^2(x - 5)$ 14. $h(x) = (x - 4)^3(x - 1)$

15. $f(x) = (x + 6)^2(3x - 2)^2$ 16. $g(x) = x(4x + 3)(x - 8)^2$ 17. $h(x) = x^2(x + 4)(2x - 3)^3$

12–17. See Additional Answers beginning on page AA1.

Graph the function. **18–23. See Additional Answers beginning on page AA1.**

18. $f(x) = (x - 3)(x + 2)(x + 1)$ 19. $g(x) = (x - 3)^2(x + 2)$

20. $h(x) = 0.3(x + 6)(x - 1)(x - 4)$ 21. $g(x) = \frac{5}{6}(x + 1)^2(x - 1)(x - 4)$

22. $h(x) = (x - 1)(x^2 + x + 1)$ 23. $f(x) = (x + 2)(x^2 + 2x + 2)$

Estimate the coordinates of each turning point and state whether each corresponds to a local maximum or a local minimum. Then estimate all real zeros and determine the least degree the function can have. **24–26. See Additional Answers beginning on page AA1.**

24.

25.

26.
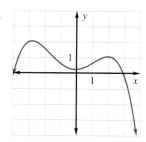

Exercise Set A (continued)

Use a graphing calculator to graph the function. Identify the x-intercepts and points where local maximums or local minimums occur.

27–32. See Additional Answers beginning on page AA1.

27. $f(x) = 3x^3 - 9x + 1$

28. $h(x) = -\dfrac{1}{3}x^3 + x - \dfrac{2}{3}$

29. $g(x) = -\dfrac{1}{4}x^4 + 2x^2$

30. $f(x) = x^5 - 6x^3 + 9x$

31. $h(x) = x^5 - 5x^3 + 4x$

32. $g(x) = x^4 - 2x^3 - 3x^2 + 5x + 2$

In Exercises 33 and 34, assume that the box is constructed using the method illustrated in Example 3 on page 99.

33. Jewelry Lila wants to make a box to hold her jewelry from a piece of metal that is 8 inches by 10 inches. What is the maximum volume of the box? What are the dimensions of the box with the maximum volume?
about 5 in. by 7 in. by 1.5 in.; about 52.5 in.^{3}

34. DVDs Chris is making a box for his DVD collection from a piece of cardboard that is 24 inches by 30 inches. What is the maximum volume of the box? What are the dimensions of the box with the maximum volume?
about 15.2 in. by 21.2 in. by 4.4 in.; about 1417.9 in.^{3}

35. Food The average number E of eggs eaten per person each year in the United States from 1970 to 2000 can be modeled by See Additional Answers beginning on page AA1.

$$E = 0.000944t^4 - 0.052t^3 + 0.95t^2 - 9.4t + 308$$

where t is the number of years since 1970.

  a. Graph the function.

  b. Identify any turning points on the domain $0 \le t \le 30$. What real-life meaning do these points have?

36. Quonset Huts A Quonset hut is a dwelling shaped like half a cylinder. You have 600 square feet of material with which to build a Quonset hut. See Additional Answers beginning on page AA1.

  a. The formula for the surface area of the hut is $S = \pi r^2 + \pi r \ell$ where r is the radius of the semicircle and ℓ is the length of the hut. Substitute 600 for S and then write an equation that gives ℓ in terms of r.

  b. The formula for the volume of the hut is $V = \dfrac{1}{2}\pi r^2 \ell$. Write an equation for the volume V of the Quonset hut as a polynomial function of r by substituting the expression for ℓ from part (a) into the volume formula.

  c. Graph the volume function from part (b). Use the function from part (b) to find the maximum volume of a Quonset hut with a surface area of 600 square feet. What are the hut's dimensions?

Exercise Set B

MM3A1b Understand the effects of the following on the graph of a polynomial function: degree, lead coefficient, and multiplicity of real zeros.

MM3A1d Investigate and explain characteristics of polynomial functions, including domain and range, intercepts, zeros, relative and absolute extrema, intervals of increase and decrease, and end behavior.

For the given degree n of a polynomial function, determine the maximum number of turns in the graph of the function.

1. $n = 9$ 8

2. $n = 6$ 5

Find all the real zeros of the function. Then determine the multiplicity of each zero and the exact number of turning points of the graph.

3–8. See Additional Answers beginning on page AA1.

3. $f(x) = (x + 2)^2(3 - x)(2x - 9)$

4. $g(x) = (x + 4)^2(3x - 5)^2$

5. $h(x) = x^3(x^2 - 1)(x + 1)$

6. $f(x) = -x(x + 6)(x + 3)(2x - 1)^2$

7. $g(x) = x^4 + x^3 - 10x^2 - 4x + 24$

8. $h(x) = 2x^5 + 9x^4 + 9x^3 - 8x^2 - 12x$

Graph the function and state the domain and range.

9–16. See Additional Answers beginning on page AA1.

9. $f(x) = (x + 1)(x^2 + 1)$

10. $g(x) = x(x + 2)^2(x - 1)^2$

11. $h(x) = (x - 1)(x + 1)^3(x - 2)^2$

12. $h(x) = -x^2(x - 3)(x - 2)^3$

13. $g(x) = x(x + 1)(x - 1)^2(x - 3)^3$

14. $f(x) = x^3(x + 3)^2(x^2 + x + 2)$

15. $f(x) = x^2(x + 1)(x - 1)^2(x - 3)^3$

16. $g(x) = (x + 7)^2(x + 4)^2(x + 2)^3$

Estimate the coordinates of each turning point and state whether each corresponds to a local maximum or a local minimum. Then estimate all real zeros and determine the least degree of the function.

17–19. See Additional Answers beginning on page AA1.

17.

18.

19.

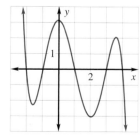

Use a graphing calculator to graph the function. Identify the x-intercepts and points where local maximums or local minimums occur.

20–25. See Additional Answers beginning on page AA1.

20. $f(x) = x^5 - 2x^4 - x^3 + 3x + 1$

21. $g(x) = 3x^3 - 6x + x^4$

22. $g(x) = 3x^4 + 4x^3 - 3$

23. $f(x) = x^5 - 5x^3 + 4x$

24. $h(x) = -\frac{1}{5}x^5 - \frac{7}{8} + x^2$

25. $f(x) = x^4 + 2.6x^3 - 10.56x^2 + 7.2x$

Exercise Set B *(continued)*

26. Critical Thinking Does a quartic function *always, sometimes,* or *never* have a turning point? *Justify* your answer. **always; the graph of every polynomial function of degree *n* has at most *n* − 1 turning points. So, a quartic function has at most 3 turning points.**

27. Critical Thinking Write a cubic function, a quartic function, and a fifth-degree polynomial function whose graphs have *x*-intercepts only at $x = -1$, 3, and 4.
See Additional Answers beginning on page AA1.

Consider the graphs $f(x) = (x + 1)^n$ where $n = 1, 2, 3, 4,$ and 5.

28. What is the *x*-intercept for all of the functions? **−1**

29. For what values of *n* does the graph have a turning point at the *x*-intercept? **2, 4**

30. For what values of *n* does the graph not have a turning point at the *x*-intercept? **1, 3, 5**

31. Generalize your findings in Exercises 29 and 30. Test your theory by graphing $f(x) = (x + 1)^6$ and $g(x) = (x + 1)^7$. **See Additional Answers beginning on page AA1.**

32. Storage A silo is a storage building shaped like a cylinder with half a sphere on top. A farmer has 1000 square feet of material with which to build a silo.
See Additional Answers beginning on page AA1.
   a. The formula for the surface area of the silo is $S = 4\pi r^2 + 2\pi rh$ where *r* is the radius of the cylinder and *h* is the height of the cylinder. Substitute 1000 for *S* and then write an equation for *h* in terms of *r*.

   b. The formula for the volume of the silo is $V = \frac{2}{3}\pi r^3 + \pi r^2 h$. Write an equation for the volume *V* of the silo as a polynomial function of *r* by substituting the expression for *h* from part (a) into the volume formula.

   c. Graph the volume function for part (b). Use the function from part (b) to find the maximum volume of a silo with a surface area of 1000 square feet. What are the silo's dimensions?

33. Temperature During a 24-hour period, the temperature *T* (in degrees Fahrenheit) in a city can be approximated by the model

$$T = 0.026x^3 - 1.03x^2 + 10.2x + 34,\ 0 \le x \le 24$$

where *x* is the number of hours since 6 A.M.
See Additional Answers beginning on page AA1.
   a. Graph the function.

   b. Identify any turning points on the domain $0 \le x \le 24$. What real-life meaning do these points have?

   c. What is the range of the function?

34. Volume A cylinder is inscribed in a sphere of radius 6. Write an equation for the volume of the cylinder as a function of *h*. Find the value of *h* that maximizes the volume of the inscribed cylinder. What is the maximum volume of the cylinder?

   $V = \pi h\left(36 - \dfrac{h^2}{4}\right)$; **about 6.9; about 522**

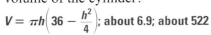

Georgia Performance Standards

MM3A1d Investigate and explain characteristics of polynomial functions, including domain and range, intercepts, zeros, relative and absolute extrema, intervals of increase and decrease, and end behavior.

Technology Activity
Local Maximums and Minimums

Use after Lesson 2.8

Question

How can you use a graphing calculator to find local maximums and minimums of a polynomial function?

An important characteristic of graphs of polynomial functions is that they have turning points corresponding to the local maximum and minimum values.

You can use a graphing calculator to find these local maximums and minimums.

Example

Find local maximums and minimums on a graphing calculator.

Use a graphing calculator to find the local maximums and minimums of the given function.

$y = x^3 - 7x + 6$

Solution

STEP 1   **Enter** the function in the equation editor.

STEP 2   **Graph** the function.

STEP 3   **Adjust** your viewing window so that you can see the local maximum and minimum.

STEP 4   **Use** the *maximum* feature to find the local maximum. The local maximum is about $(-1.53, 13.13)$.

STEP 5   **Use** the *minimum* feature to find the local minimum. The local minimum is about $(1.53, -1.13)$.

Practice

Use a graphing calculator to find the local maximums and minimums of the given function.   1–6. See Additional Answers beginning on page AA1.

1. $y = x^4 - 2x^3 - 10x^2 + 8x + 12$ **2.** $y = x^3 + 4x^2 + x - 6$

3. $y = x^4 - 13x^2 + 36$ **4.** $y = 2(x - 4)(x + 4)(x + 1)$

5. $y = -\frac{2}{3}(x - 1)(x + 2)(x + 1)(x - 3)$ **6.** $y = 0.4(x + 6)(x - 6)(x + 2)$

UNIT 2

TEST | for Unit 2

Use direct substitution to evaluate the polynomial function for the given value of *x*. Then check your answer using synthetic substitution.

1. $f(x) = -2x^3 + 8x^2 + 3x - 1; x = 4$ **11**

2. $f(x) = x^4 + 2x^2 - 16; x = -3$ **83**

For the polynomial function, (a) graph the function, (b) find the domain and range, (c) describe the degree and leading coefficient, (d) describe any symmetry, and (e) identify where the function increases and decreases.

3–5. See Additional Answers beginning on page AA1.

3. $f(x) = x^3 - x^2 - 2x$

4. $f(x) = \frac{1}{4}x^4 - 2x^2 + 16$

5. $f(x) = -2x^3 + 6x^2 - \frac{9}{2}x$

Graph the function. *Compare* the graph with the graph of $f(x) = \frac{1}{2}x^4$.

6–8. See Additional Answers beginning on page AA1.

6. $g(x) = \frac{1}{2}x^4 + 2$

7. $g(x) = \frac{1}{2}(x - 1)^4$

8. $g(x) = \frac{1}{2}(x + 4)^4 - 3$

Find the real-number solutions of the equation.

9. $20x^3 = 125x$ $-\frac{5}{2}, 0, \frac{5}{2}$

10. $x^4 - 3x^2 + 2 = 0$ $-\sqrt{2}, -1, 1\sqrt{2}$

11. $2x^3 - 6x^2 - 6x + 18 = 0$ $-\sqrt{3}, \sqrt{3}, 3$

12. $x^4 + 2x^3 - 8x - 16 = 0$ $-2, 2$

Solve the inequality using any method. 13–15. See Additional Answers beginning on page AA1.

13. $2x^3 - 5x^2 - 3x \le 0$

14. $x^4 - 4x^2 + 3 < 0$

15. $x^4 - 12 > 0$

A polynomial *f* and a factor of *f* are given. Factor *f* completely.

16. $f(x) = 2x^3 + x^2 - 5x + 2; x + 2$
$f(x) = (x + 2)(2x - 1)(x - 1)$

17. $f(x) = x^4 - 4x^3 + 8x - 32; x - 4$
$f(x) = (x - 4)(x + 2)(x^2 - 2x + 4)$

Find all real zeros of the function. 18–21. See Additional Answers beginning on page AA1.

18. $g(x) = x^3 + 6x^2 - 31x - 36$

19. $g(x) = 2x^3 + 9x^2 - 11x - 30$

20. $f(x) = 2x^4 + 5x^3 - 6x^2 - 7x + 6$

21. $f(x) = 6x^4 + 35x^3 + 35x^2 - 55x - 21$

Write a polynomial function *f* of least degree that has rational coefficients, a leading coefficient of 1, and the given zeros. 22–25. See Additional Answers beginning on page AA1.

22. $-2, 4, 6$

23. $3, 1 + \sqrt{2}$

24. $-1, 0, -i, i$

25. $-4, 1, 1 - 2i$

Find all the real zeros of the function. Then determine the multiplicity of each zero and the exact number of turning points of the graph.

26–29. See Additional Answers beginning on page AA1.

26. $f(x) = x^3(x + 4)$

27. $g(x) = (x - 9)^2(x - 1)$

28. $h(x) = x^2(x + 2)^3(x - 7)$

29. $f(x) = (x + 1)^2(4x - 3)^2$

Use a graphing calculator to graph the function. Identify the *x*-intercepts and the points where the local maximums and local minimums occur.

30 and 31. See Additional Answers beginning on page AA1.

30. $f(x) = -3x^3 - 4x^2 + x - 3$

31. $h(x) = 2x^4 - 6x^2 + 1$

TEST | for Unit 2 *(continued)*

32. **Telephone Bills** From 1995 to 2003, the average monthly local telephone bill T (in dollars) for subscribers in the United States can be modeled by

$$T = -0.0097x^4 + 0.148x^3 - 0.56x^2 + 0.5x + 20$$ **See Additional Answers beginning on page AA1.**

where x is the number of years since 1995.

a. Classify the function by degree and type.

b. Make a table of values for the function for $x = 0, 3, 5, 7, 8$.

c. Sketch a graph of the function. Do you think the model will accurately predict local telephone bills for years beyond 2003? *Explain.*

33. **Company Profit** The profit P (in millions of dollars) for a video game manufacturer can be modeled by $P = -3x^3 + 7x^2 + 11x$ where x is the number of video games produced (in millions). Currently, the company produces 3 million video games and makes a profit of $15,000,000. What lesser number of video games could the company produce and still make the same profit? **1,000,000 video games**

34. **Candles** Wes is making a candle by filling a mold with wax. It is to be shaped like a pyramid with a height that is 4 inches greater than the length of each side of its square base, as shown in the diagram. The volume of the candle is 21 cubic inches. What are the dimensions of the mold? **3 in. by 3 in. by 7 in.**

Performance Task

Art

You are making a clay sculpture that is a rectangular prism. You want the height of the sculpture to be 10 inches greater than the width of the base. The length is to be twice the width.

a. Let x represent the width (in inches) of the sculpture's base. Draw a **See Additional Answers** diagram of the sculpture, and label the dimensions in terms of x. **beginning on page AA1.**

b. Write a function that gives the volume V of the sculpture in terms of x. $V = 2x^3 + 20x^2$

c. Graph the function in part (b). Use the graph to estimate the value of x when the volume is 144 cubic inches. **See Additional Answers beginning on page AA1.**

d. Write a polynomial equation that you can use to find the value of x when the volume is 144 cubic inches. $2x^3 + 20x^2 = 144$

e. Identify the possible rational solutions of the equation in part (d). Then solve the equation. **e–g. See Additional Answers beginning on page AA1.**

f. *Compare* your answer in part (e) with your estimate from part (c). What are the dimensions of the sculpture?

g. Does the sculpture have a maximum volume? Use the end behavior of the graph in part (b) to explain your reasoning.

UNIT 3
Algebra: Rational Exponents and Square Root Functions

Investigating Math Activity
Radicals and Rational Exponents

Use before Lesson 3.1

Materials   graphing calculator

Question

How can you write the root of an integer using an exponent?

An nth root of x is written as $\sqrt[n]{x}$ where n is the index of the radical.

index $\diagup\ \sqrt[n]{x}$ —— radicand

Explore

Evaluate radical and exponential expressions.

Use a graphing calculator to evaluate each expression.

	Radical Expression	Exponential Expression	
a.	$\sqrt{4}$	$4^{1/2}$	**2, 2**
b.	$\sqrt[3]{27}$	$27^{1/3}$	**3, 3**
c.	$\sqrt[4]{625}$	$625^{1/4}$	**5, 5**
d.	$\sqrt[5]{32}$	$32^{1/5}$	**2, 2**
e.	$\sqrt[6]{729}$	$729^{1/6}$	**3, 3**

Draw Conclusions

1. What is the relationship of the values of each pair of radical and exponential expressions? **They are the same.**

2. Reasoning *Compare* the indexes in the radical expressions with the denominators of the exponents in the exponential expressions. What is the relationship of these numbers? **They are the same.**

3. Writing Write a rule that explains how to rewrite a radical expression as an exponential expression. **See Additional Answers beginning on page AA1.**

4. Use your rule from Exercise 3 to rewrite the following radical expressions as exponential expressions. Then, use your calculator to verify your rule.

   a. $\sqrt[3]{64}$ **64$^{1/3}$**   **b.** $\sqrt[4]{81}$ **81$^{1/4}$**   **c.** $\sqrt[5]{3125}$ **3125$^{1/5}$**

5. Writing Modify your rule to explain how you would rewrite the following radical expressions as exponential expressions. Then, rewrite the radical expressions as exponential expressions. Use your calculator to help you verify your new rule. **See Additional Answers beginning on page AA1.**

   a. $\left(\sqrt[3]{8}\right)^2$ **b.** $\left(\sqrt[5]{32}\right)^4$

Evaluate *n*th Roots and Use Rational Exponents

Georgia Performance Standards: MM3A2a, MM3A2b, MM3A3d

Goal Evaluate *n*th roots and study rational exponents.

Vocabulary

For an integer n greater than 1, if $b^n = a$, then b is an **nth root of a**.

An *n*th root of a is written as $\sqrt[n]{a}$ where n is the **index of the radical**. If n is odd, then a has one real *n*th root. If n is even, then a has two real *n*th roots if $a > 0$, one real *n*th root if $a = 0$, and no real *n*th roots if $a < 0$.

Example 1   Find *n*th roots

Find the indicated real *n*th root(s) of a.

a. $n = 6$, $a = 64$ **b.** $n = 5$, $a = -32$

Solution

a. Because $n = 6$ is even and $a = 64 > 0$, 64 has two real sixth roots. Because $2^6 = 64$ and $(-2)^6 = 64$, you can write $\pm\sqrt[6]{64} = \pm 2$ or $\pm 64^{1/6} = \pm 2$.

b. Because $n = 5$ is odd, -32 has one real fifth root. Because $(-2)^5 = -32$, you can write $\sqrt[5]{-32} = -2$ or $(-32)^{1/5} = -2$.

Example 2   Evaluate expressions with rational exponents

Evaluate (a) $9^{5/2}$ and (b) $27^{-2/3}$.

Rational Exponent Form	Radical Form
a. $9^{5/2} = (9^{1/2})^5 = 3^5 = 243$	$9^{5/2} = (\sqrt{9})^5 = 3^5 = 243$
b. $27^{-2/3} = \dfrac{1}{27^{2/3}} = \dfrac{1}{(27^{1/3})^2} = \dfrac{1}{3^2} = \dfrac{1}{9}$	$27^{-2/3} = \dfrac{1}{(\sqrt[3]{27})^2} = \dfrac{1}{3^2} = \dfrac{1}{9}$

Guided Practice for Examples 1 and 2

1. Find the real cube root of -343. **−7**

2. Evaluate the expression $36^{3/2}$ without using a calculator. **216**

Example 3   Approximate roots with a calculator

	Expression	Keystrokes	Display
a.	$10^{2/3}$	1 0 $\boxed{\wedge}$ $\boxed{(}$ $\boxed{2}$ $\boxed{\div}$ $\boxed{3}$ $\boxed{)}$ $\boxed{\text{ENTER}}$	4.641588834
b.	$19^{-5/4}$	1 9 $\boxed{\wedge}$ $\boxed{(}$ $\boxed{(-)}$ $\boxed{5}$ $\boxed{\div}$ $\boxed{4}$ $\boxed{)}$ $\boxed{\text{ENTER}}$	0.0252091382

Georgia Performance Standards

MM3A2a Define and understand the properties of nth roots. ☑

MM3A2b Extend properties of exponents to include rational exponents. ☑

MM3A3d Solve a variety of types of equations by appropriate means choosing among mental calculation, pencil and paper, or appropriate technology. ☑

Example 4 **Solve equations using nth roots**

Solve the equation.

a.
$$-2x^6 = -1458$$
$$x^6 = 729 \qquad \text{Divide each side by } -2.$$
$$x = \pm\sqrt[6]{729} \qquad \text{Take sixth root of each side.}$$
$$x = \pm 3 \qquad \text{Simplify.}$$

b.
$$(x+2)^5 = 35$$
$$x + 2 = \sqrt[5]{35} \qquad \text{Take fifth root of each side.}$$
$$x = -2 + \sqrt[5]{35} \qquad \text{Solve for } x.$$
$$x \approx 0.04 \qquad \text{Use a calculator.}$$

Example 5 **Use nth roots in problem solving**

Beach Ball The volume of a beach ball can be approximated using the model $V = \frac{4}{3}\pi r^3$ where r is the radius of the ball in inches. Estimate the radius of the ball if the volume is 382 cubic inches.

Solution

$$V = \frac{4}{3}\pi r^3 \qquad \text{Write model for volume.}$$

$$382 = \frac{4}{3}\pi r^3 \qquad \text{Substitute 382 for volume.}$$

$$\frac{3(382)}{4\pi} = r^3 \qquad \text{Multiply each side by } \frac{3}{4\pi}.$$

$$91.20 \approx r^3 \qquad \text{Simplify.}$$

$$4.50 \approx r \qquad \text{Take cube root of each side.}$$

Guided Practice for Examples 3, 4, and 5

Evaluate the expression using a calculator. Round the result to two decimal places when appropriate.

3. $10^{1/3}$ about 2.15 **4.** $\sqrt[6]{13}$ about 1.53 **5.** $21^{-1/4}$ about 0.47 **6.** $\left(\sqrt[4]{81}\right)^{-2}$ about 0.11

Solve the equation. Round the result to two decimal places when appropriate.

7. $-6x^2 = -180$ about ± 5.48 **8.** $x^3 - 9 = 31$ about 3.42 **9.** $(x+8)^4 = 2$ about -6.81, about -9.19

10. Rework Example 5 if the volume of a ball is 268 cubic inches. about 4 in.

UNIT 3

Exercise Set A

MM3A2a   Define and understand the properties of nth roots.

MM3A2b   Extend properties of exponents to include rational exponents.

MM3A3d   Solve a variety of types of equations by appropriate means choosing among mental calculation, pencil and paper, or appropriate technology.

Rewrite the expression using rational exponent notation.

1. $\sqrt[3]{7}$ $7^{1/3}$

2. $\left(\sqrt[3]{6}\right)^2$ $6^{2/3}$

3. $\left(\sqrt[5]{14}\right)^4$ $14^{4/5}$

4. $\left(\sqrt[7]{-21}\right)^3$ $(-21)^{3/7}$

5. $\left(\sqrt[8]{11}\right)^7$ $11^{7/8}$

6. $\left(\sqrt[9]{-2}\right)^4$ $(-2)^{4/9}$

Rewrite the expression using radical notation.

7. $17^{1/3}$ $\sqrt[3]{17}$

8. $44^{1/6}$ $\sqrt[6]{44}$

9. $33^{2/3}$ $\left(\sqrt[3]{33}\right)^2$

10. $9^{5/3}$ $\left(\sqrt[3]{9}\right)^5$

11. $(-28)^{7/5}$ $\left(\sqrt[5]{-28}\right)^7$

12. $39^{4/7}$ $\left(\sqrt[7]{39}\right)^4$

Evaluate the expression without using a calculator.

13. $\left(\sqrt[3]{8}\right)^2$ 4

14. $\left(\sqrt[4]{16}\right)^3$ 8

15. $\left(\sqrt[4]{81}\right)^4$ 81

16. $36^{3/2}$ 216

17. $4^{5/2}$ 32

18. $27^{2/3}$ 9

19. $125^{4/3}$ 625

20. $(-8)^{1/3}$ -2

21. $(-32)^{3/5}$ -8

Evaluate the expression using a calculator. Round the result to two decimal places when appropriate.

22. $\sqrt[3]{38}$ 3.36

23. $\sqrt[6]{112}$ 2.20

24. $\sqrt[7]{-215}$ -2.15

25. $(241)^{1/5}$ 3.00

26. $(-133)^{1/3}$ -5.10

27. $(69)^{1/4}$ 2.88

28. $(96)^{2/3}$ 20.97

29. $(356)^{5/9}$ 26.15

30. $(-2427)^{4/7}$ 85.97

31. **Geometry** Find the radius of a sphere with a volume of 589 cubic centimeters. **5.2 cm**

Solve the equation. Round the result to two decimal places when appropriate.

32. $x^3 + 17 = 132$ **4.86**

33. $2x^5 + 73 = 53$ **-1.58**

34. $(x + 3)^4 = 362$ **$-7.36, 1.36$**

In Exercises 35 and 36, use the following information.

Water and Ice Water, in its liquid state, has a density of 0.9971 gram per cubic centimeter. Ice has a density of 0.9168 gram per cubic centimeter. A cubic container is filled with 600 grams of liquid water. A different cubic container is filled with 600 grams of ice. Round the answers to two decimal places when appropriate.

35. Find the volume of the container filled with liquid water. Then find the length of the edges of the cubic container that is filled with liquid water. **601.75 cm³; 8.44 cm**

36. Find the volume of the container filled with ice. Then find the length of the edges of the cubic container that is filled with ice. **654.45 cm³; 8.68 cm**

UNIT 3

MM3A2a Define and understand the properties of *n*th roots.

MM3A2b Extend properties of exponents to include rational exponents.

MM3A3d Solve a variety of types of equations by appropriate means choosing among mental calculation, pencil and paper, or appropriate technology.

Rewrite the expression using rational exponent notation.

1. $\left(\sqrt[5]{63}\right)^3$ $63^{3/5}$

2. $\left(\sqrt[3]{-25}\right)^4$ $(-25)^{4/3}$

3. $\left(\sqrt[6]{124}\right)^7$ $124^{7/6}$

Rewrite the expression using radical notation.

4. $(-57)^{4/3}$ $\left(\sqrt[3]{-57}\right)^4$

5. $13^{3/2}$ $\left(\sqrt{13}\right)^3$

6. $204^{5/8}$ $\left(\sqrt[8]{204}\right)^5$

Evaluate the expression without using a calculator.

7. $\left(\sqrt[3]{27}\right)^2$ 9

8. $\left(\sqrt[4]{256}\right)^3$ 64

9. $\left(\sqrt[3]{-64}\right)^2$ 16

10. $36^{3/2}$ 216

11. $(25)^{-3/2}$ $\dfrac{1}{125}$

12. $16^{1/4}$ 2

13. $(-32)^{-3/5}$ $-\dfrac{1}{8}$

14. $(81)^{-5/2}$ $\dfrac{1}{59{,}049}$

15. $(-125)^{-5/3}$ $-\dfrac{1}{3125}$

Evaluate the expression using a calculator. Round the result to two decimal places when appropriate.

16. $\left(\sqrt[3]{23}\right)^5$ 186.01

17. $\left(\sqrt[4]{65}\right)^3$ 22.89

18. $\left(\sqrt[5]{-124}\right)^4$ 47.29

19. $(39)^{4/3}$ 132.26

20. $(-128)^{-2/5}$ 0.14

21. $(256)^{5/8}$ 32

22. $(-325)^{3/5}$ −32.15

23. $(215)^{-4/9}$ 0.09

24. $(-1012)^{8/5}$ −64,311.53

Solve the equation. Round the result to two decimal places when appropriate.

25. $x^5 = 1321$ 4.21

26. $3x^5 + 3 = 213$ 2.34

27. $(x - 3)^6 = 502$ 0.18, 5.82

28. $-4x^3 = 132$ −3.21

29. $2x^4 = 36$ ±2.06

30. $(3x + 2)^4 = 232$ −1.97, 0.63

31. $7 - x^5 = 3$ 1.32

32. $4x^5 + 96 = 24$ −1.78

33. $12 - (2x + 3)^3 = 84$ −3.58

34. **Geometry** Find the radius of a sphere with a volume of 994 cubic centimeters. **6.19 cm**

35. **Volume** A cylindrical container holds 20 ounces of liquid. One fluid ounce is approximately 1.8 cubic inches. The height of the container is 3.5 inches. Use the formula for the volume of a cylinder to find the radius of the container. **1.81 in.**

36. **Critical Thinking** Use the following examples to determine when $\sqrt[n]{a^n} \neq a$. $\sqrt[n]{a^n} \neq a$ when $a < 0$ and n is even.

 a. $\sqrt[3]{(-2)^3}$

 b. $\sqrt{(-2)^2}$

 c. $\sqrt[3]{2^3}$

 d. $\sqrt{2^2}$

Apply Properties of Rational Exponents

Georgia Performance Standards: MM3A2b

Goal Simplify expressions involving rational exponents.

Vocabulary

A radical with index n is in **simplest form** if the radicand has no perfect nth powers as factors and any denominator has been rationalized.

Two radical expressions with the same index and radicand are **like radicals.**

The expressions $a + \sqrt{b}$ and $a - \sqrt{b}$ are called **radical conjugates** of each other.

For a list of properties of rational exponents and radicals, see pages 245 and 246.

Example 1   Use properties of exponents

Use the properties of rational exponents to simplify the expression.

a. $\left(8^2 \cdot 3^2\right)^{-1/2} = \left[(8 \cdot 3)^2\right]^{-1/2} = \left(24^2\right)^{-1/2} = 24^{-1} = \dfrac{1}{24}$

b. $\left(4^{1/5} \cdot 2^{1/5}\right)^{10} = \left(4^{1/5}\right)^{10} \cdot \left(2^{1/5}\right)^{10} = 4^2 \cdot 2^2 = 16 \cdot 4 = 64$

c. $\dfrac{5^{3/4}}{5^{1/2}} \cdot 5^2 = 5^{3/4 - 1/2} \cdot 5^2 = 5^{1/4} \cdot 5^2 = 5^{1/4 + 2} = 5^{9/4}$

Example 2   Use properties of radicals

Use the properties of radicals to simplify the expression.

a. $\sqrt{8} \cdot \sqrt{50} = \sqrt{8 \cdot 50} = \sqrt{400} = 20$ Product property

b. $\dfrac{\sqrt[3]{192}}{\sqrt[3]{24}} = \dfrac{\sqrt[3]{64 \cdot 3}}{\sqrt[3]{8 \cdot 3}} = \dfrac{4\sqrt[3]{3}}{2\sqrt[3]{3}} = 2$ Quotient property

Example 3   Write radicals in simplest form

a. $\sqrt[5]{64} = \sqrt[5]{32 \cdot 2}$ Factor out perfect fifth powers.

$\phantom{\sqrt[5]{64}} = \sqrt[5]{32} \cdot \sqrt[5]{2}$ Product property

$\phantom{\sqrt[5]{64}} = 2\sqrt[5]{2}$ Simplify.

b. $\dfrac{\sqrt[3]{3}}{\sqrt[3]{4}} = \dfrac{\sqrt[3]{3}}{\sqrt[3]{4}} \cdot \dfrac{\sqrt[3]{2}}{\sqrt[3]{2}}$ Make denominator a perfect cube.

$\phantom{\dfrac{\sqrt[3]{3}}{\sqrt[3]{4}}} = \dfrac{\sqrt[3]{6}}{\sqrt[3]{8}}$ Product property

$\phantom{\dfrac{\sqrt[3]{3}}{\sqrt[3]{4}}} = \dfrac{\sqrt[3]{6}}{2}$ Simplify.

Example 4 **Add and subtract like radicals and roots**

Simplify the expression.

a. $\sqrt[4]{162} - \sqrt[4]{32} = \sqrt[4]{81} \cdot \sqrt[4]{2} - \sqrt[4]{16} \cdot \sqrt[4]{2} = 3\sqrt[4]{2} - 2\sqrt[4]{2} = (3-2)\sqrt[4]{2} = \sqrt[4]{2}$

b. $7^{3/2} + 4(7^{3/2}) = (1+4)7^{3/2} = 5(7^{3/2})$

Guided Practice for Examples 1, 2, 3, and 4

Simplify the expression.

1. $(8^{1/2} \cdot 9^{1/4})^2$ **24** 2. $\left(\dfrac{10}{10^{2/3}}\right)^2$ **$10^{2/3}$** 3. $125^{-1/3}$ **$\dfrac{1}{5}$** 4. $11^{-1/2} \cdot 11^{5/2}$ **121**

5. $\sqrt{18} \cdot \sqrt{27}$ **$9\sqrt{6}$** 6. $\sqrt[3]{16} \cdot \sqrt[3]{24}$ **$4\sqrt[3]{6}$** 7. $\dfrac{\sqrt{200}}{\sqrt{8}}$ **5** 8. $\dfrac{\sqrt[5]{160}}{\sqrt[5]{5}}$ **2**

9. $\sqrt[3]{432}$ **$6\sqrt[3]{2}$** 10. $\dfrac{\sqrt[4]{2}}{\sqrt[4]{3}}$ **$\dfrac{\sqrt[4]{54}}{3}$** 11. $3(6)^{1/4} + 5(6)^{1/4}$ **$8(6)^{1/4}$** 12. $9(54)^{1/2} - 54^{1/2}$ **$24(6)^{1/2}$**

Example 5 **Simplify expressions involving variables**

Simplify the expression. Assume all variables are positive.

a. $\sqrt[3]{\dfrac{8y^6}{z^{12}}} = \dfrac{\sqrt[3]{8y^6}}{\sqrt[3]{z^{12}}} = \dfrac{\sqrt[3]{(2y^2)^3}}{\sqrt[3]{(z^4)^3}} = \dfrac{2y^2}{z^4}$

b. $\sqrt[3]{\dfrac{a^2}{b}} = \sqrt[3]{\dfrac{a^2 \cdot b^2}{b \cdot b^2}} = \sqrt[3]{\dfrac{a^2b^2}{b^3}} = \dfrac{\sqrt[3]{a^2b^2}}{\sqrt[3]{b^3}} = \dfrac{\sqrt[3]{a^2b^2}}{b}$

c. $\dfrac{2}{c + \sqrt{d}} = \dfrac{2}{c + \sqrt{d}} \cdot \dfrac{c - \sqrt{d}}{c - \sqrt{d}} = \dfrac{2(c - \sqrt{d})}{c^2 - c\sqrt{d} + c\sqrt{d} - d} = \dfrac{2(c - \sqrt{d})}{c^2 - d}$

Example 6 **Add and subtract expressions involving variables**

Perform the indicated operation. Assume all variables are positive.

a. $-4\sqrt{k} - 5\sqrt{k} = (-4 - 5)\sqrt{k} = -9\sqrt{k}$

b. $9a^{1/3}b - 2a^{1/3}b = (9 - 2)a^{1/3}b = 7a^{1/3}b$

Guided Practice for Examples 5 and 6

Simplify the expression. Assume all variables are positive.

13. $\sqrt[4]{\dfrac{81m^4}{16n^8}}$ **$\dfrac{3m}{2n^2}$** 14. $(8p^6q^3)^{2/3}$ **$4p^4q^2$** 15. $\dfrac{3}{x - \sqrt{2y}}$ **$\dfrac{3(x + \sqrt{2y})}{x^2 - 2y}$**

16. $6\sqrt{h} - 8\sqrt{h}$ **$-2\sqrt{h}$** 17. $11a^{1/2}b - 4a^{1/2}b$ **$7a^{1/2}b$** 18. $3\sqrt{5y^4} - y\sqrt{20y^2}$ **$y^2\sqrt{5}$**

UNIT 3

Exercise Set A

MM3A2b   Extend properties of exponents to include rational exponents.

Simplify the expression using the properties of radicals and rational exponents.

1. $7^{1/3} \cdot 7^{4/3}$ $7^{5/3}$

2. $\dfrac{4^{2/3}}{4^{1/3}}$ $4^{1/3}$

3. $(6^{2/3})^{3/4}$ $6^{1/2}$

4. $5^{1/4} \cdot 3^{1/4}$ $15^{1/4}$

5. $\sqrt[4]{2} \cdot \sqrt[4]{8}$ 2

6. $\dfrac{\sqrt[4]{192}}{\sqrt[4]{6}}$ $2\sqrt[4]{2}$

7. $\dfrac{11}{\sqrt[4]{11}}$ $11^{3/4}$

8. $\sqrt[3]{7} \cdot \sqrt[3]{49}$ 7

9. $(3^{3/2})^2$ 27

10. $\left(\dfrac{54}{64}\right)^{1/3}$ $\dfrac{3\sqrt[3]{2}}{4}$

11. $\dfrac{\sqrt[4]{32}}{\sqrt[4]{2}}$ 2

12. $\dfrac{\sqrt[5]{5}}{\sqrt[5]{27}}$ $\dfrac{\sqrt[5]{45}}{3}$

Simplify the expression. Assume all variables are positive.

13. $x^{5/3} \cdot x^{4/3}$ x^3

14. $\sqrt{x^{2/5}}$ $x^{1/5}$

15. $(x^{1/2})^{2/7}$ $x^{1/7}$

16. $\left(\dfrac{x^2}{27}\right)^{1/3}$ $\dfrac{x^{2/3}}{3}$

17. $\sqrt[3]{16x^4}$ $2x\sqrt[3]{2x}$

18. $(x^{-3})^{2/5}$ $\dfrac{1}{x^{6/5}}$

19. $\dfrac{x^{7/5}}{x^{4/5}}$ $x^{3/5}$

20. $\dfrac{\sqrt[3]{64x^3y}}{4x^{-3}y}$ $\dfrac{x^4\sqrt[3]{y}}{y}$

21. $x^5 \cdot x^{\sqrt 3}$ $x^{5+\sqrt 3}$

22. $(x^{\sqrt 2})^{3\sqrt 2}$ x^6

23. $\dfrac{x^{4\sqrt 3}}{2x^{2\sqrt 3}}$ $\dfrac{x^{2\sqrt 3}}{2}$

24. $\dfrac{4x}{x+\sqrt{5y}}$ $\dfrac{4x(x-\sqrt{5y})}{x^2-5y}$

Perform the indicated operation. Assume all variables are positive.

25. $6\sqrt[3]{5} + 2\sqrt[3]{5}$ $8\sqrt[3]{5}$

26. $5\sqrt{5} - \sqrt{45}$ $2\sqrt{5}$

27. $2\sqrt{27} - 3\sqrt{48}$ $-6\sqrt{3}$

28. $2\sqrt{x} + 7\sqrt{x}$ $9\sqrt{x}$

29. $3(x^{1/2}y^3)^2 - (x^3y^{18})^{1/3}$ $2xy^6$

30. $4x^{\sqrt 3} + x^{\sqrt 3}$ $5x^{\sqrt 3}$

Write the expression in simplest form. Assume all variables are positive.

31. $\sqrt[4]{3x^7y^9z^3}$ $xy^2\sqrt[4]{3x^3yz^3}$

32. $\sqrt{x^3y^4z} \cdot \sqrt{xyz^4}$ $x^2y^2z^2\sqrt{yz}$

33. $\sqrt[3]{\dfrac{81x^2y^3}{8xy^4z}}$ $\dfrac{3\sqrt[3]{3xy^2z^2}}{2yz}$

34. Earth Science The equatorial circumference of Earth is 4.01×10^4 kilometers. One kilometer is equivalent to 3.94×10^4 inches. What is the equatorial circumference of Earth in inches?   **1.58×10^9 in.**

35. Swimming Pool A wooden deck and a circular swimming pool cover an area of 514.16 square feet of the lawn. The rectangular deck is 20 feet wide and 10 feet long. What is the radius of the pool?   **10 ft**

UNIT 3

Exercise Set B

MM3A2b   Extend properties of exponents to include rational exponents.

Simplify the expression using the properties of radicals and rational exponents.

1. $(4^{2/3} \cdot 5^{3/4})^3$ $16 \cdot 5^{9/4}$

2. $(3^{3/2} \cdot 3^3)^{1/3}$ $3^{3/2}$

3. $[(7^{2/3})^{3/5}]^3$ $7^{6/5}$

4. $\left(\dfrac{5^2}{5^{7/2}}\right)^{-1/3}$ $5^{1/2}$

5. $\left(\dfrac{16^{1/3}}{2^{1/3}}\right)^2$ 4

6. $\sqrt[4]{\sqrt[3]{\sqrt{6}}}$ $\sqrt[24]{6}$

7. $\sqrt{\dfrac{\sqrt{32}}{\sqrt{72}}}$ $\dfrac{\sqrt{6}}{3}$

8. $\sqrt[5]{(3^3)^2 \cdot (3^4)^2}$ $9 \cdot 3^{4/5}$

9. $\dfrac{\sqrt{\frac{5}{7}} \cdot \sqrt{\frac{4}{5}}}{\sqrt{10}}$ $\dfrac{\sqrt{70}}{35}$

Simplify the expression. Assume all variables are positive.

10. $x^{\sqrt{3}} \cdot x^{\sqrt{12}}$ $x^{3\sqrt{3}}$

11. $\sqrt[4]{\dfrac{x^{17}}{y^8}}$ $\dfrac{x^4 \sqrt[4]{x}}{y^2}$

12. $\left(\dfrac{x^{1/4}}{x^{1/2}}\right)^{-1}$ $x^{1/4}$

13. $\dfrac{x^{4/3}y^{7/6}}{xy}$ $x^{1/3}y^{1/6}$

14. $\left(\dfrac{2x^3y^{2/3}}{x^{5/3}y^{3/5}z}\right)^3$ $\dfrac{8x^4y^{1/5}}{z^3}$

15. $\left(\dfrac{xy^2}{3y^{4/3}z^{1/2}}\right)^{-1/2}$ $\dfrac{\sqrt{3}z^{1/4}}{x^{1/2}y^{1/3}}$

16. $\left[\dfrac{(12xz^2)^{1/2}}{(3y^3z)^{1/2}}\right]^{-3}$ $\dfrac{y^{9/2}}{8x^{3/2}z^{3/2}}$

17. $\sqrt[4]{(3x^3)^3(3x^2)^5}$ $9x^4 \sqrt[4]{x^3}$

18. $\dfrac{8x}{x - \sqrt{3y}}$ $\dfrac{8x(x + \sqrt{3y})}{x^2 - 3y}$

19. **Error Analysis** *Describe* and correct the error in simplifying the expression.

Addition was used to combine the exponents instead of subtraction; $\dfrac{y^{1/2}}{y^{-3/4}} = y^{1/2 - (-3/4)} = y^{5/4}$

$$\dfrac{y^{1/2}}{y^{-3/4}} = y^{-1/4} = \dfrac{1}{y^{1/4}} \quad \times$$

Perform the indicated operation. Assume all variables are positive.

20. $\sqrt{10\sqrt{3} - 6\sqrt{3}}$ $2\sqrt[4]{3}$

21. $2x\sqrt[3]{x^4yz^5} + \sqrt[3]{x^7yz^5}$ $3x^2z\sqrt[3]{xyz^2}$

22. $\sqrt{\sqrt[4]{16x} - \sqrt[4]{x}}$ $\sqrt[8]{x}$

23. $\sqrt[3]{\dfrac{2x}{5} + \sqrt{\dfrac{x}{25}}}$ $\dfrac{\sqrt[3]{50x + 25\sqrt{x}}}{5}$

24. $\sqrt[3]{8x} + \sqrt[6]{x^2} - \sqrt[9]{x^3}$ $2\sqrt[3]{x}$

25. $\sqrt{xyz^2} \cdot \sqrt{9x^3z} \cdot \sqrt{x} + x\sqrt{yz} \cdot \sqrt{x^3z^2}$ $4x^2z\sqrt{xyz}$

26. **Astronomy** The equatorial circumference of the Moon is 1.09×10^4 kilometers. One kilometer is equivalent to 3.94×10^4 inches. What is the equatorial circumference of the Moon in inches? 4.29×10^8 in.

27. **Bowling Ball** A bowling ball is submerged in a tub of water. As a result, a total of 333 cubic inches of water is displaced. Use the formula for the volume of a sphere to find the radius of the bowling ball. **4.3 in.**

LESSON 3.2

Problem Solving Workshop

Problem   The surface area S (in square centimeters) of a large dog's body can be approximated by the model $S = 11.2m^{2/3}$ where m is the mass (in grams) of the dog. Approximate the surface area of a dog that has a mass of 9 kilograms (9×10^3 grams).

STEP 1 Read and Understand

What do you know?   The function that models surface area of a large dog

What do you want to find out?   The surface area of a dog that has a mass of 9 kilograms

STEP 2 Make a Plan   Use what you know to substitute and solve the equation.

STEP 3 Solve the Problem   Substitute for m in the equation and simplify.

$$S = 11.2m^{2/3} \qquad \text{Write model.}$$
$$= 11.2(9 \times 10^3)^{2/3} \qquad \text{Substitute 9000 for } m.$$
$$= 11.2(9)^{2/3}(10^3)^{2/3} \qquad \text{Power of a product property}$$
$$\approx 11.2(4.33)(10^2) \qquad \text{Power of a power property}$$
$$\approx 4850 \qquad \text{Simplify.}$$

The dog's surface area is about 4850 square centimeters.

STEP 4 Look Back   Use a graphing calculator to make a table of values for the function. The table shows that the dog has a surface area of about 4846 square centimeters. The answer is correct.

X	Y1
8700	4737.7
8800	4773.9
8900	4810
9000	4846
9100	4881.8

X=9000

Practice

1. **Biology** An ant is basically cylindrical in shape, so its surface area S can be approximated by the formula for the surface area of a cylinder, $S = 2\pi rh + 2\pi r^2$, where h is the length of the ant and r is the radius. Approximate the surface area of an ant that is 5 millimeters long and has a radius of 1.1 millimeters. **about 42.2 mm²**

2. **What If?** Because the ant is cylindrical in shape, the volume of the ant can be approximated by the formula $V = \pi r^2 h$ where h is the length of the ant and r is the radius. Approximate the volume of the ant in Exercise 1. **about 19 mm³**

3. **Volume** The formula for the volume of a square pyramid is $V = \frac{1}{3}\ell^2 h$ where ℓ is the length of a side of the base and h is the height. Find the length of a pyramid that has a volume of 162 cubic feet and a height of 6 feet. **9 ft**   **4. See Additional Answers beginning on page AA1.**

4. **Biology** Let m be the mass of an average house cat. Then the mass of the Canadian lynx is $2m$. The surface areas of the house cat and the Canadian lynx can be modeled by $S_{\text{cat}} = 10m^{2/3}$ and $S_{\text{lynx}} = 10(2m)^{2/3}$. Find the ratio of the surface area of the Canadian lynx to the surface area of the cat. *Explain* what the ratio means.

UNIT 3

Graph Square Root and Cube Root Functions

Georgia Performance Standards: MM3A3d

Goal Graph square root and cube root functions.

Vocabulary

Radical functions include functions of the form $y = a\sqrt{x - h} + k$ and $y = a\sqrt[3]{x - h} + k$.

Example 1 Graph a square root function

Graph $y = 2\sqrt{x}$, and state the domain and range. Compare the graph with the graph of $y = \sqrt{x}$.

Solution

Make a table of values and sketch the graph.

x	0	1	2	3	4
y	0	2	2.83	3.46	4

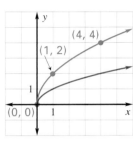

The domain is $x \geq 0$. The range is $y \geq 0$. The graph of $y = 2\sqrt{x}$ is a vertical stretch of the parent graph of $y = \sqrt{x}$.

Example 2 Graph a cube root function

Graph $y = \frac{1}{3}\sqrt[3]{x}$, and state the domain and range. Compare the graph with the graph of $y = \sqrt[3]{x}$.

Solution

Make a table of values and sketch the graph.

x	−2	−1	0	1	2	8
y	−0.42	−0.33	0	0.33	0.42	0.67

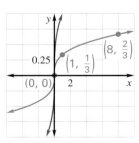

The domain and range are all real numbers. The graph of $y = \frac{1}{3}\sqrt[3]{x}$ is a vertical shrink of the parent graph of $y = \sqrt[3]{x}$ by a factor of $\frac{1}{3}$.

Guided Practice for Examples 1 and 2

Graph the function. Then state the domain and range.

1–4. See Additional Answers beginning on page AA1.

1. $y = \frac{1}{4}\sqrt{x}$ **2.** $y = -2\sqrt{x}$ **3.** $y = 3\sqrt[3]{x}$ **4.** $y = -\frac{1}{2}\sqrt[3]{x}$

UNIT 3

Georgia Performance Standards

MM3A3d Solve a variety of types of equations by appropriate means choosing among mental calculation, pencil and paper, or appropriate technology. ☑

Example 3 **Solve a multi-step problem**

The period of a pendulum can be modeled by $T = 1.34\sqrt{\ell}$ where ℓ is the length of the pendulum in feet.

a. Use a graphing calculator to graph the model.

b. Find the length of a pendulum that has a period of 2 seconds.

Solution

a. Graph the model. Enter $y = 1.34\sqrt{x}$. Use a viewing window of $0 \le x \le 3$ and $0 \le y \le 3$.

b. Use the *trace* feature to find the x-coordinate when $y = 2$. The graph shows $x \approx 2.234$.

X=2.234 Y=2.003

A pendulum with a period of 2 seconds is about 2.23 feet long.

Guided Practice for Example 3

5. Rework Example 3 to find the length of a pendulum with a period of 3 seconds. $\left(\dfrac{3}{1.34}\right)^2 \approx 5.01$ ft

Example 4 **Graph a translated radical function**

Graph $y = -\sqrt[3]{x + 2} + 1$. Then state the domain and range.

STEP 1 **Sketch** the graph of $y = -\sqrt[3]{x}$. It passes through $(-1, 1)$, $(0, 0)$ and $(1, -1)$.

STEP 2 **Note** that for $y = -\sqrt[3]{x + 2} + 1$, $h = -2$ and $k = 1$. Shift the graph left 2 units and up 1 unit. The resulting graph passes through $(-3, 2)$, $(-2, 1)$, and $(-1, 0)$. The domain and the range of the function are both all real numbers.

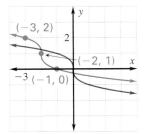

Guided Practice for Example 4

6. Graph $y = -\sqrt{x + 1} + 3$. Then state the domain and range.

7. Graph $y = 2\sqrt[3]{x - 1} + 1$. Then state the domain and range.

6 and 7. See Additional Answers beginning on page AA1.

UNIT 3

LESSON 3.3 **Exercise Set A**

MM3A3d Solve a variety of types of equations by appropriate means choosing among mental calculation, pencil and paper, or appropriate technology.

Graph the square root function. Then state the domain and range. 1–6. See Additional Answers beginning on page AA1.

1. $f(x) = \sqrt{x} - 2$

2. $f(x) = \sqrt{x-2}$

3. $f(x) = 3\sqrt{x+1}$

4. $f(x) = \sqrt{x+2} - 2$

5. $f(x) = \sqrt{x-1} + 1$

6. $f(x) = -\sqrt{x-3}$

Graph the cube root function. Then state the domain and range. 7–12. See Additional Answers beginning on page AA1.

7. $f(x) = \sqrt[3]{x} + 1$

8. $f(x) = \sqrt[3]{x-4}$

9. $f(x) = 3\sqrt[3]{x}$

10. $f(x) = \sqrt[3]{x+2}$

11. $f(x) = -\sqrt[3]{x} - 1$

12. $f(x) = \sqrt[3]{x+2} - 2$

In Exercises 13 and 14, use the following information.

Speed of Sound The speed of sound V in feet per second through air of any temperature is given by $V = \dfrac{1087\sqrt{t+273}}{16.52}$ where t is the temperature (in degrees Celsius).

13. Identify the domain and range of the function. **domain: $t \geq -273$, range: $V \geq 0$**

14. What is the temperature of the air if the speed of sound is 1250 feet per second? **87.9°C**

In Exercises 15 and 16, use the following information.

Falling Object A stone is dropped from a height of 200 feet. The time it takes for the stone to reach a height of h feet is given by the function $t = \dfrac{1}{4}\sqrt{200 - h}$ where t is the time in seconds.

15. Identify the domain and range of the function. **domain: $h \leq 200$, range: $0 \leq t \leq 3.5$**

16. What is the height of the stone after 3 seconds? **56 feet**

17. **Multiple Representations** Under certain conditions, a skydiver's terminal velocity v_t (in feet per second) is given by $v_t = 33.7\sqrt{\dfrac{W}{A}}$ where W is the weight of the skydiver (in pounds) and A is the skydiver's cross-sectional surface area (in square feet). Note that skydivers can vary their cross-sectional surface area by changing positions as they fall. **See Additional Answers beginning on page AA1.**

   a. **Writing an Equation** Write an equation that gives v_t as a function of A for a skydiver who weighs 175 pounds.

   b. **Making a Table** Make a table of values for the equation from part (a).

   c. **Drawing a Graph** Use your table to graph the equation.

MM3A3d   Solve a variety of types of equations by appropriate means choosing among mental calculation, pencil and paper, or appropriate technology.

Graph the function. Then state the domain and range.   1–9. See Additional Answers beginning on page AA1.

1. $f(x) = \sqrt{x + 4} - 2$

2. $f(x) = 2\sqrt{x - 2} + 3$

3. $f(x) = -3\sqrt{x} + 3$

4. $f(x) = -\sqrt{x + 2} + 2$

5. $f(x) = \sqrt[3]{x} + 3$

6. $f(x) = 3\sqrt[3]{x} + 2$

7. $f(x) = \sqrt[3]{x - 3} + 4$

8. $f(x) = \sqrt[3]{x - 4} + 1$

9. $f(x) = -2\sqrt[3]{x} - 3$

10. Error Analysis A student tried to explain how the graphs of $y = -2\sqrt[3]{x}$ and $y = -2\sqrt[3]{x - 1} - 3$ are related. *Describe* and correct the error.

The graph of $y = -2\sqrt[3]{x - 1} - 3$ is the graph of $y = -2\sqrt[3]{x}$ translated left 1 unit and down 3 units.

X

The graph was translated horizontally in the wrong direction; the graph of $y = -2\sqrt[3]{x - 1} - 3$ is the graph of $y = -2\sqrt[3]{x}$ translated right 1 unit and down 3 units.

Visual Thinking Using a graphing calculator, graph the functions $f(x) = \sqrt{x}$, $g(x) = \sqrt[4]{x}$, $h(x) = \sqrt[6]{x}$, and $j(x) = \sqrt[8]{x}$ on the same coordinate plane. Use the window Xmin = −1, Xmax = 2, Xscl = 1, Ymin = −1, Ymax = 2, and Yscl = 1.

11. What two points do all the graphs have in common?   **(0, 0) and (1, 1)**

12. *Describe* how the graphs are related.   **On the interval 0 to 1, the larger the root, the steeper the graph. On the interval 1 to ∞, the larger the root, the less steep the graph.**

13. Using what you have learned in Exercises 11 and 12, graph $f(x) = \sqrt[4]{x + 2} - 1$.
See Additional Answers beginning on page AA1.

Visual Thinking Using a graphing calculator, graph the functions $f(x) = \sqrt[3]{x}$, $g(x) = \sqrt[5]{x}$, $h(x) = \sqrt[7]{x}$, and $j(x) = \sqrt[9]{x}$ on the same coordinate plane. Use the window Xmin = −2, Xmax = 2, Xscl = 1, Ymin = −2, Ymax = 2, and Yscl = 1.

14. What three points do all the graphs have in common?   **(−1, −1), (0, 0) and (1, 1)**

15. *Describe* how the graphs are related.   **See Additional Answers beginning on page AA1.**

16. Using what you have learned in Exercises 14 and 15, graph $f(x) = \sqrt[5]{x - 1} + 1$.
See Additional Answers beginning on page AA1.

In Exercises 17–20, use the following information.

Falling Object A stone is dropped from a height of 175 feet. The time it takes for the stone to reach a height of h feet is given by the function $t = \frac{1}{4}\sqrt{175 - h}$ where t is the time in seconds.

17. Identify the domain and range of the function.   **domain: $h \le 175$; range: $0 \le t \le 3.3$**

18. What is the height of the stone after 1 second?   **159 feet**

19. What is the height of the stone after 3 seconds?   **31 feet**

20. When does the stone hit the ground?   **at about 3.3 seconds**

UNIT 3

Solve Radical Equations

Georgia Performance Standards: MM3A3d

Goal Solve radical equations.

Vocabulary

Equations with radicals that have variables in their radicands are called **radical equations**.

Example 1 Solve a radical equation

$\sqrt[3]{5 - 11x} = 3$	Original equation
$(\sqrt[3]{5 - 11x})^3 = 3^3$	Cube each side to eliminate the radical.
$5 - 11x = 27$	Simplify.
$x = -2$	Subtract 5 from each side. Then divide each side by -11.

CHECK Check $x = -2$ in the original equation.

$\sqrt[3]{5 - 11(-2)} \overset{?}{=} 3$	Substitute -2 for x.
$3 = 3 ✓$	Solution checks.

Example 2 Solve a radical equation given a function

Power Consumption The amount of power used by an appliance is given by $I = \sqrt{\dfrac{P}{R}}$ where I is the current (in amps), R is the resistance (in ohms), and P is the power (in watts). If the appliance uses $I = 12$ amps, and $R = 25$ ohms, find the power P.

$I = \sqrt{\dfrac{P}{R}}$	Write given function.
$12 = \sqrt{\dfrac{P}{25}}$	Substitute 12 for I and 25 for R.
$144 = \dfrac{P}{25}$	Square each side.
$3600 = P$	Multiply each side by 25.

The power consumed is 3600 watts.

Guided Practice for Examples 1 and 2

Solve the equation and check the solution.

1. $\sqrt{x + 2} = 3$ **7**

2. $\sqrt[3]{6x - 10} = 2$ **3**

3. $\sqrt[4]{x} - 5 = -3$ **16**

4. $2\sqrt[3]{x - 3} = 6$ **30**

5. Rework Example 2 to find R when $I = 10$ amps and $P = 2000$ watts. **20 ohms**

Georgia Performance Standards

MM3A3d   Solve a variety of types of equations by appropriate means choosing among mental calculation, pencil and paper, or appropriate technology.

Example 3   **Solve an equation with a rational exponent**

$(x - 1)^{3/2} - 2 = 6$	Original equation
$(x - 1)^{3/2} = 8$	Add 2 to each side.
$[(x - 1)^{3/2}]^{2/3} = 8^{2/3}$	Raise each side to the power $\frac{2}{3}$.
$x - 1 = (8^{1/3})^2$	Apply properties of exponents.
$x - 1 = 2^2$	Simplify.
$x = 5$	Add 1 to each side and simplify.

The solution is 5. Check this in the original equation.

Example 4   **Solve an equation with two radicals**

$\sqrt{x + 1} = \sqrt{3x} - 1$	Original equation
$(\sqrt{x + 1})^2 = (\sqrt{3x} - 1)^2$	Square each side.
$x + 1 = 3x - 2\sqrt{3x} + 1$	Expand right side and simplify left side.
$-2x = -2\sqrt{3x}$	Isolate radical expression.
$x = \sqrt{3x}$	Divide each side by -2.
$x^2 = 3x$	Square each side again.
$x^2 - 3x = 0$	Write in standard form.
$x(x - 3) = 0$	Factor.
$x = 0 \text{ or } x = 3$	Zero product property

CHECK $x = 0$ in the original equation.   **CHECK** $x = 3$ in the original equation.

$$\sqrt{0 + 1} \overset{?}{=} \sqrt{3(0)} - 1 \qquad\qquad \sqrt{3 + 1} \overset{?}{=} \sqrt{3(3)} - 1$$

$$1 \neq -1 \qquad\qquad\qquad\qquad\qquad 2 = 2 \checkmark$$

The only solution is 3. (The apparent solution 0 is extraneous.)

Guided Practice for Examples 3 and 4

Solve the equation. Check for extraneous solutions.

6. $2x^{3/4} = 16$ **16**

7. $\frac{1}{2}x^{5/2} = 16$ **4**

8. $\sqrt{4 - x} = x - 4$ **4**

9. $\sqrt{5x} = 4 + \sqrt{x - 4}$ **5**

LESSON 3.4 **Exercise Set A**

MM3A3d Solve a variety of types of equations by appropriate means choosing among mental calculation, pencil and paper, or appropriate technology.

Solve the equation. Check your solution.

1. $\sqrt{x} + 3 = 12$ **81**

2. $x^{1/2} - 4 = 1$ **25**

3. $3\sqrt{x+2} = 6$ **2**

4. $(2x - 3)^{1/2} + 2 = 2$ $\frac{3}{2}$

5. $5\sqrt{3x} = 15$ **3**

6. $3\sqrt{4 - 3x} = 21$ **−15**

7. $7 - \sqrt{x - 4} = -6$ **173**

8. $\sqrt{3x + 4} + \frac{3}{2} = 3$ $-\frac{7}{12}$

9. $2(x - 1)^{1/2} - 3 = 7$ **26**

Solve the equation. Check your solution.

10. $\sqrt[3]{x} + 1 = -2$ **−27**

11. $4\sqrt[3]{x} + 2 = 0$ $-\frac{1}{8}$

12. $\sqrt[3]{2x + 7} = 5$ **59**

13. $(x + 4)^{1/3} - 2 = -6$ **−68**

14. $8\sqrt[3]{x} + 3 = 11$ **1**

15. $3x^{1/3} - 2 = -4$ $-\frac{8}{27}$

16. $-2\sqrt[3]{2x + 5} + 7 = 15$ $-\frac{69}{2}$

17. $\frac{1}{2}(5x + 1)^{1/3} + \frac{5}{2} = 4$ $\frac{26}{5}$

18. $6\sqrt[3]{x - 3} + 2 = \frac{1}{2}$ $\frac{191}{64}$

Solve the equation. Check for extraneous solutions.

19. $x^{5/3} = 243$ **27**

20. $x^{3/2} + 3 = 11$ **4**

21. $2x^{5/3} = -64$ **−8**

22. $(x - 2)^{3/4} = 8$ **18**

23. $(3x + 12)^{3/2} - 3 = 24$ **−1**

24. $(3x + 21)^{3/4} + 9 = 36$ **20**

Solve the equation. Check for extraneous solutions.

25. $\sqrt{x - 3} = \sqrt{2x - 7}$ **4**

26. $\sqrt{x + 3} = \sqrt{4x - 8}$ $\frac{11}{3}$

27. $\sqrt[3]{4x - 9} = \sqrt[3]{2x - 4}$ $\frac{5}{2}$

28. $\sqrt[4]{3x + 3} = \sqrt[4]{2x - 7}$ **no solution**

29. $\sqrt{x + 1} = \sqrt{3x - 3}$ **4**

30. $\sqrt[3]{3x + 9} = \sqrt[3]{x + 6}$ $-\frac{3}{2}$

31. $x + 2 = \sqrt{2x + 7}$ **1**

32. $\sqrt{2x + 3} = 1 + \sqrt{x + 1}$ **−1, 3**

In Exercises 33–35, use the following information.

Velocity The velocity of a free falling object is given by $V = \sqrt{2gh}$ where V is velocity (in meters per second), g is acceleration due to gravity (in meters per second squared), and h is the distance (in meters) the object has fallen. The value of g depends on which body/planet is attracting the object. If an object hits the surface with a velocity of 30 meters per second, from what height was it dropped in each of the following situations?

33. You are on Earth where $g = 9.81$ m/s². **45.87 m**

34. You are on the moon where $g = 1.57$ m/s². **286.62 m**

35. You are on Mars where $g = 3.72$ m/s². **120.97 m**

LESSON 3.4 **Exercise Set B** MM3A3d Solve a variety of types of equations by appropriate means choosing among mental calculation, pencil and paper, or appropriate technology.

Solve the equation. Check your solution.

1. $(2x + 1)^{1/2} - 2 = 2$ $\frac{15}{2}$

2. $9 - \sqrt{x + 4} = 4$ 21

3. $3\sqrt{4 - 3x} + 5 = 17$ -4

4. $\sqrt{x^2 - 9} + 3 = 7$ ± 5

5. $2\sqrt{x^2 - 3} + 3 = 15$ $\pm\sqrt{39}$

6. $(3x^2 - 2)^{1/2} + 4 = 9$ ± 3

Solve the equation. Check your solution.

7. $(x - 2)^{1/3} - 3 = -5$ -6

8. $8\sqrt[3]{x} + 7 = 31$ 27

9. $\sqrt[3]{x + 5} + 2 = 7$ 120

10. $10 - 3\sqrt[3]{2x + 5} = -11$ 169

11. $(3x - 2)^{1/3} + \frac{2}{3} = 3$ $\frac{397}{81}$

12. $\sqrt[3]{x^3 + 3} + 1 = 4$ $2\sqrt[3]{3}$

Solve the equation. Check for extraneous solutions.

13. $x^{3/2} = 125$ 25

14. $(x + 3)^3 + 6 = -21$ -6

15. $3(x - 5)^{3/2} - 6 = 18$ 9

16. $\frac{1}{2}(x - 3)^{3/4} + 6 = 9$ $3 + 6\sqrt[3]{6}$

17. $(5x + 14)^{2/3} + 10 = 6$ no solution

18. $2(4x^3 - 13)^{3/5} - 5 = 49$ 4

Solve the equation. Check for extraneous solutions.

19. $\sqrt{2x - 6} = \sqrt{5x - 15}$ 3

20. $\sqrt[3]{6x - 5} - \sqrt[3]{3x + 2} = 0$ $\frac{7}{3}$

21. $\sqrt[5]{8x + 11} = \sqrt[5]{5x - 4}$ -5

22. $\sqrt{3x + 7} = x + 1$ 3

23. $\sqrt{x + 3} = \sqrt{x + 4}$ no solution

24. $\sqrt{x - 5} = \sqrt{x} - 2$ $\frac{81}{16}$

25. $\sqrt{x + 9} = 3 - \sqrt{x}$ 0

26. $\sqrt{x + 3} = 1 + \sqrt{x + 1}$ $-\frac{3}{4}$

27. $\sqrt{x - 7} = \sqrt{x + 1} + 2$ no solution

28. $\sqrt{x + 8} = \sqrt{x} + \sqrt{3}$ $\frac{25}{12}$

29. **Geometry** The lateral surface area S of a cone is given by $S = \pi r\sqrt{r^2 + h^2}$ where r is the radius and h is the height of the cone. The surface area of the base B of the cone is given by $B = \pi r^2$ where r is the radius of the cone. The total surface area of a cone with a radius of 9 inches is 216π square inches. What is the height of the cone? **12 in.**

9 in.

30. **Geometry** A container is to be made in the shape of a cylinder with a conical top. The lateral surface areas of the cylinder S_1 and cone S_2 are $S_1 = 2\pi rh$ and $S_2 = \pi r\sqrt{r^2 + h^2}$ where r is the radius and h is the height of the object. The surface area of the base B of the container is $B = \pi r^2$ where r is the radius of the container. The height of the cone is half the height of the cylinder. The radius of the container is 6 inches and its total surface area is 288π square inches. Find the total height of the container. **24 in.**

$\frac{h}{2}$

h

6 in.

Georgia Performance Standards

MM3A3d   Solve a variety of types of equations by appropriate
means choosing among mental calculation, pencil
and paper, or appropriate technology.

Technology Activity

Radical Equations

Use after Lesson 3.4

Question

How can you use a graphing calculator to solve an equation with two radicals?

You can use a graphing calculator to solve an equation with two radicals by treating each side of the equation as a function. The solution of the equation will be the point of intersection of the graphs of the two functions.

Example

Solve equations with two radicals.

Use a graphing calculator to solve the equation with two radicals.

$$\sqrt{4x + 28} = 3\sqrt{2x}$$

Solution

Let the left side of the equation represent one function, so $Y_1 = \sqrt{4x + 28}$.

Let the right side of the equation represent another function, so $Y_2 = 3\sqrt{2x}$.

STEP 1   **Enter** the equations in the equation editor window.

STEP 2   **Graph** the functions in a standard viewing window.

STEP 3   **Use** the *intersect* feature of the calculator to find the point of intersection.

You can see that the point of intersection is $(2, 6)$. So, the solution is $x = 2$.

Practice

Use a graphing calculator to find the solution of the equation with two radicals.

1. $\sqrt{x + 2} = \sqrt{10 - 3x}$ 2

2. $\sqrt{x + 5} = 5 - \sqrt{x}$ 4

3. $\sqrt{2x + 3} = 3 - \sqrt{2x}$ $\frac{1}{2}$

4. $\sqrt{2x - 1} = \sqrt{x + 4}$ 5

5. $\sqrt{2x + 10} = 2\sqrt{x}$ 5

6. $\sqrt{x - 6} = \sqrt{\frac{1}{3}x}$ 9

UNIT 3

TEST | for Unit 3

Evaluate the expression without using a calculator.

1. $\left(\sqrt[3]{8}\right)^5$ **32**

2. $\left(\sqrt[4]{256}\right)^3$ **64**

3. $\left(\sqrt[4]{81}\right)^2$ **9**

4. $16^{3/4}$ **8**

5. $125^{4/3}$ **625**

6. $49^{3/2}$ **343**

Solve the equation. Round the result to two decimal places when appropriate.

7. $x^5 = 327$ **3.18**

8. $2x^4 + 17 = 209$ **3.13**

9. $5x^3 - 12 = 83$ **2.67**

10. $(x + 6)^4 = 334$ **−1.72**

11. $(2x - 5)^5 = 728$ **4.37**

12. $(x + 7)^3 - 27 = 531$ **1.23**

Simplify the expression. Assume all variables are positive.

13. $\sqrt{x^{2/3}}$ $x^{1/3}$

14. $x^{3/4} \cdot x^{7/4}$ $x^{5/2}$

15. $\left(x^{2/3}\right)^{6/5}$ $x^{4/5}$

16. $\left(\dfrac{x^4}{64}\right)^{1/3}$ $\dfrac{x^{4/3}}{4}$

17. $\sqrt[3]{81x^5}$ $3x^{5/3}\sqrt[3]{3}$

18. $\dfrac{6}{x + \sqrt{7y}}$ $\dfrac{6(x - \sqrt{7y})}{x^2 - 7y}$

Perform the indicated operation. Assume all variables are positive.

19. $7\sqrt{5} + 5\sqrt{5}$ $12\sqrt{5}$

20. $\sqrt{54} - 5\sqrt{6}$ $-2\sqrt{6}$

21. $2\sqrt{18} + \sqrt{8}$ $8\sqrt{2}$

22. $6\sqrt{x} - \sqrt{4x}$ $4\sqrt{x}$

23. $\sqrt{\left(11\sqrt{2} - 2\sqrt{2}\right)}$ $3\sqrt[4]{2}$

24. $5x\sqrt[3]{xy^7} - 3y\sqrt[3]{x^4y^4}$ $2xy^2\sqrt[3]{xy}$

Graph the function. Then state the domain and range. **25–33. See Additional Answers beginning on page AA1.**

25. $f(x) = \sqrt{x} + 5$

26. $f(x) = \sqrt{x - 4} + 6$

27. $f(x) = -3\sqrt[3]{x}$

28. $f(x) = 2\sqrt{x + 2} - 2$

29. $f(x) = \dfrac{3}{5}\sqrt[3]{x + 4} - 1$

30. $f(x) = -\dfrac{1}{2}\sqrt[3]{x - 2} + 2$

31. $f(x) = -2\sqrt{x + 3} + 1$

32. $f(x) = -\dfrac{1}{3}\sqrt[3]{x - 1} + 3$

33. $f(x) = \dfrac{1}{2}\sqrt[3]{x + 3} + 2$

Solve the equation. Check your solution.

34. $\sqrt{x} - 4 = 5$ **81**

35. $7\sqrt[3]{x} - 4 = 3$ **1**

36. $(x + 1)^{1/2} + 5 = 8$ **8**

37. $4 = \sqrt[3]{2x - 8}$ **36**

38. $\sqrt{3x + 12} = 6$ **8**

39. $(4x + 7)^{1/3} - 5 = -2$ **5**

Solve the equation. Check for extraneous solutions.

40. $(x + 12)^{3/2} - 15 = 12$ **−3**

41. $x + 2 = \sqrt{28 - x}$ **3**

42. $x - 1 = \sqrt{x + 41}$ **8**

43. $x + 1 = \sqrt{19 - x}$ **3**

44. $\sqrt{3x + 5} = \sqrt{4x - 2}$ **7**

45. $\sqrt[3]{5x + 4} = \sqrt[3]{2x - 8}$ **−4**

46. Geometry Find the radius of a circle with an area of 907 square centimeters. **17 centimeters**

47. Geometry Find the radius of a sphere with a volume of 2.14 cubic feet. **0.8 foot**

48. **Physics** In physics, transitional kinetic energy E (in Joules) is given by the equation $E = \frac{1}{2}mv^2$ where m represents the mass in kilograms, and v represents the velocity (in meters per second). Find the velocity of a thrown baseball at time of release whose mass is 0.148 kilogram, and whose transitional kinetic energy is 90.65 Joules. **35 meters per second**

49. **Placemat** A rectangular placemat on a table is 15 inches long and 9 inches wide. A circular plate is sitting on the placemat. The area of the placemat that is not covered by the plate is 84.76 square inches. What is the radius of the plate? **4 inches**

50. **Pendulum** The period T (in seconds) of a pendulum can be modeled by $T = 1.11\sqrt{\ell}$ where ℓ is the pendulum's length (in feet). How long is a pendulum with a period of 5 seconds? **20.3 feet**

51. **Pendulum** Use the equation from Exercise 50 to determine the length of a pendulum with a period of 1.4 seconds. **1.6 feet**

52. **Velocity** The velocity of a free falling object is given by $V = \sqrt{19.62h}$, where V is velocity (in meters per second) and h is the distance (in meters) the object has fallen. If an object hit the ground with a velocity of 55 meters per second, from what height was it dropped? **154 meters**

53. Surface Area The lateral surface area of a cone is given by $S = \pi r\sqrt{r^2 + h^2}$ where r is the radius and h is the height of the cone. A cone has a radius of 12 inches and a lateral surface area of 912 square inches. What is the height of the cone? **21 inches**

Performance Task

Park Design

A park has a circular pond and a square picnic area. The length of a side of the picnic area is the same as the diameter of the pond.

a. The area of the picnic area is 2809 square feet. What is the radius of the pond? **26.5 feet**

b. Solve the equation $A = \pi r^2$ for r. $r = \sqrt{\dfrac{A}{\pi}}$

c. Write the equation you found in part (b) using rational exponents. $r = \left(\dfrac{A}{\pi}\right)^{1/2}$

d. Graph the equation you found in part (b). How does the graph of the equation differ from the graph of $f(x) = \sqrt{x}$? **See Additional Answers beginning on page AA1.**

e. Suppose the park is going to build a cone-shaped cover for the pond, without a bottom. The amount of material needed for the cover is 2387 square feet. Use the formula for the lateral surface area of a cone, $S = \pi r\sqrt{r^2 + h^2}$, to determine the height of the cone-shaped cover. **11 feet**

f. Find the height of the cone-shaped cover if only 2230 square feet of material is available. **4 feet**

UNIT 4
Algebra: Exponential and Logarithmic Functions

Graph Exponential Growth Functions

Georgia Performance Standards: MM3A2e, MM3A2f, MM3A2g

Goal Graph and use exponential growth functions.

Vocabulary

An **exponential function** has the form $y = ab^x$, where $a \neq 0$ and the base b is a positive number other than 1.

If $a > 0$ and $b > 1$, then the function $y = ab^x$ is an **exponential growth function,** and b is called the **growth factor.**

An **asymptote** is a line that a graph approaches more and more closely.

Exponential Growth Model When a real-life quantity increases by a fixed percent each year (or other time period), the amount y of the quantity after t years can be modeled by the equation $y = a(1 + r)^t$, where a is the initial amount and r is the percent increase expressed as a decimal. Note that the quantity $1 + r$ is the growth factor.

Example 1   **Graph $y = b^x$ for $b > 1$**

Graph $y = 5^x$.

STEP 1 **Make** a table of values.

x	−2	−1	0	1	2
y	$\frac{1}{25}$	$\frac{1}{5}$	1	5	25

STEP 2 **Plot** the points from the table.

STEP 3 **Draw,** from *left* to *right*, a smooth curve that begins just above the x-axis, passes through the plotted points, and moves up to the right.

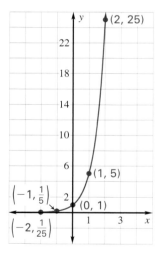

Example 2   **Graph $y = ab^x$ for $b > 1$**

Graph $y = \left(-\dfrac{1}{4}\right) \cdot 2^x$.

Plot $\left(0, -\dfrac{1}{4}\right)$ and $\left(1, -\dfrac{1}{2}\right)$. From *left* to *right*, draw a curve that begins just below below the x-axis, passes through the two points, and moves down to the right.

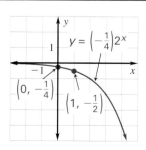

Example 3 Graph $y = ab^{x-h} + k$ for $b > 1$

Graph $y = 3 \cdot 2^{x+1} + 2$. State the domain and range.

Begin by sketching the graph of $y = 3 \cdot 2^x$, which passes through (0, 3) and (1, 6). Because the function is of the form $y = ab^{x-h} + k$ where $h = -1$ and $k = 2$, translate the graph of $y = 3 \cdot 2^x$ left 1 unit and up 2 units.

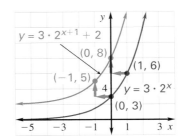

The asymptote of the graph is the line $y = 2$. The domain is all real numbers, and the range is $y > 2$.

Example 4 Find the doubling time for an account

Finance You deposit $3000 in an account that pays 6% interest compounded annually. In about how many years will the balance double?

STEP 1 **Write** an exponential growth function using the compound interest formula.

$$A = P\left(1 + \frac{r}{n}\right)^{nt}$$

$$A = 3000\left(1 + \frac{0.06}{1}\right)^{(1)t}$$

$$A = 3000(1.06)^t$$

STEP 2 **Graph** the model.

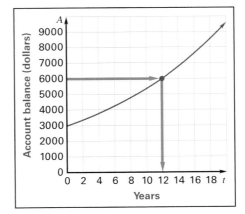

STEP 3 **Use** the graph to estimate the year when the balance of the account is $6000, double the initial balance.

The balance of the account doubles in about 12 years.

Guided Practice for Examples 1, 2, 3, and 4

Graph the function. State the domain and range. 1–3. See Additional Answers beginning on page AA1.

1. $y = 6^x$

2. $f(x) = -\left(\frac{1}{4}\right) \cdot 8^x$

3. $y = \frac{1}{2} \cdot 3^{x-5} + 4$

4. You deposit $2000 in an account that pays 4.75% interest compounded annually. In about how many years will the balance double? **15 yr**

MM3A2e	Investigate and explain characteristics of exponential and logarithmic functions including domain and range, asymptotes, zeros, intercepts, intervals of increase and decrease, and rate of change.
MM3A2f	Graph functions as transformations of $f(x) = a^x$, $f(x) = \log_a x$, $f(x) = e^x$, $f(x) = \ln x$.
MM3A2g	Explore real phenomena related to exponential and logarithmic functions including half-life and doubling time.

Match the function with its graph.

1. $y = 4 \cdot 2^x$ **B**

2. $y = 2 \cdot 4^x$ **C**

3. $y = -4 \cdot 2^x$ **A**

A.

B.

C.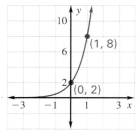

Graph the function. State the domain and range.

4–12. See Additional Answers beginning on page AA1.

4. $y = 5^x$

5. $f(x) = 9^x$

6. $y = \dfrac{1}{3} \cdot 6^x$

7. $f(x) = -\left(\dfrac{3}{2}\right)^x$

8. $f(x) = 2 \cdot \left(\dfrac{5}{4}\right)^x$

9. $y = 5^x + 1$

10. $f(x) = -3 \cdot 2^{x+3} + 1$

11. $y = 2 \cdot 5^{x-3} - 5$

12. $y = 5 \cdot 3^{x-4} - 6$

13. **Error Analysis** *Describe* and correct the error in graphing the function $y = \dfrac{1}{2} \cdot 6^x$.

The function was not evaluated correctly when $x = 0$. The correct point is (0, 0.5), not (0, 1).

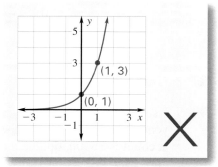

14. **Account Balance** You deposit $2000 in an account that pays 4.5% interest compounded annually. Write a model giving the account balance A after t years. In about how many years will the balance double? $A = 2000(1.045)^t$; 16 yr

15. **Enrollment** The student enrollment of a high school was 1350 in 2008 and increases by 9% each year.

a. Write a model giving the enrollment E of the high school t years after 2008. What is the student enrollment in 2011? $E = 1350(1.09)^t$; about 1748 students

b. Estimate when the enrollment will double. **2016**

Exercise Set B

MM3A2e Investigate and explain characteristics of exponential and logarithmic functions including domain and range, asymptotes, zeros, intercepts, intervals of increase and decrease, and rate of change.

MM3A2f Graph functions as transformations of $f(x) = a^x$, $f(x) = \log_a x$, $f(x) = e^x$, $f(x) = \ln x$.

MM3A2g Explore real phenomena related to exponential and logarithmic functions including half-life and doubling time.

Graph the function. State the domain and range. 1–9. See Additional Answers beginning on page AA1.

1. $y = 7^x$

2. $f(x) = 5 \cdot 2^x$

3. $y = -2(2.5)^x$

4. $f(x) = -3 \cdot 2^{x+4}$

5. $f(x) = 5 \cdot 4^x - 7$

6. $y = 3^{x+1} + 3$

7. $f(x) = 8 \cdot 2^{x-3} - 1$

8. $y = -3.5^{x-1} + 2$

9. $y = 5 \cdot 2^{x-1} - 2$

In Exercises 10–12, use the following information.

Account Balance You deposit $4500 in an account that earns 3.5% annual interest. Find the balance after one year if the interest is compounded with the given frequency.

10. annually
$4657.50

11. monthly
$4660.05

12. quarterly
$4659.58

13. **Population** In 1990, the population of Austin, Texas, was 494,290. During the next 10 years, the population increased by about 3% per year. See Additional Answers beginning on page AA1.

a. Write a model giving the population P (in thousands) of Austin t years after 1990. What was the population in 2000?

b. Graph the model and state the domain and range.

c. Estimate the year when the population was about 540,000.

14. **Antiques** You purchase an antique end table in 2008 for $325. The value of the table is expected to increase by 5% per year. See Additional Answers beginning on page AA1.

a. Write a model giving the value v of the end table t years after 2008. What was the value of the table in 2010?

b. Graph the model and state the domain and range. Use the graph to estimate the year when the value of the end table will double its initial value.

15. **Multiple Representations** In 1977, there were 41 breeding pairs of bald eagles in Maryland. Over the next 24 years, the number of breeding pairs increased by about 8.9% per year. See Additional Answers beginning on page AA1.

a. **Writing a Model** Write a model giving the number n of breeding pairs of bald eagles in Maryland t years after 1977.

b. **Making a Table** Make a table of values for the model.

c. **Graphing a Model** Graph the model.

d. **Estimating a Value** Estimate the year in which the number of breeding pairs was double the number in 1977.

UNIT 4

Georgia Performance Standards

MM3A2g Explore real phenomena related to exponential and logarithmic functions including half-life and doubling time.

MM3A3d Solve a variety of types of equations by appropriate means choosing among mental calculation, pencil and paper, or appropriate technology.

LESSON 4.1

Problem Solving Workshop

Problem In 1998, there were about 29,670,000 Internet hosts. During the next 7 years, the number of hosts increased by about 39% each year. Write an exponential growth model giving the number h (in millions) of hosts t years after 1998. Use a graph to estimate the year when there were about 80 million hosts.

STEP 1 Read and Understand

What do you know? The number of Internet hosts in 1998 and the percent increase for the next 7 years

What do you want to find out? The exponential growth model and points on the model

STEP 2 Make a Plan Use what you know to substitute and solve the equation.

STEP 3 Solve the Problem The initial amount is $a = 29.67$ million and the percent increase is $r = 0.39$. So the exponential growth model is:

$h = a(1 + r)^t$ Write exponential growth model.

$= 29.67(1 + 0.39)^t$ Substitute 29.67 for a and 0.39 for r.

$= 29.67(1.39)^t$ Simplify.

The graph passes through the points (0, 29.67) and (1, 41.24). Plot a few other points. Then draw a smooth curve through the points.

Using the graph, you can estimate that the number of hosts was about 80 million during 2001 ($t \approx 3$).

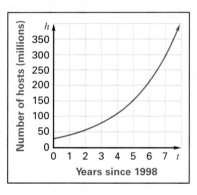

STEP 4 Look Back Substitute $t = 3$ into the equation to see that there were about $29.67(1.39)^3 \approx 79.68$ million hosts in 2001 which is reasonably close to 80 million. The answer is correct.

Practice

1. **Medicare** In 2000, the amount of federal budget outlays for Medicare was $197.1 billion. During the next 5 years, the amount increased by about 8% each year. Write an exponential growth model giving the amount M (in billions of dollars) of outlays for Medicare t years after 2000. Use a graph to estimate the year when about $250 billion was given to Medicare. **$M = 197.1(1.08)^t$; 2003**

2. **Population** In 2000, the population of a town was 2200. During the next 15 years, the population of the town increased by about 3% each year. Write an exponential growth model giving the number p of people in the town t years after 2000. Use a graph to estimate the year when there were about 2800 people in the town. **$p = 2200(1.03)^t$; 2008**

Graph Exponential Decay Functions

Georgia Performance Standards: MM3A2e, MM3A2f, MM3A2g

Goal Graph and use exponential decay functions.

Vocabulary

An **exponential decay function** has the form $y = ab^x$, where $a > 0$ and $0 < b < 1$.

The base b of an exponential decay function is called the **decay factor.**

The time required for a substance to fall to half its initial value is called **half-life.**

Exponential Decay Model When a real-life quantity decreases by a fixed percent each year (or other time period), the amount y of the quantity after t years can be modeled by the equation $y = a(1 - r)^t$, where a is the initial amount and r is the percent decrease expressed as a decimal. Note that the quantity $1 - r$ is the decay factor.

Example 1 Graph $y = b^x$ for $0 < b < 1$

Graph $y = \left(\dfrac{1}{2}\right)^x$.

Solution

STEP 1 Make a table of values.

x	−2	−1	0	1	2
y	4	2	1	$\dfrac{1}{2}$	$\dfrac{1}{4}$

STEP 2 Plot the points from the table.

STEP 3 Draw, from *right* to *left*, a smooth curve that begins just above the *x*-axis, passes through the plotted points, and moves up to the left.

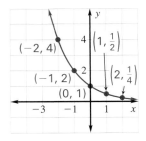

Example 2 Graph $y = ab^x$ for $0 < b < 1$

Graph $y = -3\left(\dfrac{2}{5}\right)^x$.

Solution

Plot $(0, -3)$ and $\left(1, -\dfrac{6}{5}\right)$. From *right* to *left*, draw a curve that begins just below the *x*-axis, passes through the two points, and moves down to the left.

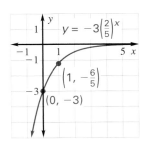

Georgia Performance Standards

MM3A2e Investigate and explain characteristics of exponential and logarithmic functions including domain and range, asymptotes, zeros, intercepts, intervals of increase and decrease, and rate of change. ☑

MM3A2f Graph functions as transformations of $f(x) = a^x$, $f(x) = \log_a x$, $f(x) = e^x$, $f(x) = \ln x$. ☑

MM3A2g Explore real phenomena related to exponential and logarithmic functions including half-life and doubling time. ☑

Example 3 **Graph $y = ab^{x-h} + k$ for $0 < b < 1$**

Graph $y = 3\left(\dfrac{1}{2}\right)^{x+1} - 2$. State the domain and range.

Begin by sketching the graph of $y = 3\left(\dfrac{1}{2}\right)^x$ which passes through $(0, 3)$ and $\left(1, \dfrac{3}{2}\right)$. Then translate the graph left 1 unit and down 2 units. The graph passes through $(-1, 1)$ and $\left(0, -\dfrac{1}{2}\right)$.

The asymptote of the graph is the line $y = -2$. The domain is all real numbers, and the range is $y > -2$.

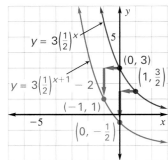

Example 4 **Using a half-life model**

Biology When a plant dies, it stops acquiring carbon-14 from the atmosphere. Carbon-14 decays over time with a half-life of about 5730 years. The percent P (in decimal form) of the original amount of carbon-14 that remains in a sample after t years is given by $P = 1\left(\dfrac{1}{2}\right)^{t/5730}$. About how many years after a plant dies will 60% of the carbon-14 in the plant remain?

STEP 1 **Graph** the model.

The graph passes through the point $(0, 1)$. Plot a few other points. Then draw a smooth curve through the points.

STEP 2 **Use** the graph to estimate.

About 4200 years after the plant dies, 60% of the carbon-14 remains in the plant.

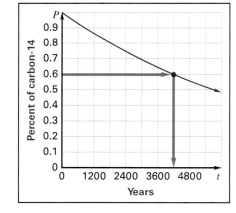

Guided Practice for Examples 1, 2, 3, and 4

Graph the function. State the domain and range. 1–3. See Additional Answers beginning on page AA1.

1. $y = \left(\dfrac{1}{5}\right)^x$

2. $f(x) = -2\left(\dfrac{2}{3}\right)^x$

3. $y = 5\left(\dfrac{1}{3}\right)^{x+2} - 1$

4. About how many years after a plant dies will 50% of the carbon-14 in the plant remain? **5730 yr**

LESSON 4.2 **Exercise Set A**

MM3A2e Investigate and explain characteristics of exponential and logarithmic functions including domain and range, asymptotes, zeros, intercepts, intervals of increase and decrease, and rate of change.

MM3A2f Graph functions as transformations of $f(x) = a^x$, $f(x) = \log_a x$, $f(x) = e^x$, $f(x) = \ln x$.

MM3A2g Explore real phenomena related to exponential and logarithmic functions including half-life and doubling time.

Tell whether the function represents *exponential growth* or *exponential decay*.

1. $y = 9 \cdot \left(\dfrac{3}{4}\right)^x$

exponential decay

2. $y = 3 \cdot \left(\dfrac{5}{2}\right)^x$

exponential growth

3. $y = 5 \cdot (0.5)^x$

exponential decay

Match the function with its graph.

4. $y = 4 \cdot \left(\dfrac{1}{4}\right)^x$ **B**

5. $y = 4 \cdot 4^x$ **C**

6. $y = \left(\dfrac{1}{4}\right)^x + 4$ **A**

A.

B.

C.
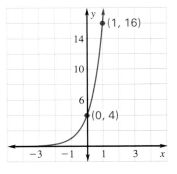

Graph the function. State the domain and range.

7–12. See Additional Answers beginning on page AA1.

7. $y = \left(\dfrac{1}{6}\right)^x$

8. $f(x) = \left(\dfrac{1}{3}\right)^x + 1$

9. $y = -\left(\dfrac{1}{2}\right)^{x+3}$

10. $f(x) = -8\left(\dfrac{1}{2}\right)^{x-4}$

11. $y = 6\left(\dfrac{1}{3}\right)^{x-4} + 2$

12. $y = \left(\dfrac{2}{5}\right)^{x+1} - 2$

13. Medicine The half-life of a drug is the amount of time it takes for half of the active elements to be eliminated from the body. The amount A (in milligrams) of 200 milligrams of a certain drug that remains in the bloodstream after t hours is given by $A = 200\left(\dfrac{1}{2}\right)^{t/3}$. In about how many hours will 100 milligrams of the drug remain in the bloodstream? **3 h**

14. Radioactive Decay The half-life of radium-226 is about 1600 years. The amount A (in grams) of radioactive radium-226 that remains in a sample after t years is given by $A = 10(0.5)^{t/1600}$.

a. What is the initial amount of radium-226? ($t = 0$) **10 g**

b. In about how many years will 2.5 grams of radium-226 remain? **3200 yr**

UNIT 4

MM3A2e Investigate and explain characteristics of exponential and logarithmic functions including domain and range, asymptotes, zeros, intercepts, intervals of increase and decrease, and rate of change.

MM3A2f Graph functions as transformations of $f(x) = a^x$, $f(x) = \log_a x$, $f(x) = e^x$, $f(x) = \ln x$.

MM3A2g Explore real phenomena related to exponential and logarithmic functions including half-life and doubling time.

Graph the function. State the domain and range. 1–9. See Additional Answers beginning on page AA1.

1. $f(x) = 3\left(\frac{1}{5}\right)^x$

2. $y = -(0.2)^x$

3. $f(x) = -3\left(\frac{1}{4}\right)^x$

4. $f(x) = \left(\frac{1}{5}\right)^x - 4$

5. $y = -\left(\frac{2}{3}\right)^{x+3}$

6. $f(x) = -2\left(\frac{1}{2}\right)^{x+2} - 5$

7. $y = -\left(\frac{1}{2}\right)^{x+8} - 2$

8. $y = 10\left(\frac{1}{4}\right)^{x-5} + 1$

9. $y = \left(\frac{3}{5}\right)^{x+1} - 2$

10. Multiple Representations You buy a new mountain bike for $200. The value of the bike decreases by 25% each year. **See Additional Answers beginning on page AA1.**

    a. Writing a Model Write a model giving the mountain bike's value y (in dollars) after t years.

    b. Making a Table Make a table of values for the model.

    c. Graphing a Model Graph the model.

    d. Estimating a Value Estimate when the value of the model will be $50.

11. Error Analysis You invest $700 in the stock of a company. The value of the stock decreases 3% each year. *Describe* and correct the error in writing a model for the value of the stock after t years. **The decay factor should be 1 − 0.03 = 0.97, not 0.03.**

$$y = \left(\begin{array}{c}\text{Initial}\\\text{amount}\end{array}\right)\left(\begin{array}{c}\text{Decay}\\\text{factor}\end{array}\right)^t$$

$$y = 700(0.03)^t$$

✗

12. Medicine The amount A (in milligrams) of a certain drug that remains in the bloodstream after t hours is given by $A = 500\left(\frac{1}{2}\right)^{t/4}$. The initial amount of the drug is 500 milligrams. What is the half-life of the medication? **4 h**

13. Half-life Models The half-life of phosphorus-32 is about 14 days. The amount A (in grams) of radioactive phosphorus-32 that remains in a sample after t days is given by $A = 400\left(\frac{1}{2}\right)^{t/14}$.

    a. What is the initial amount of phosphorus-32? ($t = 0$) **400 g**

    b. How much phosphorus-32 is present after 10 days? **243.8 g**

    c. In about how many days will 100 grams of phosphorus-32 remain? **28 days**

Georgia Performance Standards

MM3A2g   Explore real phenomena related to exponential and
logarithmic functions including half-life and doubling time.

Technology Activity

Evaluate Exponential Decay Models

Use after Lesson 4.2

Question

How can you use the *table* feature of a graphing calculator to evaluate an exponential decay model?

When a real-life quantity decreases by a fixed percent each year (or other time period), the amount y of the quantity after t years can be modeled by the equation $y = a(1 - r)^t$ where a is the initial amount and r is the percent decrease expressed as a decimal. Note that the quantity $1 - r$ is the decay factor. You can use the *table* feature of a graphing calculator to evaluate a model at different times.

Example

Use the *table* feature of a graphing calculator.

A new car costs \$23,000. The value of the car will depreciate 14% each year for the first three years. Find the value of the car after two years.

Solution

The exponential decay model is $y = 23{,}000(1 - 0.14)^x$ or $y = 23{,}000(0.86)^x$, where x represents the number of years.

Use the *table* feature of a graphing calculator to find the value of the car after two years.

X	Y1
1	19780
2	**17011**
3	14629
4	12581
5	10820

Y1=17010.8

STEP 1 **Enter** the equation in the equation editor window.

STEP 2 **Set** up a table to display the x-values starting at 1 and increasing in increments of 1.

STEP 3 **View** the table. In the table, x represents the number of years and Y_1 represents the value of the car. So, you can easily see that the value of the car after two years is about \$17,011.

Practice

Use the *table* feature of a graphing calculator to complete the following.

1. A new motorcycle costs \$18,000. The value of the motorcycle will depreciate 12% each year. Write an exponential decay model for the situation. What is the value of the motorcycle after three years? $y = 18{,}000(0.88)^x$; \$12,266.50

2. You buy a used motorcycle for \$10,000. The value of the motorcycle will depreciate 15% each year. Write an exponential decay model for the situation. When will the value of the motorcycle be about \$2700? $y = 10{,}000(0.85)^x$; 8 yr

Use Functions Involving *e*

Georgia Performance Standards: MM3A2e, MM3A2f, MM3A2g, MM3A3d

Goal Study functions involving the natural base *e*.

Vocabulary

The number denoted by the letter *e* is called the **natural base** *e* or the *Euler number*.

It is an irrational number defined as follows: As *n* approaches $+\infty$, $\left(1 + \dfrac{1}{n}\right)^n$ approaches $e \approx 2.718281828$.

A function of the form $f(x) = ae^{rx}$ is called a *natural base exponential function*.

Continuously Compounded Interest When interest is compounded *continuously*, the amount *A* in an account after *t* years is given by the formula $A = Pe^{rt}$, where *P* is the principal and *r* is the annual interest rate expressed as a decimal.

Example 1   Simplify natural base expressions

Simplify the expression.

a. $e^6 \cdot e^4 = e^{6+4} = e^{10}$

b. $\dfrac{21e^8}{7e^2} = 3e^{8-2} = 3e^6$

c. $(-2e^x)^3 = (-2)^3(e^x)^3 = -8e^{3x}$

Example 2   Graph natural base functions

Graph the function. State the domain and range.

a. $y = 4e^{-x} + 5$

Because $a = 4$ is positive and $r = -1$ is negative, the function is an exponential decay function. Translate the graph of $y = 4e^{-x}$ up 5 units.

The domain is all real numbers, and the range is $y > 5$.

b. $y = e^{2(x+1)} - 2$

Because $a = 1$ is positive and $r = 2$ is positive, the function is an exponential growth function. Translate the graph of $y = e^{2x}$ left 1 unit and down 2 units.

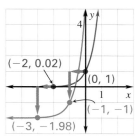

The domain is all real numbers, and the range is $y > -2$.

Example 3 Solve a multi-step problem

Bacteria Growth A population of bacteria can be modeled by the function $P = 70e^{0.22t}$ where t is the time (in hours). Graph the model and use the graph to estimate the population after 4 hours.

STEP 1 Graph the model, as shown.

STEP 2 Use the *trace* feature to find that
$P \approx 168.76298$ when $t = 4$.

The population of bacteria is about 169 after 4 hours.

Example 4 Model continuously compounded interest

Compound Interest You deposit $500 in an account that pays 3% annual interest compounded continuously. What is the balance after 2 years?

Solution

Use the formula for continuously compounded interest.

$A = Pe^{rt}$ Write formula.

$= 500e^{0.03(2)}$ Substitute 500 for P, 0.03 for r, and 2 for t.

≈ 530.92 Use a calculator.

The balance at the end of 2 years is $530.92.

Guided Practice for Examples 1, 2, 3, and 4

Simplify the expression.

1. $e^8 \cdot e \; e^9$ **2.** $4e^{-5} \cdot 7e^8 \;\; 28e^3$ **3.** $\dfrac{18e^{10}}{3e^5} \;\; 6e^5$ **4.** $(11e^{-3x})^2 \;\; 121e^{-6x}$

Graph the function. State the domain and range.

5–6. See Additional Answers beginning on page AA1.

5. $y = 2e^{0.6x} - 1$ **6.** $y = 5e^{-2x}$ **7.** $y = \dfrac{2}{3}e^{x+3} + 2$

8. You deposit $2000 in an account that pays 4% annual interest compounded continuously. Find the balance after each amount of time.

     a. 1 year **$2081.62**   **b.** 3 years **$2254.99**   **c.** 5.5 years **$2492.15**

Exercise Set A

MM3A2e Investigate and explain characteristics of exponential and logarithmic functions including domain and range, asymptotes, zeros, intercepts, intervals of increase and decrease, and rate of change.

MM3A2f Graph functions as transformations of $f(x) = a^x$, $f(x) = \log_a x$, $f(x) = e^x$, $f(x) = \ln x$.

MM3A2g Explore real phenomena related to exponential and logarithmic functions including half-life and doubling time.

MM3A3d Solve a variety of types of equations by appropriate means, choosing among mental calculation, pencil and paper, or appropriate technology.

Simplify the expression.

1. $e^{-5} \cdot e^2$ $\dfrac{1}{e^3}$

2. $e^3 \cdot e^{-3}$ 1

3. $(e^4)^{-3}$ $\dfrac{1}{e^{12}}$

4. $(2e^3)^2$ $4e^6$

5. $\left(\dfrac{3e^3}{6e^2}\right)^2$ $\dfrac{e^2}{4}$

6. $\left(\dfrac{8e^2}{2e^5}\right)^{-1}$ $\dfrac{e^3}{4}$

7. $3e^x \cdot 2e^{4x}$ $6e^{5x}$

8. $\sqrt{9e^4} \cdot 2e^{-3}$ $\dfrac{6}{e}$

9. $\dfrac{e^3}{e^{x+3}}$ $\dfrac{1}{e^x}$

10. *Error Analysis* *Describe* and correct the error in simplifying the expression.

The 3 should also be raised to the second power;
$(3e^{5x})^2 = 3^2 e^{(5x)(2)} = 9e^{10x}$

$$(3e^{5x})^2 = 3e^{(5x)(2)}$$
$$= 3e^{10x} \qquad \times$$

Use a calculator to evaluate the expression. Round the result to three decimal places.

11. e^7 1096.633

12. $e^{-3/2}$ 0.223

13. $e^{0.6}$ 1.822

14. $e^{\sqrt{3}}$ 5.652

Tell whether the function is an example of *exponential growth* or *exponential decay*.

15. $f(x) = 4e^{2x}$ exponential growth

16. $f(x) = e^{-5x}$ exponential decay

17. $f(x) = 6e^{-x}$ exponential decay

18. $f(x) = \dfrac{1}{4}e^{4x}$ exponential growth

19. $f(x) = \dfrac{1}{8}e^{-x}$ exponential decay

20. $f(x) = -e^{-x/2}$ exponential growth

Graph the function. State the domain and range.

21–26. See Additional Answers beginning on page AA1.

21. $f(x) = 3e^x$

22. $f(x) = 3e^{-x}$

23. $f(x) = -e^x + 3$

24. $f(x) = 2e^{x-1} + 1$

25. $f(x) = \dfrac{1}{2}e^{x-2} - 3$

26. $f(x) = e^{2x+1} + 2$

In Exercises 27 and 28, use the following information.

Finance You deposit $2200 in an account that pays 3% annual interest. After 15 years, you withdraw the money.

27. What is the balance if the interest is compounded quarterly? **$3444.50**

28. What is the balance if the interest is compounded continuously? **$3450.29**

Exercise Set B

MM3A2e Investigate and explain characteristics of exponential and logarithmic functions including domain and range, asymptotes, zeros, intercepts, intervals of increase and decrease, and rate of change.

MM3A2f Graph functions as transformations of $f(x) = a^x$, $f(x) = \log_a x$, $f(x) = e^x$, $f(x) = \ln x$.

MM3A2g Explore real phenomena related to exponential and logarithmic functions including half-life and doubling time.

MM3A3d Solve a variety of types of equations by appropriate means, choosing among mental calculation, pencil and paper, or appropriate technology.

Simplify the expression.

1. $\frac{1}{2}e^{-2}(2e^4)^3$ $4e^{10}$

2. $\left(\frac{e^3}{3e}\right)^{-2}$ $\frac{9}{e^4}$

3. $\left(\frac{2e^{-4}}{6}\right)^{-3}$ $27e^{12}$

4. $(2e^{1.2x})^5$ $32e^{6x}$

5. $\left(\frac{e^{4x-1}}{\sqrt{4e^{2x}}}\right)^3$ $\frac{e^{9x-3}}{8}$

6. $\sqrt[3]{16e^{10x}}$ $2e^{3x}\sqrt[3]{2e^x}$

Use a calculator to evaluate the expression. Round the result to three decimal places.

7. e^5 148.413

8. $e^{-\sqrt{3}/2}$ 0.421

9. $e^{-1.6}$ 0.202

10. e^e 15.154

Graph the function. State the domain and range. 11–16. See Additional Answers beginning on page AA1.

11. $f(x) = 2e^x - 3$

12. $f(x) = \frac{1}{2}e^{-x} + 1$

13. $f(x) = -e^{x+2} + 2$

14. $f(x) = \frac{1}{4}e^{2x-1} + 1$

15. $f(x) = \frac{3}{5}e^{2-x} - 4$

16. $f(x) = \frac{3}{2}e^{3(x-2)} - 3$

In Exercises 17–21, use the following information.

Learning Curve The management at a factory has determined that a worker can produce a maximum of 45 units per day. The model $y = 45 - 42e^{-0.05t}$ indicates the number of units y that a new employee can produce per day after t days on the job.

17. Is the model an example of exponential growth or exponential decay? **exponential growth**

18. Graph the function. **See Additional Answers beginning on page AA1.**

19. How many units can be produced by an employee on the first day? **3**

20. How many units can be produced per day by an employee who has been on the job 13 days? **23**

21. Use the graph to estimate how many days of employment are required for a worker to produce 30 units per day. **21**

Investigating Math Activity

Explore Exponential and Logarithmic Equations

Use before Lesson 4.4

Question

How can you rewrite an exponential equation as a logarithmic equation?

It is simple to evaluate a numerical exponential expression. For example, the exponential expression 4^2 has a value of 16. It is more difficult, however, to determine the value of x that would satisfy $3^x = 15$. Mathematicians define this x-value as a logarithm and write $x = \log_3 15$.

Explore

Evaluate exponential expressions.

Evaluate the exponential expression. Notice how the resulting equation compares with the corresponding logarithmic equation.

Exponential Equation	**Logarithmic Equation**
a. $3^2 = \underline{\ ?\ }$ 9	$\log_3 9 = 2$
b. $2^{-3} = \underline{\ ?\ }$ $\frac{1}{8}$	$\log_2 \frac{1}{8} = -3$
c. $5^0 = \underline{\ ?\ }$ 1	$\log_5 1 = 0$
d. $\left(\frac{1}{6}\right)^{-2} = \underline{\ ?\ }$ 36	$\log_{1/6} 36 = -2$

Draw Conclusions 1–4. See Additional Answers beginning on page AA1.

1. *Compare* your answers in the *Exponential Equation* column with a classmate.

2. In an exponential expression, the number being raised to a power is called the *base*. In a logarithmic expression, the number that is written as the subscript of *log* is known as the *base*. How does the base in the exponential equation compare with the base in the logarithmic equation for each pair of equations?

3. How does the exponent in the exponential equation compare with the value of the logarithmic equation for each pair of equations? How does the value of the exponential equation compare with the number following the subscript in the logarithmic equation for each pair of equations?

4. Writing *Explain* how to rewrite exponential equations as logarithmic equations. Then rewrite the following exponential equations as logarithmic equations.

   a. $2^5 = 32$ **b.** $4^{-2} = \frac{1}{16}$ **c.** $3^4 = 81$

UNIT 4

Evaluate Logarithms and Graph Logarithmic Functions

Georgia Performance Standards: MM3A2c, MM3A2e, MM3A2f

Goal Evaluate logarithms and graph logarithmic functions.

Vocabulary

Let b and y be positive numbers with $b \neq 1$. The **logarithm of y with base b** is denoted by $\log_b y$ and is defined as follows: $\log_b y = x$ if and only if $b^x = y$.

A **common logarithm** is a logarithm with base 10, denoted by log.

A **natural logarithm** is a logarithm with base e, denoted by ln.

A **logarithmic function** is a function of the form $f(x) = \log_b x$.

By definition of a logarithm, it follows that the logarithmic function $g(x) = \log_b x$ is the inverse of the exponential function $f(x) = b^x$. This means that $g(f(x)) = \log_b b^x = x$ and $f(g(x)) = b^{\log_b x} = x$.

Example 1 Rewrite logarithmic equations

Logarithmic Form	**Exponential Form**
a. $\log_2 16 = 4$	$2^4 = 16$
b. $\log_4 1 = 0$	$4^0 = 1$
c. $\log_9 9 = 1$	$9^1 = 9$
d. $\log_{1/5} 25 = -2$	$\left(\frac{1}{5}\right)^{-2} = 25$

Example 2 Evaluate logarithms

Evaluate the logarithm.

a. $\log_3 81$ **b.** $\log_4 0.25$ **c.** $\log_{1/6} 36$ **d.** $\log_{27} 3$

Solution

a. $3^4 = 81$, so $\log_3 81 = 4$. **b.** $4^{-1} = 0.25$, so $\log_4 0.25 = -1$.

c. $\left(\frac{1}{6}\right)^{-2} = 36$, so $\log_{1/6} 36 = -2$. **d.** $27^{1/3} = 3$, so $\log_{27} 3 = \frac{1}{3}$.

Guided Practice for Examples 1 and 2

Rewrite the equation in exponential form.

1. $\log_5 125 = 3$
  $5^3 = 125$
2. $\log_{11} 11 = 1$
  $11^1 = 11$
3. $\log_8 1 = 0$
  $8^0 = 1$
4. $\log_{1/3} 27 = -3$
  $\left(\frac{1}{3}\right)^{-3} = 27$

Evaluate the logarithm.

5. $\log_6 216$ 3 **6.** $\log_5 \frac{1}{25}$ −2 **7.** $\log_{1/2} 64$ −6 **8.** $\log_{32} 2$ $\frac{1}{5}$

Example 3   **Simplify using inverse properties**

   a. $10^{\log 9.6} = 9.6$ $\log_b b^x = x$

   b. $\log_7 49^{2x} = \log_7 (7^2)^{2x}$ Express 49 as a power with base 7.

           $= \log_7 (7)^{4x}$ Power of a power property

           $= 4x$ $\log_b b^x = x$

Example 4   **Find inverse functions**

Find the inverse of the function.

   a. $y = 8^x$; From the definition of logarithm, the inverse of $y = 8^x$ is $y = \log_8 x$.

   b. $y = \ln(x - 2)$ Original function

           $x = \ln(y - 2)$ Switch x and y.

           $e^x = y - 2$ Write in exponential form.

      $e^x + 2 = y$ Solve for y.

     The inverse of $y = \ln(x - 2)$ is $y = e^x + 2$.

Example 5   **Translate a logarithmic graph**

Graph $y = \log_3(x + 1) - 2$. State the domain and range.

STEP 1   **Sketch** the graph of the parent function $y = \log_3 x$, which passes through $(1, 0)$, $(3, 1)$, and $(9, 2)$.

STEP 2   **Translate** the parent graph left 1 unit and down 2 units. The translated graph passes through $(0, -2)$, $(2, -1)$, and $(8, 0)$. The graph's asymptote is $x = -1$.

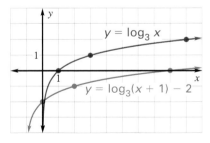

The domain is $x > -1$, and the range is all real numbers.

Guided Practice for Examples 3, 4, and 5

Simplify the expression.

   9. $e^{\ln 4.5}$ **4.5**   **10.** $\ln e^{-2x}$ **−2x**   **11.** $\log_4 4^{7x}$ **7x**   **12.** $10^{\log 3x}$ **3x**

   13.   Find the inverse of $y = \ln(x + 1)$.   **14.**   Find the inverse of $y = 5^x$.
        $y = e^x - 1$ $y = \log_5 x$

   15.   Graph $y = \log_2(x - 4) - 3$. State the domain and range.   **See Additional Answers beginning on page AA1.**

LESSON 4.4	**Exercise Set A**

MM3A2c	Define logarithmic functions as inverses of exponential functions.
MM3A2e	Investigate and explain characteristics of exponential and logarithmic functions including domain and range, asymptotes, zeros, intercepts, intervals of increase and decrease, and rate of change.
MM3A2f	Graph functions as transformations of $f(x) = a^x$, $f(x) = \log_a x$, $f(x) = e^x$, $f(x) = \ln x$.

Rewrite the equation in exponential form.

1. $\log_7 49 = 2$ $7^2 = 49$

2. $\log_2 16 = 4$ $2^4 = 16$

3. $\log_5 125 = 3$ $5^3 = 125$

4. $\log_{16} 4 = \frac{1}{2}$ $16^{1/2} = 4$

5. $\log_4 \frac{1}{4} = -1$ $4^{-1} = \frac{1}{4}$

6. $\log_3 \frac{1}{9} = -2$ $3^{-1} = \frac{1}{9}$

Evaluate the logarithm without using a calculator.

7. $\log_9 81$ 2

8. $\log_8 1$ 0

9. $\log_3 \frac{1}{3}$ −1

10. $\log_4 2$ $\frac{1}{2}$

11. $\log_{27} 3$ $\frac{1}{3}$

12. $\log_4 4^{2/3}$ $\frac{2}{3}$

Use a calculator to evaluate the logarithm. Round the result to three decimal places.

13. $\ln \sqrt{5}$ 0.805

14. $\log 110$ 2.041

15. $\ln \frac{1}{2}$ −0.693

Find the inverse of the function.

16. $y = \log_5 x$ $f^{-1}(x) = 5x$

17. $y = \ln x$ $f^{-1}(x) = e^x$

18. $y = \log_{1/5} x$ $f^{-1}(x) = \left(\frac{1}{5}\right)^x$

19. $y = \log \frac{x}{2}$
$f^{-1}(x) = 2(10^x)$

20. $y = \log_6(x + 2)$
$f^{-1}(x) = 6^x - 2$

21. $y = \log_3 9x$
$f^{-1}(x) = 3^{x-2}$

Graph the function. State the domain and range.

22–24. See Additional Answers beginning on page AA1.

22. $f(x) = \log_3 x$

23. $f(x) = \log_3(x + 2)$

24. $f(x) = -\log_3 x - 1$

25. Galloping Speed Four-legged animals run with two different types of motion: trotting and galloping. An animal that is trotting has at least one foot on the ground at all times. An animal that is galloping has all four feet off the ground at times. The number S of strides per minute at which an animal breaks from a trot to a gallop is related to the animal's weight w (in pounds) by the model $S = 256.2 - 47.9 \log w$. Approximate the number of strides per minute for a 450 pound horse when it breaks from a trot to a gallop. **129**

26. Tornadoes The wind speed S (in miles per hour) near the center of a tornado is related to the distance d (in miles) the tornado travels by the model $S = 93 \log d + 65$. Approximate the wind speed of a tornado that traveled 75 miles. **239.4 mi/h**

MM3A2c Define logarithmic functions as inverses of exponential functions.

MM3A2e Investigate and explain characteristics of exponential and logarithmic functions including domain and range, asymptotes, zeros, intercepts, intervals of increase and decrease, and rate of change.

MM3A2f Graph functions as transformations of $f(x) = a^x$, $f(x) = \log_a x$, $f(x) = e^x$, $f(x) = \ln x$.

Rewrite the equation in exponential form.

1. $\log_4 2 = \dfrac{1}{2}$ $4^{1/2} = 2$

2. $\log_3 81 = 4$ $3^4 = 81$

3. $\log_{1/4} 64 = -3$ $\left(\dfrac{1}{4}\right)^{-3} = 64$

Evaluate the logarithm without using a calculator.

4. $\log_4 \dfrac{1}{64}$ -3

5. $\log 10\sqrt{10}$ $\dfrac{3}{2}$

6. $\log_4 32$ $\dfrac{5}{2}$

7. $\log_8 4$ $\dfrac{2}{3}$

8. $\log_{16} \dfrac{1}{2}$ $-\dfrac{1}{4}$

9. $\log_{25} 125$ $\dfrac{3}{2}$

Use a calculator to evaluate the logarithm. Round the result to three decimal places.

10. $1 + \ln 7$ **2.946**

11. $\dfrac{\log 82}{0.24}$ **7.974**

12. $\dfrac{\ln 15}{2 - \ln 10}$ **−8.950**

Find the inverse of the function.

13. $y = \log_7 x$ $f^{-1}(x) = 7^x$

14. $y = \log_3 4x$ $f^{-1}(x) = \dfrac{3^x}{4}$

15. $y = \log_{1/2}(2x) + 3$ $f^{-1}(x) = \left(\dfrac{1}{2}\right)^{x-2}$

16. $y = \ln x + 2$ $f^{-1}(x) = e^{x-2}$

17. $y = \ln(x - 1) - 3$ $f^{-1}(x) = e^{x+3} + 1$

18. $y = \log_2 8^{x-1}$ $f^{-1}(x) = \dfrac{1}{3}x + 1$

Graph the function. State the domain and range.   19–21. See Additional Answers beginning on page AA1.

19. $f(x) = \log_2(x + 2)$

20. $f(x) = -\log_2(x + 2) - 1$

21. $f(x) = 5(\log(x - 1))$

In Exercises 22–24, use the following information.

400-Meter Relay The winning time (in seconds) in the women's 400-meter relay at the Olympic Games from 1928 to 1996 can be modeled by the function $f(t) = 67.99 - 5.82 \ln t$ where t is the number of years since 1900.

22. What was the winning time in 1976?   **42.79 sec**

23. Graph the model.   **See Additional Answers beginning on page AA1.**

24. Use the graph to approximate the winning time in the 2004 Olympic Games.   **40.96 sec**

UNIT 4

Interpret Graphs of Exponential and Logarithmic Functions

Georgia Performance Standards: MM3A2e, MM3A2f

Goal Interpret graphs of exponential and logarithmic functions.

Vocabulary

The **zeros** of a function $f(x)$ are the values of x for which $f(x) = 0$. The zero of a function is the x-coordinate of the x-intercept.

A function $f(x)$ is increasing on an interval if the graph moves upward as you move from left to right.

A function $f(x)$ is decreasing on an interval if the graph moves downward as you move from left to right.

For nonlinear functions, the **average rate of change** r between two points (x_1, y_1) and (x_2, y_2) is given by the formula $r = \dfrac{y_2 - y_1}{x_2 - x_1}$.

Example 1   **Analyzing the graph of an exponential function**

Analyze the graph of the function
$y = 2^x - 4$.

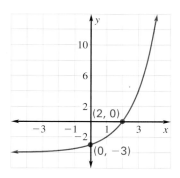

a. Identify the intercepts of the graph and the zeros of the function, if any.

b. Determine the intervals over which the function is increasing and decreasing.

c. Determine whether the average rate of change is greater between (2, 0) and (3, 4) or (3, 4) and (4, 12).

Solution

a. The graph intersects the x-axis at point (2, 0). So the x-intercept is (2, 0) and the zero of the function is $x = 2$. The graph intersects the y-axis at point (0, -3). So the y-intercept is (0, -3).

You can check your answer using a graphing calculator. Graph the function $y = 2^x - 4$. Then use the *zero* and *table* features.

b. The graph is moving upward as you move from left to right. So, the function is increasing over the entire real number line. There are no intervals of decrease because the function is always increasing.

c. The average rate of change between (2, 0) and (3, 4) is $\dfrac{y_2 - y_1}{x_2 - x_1} = \dfrac{4 - 0}{3 - 2} = 4$.

The average rate of change between (3, 4) and (4, 12) is $\dfrac{y_2 - y_1}{x_2 - x_1} = \dfrac{12 - 4}{4 - 3} = 8$.

So, the average rate of change is greater between (3, 4) and (4, 12).

UNIT 4

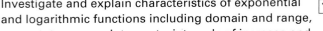

Georgia Performance Standards

MM3A2e Investigate and explain characteristics of exponential and logarithmic functions including domain and range, asymptotes, zeros, intercepts, intervals of increase and decrease, and rate of change.

MM3A2f Graph functions as transformations of $f(x) = a^x$, $f(x) = \log_a x$, $f(x) = e^x$, $f(x) = \ln x$.

Example 2 **Analyzing the graph of a logarithmic function**

Analyze the graph of the function
$y = \log_2 x.$

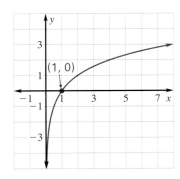

a. Identify the zeros of the function, if any.

b. Determine the intervals over which the function is increasing and decreasing.

c. Determine whether the average rate of change is greater between $(1, 0)$ and $(2, 1)$ or $(3, 1.585)$ and $(4, 2)$.

Solution

a. The graph intersects the x-axis at point $(1, 0)$. So the zero of the function is $x = 1$.

b. The graph is moving upward as you move from left to right. So, the function is increasing over the entire real number line. There are no intervals of decrease because the function is always increasing.

c. You can see from the graph that the average rate of change is greater between the points $(1, 0)$ and $(2, 1)$.

Guided Practice for Examples 1 and 2

For Exercises 1 and 2, analyze the graph. 1–2. See Additional Answers beginning on page AA1.

a. Identify the intercepts of the graph and the zeros of the function, if any.

b. Determine the intervals for which the function is increasing and decreasing.

c. Determine whether the average rate of change is greater between points A and B or between C and D.

1.

2.

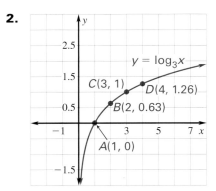

Example 3 **Graph a natural logarithmic function**

Graph the function $y = \ln x$.

Solution

STEP 1 Make a table of values.

x	1	2	3	4	5
y	0	0.693	1.099	1.386	1.609

STEP 2 Plot the points from the table. The y-axis is a vertical asymptote.

STEP 3 Draw, from left to right, a smooth curve that starts just to the right of the y-axis and moves up through the plotted points.

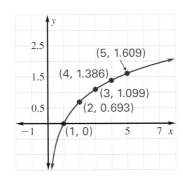

You can translate the graph of a function of the form $y = \ln(x - h) + k$ by translating the graph of the parent function $y = \ln x$.

Example 4 **Translate a natural logarithmic graph horizontally**

Graph $y = \ln(x + 2)$. State the domain and the range.

Solution

STEP 1 Sketch the graph of the parent function $y = \ln x$.

STEP 2 Translate the parent graph left 2 units. The translated graph passes through $(-1, 0)$, $(0, 0.693)$, $(1, 1.099)$. The graph's asymptote is $x = -2$.

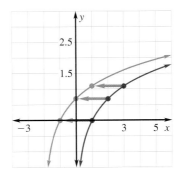

The domain is $x > -2$, and the range is all real numbers.

Guided Practice for Examples 3 and 4

Graph the function. State the domain and range. 3–4. See Additional Answers beginning on page AA1.

3. $y = \ln(x - 8)$

4. $y = \ln(x + 4)$

Example 5 **Translate a natural logarithmic graph vertically**

Graph $y = \ln x + 5$. State the domain and the range.

Solution

STEP 1 **Sketch** the graph of the parent function $y = \ln x$.

STEP 2 **Translate** the parent graph up 5 units. The translated graph passes through $(1, 5)$, $(2, 5.693)$, $(3, 6.099)$. The graph's asymptote is $x = 0$.

The domain is $x > 0$, and the range is all real numbers.

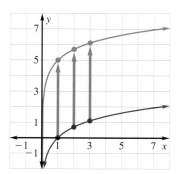

Example 6 **Graph and interpret a natural logarithmic function**

Graph $y = \ln(x - 1) - 4$. State the domain and the range and analyze the graph of the function.

Solution

STEP 1 **Sketch** the graph of the parent function $y = \ln x$.

STEP 2 **Translate** the parent graph right 1 unit and down 4 units. The translated graph passes through $(2, -4)$, $(3, -3.307)$, $(4, -2.901)$. The graph's asymptote is $x = 1$. The domain is $x > 1$, and the range is all real numbers.

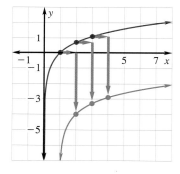

STEP 3 **Analyze** the graph.

The graph does not intersect the x-axis, so it does not have a zero. The graph moves upward as you move from left to right. So, the function is increasing over the entire real number line. There are no intervals of decrease because the function is always increasing. Of the points shown, the average rate of change is greatest between points $(2, -4)$ and $(3, -3.307)$.

Guided Practice for Examples 5 and 6

Graph the function. State the domain and range.   5–8. See Additional Answers beginning on page AA1.

5. $y = \ln x + 0.5$

6. $y = \ln(x + 2) + 3$

7. $y = \ln x - 3$

8. $y = \ln(x - 4) - 5$

LESSON 4.5 **Exercise Set A**

| MM3A2e | Investigate and explain characteristics of exponential and logarithmic functions including domain and range, asymptotes, zeros, intercepts, intervals of increase and decrease, and rate of change. |
| MM3A2f | Graph functions as transformations of $f(x) = a^x$, $f(x) = \log_a x$, $f(x) = e^x$, $f(x) = \ln x$. |

Analyze the graph. (a) Identify the intercepts of the graph and the zeros of the function, if any. (b) Determine the intervals for which the function is increasing and decreasing. (c) Determine whether the average rate of change is greater between points A and B or between C and D.

1.

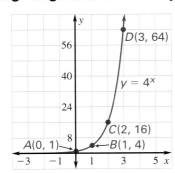

a. y-intercept: $(0, 1)$; no x-intercept; no zeros
b. increasing: $(-\infty, \infty)$
c. C and D

2.

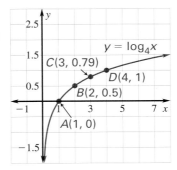

a. no y-intercept; x-intercept: $(1, 0)$; zero: $x = 1$
b. increasing: $(0, \infty)$
c. A and B

3. **Error Analysis** *Describe* and correct the error in identifying the zeros of the function $y = -3^x + 9$.

The zero is the x-coordinate of the x-intercept, not the y-coordinate of the y-intercept. The zero is $x = 2$.

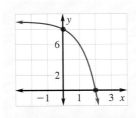

The zero of the function is $x = 8$.

X

Graph the function. State the domain and range.

4–6. See Additional Answers beginning on page AA1.

4. $y = \ln(x + 12)$ **5.** $y = \ln x - 0.25$ **6.** $f(x) = \ln(x - 1) + 5$

Use a graphing calculator to graph the function. (a) Approximate the zeros of the function, if any. (b) Determine the intervals for which the function is increasing and decreasing.

7. $f(x) = -5^x$ a. no zeros
b. decreasing: $(-\infty, \infty)$

8. $f(x) = \log_5 x$ a. zero: $x = 1$
b. decreasing: $(0, \infty)$

9. $f(x) = -\ln x$ a. $x = 1$
b. decreasing: $(0, \infty)$

10. **Car Value** The value V (in dollars) of a car t years after it is purchased is shown.

a. Identify the zeros of the function and the interval(s) for which the function is increasing and decreasing. What does this mean?

b. Determine whether the average rate of change is greater between years 1 and 2 or between 4 and 5. What does this mean in the context of the problem?

See Additional Answers beginning on page AA1.

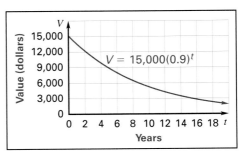

UNIT 4

Exercise Set B

MM3A2e   Investigate and explain characteristics of exponential and logarithmic functions including domain and range, asymptotes, zeros, intercepts, intervals of increase and decrease, and rate of change.

MM3A2f   Graph functions as transformations of $f(x) = a^x$, $f(x) = \log_a x$, $f(x) = e^x$, $f(x) = \ln x$.

Analyze the graph. (a) Identify the zeros of the function, if any. (b) Determine the intervals for which the function is increasing and decreasing. (c) Determine whether the average rate of change is greater between points A and B or between C and D.

1.

a. $x = 0$
b. increasing: $(-\infty, \infty)$
c. C and D

2.

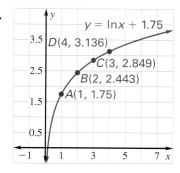

a. zero: $x \approx 0.1738$
b. increasing: $(0, \infty)$
c. A and B

Use a graphing calculator to graph the function. (a) Approximate the zeros of the function, if any. (b) Determine the intervals for which the function is increasing and decreasing. 3–8. See Additional Answers beginning on page AA1.

3. $y = 3^{x+1}$

4. $f(x) = -8^x - 2$

5. $y = 2^{x+1} + 3$

6. $f(x) = \log_9 x + 3$

7. $f(x) = \log(x + 1) - 1$

8. $y = \log_4 x + \log_2 x$

Graph the function. State the domain and range. 9–11. See Additional Answers beginning on page AA1.

9. $y = \ln(x + 1.2)$

10. $y = \ln(x - 0.5) + 1.5$

11. $f(x) = \ln(x + 7.8) - 3.2$

12. **Multiple Representations** You buy an antique chair. The value V (in dollars) of a chair can be modeled by the function $V = 250(1.1)^t$, where t is the number of years since the date of purchase. **See Additional Answers beginning on page AA1.**

  a. **Making a Table** Make a table with t-values of 0, 1, 2, 3, 4, and 5.

  b. **Graphing a Model** Graph the model. Identify the zeros of the function, if any. What does this mean?

  c. **Identifying Intervals** Identify the interval(s) for which the value of the chair is increasing and decreasing. What does this mean in the context of the problem?

  d. **Determining Rate of Change** Determine whether the average rate of change is greater between years 1 and 2 or 4 and 5. What does this mean in the context of the problem?

13. **Biology** Biologists have found that an alligator's length ℓ (in inches) and weight w (in pounds) can be related by the function $\ell = 27.1 \ln w - 32.8$ when $w > 4$. **See Additional Answers beginning on page AA1.**

  a. Use a graphing calculator to graph the model. Identify the zeros of the function, if any.

  b. Find the intervals for which the function is increasing and decreasing. What does this mean in the context of the problem?

Apply Properties of Logarithms

Georgia Performance Standards: MM3A2d, MM3A2g

Goal Rewrite logarithmic expressions.

Vocabulary

Properties of logarithms

Because of the relationship between logarithms and exponents, the properties of exponents have corresponding properties involving logarithms.

Let b, m, and n be positive numbers such that $b \neq 1$.

Product Property: $\log_b mn = \log_b m + \log_b n$

Quotient Property: $\log_b \dfrac{m}{n} = \log_b m - \log_b n$

Power Property: $\log_b m^n = n \log_b m$

Example 1   **Use properties of logarithms**

Use $\log_3 5 \approx 1.465$ and $\log_3 6 \approx 1.631$ to evaluate the logarithm.

a. $\log_3 \dfrac{6}{5} = \log_3 6 - \log_3 5$ Quotient property

$\approx 1.631 - 1.465$ Use the given values of $\log_3 5$ and $\log_3 6$.

$= 0.166$ Simplify.

b. $\log_3 30 = \log_3(5 \cdot 6)$ Write 30 as $5 \cdot 6$.

$= \log_3 5 + \log_3 6$ Product property

$\approx 1.465 + 1.631$ Use the given values of $\log_3 5$ and $\log_3 6$.

$= 3.096$ Simplify.

c. $\log_3 36 = \log_3 6^2$ Write 36 as 6^2.

$= 2 \log_3 6$ Power property

$\approx 2(1.631)$ Use the given value of $\log_3 6$.

$= 3.262$ Simplify.

Example 2   **Expand a logarithmic expression**

$\log_8 \dfrac{3x}{y} = \log_8 3x - \log_8 y$ Quotient property

$= \log_8 3 + \log_8 x - \log_8 y$ Product property

Example 3   **Condense a logarithmic expression**

$\ln x + 3 \ln y - 2 \ln 4 = \ln x + \ln y^3 - \ln 4^2$ Power property

$= \ln(x \cdot y^3) - \ln 4^2$ Product property

$= \ln \dfrac{xy^3}{16}$ Quotient property

Georgia Performance Standards

MM3A2d Understand and use properties of logarithms by extending laws of exponents.

MM3A2g Explore real phenomena related to exponential and logarithmic functions including half-life and doubling time.

Guided Practice for Examples 1, 2, and 3

Use $\log_2 7 \approx 2.807$ and $\log_2 3 \approx 1.585$ to evaluate the logarithm.

1. $\log_2 \dfrac{7}{3}$ **1.222**   **2.** $\log_2 21$ **4.392**   **3.** $\log_2 49$ **5.614**   **4.** $\log_2 27$ **4.755**

5. Expand $\ln x^5 y^2 z$. **$5 \ln x + 2 \ln y + \ln z$**   **6.** Condense $8 \log x + \dfrac{1}{2} \log y$. **$\log x^8 y^{1/2}$**

Change-of-Base Formula Logarithms with any base other than 10 or e can be written in terms of common or natural logarithms using the change-of-base formula.

Let x and c be positive numbers with $c \neq 1$. Then $\log_c x = \dfrac{\log x}{\log c}$ and $\log_c x = \dfrac{\ln x}{\ln c}$.

Example 4 **Use the change-of-base formula**

Evaluate $\log_2 12$ using common logarithms and natural logarithms.

Using common logarithms:

$$\log_2 12 = \frac{\log 12}{\log 2} \approx \frac{1.0792}{0.3010} \approx 3.585$$

Using natural logarithms:

$$\log_2 12 = \frac{\ln 12}{\ln 2} \approx \frac{2.4849}{0.6931} \approx 3.585$$

Example 5 **Use properties of logarithms in real life**

Average student scores on a memory exam are modeled by the function $f(t) = 100 - 12 \log(t + 1)$ where t is the time in months.

a. Use properties of logarithms to write the model in condensed form.

b. Find the average score after 3 months.

Solution

a. $f(t) = 100 - 12 \log(t + 1)$ Write original model.

  $f(t) = 100 - \log(t + 1)^{12}$ Power property

b. $f(3) = 100 - \log(3 + 1)^{12}$ Substitute 3 for t.

  ≈ 92.775 Use a calculator.

Guided Practice for Examples 4 and 5

Use the change-of-base formula to evaluate the logarithm.

7. $\log_2 6$ **2.585**   **8.** $\log_4 18$ **2.085**   **9.** $\log_9 4$ **0.631**   **10.** $\log_{12} 26$ **1.311**

11. Rework Example 5 to find the average score after 6 months. **about 89.8588**

UNIT 4

LESSON
4.6

Exercise Set A

MM3A2d Understand and use properties of logarithms by extending laws of exponents.

MM3A2g Explore real phenomena related to exponential and logarithmic functions including half-life and doubling time.

Match the expression with the logarithm that has the same value.

1. $\log \sqrt{2} + \log \sqrt{8}$ **C**
2. $\log 4 - \log 10$ **A**
3. $2 \log 4 - \log 2$ **D**
4. $-3 \log \frac{1}{3}$ **B**

A. $\log \frac{2}{5}$
B. $\log 27$
C. $\log 4$
D. $\log 8$

Use $\log 4 \approx 0.602$ and $\log 7 \approx 0.845$ to evaluate the logarithm.

5. $\log 28$ **1.447**
6. $\log \frac{7}{4}$ **0.243**
7. $\log 16$ **1.204**

8. $\log 49$ **1.690**
9. $\log \frac{1}{4}$ **−0.602**
10. $\log \frac{49}{64}$ **−0.116**

Expand the expression.

11. $\log_7 x^2 y$ **$2 \log_7 x + \log_7 y$**
12. $\log_2 \frac{x^2}{4}$ **$2 \log_2 x - \log_2 4$**
13. $\log 5 \sqrt[3]{x}$ **$\log 5 + \frac{1}{3} \log x$**

14. $\ln \frac{1}{2x^2}$ **$-\ln 2 - 2 \ln x$**
15. $\log_9 \frac{2x^3}{3}$
16. $\log_6 \frac{xy^2}{\sqrt{z}}$

 $\log_9 2 + 3 \log_9 x - \frac{1}{2}$
 $\log_6 x + 2 \log_6 y - \frac{1}{2} \log_6 z$

Condense the expression.

17. $\log_3 4 + \log_3 2 + \log_3 2$ **$\log_3 16$**
18. $2 \ln x - \ln 3 + \ln 6$ **$\ln 2x^2$**

19. $3 \log x + \log 4 - \log x - \log 6$ **$\log \frac{2x^2}{3}$**
20. $3 \ln(x + 1) - 2 \ln y + \ln y + \ln 2$ **$\ln \frac{2(x + 1)^3}{y}$**

Use the change-of-base formula to evaluate the logarithm.
Round your result to three decimal places.

21. $\log_7 12$ **1.277**
22. $\log_4 112$ **3.404**
23. $\log_5 1.25$ **0.139**

24. $\log_{2.2} 22$ **3.920**
25. $\log_{4.2} 18.1$ **2.018**
26. $\log_{1/3} 0.0005$ **6.919**

27. Henderson-Hasselbach Formula The pH of a patient's blood can be calculated using the Henderson-Hasselbach Formula, $\text{pH} = 6.1 + \log \frac{B}{C}$, where B is the concentration of bicarbonate and C is the concentration of carbonic acid. The normal pH of blood is approximately 7.4.

  a. Expand the right side of the formula. **$\text{pH} = 6.1 + \log B - \log C$**
  b. Find the pH of blood that has bicarbonate concentration of 38 and carbonic acid concentration of 2.0. **7.38**
  c. Is the pH in part (b) above normal or below normal? **just below normal**

UNIT 4

Exercise Set B

MM3A2d Understand and use properties of logarithms by extending laws of exponents.

MM3A2g Explore real phenomena related to exponential and logarithmic functions including half-life and doubling time.

Use ln 2 ≈ 0.693, ln 3 ≈ 1.099, and ln 7 ≈ 1.946 to evaluate the logarithm.

1. $\ln 28$ **3.332**

2. $\ln \frac{7}{4}$ **0.560**

3. $\ln 16$ **2.772**

4. $\ln 42$ **3.738**

5. $\ln \frac{21}{4}$ **1.659**

6. $\ln \frac{24}{9}$ **0.980**

Expand the expression.

7. $\log_2 \frac{x^3}{yz^2}$ **3 log₂ x − log₂ y − 2 log₂ z**

8. $\ln \sqrt{x^3 y}$ **$\frac{3}{2}$ ln x + $\frac{1}{2}$ ln y**

9. $\log \frac{\sqrt{4x}}{y^2}$ **log 2 + $\frac{1}{2}$ log x − 2 log y**

10. $\ln \frac{7y}{x^2}$ **ln 7 + ln y − 2 ln x**

11. $\log_9(2x^2yz)^5$ **5[log₉ 2 + 2 log₉ x + log₉ y + log₉ z]**

12. $\log_6 \frac{(x+3)^2}{3y^3}$ **2 log₆(x + 3) − log₆ 3 − 3 log₆ y**

Condense the expression. 13–18. See Additional Answers beginning on page AA1.

13. $\log_3 4 + \log_3 5 - \log_3 2 - \log_3 6$

14. $2 \log 5 - 2 \log x + \log y$

15. $2\left(\log_2 3 + \frac{1}{2} \log_2 x\right) - \log_2 y - 4 \log_2 x$

16. $2 \ln(x - 3) - \ln 6 - 3 \ln(x + 2)$

17. $\frac{3}{2} \log (x + 4) - 3 \log x - \ln 6$

18. $\frac{1}{2}[\ln 3 + 4 \ln x - 2 \ln(x - 1)]$

Use the change-of-base formula to evaluate the logarithm.
Round your result to three decimal places.

19. $\log_{15} 158$ **1.869**

20. $\log_{0.05} 22$ **−1.032**

21. $\log_{32} 10{,}254$ **2.665**

22. **Annuities** An ordinary annuity is an account in which you make a fixed deposit at the end of each compounding period. You want to use an annuity to help you save money for college. The formula

$$t = \frac{\ln\left[\dfrac{Sr + Pn}{Pn}\right]}{n \ln\left[\dfrac{n + r}{n}\right]}$$

gives the time t (in years) required to have S dollars in the annuity if your periodic payments P (in dollars) are made n times a year and the annual interest rate is r (in decimal form).

a. Expand the right side of the formula. $t = \dfrac{\ln(Sr + Pn) - \ln P - \ln n}{n(\ln(n + r) - \ln n)}$

b. How long will it take you to save $35,000 in an annuity that earns an annual interest rate of 5% if you make monthly payments of $150? **13.6 yr**

c. How long will it take you to save $35,000 in an annuity that earns an annual interest rate of 4% if you make monthly payments of $250? **9.6 yr**

UNIT 4

Solve Exponential and Logarithmic Equations

Georgia Performance Standards: MM3A3b, MM3A3d

Goal Solve exponential and logarithmic equations.

Vocabulary

Exponential equations are equations in which variable expressions occur as exponents.

Logarithmic equations are equations that involve logarithms of variable expressions.

Property of Equality for Exponential Equations If b is a positive number other than 1, then $b^x = b^y$ if and only if $x = y$.

Property of Equality for Logarithmic Equations If b, x, and y are positive numbers with $b \neq 1$, then $\log_b x = \log_b y$ if and only if $x = y$.

Example 1 **Solve by equating exponents**

Solve $8^x = 4^{x+1}$.

Solution

$8^x = 4^{x+1}$	Write original equation.
$(2^3)^x = (2^2)^{x+1}$	Rewrite 8 and 4 as powers with base 2.
$2^{3x} = 2^{2x+2}$	Power of a power property
$3x = 2x + 2$	Property of equality for exponential equations
$x = 2$	Solve for x.

CHECK Check the apparent solution using a graph. Graph $y = 8^x$ and $y = 4^{x+1}$ in the same coordinate plane. The graphs intersect when $x = 2$. So, the solution is 2.

Intersection
X=2   Y=64

Example 2 **Solve by taking a logarithm of each side**

Solve $8^x = 23$.

Solution

$8^x = 23$	Write original equation.
$\log_8 8^x = \log_8 23$	Take $\log_8$ of each side.
$x = \log_8 23$	$\log_b b^x = x$
$x = \dfrac{\log 23}{\log 8}$	Use change-of-base formula.
$x \approx 1.51$	Use a calculator.

Georgia Performance Standards

MM3A3b   Solve polynomial, exponential, and logarithmic
equations analytically, graphically, and using
appropriate technology.

MM3A3d   Solve a variety of types of equations by appropriate
means choosing among mental calculation, pencil
and paper, or appropriate technology.

Example 3   Solve a logarithmic equation

$$\log_8(x + 6) = \log_8(4 - x)$$ Original equation

$$x + 6 = 4 - x$$ Property of equality for logarithmic equations

$$2x + 6 = 4$$ Add x to each side.

$$2x = -2$$ Subtract 6 from each side.

$$x = -1$$ Divide each side by 2.

Example 4   Exponentiate each side of an equation

Find the solution(s) of log x + log(x + 3) = 1.

METHOD 1 Solve analytically.

$$\log x + \log(x + 3) = 1$$ Write original equation.

$$\log[x(x + 3)] = 1$$ Product property of logarithms

$$10^{\log[x(x + 3)]} = 10^1$$ Exponentiate each side using base 10.

$$x(x + 3) = 10$$ $b^{\log_b x} = x$

$$x^2 + 3x = 10$$ Distributive property

$$x^2 + 3x - 10 = 0$$ Write in standard form.

$$(x + 5)(x - 2) = 0$$ Factor.

$$x = -5 \text{ or } x = 2$$ Zero product property

METHOD 2 Use a graph.

STEP 1 Graph $y = \log x + \log(x + 3)$ and $y = 1$
in the same viewing window. Set the viewing
window to show $-6 \le x \le 6$ and $-2 \le y \le 4$.

STEP 2 Use the *intersect* feature to determine
where the graphs intersect. The graphs intersect
only when $x = 2$.

So, 2 is the only solution.

Intersection
X=2   Y=1

Guided Practice for Examples 1, 2, 3, and 4

Solve the equation. Check for extraneous solutions.

1. $5^{3x + 1} = 25^{x + 1}$ **1**

2. $4^{3x} = 9$ **about 0.528**

3. $\log_7(x + 2) = \log_7(2 - 3x)$ **0**

4. $\ln(4 - 5x) = \ln(x + 10)$ **−1**

5. $\log_6 x + \log_6(x - 5) = 2$ **9**

6. $2 \ln x = \ln(2x - 3) + \ln(x - 2)$ **6**

Exercise Set A

MM3A3b Solve polynomial, exponential, and logarithmic equations analytically, graphically, and using appropriate technology.

MM3A3d Solve a variety of types of equations by appropriate means choosing among mental calculation, pencil and paper, or appropriate technology.

Solve the exponential equation. Check for extraneous solutions. Round the result to three decimal places if necessary.

1. $e^x = 1$ **0**

2. $e^x + 1 = 7$ **1.792**

3. $5^x = 12$ **1.544**

4. $4^x - 6 = 4$ **1.661**

5. $3e^{3x} = 12$ **0.462**

6. $10^{2x-3} + 3 = 19$ **2.102**

7. $3^{-3x+1} = 3^{x-9}$ $\dfrac{5}{2}$

8. $8^{2x} = 8^{x+7}$ **7**

9. $7^{2x-3} - 4 = 14$ **2.243**

10. $4e^{3x} = 1$ **−0.462**

11. $e^{5x+2} = e^{3x+12}$ **5**

12. $3e^{3-x} = 15$ **1.391**

13. $9^{2x} = 3^{2x+4}$ **2**

14. $25^{x-4} = 5^{3x+1}$ **−9**

15. $8^{x-1} = \left(\dfrac{1}{2}\right)^{2x-1}$ $\dfrac{4}{5}$

16. $3(2^{x+6}) = 17$ **−3.497**

17. $5^{0.5x} + 12 = 21$ **2.730**

18. $-5e^x - 3 = 24$ **no solution**

19. $\dfrac{3}{4}e^{3x} - 8 = -6$ **0.327**

20. $\dfrac{2}{3}(4^{3x}) - 5 = -2$ **0.362**

21. $10^{2x+1} + 2 = 2$ **no solution**

Solve the logarithmic equation. Check for extraneous solutions. Round the result to three decimal places if necessary.

22. $\log x = 3$ **1000**

23. $\ln x = 4$ **54.598**

24. $\log_3 x = 5$ **243**

25. $\log_7(2 - x) = \log_7 5x$ $\dfrac{1}{3}$

26. $\ln(3x - 3) = \ln(x - 6)$ **no solution**

27. $7 - \log_3 8x = 2$ **30.375**

28. $2\log_7(1 - 2x) = 12$ **−58,824**

29. $3\ln x - 7 = 4$ **39.121**

30. $\ln(1 - 3x) + 3 = 9$ **−134.143**

31. $\log 7x + 4 = 5$ $\dfrac{10}{7}$

32. $4 + \log_9(3x - 7) = 6$ **29.333**

33. $\log_2 2x + \log_2 x = 5$ **4**

34. $\log_6(2x - 6) + \log_6 x = 2$ **6**

35. $\ln 3x - \ln 2 = 4$ **36.399**

36. $\ln(-5x + 3) = \ln 2x + 2$ **0.152**

37. **Multiple Choice** You deposit $500 in an account that pays 3.25% annual interest compounded monthly. About how long does it take for the balance to quadruple? **B**

    A. 36.3 years   **B.** 42.7 years   **C.** 45.1 years

In Exercises 38–40, use the following information.

Compounding Interest You deposit $700 in an account that pays 2.75% annual interest. How long does it take the balance to reach the following amounts?

38. $1000 when interest is compounded quarterly **13.0 yr**

39. $1500 when interest is compounded yearly **28.1 yr**

40. $2000 when interest is compounded continuously **38.2 yr**

41. **Rocket Velocity** Disregarding the force of gravity, the maximum velocity v of a rocket is given by $v = t \ln M$ where t is the velocity of the exhaust and M is the ratio of the mass of the rocket with fuel to its mass without fuel. A solid propellant rocket has an exhaust velocity of 2.3 kilometers per second. Its maximum velocity is 7.2 kilometers per second. Find its mass ratio M. **22.88**

MM3A3b Solve polynomial, exponential, and logarithmic equations analytically, graphically, and using appropriate technology.

MM3A3d Solve a variety of types of equations by appropriate means choosing among mental calculation, pencil and paper, or appropriate technology.

Solve the exponential equation. Check for extraneous solutions. Round the result to three decimal places if necessary.

1. $e^x = 5$ **1.609**

2. $e^{x-2} = 14$ **4.639**

3. $e^{2x} + 5 = 12$ **0.973**

4. $2^x = 22$ **4.459**

5. $3^x - 4 = 6$ **2.096**

6. $4^{4x+2} = 54$ **0.219**

7. $e^{2x-3} + 6 = 13$ **2.473**

8. $2e^{2-3x} - 3 = 11$ **0.018**

9. $9^{x-5} + 4 = 15$ **6.091**

10. $3^{x+1} + 4 = 8$ **0.262**

11. $\frac{1}{2}(10^{x+6}) - 5 = 14$ **−4.420**

12. $4^{3-x} + 2 = \frac{5}{2}$ **3.5**

13. $3e^{3x} - 1 = 1$ **−0.135**

14. $e^{x^2-2} = e^x$ **−1, 2**

15. $3^{x^2} + 5 = 6$ **0**

16. $27^x = 3^{2x+3}$ **3**

17. $216^{2x-1} = 36^{4x+3}$ **$-\frac{9}{2}$**

18. $16^{x-5} = \left(\frac{1}{2}\right)^{2x-1}$ **$\frac{7}{2}$**

Solve the logarithmic equation. Check for extraneous solutions. Round the result to three decimal places if necessary.

19. $\log(x+2) = 4$ **9998**

20. $2 \ln x - 7 = -5$ **e**

21. $\log_3(x-3) + 3 = 5$ **12**

22. $\log_7(2-x) = 3$ **−341**

23. $\ln(2x-1) + \ln x = 0$ **1**

24. $\log_2 x + \log_2(x+1) = 1$ **1**

25. $\log_3 x + \log_3(x+8) = 2$ **1**

26. $\log_4(x-3) + \log_4(x-4) = \frac{1}{2}$ **5**

27. $\log(x-5) = \log(x-2) + 1$ **no solution**

28. $2\log_7(1-x) = \log_7(7-x)$ **−2**

29. $\ln(2x^2 - 3) = \ln(9x - 13)$ **$2, \frac{5}{2}$**

30. $\log_2(x-3) + \log_2(x+1) = \log_2(6x-18)$ **5**

31. $\log_2 x + \log_2(x+4) - \log_2(x-2) = 4$ **4, 8**

32. $\log_2(7x-8) - \log_2(x+1) - \log_2(x-1) = 1$ **$\frac{3}{2}, 2$**

Solve the exponential equation. Round the result to three decimal places.

33. $3^{x+1} = 2^{4x}$ **0.656**

34. $e^{x-2} = 10^{2-x}$ **2**

35. $4^{2x+3} = 5^{x-4}$ **−9.110**

In Exercises 36–38, use the following information.

Loan Repayment The formula $L = P\left[\dfrac{1 - \left(1 + \dfrac{r}{n}\right)^{-nt}}{\dfrac{r}{n}}\right]$ gives the amount of a loan L

in terms of the amount of each payment P, the interest rate r as a decimal, the number of payments per year n, and the number of years t.

36. How long will it take to pay off a $120,000 loan at 6% interest when making monthly payments of $860? **20 yr**

37. When the loan is paid off, how much money will you have paid the bank? **$206,400**

38. How much did you pay in interest? **$86,400**

Solve Exponential and Logarithmic Inequalities

Georgia Performance Standards: MM3A3c

Goal Solve exponential and logarithmic inequalities.

Vocabulary

An **exponential inequality in one variable** is an inequality that can be written in the form $ab^x + k < 0$, $ab^x + k > 0$, $ab^x + k \leq 0$, or $ab^x + k \geq 0$, where $a \neq 0$, $b > 0$, and $b \neq 1$.

A **logarithmic inequality in one variable** is an inequality that can be written in the form $\log_b x + k < 0$, $\log_b x + k > 0$, $\log_b x + k \leq 0$, or $\log_b x + k \geq 0$, where $b > 0$, and $b \neq 1$.

The same methods used to solve polynomial inequalities in Lesson 2.4 can be used to solve exponential and logarithmic inequalities.

Example 1   **Solve an exponential inequality analytically**

Solve $4^{x+1} \geq 32$.

Solution

STEP 1 **Write** and solve the equation obtained by replacing $\geq$ with $=$.

$4^{x+1} = 32$	Write equation that corresponds to inequality.
$\log_4 4^{x+1} = \log_4 32$	Take $\log_4$ of each side.
$x + 1 = \log_4 32$	$\log_b b^x = x$
$x = \log_4 32 - 1$	Subtract 1 from each side.
$x = \dfrac{\log 32}{\log 4} - 1$	Change-of-base formula
$x = 1.5$	Use a calculator.

STEP 2 **Plot** the solution from Step 1 on a number line. Use a solid dot to indicate 1.5 is a solution of the inequality. The solution $x = 1.5$ represents the *critical x-value* of the inequality $4^{x+1} \geq 32$. The critical x-value partitions the number line into two intervals. Test an x-value in each interval to see if it is a solution of the inequality.

Test $x = 0$:
$4^{0+1} \overset{?}{\geq} 32$
$4 \neq 32$

Test $x = 3$:
$4^{3+1} \overset{?}{\geq} 32$
$256 \geq 32$ ✓

The solution consists of all real numbers in the interval $[1.5, +\infty)$.

Georgia Performance Standards

MM3A3c Solve polynomial, exponential, and logarithmic inequalities analytically, graphically, and using appropriate technology. Represent solution sets of inequalities using interval notation. ☑

Example 2 Solve an exponential inequality using technology

Car Value Your family purchases a new car for $25,000. Its value depreciates by 12% each year. During what interval of time does the car's value exceed $16,000?

Solution

Let y represent the value of the car (in dollars) x years after it is purchased. A function relating x and y is:

$$y = 25,000(1 - 0.12)^x \qquad \text{Original function}$$

$$y = 25,000(0.88)^x \qquad \text{Simplify.}$$

To find the values of x for which y exceeds 16,000, solve the inequality $25,000(0.88)^x > 16,000$.

METHOD 1 Use a table.

STEP 1 Enter the function $y = 25,000(0.88)^x$ into a graphing calculator. Set up a table to display the x-values starting at 0 and increasing in increments of 0.1.

X	Y1
3.2	16607
3.3	16396
3.4	16188
3.5	15982
3.6	15779
3.7	15779

X=3.4

STEP 2 Use the *table* feature to create a table of values. Scrolling through the table shows that $y > 16,000$ when $0 \le x \le 3.4$.

The car's value exceeds $16,000 for about the first 3.4 years after it is purchased.

METHOD 2 Use a graph.

STEP 1 Graph $y = 25,000(0.88)^x$ and $y = 16,000$ in the same viewing window. Set the viewing window to show $0 \le x \le 8$ and $0 \le y \le 25,000$.

STEP 2 Use the intersect feature to determine where the graphs intersect. The graphs intersect when $x \approx 3.49$.

Intersection
X=3.4911627   Y=16000

The graph of $y = 25,000(0.88)^x$ is above the graph of $y = 16,000$ when $0 \le x \le 3.49$. So, the car's value exceeds $16,000 for about the first 3.5 years after it is purchased.

Guided Practice for Examples 1 and 2

Solve the exponential inequality.

1. $5^{x-4} \ge 625$ [8, +∞)
2. $32^{x-1} \le 4$ (−∞, 1.4]
3. $7^{3x-4} < 18$ (−∞, 1.83)

4. **Car Value** In Example 2, during what interval of time does the car's value fall below $10,000? **About 7.17 years after the car is purchased and for the remaining life of the car.**

| Example 3 | **Solve a logarithmic inequality analytically** |

Solve the logarithmic inequality.

a. $\log_5 x < 2$

b. $\log_4 x + 8 \geq 11$

Solution

a. *STEP 1* **Write** and solve the equation obtained by replacing $<$ with $=$.

$\log_5 x = 2$ Write equation that corresponds to inequality.

$5^{\log_5 x} = 5^2$ Exponentiate each side using base 5.

$x = 25$ $b^{\log_b x} = x$

STEP 2 **Plot** the solution from Step 1 using an open dot. The value x must be a positive number, so the number line should show only positive numbers. The solution $x = 25$ represents the critical x-value of the inequality $\log_5 x < 2$. Test an x-value in each interval to see if it is a solution of the inequality.

Test $x = 5$:
$\log_5 5 \overset{?}{<} 2$
$1 < 2\checkmark$

Test $x = 40$:
$\log_5 40 \overset{?}{<} 2$
$2.29 \not< 2$

The solution consists of all real numbers in the interval $(0, 25)$.

b. *STEP 1* **Write** and solve the equation obtained by replacing $\geq$ with $=$.

$\log_4 x + 8 = 11$ Write equation that corresponds to inequality.

$\log_4 x = 3$ Subtract 8 from each side.

$4^{\log_4 x} = 4^3$ Exponentiate each side using base 4.

$x = 64$ $b^{\log_b x} = x$

STEP 2 **Plot** the solution from Step 1 using a solid dot. The solution $x = 64$ represents the critical x-value of the inequality $\log_4 x + 8 \geq 11$. Test an x-value in each interval to see if it is a solution of the inequality.

Test $x = 16$:
$\log_4 16 + 8 \overset{?}{\geq} 11$
$10 \not\geq 11$

Test $x = 128$:
$\log_4 128 + 8 \overset{?}{\geq} 11$
$11.5 \geq 11\checkmark$

The solution consists of all real numbers in the interval $[64, +\infty)$.

Guided Practice for Example 3

Solve the logarithmic inequality.

5. $\log_3 x - 3 > 1$

$(81, +\infty)$

6. $\log_6 2x + 7 < 10$

$(0, 108)$

7. $\log_9(x - 8) \geq \dfrac{3}{2}$

$[35, +\infty)$

Example 4 **Solve a logarithmic inequality using technology**

Solve $\log_3 x \le 2$.

Solution

METHOD 1 Use a table.

STEP 1 **Enter** the function $y = \log_3 x$ into a graphing calculator as $y = \dfrac{\log x}{\log 3}$.

STEP 2 **Use** the *table* feature to create a table of values. Identify the interval for which $y \le 2$. These x-values can be represented by the interval $(0, 9]$.

Make sure that the x-values are reasonable and in the domain of the function $(x > 0)$.

The solution of $\log_3 x \le 2$ is $(0, 9]$.

METHOD 2 Use a graph.

STEP 1 Graph $y = \log_3 x$ and $y = 2$ in the same viewing window.

STEP 2 Using the *intersect* feature, you can determine that the graphs intersect when $x = 9$.

The graph of $y = \log_3 x$ is on or below the graph of $y = 2$ during the x interval $(0, 9]$.

So, the solution of $\log_3 x \le 2$ is $(0, 9]$.

Guided Practice for Example 4

Use a graphing calculator to solve the logarithmic inequality.

8. $\log_2 x < 3$ $(0, 8)$

9. $\log_5(x - 2) \ge \dfrac{1}{3}$ $[3.71, +\infty)$

10. $\log_4 3x > \dfrac{2}{5}$ $(0.58, +\infty)$

MM3A3c Solve polynomial, exponential, and logarithmic inequalities analytically, graphically, and using appropriate technology. Represent solution sets of inequalities using interval notation.

Solve the exponential inequality analytically.

1. $4^x < 64$ $(-\infty, 3)$

2. $\left(\frac{1}{4}\right)^x \geq 16$ $(-\infty, -2]$

3. $3^x < 81$ $(-\infty, 4)$

4. $25 \leq 5^{x+1}$ $[1, \infty)$

5. $4^{x+1} > 64$ $(2, \infty)$

6. $27\left(\frac{2}{3}\right)^x \leq \frac{16}{3}$ $[4, \infty)$

Use a graphing calculator to solve the exponential inequality.

7. $3 \leq 8\left(\frac{3}{4}\right)^x$ $(-\infty, 3.409]$

8. $244(0.35)^x > 100$ $(-\infty, 0.85)$

9. $5(0.4)^{x-2} \geq 5$ $(-\infty, 2]$

Solve the logarithmic inequality analytically.

10. $\log_3 x < 2$ $(0, 9)$

11. $\log_5 x \leq 1$ $(0, 5]$

12. $\log_7 x < 2$ $(0, 49)$

13. $\log_4 x \leq \frac{3}{2}$ $(0, 8]$

14. $\log_5 x - 7 \geq -6$ $[5, \infty)$

15. $\log_6 x + 4 < 5$ $(0, 6)$

Use a graphing calculator to solve the logarithmic inequality.

16. $8 \ln x \geq 1$ $[1.133, \infty)$

17. $6 \log_2 x > 14$ $(5.04, \infty)$

18. $-2 \log_7 x + 9 > 11$ $(0, 0.143)$

19. **Finance** You deposit $2000 in an account that pays 5% annual interest compounded monthly. During which time interval will your balance exceed $2500? **after about 4.5 years**

20. **Finance** You deposit $800 in an account that pays 4.5% annual interest compounded continuously. During which time interval will your balance be less than $900? **in the first 2.6 years after the initial deposit**

21. **Multiple Representations** Suppose the annual rate of inflation averages 4% over the next 20 years. **See Additional Answers beginning on page AA1.**

  a. **Writing a Model** Let P represent the present cost of an item. Write a model that gives the cost C (in dollars) of an item after t years.

  b. **Using a Table** A can of corn currently costs $.99. Write an inequality that gives the time interval for which the cost of a can of corn is between $.99 and $1.50. Then use a table to predict when this will occur.

  c. **Using a Graph** Write an inequality that gives the time interval in which the cost of a can of corn exceeds $2.00. Then use a graph to predict when this will occur.

22. **Tornadoes** The wind speed s (in miles per hour) near the center of a tornado can be modeled by $s = 93 \log d + 65$, where d is the distance (in miles) that the tornado travels.

  a. Approximate the distances for which a tornado must travel to have a center wind speed between 150 miles per hour and 200 miles per hour. **between 8.2 miles and 28.3 miles, (8.2, 28.3)**

  b. Approximate the distances for which a tornado must travel to have a center wind speed of at least 175 miles per hour. **greater than 15.2 miles, (15.2, ∞)**

LESSON
4.8

**Exercise
Set B**

MM3A3c   Solve polynomial, exponential, and logarithmic
inequalities analytically, graphically, and using
appropriate technology. Represent solution sets of
inequalities using interval notation.

Solve the exponential inequality analytically.

1. $7^{x-2} \le 1.5$ $(-\infty, 2.21]$

2. $\left(\dfrac{3}{2}\right)^{x+1} < 10$ $(-\infty, 4.68)$

3. $14\left(\dfrac{5}{6}\right)^{x} \ge 9$ $[2.42, +\infty)$

4. $-135\left(\dfrac{9}{7}\right)^{x} \ge -475$ $(-\infty, 5)$

5. $-3e^{x} < -7$ $(0.85, +\infty)$

6. $4^{5x+1} \ge 0.5$ $[-0.3, +\infty)$

Use a graphing calculator to solve the exponential inequality.

7. $-(0.82)^{5x} \le -10$
   $(-\infty, -2.32)$

8. $20(1.4)^{3.5x} > 1000$
   $(3.322, +\infty)$

9. $50e^{-0.02x} < 70$
   $(-16.82, +\infty)$

Solve the logarithmic inequality analytically.

10. $\log_2 x < 3.5$ $(0, 11.31)$

11. $\ln x + 1 \ge 2$ $[2.72, +\infty)$

12. $\log_3 4x + 7 \le 12$ $(0, 60.75]$

13. $\log_9(x-1) \ge 1.5$ $[28, +\infty)$

14. $2\log_4(x+3) - 1 > 5$
    $(61, +\infty)$

15. $4\log_7 3x - 4 \le 7$ $(0, 70.29]$

Use a graphing calculator to solve the logarithmic inequality.

16. $\log_5(x-4) + 6 \le 8$ $(4, 29]$

17. $\ln 3x + 3 < 8$ $(0, 49.74)$

18. $-4\log_2 x > 2x - 7$ $(0, 1.8)$

19. **Radioactive Decay** Two hundred grams of radium are stored in a container.
    The amount R (in grams) of radium present after t years can be modeled by
    $R = 200e^{-0.00043t}$. Write and solve an inequality that can be used to determine
    when the mass of the radium will be less than 10 grams. $200e^{-0.00043t} < 10$; **after about 6966.8 years**

20. **Newton's Law of Cooling** Newton's law of cooling states that the temperature T
    of a cooling substance at time t (in minutes) can be modeled by the equation
    $T = (T_0 - T_R)e^{-rt} + T_R$, where T_0 is the initial temperature of the substance, T_R
    is the room temperature, and r is a constant that represents the cooling rate of
    the substance. **See Additional Answers beginning on page AA1.**

    a. You take a pot of soup off the stove. It has an initial temperature of 212°F, and the
       room temperature is 72°F. The soup is cooling at a rate of 0.03. You want to eat
       the soup when the temperature is between 130°F and 140°F. Write an inequality that
       gives the time interval in which this would occur.

    b. Solve the inequality to find the time interval described in part (a).

    c. Will the temperature ever drop below 70°F? *Explain.*

21. **Business** The demand equation for a certain product is modeled by the equation

    $$p = 6000\left(1 - \dfrac{4}{4 + e^{-0.002x}}\right)$$

    where p is the price and x is the number of units. In order to make a profit, the
    company cannot sell its product for less than $80. Approximate the prices in which
    the company will make a profit and yield a demand of at least 1000 units.
    $80 \le p \le 196.36$

Write and Apply Exponential and Power Functions

Georgia Performance Standards: MM3A2g

Goal Write exponential and power functions.

Example 1   Write an exponential function

Write an exponential function $y = ab^x$ whose graph passes through (1, 6) and (2, 18).

STEP 1 Substitute the coordinates of the two given points into $y = ab^x$.

$$6 = ab^1 \qquad\qquad 18 = ab^2$$

STEP 2 Solve for a in the first equation and substitute into the second equation.

$$18 = \left(\frac{6}{b}\right)b^2 \qquad \text{Substitute } \frac{6}{b} \text{ for } a.$$

$$3 = b \qquad\qquad \text{Solve for } b.$$

STEP 3 Because $b = 3$, it follows that $a = \frac{6}{3} = 2$. So, $y = 2 \cdot 3^x$.

Transforming Exponential Data A set of more than two points (x, y) fits an exponential pattern if and only if the set of transformed points $(x, \ln y)$ fits a linear pattern.

Example 2   Find an exponential model

Insects The table shows the number of insects y in a controlled experiment during the xth month of the experiment. Draw a scatter plot of the data pairs $(x, \ln y)$. Then find an exponential model for the original data.

Month, x	1	2	3	4	5	6
Population, y	2.73	5.73	12.04	25.28	53.09	111.50

STEP 1 Use a calculator to find the data pairs $(x, \ln y)$; (1, 1.004), (2, 1.746), (3, 2.488), (4, 3.230), (5, 3.972), and (6, 4.714).

STEP 2 Plot the new points and observe that they lie close to a line. So, an exponential model should be a good fit for the original data.

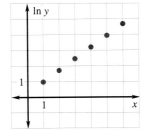

STEP 3 To find an exponential model $y = ab^x$, choose two points (1, 1.004) and (6, 4.714) and find an equation of a line. Then solve for y.

$$\ln y - 1.004 = 0.742(x - 1) \qquad \text{Equation of line}$$

$$\ln y = 0.742x + 0.262 \qquad \text{Simplify.}$$

$$y = e^{0.742x + 0.262} \qquad \text{Exponentiate each side using base } e.$$

$$y = e^{0.262}\left(e^{0.742}\right)^x \qquad \text{Use properties of exponents.}$$

$$y \approx 1.3(2.1)^x \qquad \text{Exponential model}$$

Georgia Performance Standards

MM3A2g Explore real phenomena related to exponential and logarithmic functions including half-life and doubling time.

Guided Practice for Examples 1 and 2

Write an exponential function $y = ab^x$ whose graph passes through the given points. **1–3. See Additional Answers beginning on page AA1.**

1. $(1, 8), (2, 16)$ **2.** $(2, 8), (3, 32)$ **3.** $(1, 15), (2, 75)$

4. How would the exponential model in Example 2 change if the insect population increased as shown in the table below? $y = 1.5(2^x)$

Month, x	1	2	3	4	5	6
Population, y	3	6	12	24	48	96

Example 3 **Write a power function**

Write a power function $y = ax^b$ whose graph passes through (2, 1) and (4, 3).

Solution

STEP 1 Substitute the coordinates of the two given points into $y = ax^b$.

$1 = a \cdot 2^b$ Substitute 1 for y and 2 for x.

$3 = a \cdot 4^b$ Substitute 3 for y and 4 for x.

STEP 2 Solve for a in the first equation and substitute into the second equation.

$3 = \dfrac{1}{2^b} \cdot 4^b$ Substitute $\dfrac{1}{2^b}$ for a.

$3 = 2^b$ Simplify.

$\log_2 3 = b$ Take $\log_2$ of each side.

$\dfrac{\log 3}{\log 2} = b$ Change-of-base formula

$1.58 \approx b$ Use a calculator.

STEP 3 Because $b \approx 1.58$, it follows that $a \approx \dfrac{1}{2^{1.58}} \approx 0.33$. So, $y = 0.33x^{1.58}$.

Transforming Power Data A set of more than two points (x, y) fits a power pattern if and only if the set of transformed points $(\ln x, \ln y)$ fits a linear pattern.

Guided Practice for Example 3

Write a power function $y = ax^b$ whose graph passes through the given points.

5. $(2, 9), (3, 27)$ **6.** $(1, 8), (2, 32)$ **7.** $(1, 1), (4, 8)$

     $y = 1.38x^{2.71}$ $y = 8x^2$ $y = x^{1.5}$

UNIT 4

MM3A2g Explore real phenomena related to exponential and logarithmic functions including half-life and doubling time.

Write an exponential function $y = ab^x$ whose graph passes through the given points.

1. $\left(0, \frac{1}{2}\right), \left(2, \frac{9}{2}\right)$ $y = \frac{1}{2}(3)^x$

2. $\left(1, \frac{2}{5}\right), \left(3, \frac{8}{5}\right)$ $y = \frac{1}{5}(2)^x$

3. $(1, 12), \left(-1, \frac{3}{4}\right)$ $y = 3(4)^x$

4. $(2, 2), (3, 1)$ $y = 8\left(\frac{1}{2}\right)^x$

5. $(0, 5), \left(2, \frac{20}{9}\right)$ $y = 5\left(\frac{2}{3}\right)^x$

6. $\left(0, \frac{3}{4}\right), \left(1, \frac{1}{4}\right)$ $y = \left(\frac{3}{4}\right)\left(\frac{1}{3}\right)^x$

Find an exponential model by solving for y.

7. $\ln y = 1.924x + 3.634$
  $y = 37.86(6.85)^x$

8. $\ln y = 0.283x - 6.275$
  $y = 0.0019(1.33)^x$

9. $\ln y = -3.5x + 4.129$
  $y = 62.12(0.03)^x$

10. Use the points (x, y) to draw a scatter plot of the points $(x, \ln y)$. Then find an exponential model for the data. **See Additional Answers beginning on page AA1.**

x	1	2	3	4	5	6
y	3.36	9.41	26.34	73.76	206.52	578.27

Write a power function $y = ax^b$ whose graph passes through the given points.

11. $(1, 3), (2, 24)$ $y = 3x^3$

12. $(1, 0.5), (4, 8)$ $y = \frac{1}{2}x^2$

13. $(1, 2), (4, 16)$ $y = 2x^{1.5}$

14. $(1, -4), (4, -64)$
  $y = -4x^2$

15. $(4, 0.5), (9, 0.75)$
  $y = \frac{1}{4}x^{0.5}$

16. $(3, -7.794), (7, -64.82)$
  $y = -\frac{1}{2}x^{2.5}$

Find a power model by solving for y.

17. $\ln y = 3.3 \ln x + 2.56$
  $y = 12.94x^{3.3}$

18. $\ln y = 1.05 \ln x - 4.28$
  $y = 0.014x^{1.05}$

19. $\ln y = 2 \ln 2x + 3.15$
  $y = 93.34x^2$

20. Use the points (x, y) to draw a scatter plot of the points $(\ln x, \ln y)$. Then find a power model for the data. **See Additional Answers beginning on page AA1.**

x	1	2	3	4	5	6
y	2.1	7.313	15.172	25.464	38.051	52.831

21. **Minimum Wage** The table shows the minimum hourly wage in the United States since 1960. Let $x = 1$ represent the year 1960, $x = 2$ represent the year 1965, and so on. Let y represent the minimum hourly wage. Use a graphing calculator to find a power model for the data. Use the model to estimate the minimum hourly wage in 2020. $y = 0.81x^{0.79}$; $6.14

Year	1960	1965	1970	1975	1980	1985	1990	1995	2000	2005
Wage	$1.00	$1.25	$1.60	$2.10	$3.10	$3.35	$3.80	$4.25	$5.15	$5.15

UNIT 4

LESSON
4.9

Exercise
Set B

MM3A2g   Explore real phenomena related to exponential
and logarithmic functions including half-life and
doubling time.

Write an exponential function $y = ab^x$ whose graph passes through the given points.

1. $(1, 2.88), (3, 16.589)$ $y = 1.2(2.4)^x$

2. $(2, 7.35), (4, 90.038)$ $y = 0.6(3.5)^x$

3. $(3, 200.04), (6, 14{,}820.386)$ $y = 2.7(4.2)^x$

Use the points (x, y) to draw a scatter plot of the points $(x, \ln y)$. Then find an exponential model for the data.   4–5. See Additional Answers beginning on page AA1.

4.

x	1	2	3	4	5	6
y	5.4	9.72	17.496	31.493	56.687	102.04

5.

x	1	2	3	4	5	6
y	3.6	14.4	57.6	230.4	921.6	3686.4

Write a power function $y = ax^b$ whose graph passes through the given points.

6. $(1, 0.3), (4, 2.4)$
   $y = 0.3x^{1.5}$

7. $(2, 27.292), (5, 809.86)$
   $y = 2.1x^{3.7}$

8. $(6, 17.2), (14, 24.14)$
   $y = 8.4x^{0.4}$

In Exercises 9–12, use the following information.

Gas Prices The data gives the average cost of gasoline in dollars per gallon in the United States during August 2005. Each increment of x represents six days with the first data point, $x = 1$, corresponding to August 3, the second data point, $x = 2$, corresponding to August 9, and so on.

x	1	2	3	4	5	6
y	2.30	2.39	2.54	2.59	2.59	3.08

9. Use the points (x, y) to draw a scatter plot of the points $(\ln x, \ln y)$.
   Then find a power model for the data.   **See Additional Answers beginning on page AA1.**

10. Use your graphing calculator to find an exponential model
    for the data. $y = 2.164(1.05)^x$

11. Use your graphing calculator to find a power model for the data. $y = 2.233x^{0.129}$

12. Which model is the better fitting model? *Explain* your answer.   **The exponential model is better fitting because the relationship between x and $\ln y$ is closer to linear than the relationship between $\ln x$ and $\ln y$.**

TEST | for Unit 4

Graph the function. State the domain and range. 1–6. See Additional Answers beginning on page AA1.

1. $y = 7^x$

2. $f(x) = 0.25 \cdot 2^{x+3}$

3. $f(x) = 3(0.75)^x$

4. $f(x) = 8 \cdot (0.25)^x$

5. $y = (0.8)^x - 3$

6. $y = e^{x+3} + 1$

Find the inverse of the function.

7. $y = \log_3 x$ $y = 3^x$

8. $f(x) = \ln x$ $y = e^x$

9. $y = \log(x + 5)$ $y = 10^x - 5$

Graph the function. State the domain and range. 10–12. See Additional Answers beginning on page AA1.

10. $y = \log_4 x$

11. $y = \log(x - 1) + 5$

12. $f(x) = \ln x - 4$

Analyze the graph. (a) Identify the zeros of the function, if any. (b) Determine the intervals for which the function is increasing and decreasing. (c) Determine whether the average rate of change is greater between points A and B or between C and D.

13.

a. $x \approx -1585$
b. decreasing: $(-\infty, \infty)$
c. A and B

14.

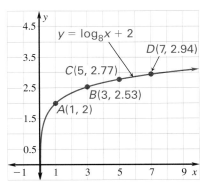

a. $x \approx 0.0156$
b. increasing: $(0, \infty)$
c. A and B

Expand the expression.

15. $\log_3 4x$ $\log_3 4 + \log_3 x$

16. $\log_2 \dfrac{x^2}{5}$ $2\log_2 x - \log_2 3$

17. $\ln \dfrac{4}{x^3}$ $\ln 4 - 3 \ln x$

Condense the expression.

18. $\ln x - 2 \ln 4 + \ln 5$ $\ln \dfrac{5x}{16}$

19. $\log_4 5 - \log_4 3$ $\log_4 \dfrac{5}{3}$

20. $3 \log x - \log 5 - \log y$ $\log \dfrac{x^3}{5y}$

Use the change-of-base formula to evaluate the logarithm. Round your result to three decimal places.

21. $\log_{12} 122$ **1.933**

22. $\log_{0.2} 492$ **−3.851**

23. $\log_{50} 1420$ **1.855**

Solve the equation. Check for extraneous solutions. Round the result to three decimal places if necessary.

24. $e^{2x} = 4$ **0.693**

25. $4^x + 1 = 0.5$ **no solution**

26. $\log_2 4x = \log_2(x + 15)$ **5**

Solve the inequality using any method.

27. $\left(\dfrac{2}{3}\right)^x \geq 4$ **(−∞, −3.419)**

28. $5^{x+2} < 6280$ **(−∞, 3.434)**

29. $-0.5 \log_3 x + 5 \leq 4.5$ **(3, ∞)**

Write a power function $y = ax^b$ whose graph passes through the given points.

30. $(1, 2), (4, 256)$ $y = 2x^{3.5}$ **31.** $(1, 0.2), (2, 51.2)$ $y = 0.2x^8$ **32.** $(-1, -5), (3, -405)$ $y = -5x^4$

33. Half-life Models The half-life of nitrogen-13 is about 10 minutes. The amount A (in grams) of radioactive nitrogen-13 that remains in a sample after t minutes is given by $A = 2000\left(\dfrac{1}{2}\right)^{t/10}$.

  a. What is the initial amount of nitrogen-13? ($t = 0$) **2000 g**

  b. How much nitrogen-13 is present after half an hour? **250 g**

  c. In about how many hours will 500 grams of nitrogen-13 remain? **20 min**

34. Bacteria Growth A population of bacteria can be modeled by the function $P = 60e^{0.3t}$ where t is the time (in hours). Graph the model and use the graph to estimate the population after 5 hours. **See Additional Answers beginning on page AA1.**

35. Chemistry The pH value for a substance measures how acidic or alkaline the substance is. It is given by the formula pH $= -\log [H^+]$ where H^+ is the hydrogen ion concentration (in moles per liter). What is the pH value of a substance with a hydrogen ion concentration of $10^{-5.7}$ moles per liter? **pH = 5.7**

36. Finance You deposit $2000 in an account that pays 3.5% annual interest compounded continuously. When will your balance exceed $2500? When will your balance double? **after about 6.4 years; about 19.8 years**

Performance Task

Finance

You have $500 to invest, and you are trying to decide between two different banks. The first bank pays 5% annual interest compounded monthly. **See Additional Answers beginning on page AA1.**

  a. Write a model giving the account balance A after t years for the first bank.

  b. Make a table of values and graph the model for the first bank. In about how many years will your balance double in the first bank?

  c. Analyze the graph in part (b). Identify the zeros of the function, and determine the intervals for which the function is increasing and decreasing. *Explain* what these mean in the context of the problem.

  d. A bank representative from the second bank provides the following table of how your money will perform over the next 5 years if deposited in that bank. Draw a scatter plot of the data. Then find an exponential model for the data.

Time, t	1	2	3
Account balance, A	530.00	561.80	595.51

  e. If you deposit your money in the second bank, when will your balance exceed $750? Which bank seems to be the better choice? *Explain.*

UNIT 5
Geometry

Graph and Write Equations of Parabolas

LESSON 5.1

Georgia Performance Standards: MM3G2b, MM3G2c

Goal Graph and write equations of parabolas.

Vocabulary

A **parabola** is the set of points equidistant from a point called the **focus** and a line called the **directrix**. The line perpendicular to the parabola's directrix and passing through its focus is the **axis of symmetry**. The point on the parabola that lies on the axis of symmetry is the **vertex**.

The standard form of the equation of a parabola with vertex at $(0, 0)$ is as follows:

Equation	Focus	Directrix	Axis of Symmetry
$x^2 = 4py$	$(0, p)$	$y = -p$	Vertical $(x = 0)$
$y^2 = 4px$	$(p, 0)$	$x = -p$	Horizontal $(y = 0)$

Example 1 **Graph an equation of a parabola**

Graph $x = \frac{1}{4}y^2$. Identify the focus, directrix, and axis of symmetry.

STEP 1 **Rewrite** the equation in standard form.

$x = \frac{1}{4}y^2$ Write original equation.

$4x = y^2$ Multiply each side by 4.

STEP 2 **Identify** the focus, directrix, and axis of symmetry. The equation has the form $y^2 = 4px$ where $p = 1$. The focus is $(p, 0)$, or $(1, 0)$. The directrix is $x = -p$, or $x = -1$. Because y is squared, the axis of symmetry is the x-axis.

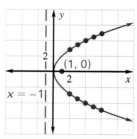

STEP 3 **Draw** the parabola by making a table of values and plotting points. Because $p > 0$, the parabola opens to the right. Use only positive x-values.

x	2	3	4	5	6
y	± 2.83	± 3.46	± 4	± 4.47	± 4.90

Guided Practice for Example 1

Graph the equation. Identify the focus, directrix, and axis of symmetry of the parabola. 1–4. See Additional Answers beginning on page AA1.

1. $x^2 = \frac{1}{4}y$ **2.** $y^2 = -2x$ **3.** $x = \frac{1}{2}y^2$ **4.** $y = -\frac{1}{3}x^2$

Example 2 ## Write an equation of a parabola

Write an equation of the parabola shown.

The graph shows that the vertex is $(0, 0)$ and the directrix is $y = -p = \frac{1}{2}$. Substitute $-\frac{1}{2}$ for p in the standard form of the equation of a parabola.

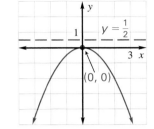

$x^2 = 4py$ Standard form, vertical axis of symmetry

$x^2 = 4\left(-\frac{1}{2}\right)y$ Substitute $-\frac{1}{2}$ for p.

$x^2 = -2y$ Simplify.

Example 3 ## Solve a multi-step problem

Parabolic Reflector The cross section of a parabolic reflector is 10 yards across and the focus of the reflector is located 4 yards above the vertex. Write an equation for the cross section of a reflector opening upward with its vertex at $(0, 0)$. What is the depth of the reflector?

STEP 1 **Write** an equation for the cross section. Because the focus is above the vertex, p is positive, so $p = 4$. An equation for the cross section of the reflector with its vertex at the origin is as follows.

$x^2 = 4py$ Standard form, vertical axis of symmetry

$x^2 = 4(4)y$ Substitute 4 for p.

$x^2 = 16y$ Simplify.

STEP 2 **Find** the depth of the reflector. The depth is the y-value at the reflector's outer edge. The reflector extends 5 yards to either side of the vertex $(0, 0)$, so substitute 5 for x in the equation from Step 1.

$x^2 = 16y$ Equation for the cross section

$5^2 = 16y$ Substitute 5 for x.

$1.56 \approx y$ Solve for y.

The reflector is about 1.56 yards deep.

Guided Practice for Examples 2 and 3

5. Write the standard form of the equation of the parabola with vertex at $(0, 0)$ and directrix $x = 3$. $y^2 = -12x$

6. The cross section of parabolic reflector is 14 meters across and the focus of the reflector is 5 meters above the vertex. Write an equation for the cross section of a reflector opening upward with its vertex at $(0, 0)$. What is the reflector's depth? $x^2 = 20y$; 2.45 m

UNIT 5

Tell whether the parabola opens *up*, *down*, *left*, or *right*.

1. $x^2 = -4y$ down

2. $y^2 = 7x$ right

3. $y^2 = -2x$ left

Graph the equation. Identify the focus and directrix of the parabola. 4–9. See Additional Answers beginning on page AA1.

4. $x^2 = 12y$

5. $y^2 = -4x$

6. $x^2 = -y$

7. $y^2 - 6x = 0$

8. $x^2 + 8y = 0$

9. $2x^2 - y = 0$

10. **Error Analysis** *Describe* and correct the error in graphing $-5x + y^2 = 0$.
See Additional Answers beginning on page AA1.

$-5x + y^2 = 0$

(0, 1.25)

0.5

0.5

$y = -1.25$

Write the standard form of the equation of the parabola with the given focus and vertex at (0, 0).

11. $(2, 0)$ $y^2 = 8x$

12. $(0, 1)$ $x^2 = 4y$

13. $(-1, 0)$ $y^2 = -4x$

14. $\left(0, \frac{1}{2}\right)$ $x^2 = 2y$

15. $(3, 0)$ $y^2 = 12x$

16. $(0, -6)$ $x^2 = -24y$

Write the standard form of the equation of the parabola with the given directrix and vertex at (0, 0).

17. $x = 3$ $y^2 = -12x$

18. $y = -2$ $x^2 = 8y$

19. $x = -1$ $y^2 = 4x$

20. $y = 4$ $x^2 = -16y$

21. $x = \frac{1}{4}$ $y^2 = -x$

22. $y = -\frac{1}{2}$ $x^2 = 2y$

23. **Television Antenna Dish** The cross section of a television antenna dish is a parabola. The receiver is located at the focus, 2.5 feet above the vertex. Assume the vertex is at the origin. Write an equation for the cross section of the dish opening upward. $x^2 = 10y$

24. **Headlight** The filament of a light bulb is a thin wire that glows when electricity passes through it. The filament of a car headlight is at the focus of a parabolic reflector, which sends light out in a straight beam. Given that the filament is 1.5 inches from the vertex, write an equation for the cross section of the reflector opening to the right with vertex at (0, 0). $y^2 = 6x$

MM3G2b Graph conic sections, identifying fundamental characteristics.

MM3G2c Write equations of conic sections given appropriate information.

Graph the equation. Identify the focus and directrix of the parabola.

1–9. See Additional Answers beginning on page AA1.

1. $x^2 = 12y$

2. $y^2 = -16x$

3. $8x^2 = -y$

4. $2y^2 - 8x = 0$

5. $4x^2 + y = 0$

6. $4x^2 - 6y = 0$

7. $x^2 - 40y = 0$

8. $x + \left(\frac{1}{20}\right)y^2 = 0$

9. $3x^2 = 4y$

Write the standard form of the equation of the parabola with the given focus and vertex at (0, 0).

10. $(3, 0)$ $y^2 = 12x$

11. $(0, 6)$ $x^2 = 24y$

12. $(-2, 0)$ $y^2 = -8x$

13. $(5, 0)$ $y^2 = 20x$

14. $\left(-\frac{1}{4}, 0\right)$ $y^2 = -x$

15. $\left(0, -\frac{3}{8}\right)$ $x^2 = -\frac{3}{2}y$

16. $\left(0, \frac{1}{4}\right)$ $x^2 = y$

17. $\left(-\frac{3}{2}, 0\right)$ $y^2 = -6x$

18. $\left(0, -\frac{1}{8}\right)$ $x^2 = -\frac{1}{2}y$

Write the standard form of the equation of the parabola with the given directrix and vertex at (0, 0).

19. $x = 2$ $y^2 = -8x$

20. $y = -12$ $x^2 = 48y$

21. $x = -6$ $y^2 = 24x$

22. $y = -5$ $x^2 = 20y$

23. $x = 4$ $y^2 = -16x$

24. $x = -\frac{1}{12}$ $y^2 = \frac{1}{3}x$

25. $y = \frac{5}{8}$ $x^2 = -\frac{5}{2}y$

26. $x = -\frac{7}{4}$ $y^2 = 7x$

27. $y = -\frac{5}{2}$ $x^2 = 10y$

28. Solar Energy Cross sections of parabolic mirrors at a solar-thermal complex can be modeled by the equation $\frac{1}{20}x^2 = y$ where x and y are measured in feet. The oil-filled heating tube is located at the focus of the parabola. How high above the vertex of the mirror is the heating tube? **5 ft**

29. Storage Building A storage building for rock salt has the shape of a paraboloid which has vertical cross sections that are parabolas. The equation of a vertical cross section is $y = -\frac{1}{8}x^2$. If the building is 24 feet high, how much rock salt will it hold? (*Hint:* The volume of a paraboloid is $v = \frac{1}{2}\pi r^2 h$ where r is the radius of the base and h is the height.) **7238.2 ft³**

24 ft

Graph and Write Equations of Circles

Georgia Performance Standards: MM3G1a, MM3G1b, MM3G1c

Goal Graph and write equations of circles.

Vocabulary

A **circle** is the set of all points (x, y) in a plane that are equidistant from a fixed point, called the **center** of the circle. The distance r between the center and any point (x, y) on the circle is the **radius.** The standard form of the equation of a circle with center at $(0, 0)$ and radius r is $x^2 + y^2 = r^2$.

Example 1 Graph the equation of a circle

Graph $x^2 = 25 - y^2$. Identify the radius of the circle.

STEP 1 **Rewrite** the equation $x^2 = 25 - y^2$ in standard form as $x^2 + y^2 = 25$.

STEP 2 **Identify** the center and radius. From the equation, the graph is a circle centered at the origin with radius $r = \sqrt{25} = 5$.

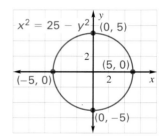

STEP 3 **Draw** the circle. First plot convenient points that are 5 units from the origin, such as $(0, 5)$, $(0, -5)$, $(5, 0)$, and $(-5, 0)$. Draw the circle that passes through the points.

Example 2 Write an equation of a circle

The point (6, 2) lies on a circle whose center is the origin. Write the standard form of the equation of the circle.

Because the point $(6, 2)$ lies on the circle, the circle's radius must be the distance between the center $(0, 0)$ and the point $(6, 2)$. Use the distance formula.

$$r = \sqrt{(6 - 0)^2 + (2 - 0)^2} = \sqrt{36 + 4} = \sqrt{40} \qquad \text{The radius is } \sqrt{40}.$$

Use the standard form with $r = \sqrt{40}$ to write an equation of the circle.

$$x^2 + y^2 = r^2 \qquad \text{Standard form}$$
$$x^2 + y^2 = (\sqrt{40})^2 \qquad \text{Substitute } \sqrt{40} \text{ for } r.$$
$$x^2 + y^2 = 40 \qquad \text{Simplify.}$$

Guided Practice for Examples 1 and 2

1–3. See Additional Answers beginning on page AA1.

Graph the equation. Identify the radius of the circle.

1. $x^2 + y^2 = 16$ **2.** $x^2 = 81 - y^2$ **3.** $y^2 - 9 = -x^2$

4. Write the standard form of the equation of the circle that passes through $(3, 2)$ and whose center is the origin. $x^2 + y^2 = 13$

Example 3   Find an equation of a line tangent to a circle

Find an equation of the line tangent to the circle $x^2 + y^2 = 10$ at $(-1, 3)$.

Solution

A line tangent to a circle is perpendicular to the radius at the point of tangency. Because the radius to the point $(-1, 3)$ has slope $m = \dfrac{3 - 0}{-1 - 0} = -3$, the slope of the tangent line at $(-1, 3)$ is the negative reciprocal of -3, or $\dfrac{1}{3}$. An equation of the tangent line is as follows:

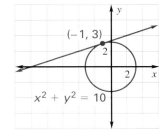

$y - 3 = \dfrac{1}{3}(x - (-1))$ Point-slope form

$y - 3 = \dfrac{1}{3}x + \dfrac{1}{3}$ Distributive property

$y = \dfrac{1}{3}x + \dfrac{10}{3}$ Solve for y.

Example 4   Write a circular model

Store Delivery A furniture store advertises free delivery up to a 50 mile radius from the store. If a customer lives 28 miles east and 41 miles north of the store, does the customer qualify for free delivery?

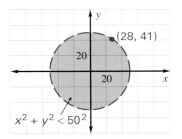

In the diagram above, the origin represents the store and the positive y-axis represents north.

STEP 1 **Write** an inequality for the region covered by free delivery. From the diagram, this region is all points that satisfy the inequality $x^2 + y^2 < 50^2$.

STEP 2 **Substitute** the coordinates $(28, 41)$ into the inequality.

$x^2 + y^2 < 50^2$ Inequality from Step 1

$28^2 + 41^2 \overset{?}{<} 50^2$ Substitute for x and y.

$2465 < 2500$ The inequality is true.

The customer does qualify for free delivery.

Guided Practice for Examples 3 and 4

5. Write an equation of the line tangent to the circle $x^2 + y^2 = 20$ at $(2, 4)$. $y = -\dfrac{1}{2}x + 5$

6. In Example 4, determine if a customer who lives 30 miles west and 41 miles south qualifies for free delivery. **The customer does not qualify for free delivery.**

UNIT 5

LESSON 5.2 **Exercise Set A**

MM3G1a   Find equations of circles.

MM3G1b   Graph a circle given an equation in general form.

MM3G1c   Find the equation of a tangent line to a circle at a given point.

Graph the equation. Identify the radius of the circle.

1–6. See Additional Answers beginning on page AA1.

1. $x^2 + y^2 = 9$

2. $x^2 + y^2 = 20$

3. $x^2 + y^2 = 64$

4. $x^2 + y^2 = 50$

5. $5x^2 + 5y^2 = 80$

6. $3x^2 + 3y^2 = 120$

7. **Error Analysis** *Describe* and correct the error in graphing $5x^2 + 5y^2 = 80$.
See Additional Answers beginning on page AA1.

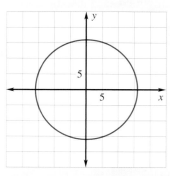

The radius of the circle is 16.

Write the standard form of the equation of the circle with the given radius and whose center is the origin.

8. 11 $x^2 + y^2 = 121$

9. $4\sqrt{5}$ $x^2 + y^2 = 80$

10. $2\sqrt{7}$ $x^2 + y^2 = 28$

11. $\sqrt{7}$ $x^2 + y^2 = 7$

12. $2\sqrt{5}$ $x^2 + y^2 = 20$

13. $3\sqrt{10}$ $x^2 + y^2 = 90$

Write the standard form of the equation of the circle that passes through the given point and whose center is the origin.

14. $(0, -10)$ $x^2 + y^2 = 100$

15. $(-3, -4)$ $x^2 + y^2 = 25$

16. $(-4, -1)$ $x^2 + y^2 = 17$

17. $(2, 3)$ $x^2 + y^2 = 13$

18. $(-3, 5)$ $x^2 + y^2 = 34$

19. $(4, -6)$ $x^2 + y^2 = 52$

The equations of both circles and parabolas are given. Graph the equation.

20. $x^2 + 3y = 0$

21. $2x^2 + 2y^2 = 8$

22. $x^2 - 8y = 0$

20–22. See Additional Answers beginning on page AA1.

Write an equation of the line tangent to the given circle at the given point.

23. $x^2 + y^2 = 17; (1, 4)$ $y = -\frac{1}{4}x + \frac{17}{4}$

24. $x^2 + y^2 = 52; (-4, 6)$ $y = \frac{2}{3}x + \frac{26}{3}$

25. **Capitol Dome** The Capitol Dome sits atop the Capitol Building in Washington, D.C. The base of the dome is a circle with a diameter of 96 feet. Suppose a coordinate plane was placed over the base of the dome with the origin at the center of the dome. Write an equation in standard form for the outside boundary of the base of the dome. $x^2 + y^2 = 2304$

UNIT 5

MM3G1a Find equations of circles.

MM3G1b Graph a circle given an equation in general form.

MM3G1c Find the equation of a tangent line to a circle at a given point.

Graph the equation. Identify the radius of the circle. 1–6. See Additional Answers beginning on page AA1.

1. $x^2 + y^2 = 100$

2. $\frac{1}{3}x^2 + \frac{1}{3}y^2 = 12$

3. $2x^2 + 2y^2 = 98$

4. $4x^2 + 4y^2 = 96$

5. $3x^2 + 3y^2 = 54$

6. $7x^2 + 7y^2 = 196$

Write the standard form of the equation of the circle with the given radius and whose center is the origin.

7. $\sqrt{13}$ $x^2 + y^2 = 13$

8. $2\sqrt{7}$ $x^2 + y^2 = 28$

9. $4\sqrt{17}$ $x^2 + y^2 = 272$

Write the standard form of the equation of the circle that passes through the given point and whose center is the origin.

10. $(7, -4)$ $x^2 + y^2 = 65$

11. $(10, 2)$ $x^2 + y^2 = 104$

12. $(2, -12)$ $x^2 + y^2 = 148$

13. $(-2, -4)$ $x^2 + y^2 = 20$

14. $(3, \sqrt{5})$ $x^2 + y^2 = 14$

15. $\left(\frac{1}{2}, -5\right)$ $x^2 + y^2 = \frac{101}{4}$

Write an equation of the line tangent to the given circle at the given point.

16. $x^2 + y^2 = 13; (3, -2)$ $y = \frac{3}{2}x - \frac{13}{2}$

17. $x^2 + y^2 = 40; (2\sqrt{6}, 4)$ $y = \frac{-\sqrt{6}}{2}x + 10$

18. **Length of a Chord** A circle has a radius of 4 and is centered at the origin. The line $y = 2$ intersects the circle to form a chord. What is the length of the chord? Round your answer to two decimal places. **6.93**

19. **Multiple Representations** The Modified Mercalli Intensity Scale rates an earthquake's "shaking strength." Suppose an earthquake has a 5.0 rating at its epicenter, a 4.6 rating 20 miles away from the epicenter, and a 4.2 rating 35 miles away.
See Additional Answers beginning on page AA1.
   a. **Drawing Graphs** Draw circles in a coordinate plane that represent the locations with a 4.6 rating and the locations with a 4.2 rating. Place the epicenter at the origin.

   b. **Writing Inequalities** For the circles in part (a), write inequalities describing the coordinates of locations with a rating of 4.6 or greater and with a rating of 4.2 or greater.

   c. **Making a Prediction** What can you predict about the rating of locations 16 miles east and 18 miles north of the epicenter? *Explain.*

20. **Semicircle** In the diagram to the right, the semicircle has a radius of $x + 5$ and the center C is the origin. The point $(15, x)$ lies on the semicircle. Find the value of x. **20**

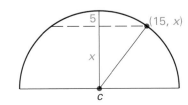

UNIT 5

LESSON 5.2

Problem Solving Workshop

Problem An air traffic control tower can detect airplanes up to 50 miles away. A plane is 38 miles east and 41 miles south of the control tower. Is the plane in the tower's range?

STEP 1 Read and Understand

What do you know? The radius of the tower's range

What do you want to find out? Whether the plane is in the tower's range

STEP 2 Make a Plan Use what you know to write and solve an inequality.

STEP 3 Solve the Problem Write an inequality for the region covered by the tower. From the diagram, this region is all points that satisfy the following inequality:
$x^2 + y^2 \le 50^2$

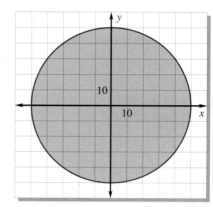

Substitute the coordinates (38, 41) into the inequality.

$$x^2 + y^2 \le 50^2 \qquad \text{Write inequality.}$$

$$38^2 + 41^2 \overset{?}{\le} 50^2 \qquad \text{Substitute for } x \text{ and } y.$$

$$3125 \not\le 2500 \qquad \text{The inequality is false.}$$

So, the plane is not in the tower's range.

STEP 4 Look Back The distance between the tower, located at the origin, and (38, 41) is $d = \sqrt{(38 - 0)^2 + (41 - 0)^2} \approx 55.9$ miles which is greater than the 50 mile range of the tower. The answer is correct.

Practice

1. **Earthquakes** Suppose an earthquake can be felt up to 80 miles from its epicenter. You are located at a point 65 miles west and 50 miles south of the epicenter. Do you feel the earthquake? **no**

2. **Radio Signals** The signals of a radio station can be received up to 65 miles away. Your house is 30 miles east and 56 miles south of the radio station. Can you receive the radio station's signals? **yes**

3. **What If?** Suppose in Exercise 2 that you want to drive west from your house. For how many miles will you be able to receive the radio station's signal? **63 mi**

4. **Lawn Sprinklers** A sprinkler can water a region with an 8 foot radius. A plant is 4 feet east and 6 feet north of the sprinkler. Is the plant in the sprinkler's range? **yes**

5. **What If?** Suppose in Exercise 4 that there is another plant located 3 feet west and 7 feet south of the sprinkler. Is this plant in the sprinkler's range? **yes**

6. **Ocean Navigation** The beam of a lighthouse can be seen for up to 25 miles. You are on a ship that is 19 miles east and 21 miles north of the lighthouse. Can you see the lighthouse beam? **no**

UNIT 5

Investigating Math Activity
Draw an Ellipse

Use before Lesson 5.3

Materials   **thumbtacks, string, cardboard, and tape**

Question

What is the relationship between an ellipse and its foci?

Explore

Draw an ellipse.

Read through the following steps on how to draw an ellipse and the questions that follow. You will need to make some observations as you are drawing your ellipse.

STEP 1   Get two thumbtacks, a piece of string, a piece of cardboard, and tape from your teacher.

STEP 2   Use the tape to attach a piece of paper to the piece of cardboard.

STEP 3   Use your pencil to mark two points on the paper, and label them F_1 and F_2. These will be your *foci*.

STEP 4   Place one thumbtack on each point.

STEP 5   Tie each end of the string to a thumbtack.

STEP 6   Place your pencil in the string and pull it until it is tight.

STEP 7   Carefully move your pencil around the foci until you reach your starting point. Remember to keep the string tight.

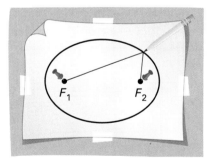

Draw Conclusions

1. What happened to the length of the string from F_2 to a point on the ellipse as the length of the string from F_1 to the same point on the ellipse increased? **The length decreased.**

2. What happened to the length of the string from F_2 to a point on the ellipse as the length of the string from F_1 to the same point on the ellipse decreased? **The length increased.**

3. Did the total length of the string ever change? **no**

4. Writing F_1 and F_2 are the *foci* of the ellipse. What must be true about the sum of the distances from the foci to any point on the ellipse? Write a definition for an ellipse in terms of the relationship of the points on the ellipse to the foci. **See Additional Answers beginning on page AA1.**

UNIT 5

Graph and Write Equations of Ellipses

Georgia Performance Standards: MM3G2b, MM3G2c

Goal Graph and write equations of ellipses.

Vocabulary

An **ellipse** is the set of all points P in a plane such that the sum of the distances between P and two fixed points, called the **foci,** is a constant. The line through the foci intersects the ellipse at two **vertices.** The **major axis** joins the vertices. Its midpoint is the ellipse's **center.** The line perpendicular to the major axis at the center intersects the ellipse at the two **co-vertices,** which are joined by the **minor axis.**

The standard form of the equation of an ellipse with center at the origin is as follows:

Equation	Major Axis	Vertices	Co-Vertices
$\dfrac{x^2}{a^2} + \dfrac{y^2}{b^2} = 1$	Horizontal	$(\pm a, 0)$	$(0, \pm b)$
$\dfrac{x^2}{b^2} + \dfrac{y^2}{a^2} = 1$	Vertical	$(0, \pm a)$	$(\pm b, 0)$

The major and minor axes are of lengths $2a$ and $2b$, respectively, where $a > b > 0$. The foci lie on the major axis at a distance of c units from the center, where $c^2 = a^2 - b^2$.

Example 1 **Graph an equation of an ellipse**

Graph the equation $9x^2 + y^2 = 36$. Identify the vertices, co-vertices, and foci of the ellipse.

STEP 1 **Rewrite** the equation in standard form.

$$9x^2 + y^2 = 36 \qquad \text{Write original equation.}$$

$$\frac{9x^2}{36} + \frac{y^2}{36} = \frac{36}{36} \qquad \text{Divide each side by 36.}$$

$$\frac{x^2}{4} + \frac{y^2}{36} = 1 \qquad \text{Simplify.}$$

STEP 2 **Identify** the vertices, co-vertices, and foci. Note that $b^2 = 4$ and $a^2 = 36$, then $b = 2$ and $a = 6$. The denominator of the y^2-term is greater than that of the x^2-term, so the major axis is vertical. The vertices of the ellipse are at $(0, \pm a) = (0, \pm 6)$. The co-vertices are at $(\pm b, 0) = (\pm 2, 0)$. Find the foci.

$$c^2 = a^2 - b^2 = 6^2 - 2^2 = 32, \text{ so } c = \sqrt{32} = 4\sqrt{2}$$

The foci are at $\left(0, \pm 4\sqrt{2}\right)$, or about $(0, \pm 5.7)$.

STEP 3 **Draw** the ellipse that passes through each vertex and co-vertex.

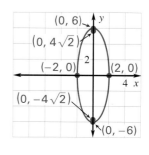

UNIT 5

Georgia Performance Standards

MM3G2b   Graph conic sections, identifying fundamental
characteristics.   ☑

MM3G2c   Write equations of conic sections given appropriate
information.   ☑

Guided Practice for Example 1

Graph the equation. Identify the vertices, co-vertices, and foci of the ellipse.   1–3. See Additional Answers beginning on page AA1.

1. $\dfrac{x^2}{16} + \dfrac{y^2}{25} = 1$

2. $\dfrac{x^2}{25} + \dfrac{y^2}{9} = 1$

3. $4x^2 + 9y^2 = 36$

Example 2   Write an equation given a vertex and co-vertex

Write an equation of the ellipse that has a vertex at (5, 0), a co-vertex at (0, 4), and center at (0, 0).

By symmetry, the ellipse must also have a vertex at $(-5, 0)$ and a co-vertex at $(0, -4)$. The major axis is horizontal with $a = 5$, and the minor axis is vertical with $b = 4$.

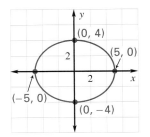

An equation is $\dfrac{x^2}{5^2} + \dfrac{y^2}{4^2} = 1$, or $\dfrac{x^2}{25} + \dfrac{y^2}{16} = 1$.

Example 3   Write an equation given a vertex and a focus

Write an equation of the ellipse that has a vertex at (0, 13), a focus at (0, −5), and center at (0, 0).

Make a sketch of the ellipse. Because the given vertex and focus lie on the y-axis, the major axis is vertical, with $a = 13$ and $c = 5$. To find b, use the equation $c^2 = a^2 - b^2$.

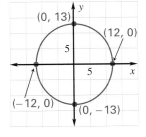

$5^2 = 13^2 - b^2$

$b^2 = 13^2 - 5^2$

$b^2 = 144$

$b = \sqrt{144}$

$b = 12$

An equation is $\dfrac{x^2}{12^2} + \dfrac{y^2}{13^2} = 1$, or $\dfrac{x^2}{144} + \dfrac{y^2}{169} = 1$.

Guided Practice for Examples 2 and 3

Write an equation of the ellipse with the given characteristics and center at (0, 0).

$x^2 + \dfrac{y^2}{9} = 1$

$\dfrac{x^2}{64} + \dfrac{y^2}{28} = 1$

4. Vertex: $(0, 3)$; Co-vertex: $(-1, 0)$

5. Vertex: $(8, 0)$; Focus: $(-6, 0)$

6. Vertex: $(0, -3)$; Co-vertex: $(2, 0)$

7. Vertex: $(-6, 0)$; Focus: $(2, 0)$ $\dfrac{x^2}{36} + \dfrac{y^2}{32} = 1$

$\dfrac{x^2}{4} + \dfrac{y^2}{9} = 1$

UNIT 5

MM3G2b Graph conic sections, identifying fundamental characteristics.

MM3G2c Write equations of conic sections given appropriate information.

Graph the equation. Identify the vertices, co-vertices, and foci of the ellipse.

1–9 See Additional Answers beginning on page AA1.

1. $\dfrac{x^2}{16} + \dfrac{y^2}{36} = 1$

2. $\dfrac{x^2}{49} + \dfrac{y^2}{4} = 1$

3. $\dfrac{x^2}{64} + \dfrac{y^2}{100} = 1$

4. $\dfrac{x^2}{25} + \dfrac{y^2}{81} = 1$

5. $16x^2 + y^2 = 16$

6. $49x^2 + 4y^2 = 196$

7. $9x^2 + 4y^2 = 36$

8. $16x^2 + 25y^2 = 400$

9. $4x^2 + 81y^2 = 324$

Write an equation of the ellipse with the given characteristics and center at (0, 0).

10. Vertex: (3, 0) $\dfrac{x^2}{9} + \dfrac{y^2}{4} = 1$
Co-vertex: (0, 2)

11. Vertex: (0, 5) $\dfrac{x^2}{1} + \dfrac{y^2}{25} = 1$
Co-vertex: (1, 0)

12. Vertex: (−6, 0) $\dfrac{x^2}{36} + \dfrac{y^2}{9} = 1$
Co-vertex: (0, −3)

13. Vertex: (0, 4) $\dfrac{x^2}{4} + \dfrac{y^2}{16} = 1$
Focus: $(0, 2\sqrt{3}\,)$

14. Vertex: (−7, 0) $\dfrac{x^2}{49} + \dfrac{y^2}{25} = 1$
Focus: $(2\sqrt{6}, 0)$

15. Co-vertex: (0, 6) $\dfrac{x^2}{64} + \dfrac{y^2}{36} = 1$
Focus: $(-2\sqrt{7}, 0)$

The equations of a parabola, a circle, and an ellipse are given. Graph the equation. **16–18 See Additional Answers beginning on page AA1.**

16. $x^2 + 12y = 0$

17. $3x^2 + 3y^2 = 48$

18. $6x^2 + 8y^2 = 96$

19. **Swimming Pool** An elliptical pool is 20 feet long and 16 feet wide. Write an equation for the boundary of the swimming pool. Assume the major axis of the pool is vertical. $\dfrac{x^2}{64} + \dfrac{y^2}{100} = 1$

20. **Race Track** The shape of a dirt race track for car racing is approximately an ellipse. The track is 400 feet long and 250 feet wide. Write an equation for the boundary of the race track. Assume the major axis of the track is horizontal. $\dfrac{x^2}{40,000} + \dfrac{y^2}{15,625} = 1$

21. **Zoo Trains** The train at a zoo encloses an area designated as the children's zoo. The track is in the shape of an ellipse that is 500 yards long and 300 yards wide.

300 yds

CHILDREN'S ZOO

500 yds

a. Write an equation for the track. Assume the major axis of the track is horizontal.

b. The area of an ellipse is $A = \pi ab$. What is the area of the children's zoo? **a.** $\dfrac{x^2}{62,500} + \dfrac{y^2}{22,500} = 1$ **b.** $37,500\pi$ yd^2

22. **Australian Football** The playing field for Australian football is an ellipse that is between 135 and 185 meters long and between 110 and 155 meters wide. Write equations of ellipses with vertical major axes that model the largest and smallest fields described. Then write on inequality that describes the possible areas of these fields. (The area of an ellipse is $A = \pi ab$.)

Largest field: $\dfrac{x^2}{6006.25} + \dfrac{y^2}{8556.25} = 1$; smallest field: $\dfrac{x^2}{3025} + \dfrac{y^2}{4556.25} = 1$; $11{,}663 \le A \le 22{,}521$ m^2

Exercise Set B

MM3G2b   Graph conic sections, identifying fundamental characteristics.

MM3G2c   Write equations of conic sections given appropriate information.

Graph the equation. Identify the vertices, co-vertices, and foci of the ellipse.

1. $\dfrac{x^2}{3} + 3y^2 = 3$

2. $\dfrac{9x^2}{16} + \dfrac{4y^2}{25} = 1$

3. $\dfrac{x^2}{48} + \dfrac{y^2}{27} = 3$ **1–6 See Additional Answers beginning on page AA1.**

4. $4x^2 + 5y^2 = 40$

5. $9x^2 + 6y^2 = 72$

6. $\dfrac{28x^2}{81} + \dfrac{63y^2}{25} = 7$

Write an equation of the ellipse with the given characteristics and center at (0, 0).

7. Vertex: $(8, 0)$ $\dfrac{x^2}{64} + \dfrac{y^2}{25} = 1$
Co-vertex: $(0, -5)$

8. Vertex: $(0, -7)$ $\dfrac{x^2}{9} + \dfrac{y^2}{49} = 1$
Co-vertex: $(3, 0)$

9. Vertex: $(13, 0)$ $\dfrac{x^2}{169} + \dfrac{y^2}{31} = 1$
Co-vertex: $(0, \sqrt{31})$

10. Vertex: $(6, 0)$ $\dfrac{x^2}{36} + \dfrac{y^2}{24} = 1$
Focus: $(2\sqrt{3}, 0)$

11. Co-vertex: $(0, 9)$ $\dfrac{x^2}{169} + \dfrac{y^2}{81} = 1$
Focus: $(2\sqrt{22}, 0)$

12. Co-vertex: $(-1, 0)$ $x^2 + \dfrac{y^2}{36} = 1$
Focus: $(0, -\sqrt{35})$

13. Gears In some industrial machines, elliptical gears are used instead of circular ones. One of these elliptical gears is 12 centimeters tall and 8 centimeters wide. Write an equation for the outline of this elliptical gear. Assume the major axis of the gear is vertical. $\dfrac{x^2}{16} + \dfrac{y^2}{36} = 1$

14. Company Logo You are in charge of designing a company logo similar to the figure at the right. The only stipulations are that the border must be an ellipse and the width of the ellipse must be three times the height. Write an equation in standard form for the outline of the logo in terms of the height h. $\dfrac{4x^2}{9h^2} + \dfrac{4y^2}{h^2} = 1$

15. Boat Tours A tour boat travels between two islands that are 12 miles apart. For a trip between the islands, there is enough fuel for a 20-mile tour.

a. The region in which the boat can travel is bounded by an ellipse. *Explain* why this is so.

b. Let $(0, 0)$ represent the center of the ellipse. Find the coordinates of each island.   **Island 1: $(-6, 0)$; Island 2: $(6, 0)$**

c. Suppose the boat travels from one island, straight past the other island to the vertex of the ellipse and back to the second island. How many miles does the boat travel? Use your answer to find the coordinates of the vertex.   **20 mi; $(\pm 10, 0)$**

d. Write an equation of the ellipse. $\dfrac{x^2}{100} + \dfrac{y^2}{64} = 1$

a. The greatest distance the boat can travel between islands is 20 mi, going straight out to a point and then straight to the other island. This is the definition of an ellipse.

UNIT 5

Graph and Write Equations of Hyperbolas

Georgia Performance Standards: MM3G2b, MM3G2c

Goal Graph and write equations of hyperbolas.

Vocabulary

A **hyperbola** is the set of all points P in a plane such that the *difference* of the distances between P and two fixed points, again called the **foci,** is a constant. The line through the foci intersects the hyperbola at the two **vertices.** The **transverse axis** joins the vertices. Its midpoint is the hyperbola's **center.**

The standard form of the equation of an ellipse with center at the origin is as follows:

Equation	Transverse Axis	Asymptotes	Vertices
$\dfrac{x^2}{a^2} - \dfrac{y^2}{b^2} = 1$	Horizontal	$y = \pm\dfrac{b}{a}x$	$(\pm a, 0)$
$\dfrac{y^2}{a^2} - \dfrac{x^2}{b^2} = 1$	Vertical	$y = \pm\dfrac{a}{b}x$	$(0, \pm a)$

The foci lie on the transverse axis, c units from the center, where $c^2 = a^2 + b^2$.

Example 1   Graph an equation of a hyperbola

Graph $4x^2 - 9y^2 = 36$. Identify the vertices, foci, and asymptotes of the hyperbola.

STEP 1 **Rewrite** the equation in standard form.

$$4x^2 - 9y^2 = 36 \qquad \text{Write original equation.}$$

$$\frac{4x^2}{36} - \frac{9y^2}{36} = \frac{36}{36} \qquad \text{Divide each side by 36.}$$

$$\frac{x^2}{9} - \frac{y^2}{4} = 1 \qquad \text{Simplify.}$$

STEP 2 **Identify** the vertices, foci, and asymptotes. Note that $a^2 = 9$ and $b^2 = 4$, then $a = 3$ and $b = 2$. The x^2-term is positive, so the transverse axis is horizontal and the vertices are at $(\pm 3, 0)$. Find the foci.

$$c^2 = a^2 + b^2 = 3^2 + 2^2 = 13, \text{ so } c = \sqrt{13}$$

The foci are at $(\pm\sqrt{13}, 0) \approx (\pm 3.6, 0)$.

The asymptotes are $y = \pm\dfrac{b}{a}x$, or $y = \pm\dfrac{2}{3}x$.

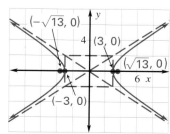

STEP 3 **Draw** the hyperbola. First draw a rectangle centered at the origin that is $2b = 4$ units high and $2a = 6$ units wide. The asymptotes pass through opposite corners of the rectangle. Draw the hyperbola passing through the vertices and approaching the asymptotes.

Example 2 Write an equation of a hyperbola

Write an equation of the hyperbola with foci at (0, 7) and (0, −7) and vertices at (0, 6) and (0, −6).

The foci and vertices lie on the y-axis equidistant from the origin, so the transverse axis is vertical and the center is the origin. The foci are each 7 units from the center, so $c = 7$. The vertices are each 6 units from the center, so $a = 6$.

Because $c^2 = a^2 + b^2$, you have $b^2 = c^2 - a^2$. Find b^2.

$$b^2 = c^2 - a^2 = 7^2 - 6^2 = 13$$

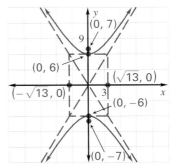

Because the transverse axis is vertical, the standard form of the equation is as follows:

$$\frac{y^2}{6^2} - \frac{x^2}{13} = 1 \qquad \text{Substitute 6 for } a \text{ and 13 for } b^2.$$

$$\frac{y^2}{36} - \frac{x^2}{13} = 1 \qquad \text{Simplify.}$$

Example 3 Solve a multi-step problem

Hyperbolic Mirror The focus of hyperbolic mirror has coordinates (15, 0). Find the vertex $(a, 0)$ of the mirror, if the point (15, 16) is on the mirror.

STEP 1 The major axis is horizontal with $c = 15$. To write an equation for the mirror, use $b^2 = c^2 - a^2$ and the point (15, 16).

$$\frac{15^2}{a^2} - \frac{16^2}{c^2 - a^2} = 1$$

STEP 2 Solve $\dfrac{15^2}{a^2} - \dfrac{16^2}{15^2 - a^2} = 1$ for a. Because the mirror is represented by the right branch of the hyperbola and the vertex lies between the center (0, 0) and the focus (15, 0), use the solution $a = 9$.

The vertex is (9, 0).

Guided Practice for Examples 1, 2, and 3

1. Graph $x^2 - 4y^2 = 16$. Identify the vertices, foci, and asymptotes.
    See Additional Answers beginning on page AA1.

2. Write an equation of the hyperbola with foci at $\left(0, \sqrt{13}\right)$ and $\left(0, -\sqrt{13}\right)$ and vertices at (0, 3) and (0, −3). $\dfrac{y^2}{9} - \dfrac{x^2}{4} = 1$

3. In Example 3, find the vertex if the focus is (20, 0) and the point on the mirror is (15, 12). **(12, 0)**

UNIT 5

LESSON 5.4 **Exercise Set A**

MM3G2b   Graph conic sections, identifying fundamental characteristics.

MM3G2c   Write equations of conic sections given appropriate information.

Graph the equation. Identify the vertices, foci, and asymptotes of the hyperbola. 1–6. See Additional Answers beginning on page AA1.

1. $\dfrac{x^2}{16} - \dfrac{y^2}{4} = 1$

2. $\dfrac{x^2}{9} - \dfrac{y^2}{36} = 1$

3. $\dfrac{y^2}{25} - \dfrac{x^2}{4} = 1$

4. $x^2 - 4y^2 = 4$

5. $2y^2 - 10x^2 = 40$

6. $16y^2 - 4x^2 = 64$

7. Error Analysis *Describe* and correct the error in graphing $\dfrac{x^2}{64} - \dfrac{y^2}{16} = 1$.
See Additional Answers beginning on page AA1.

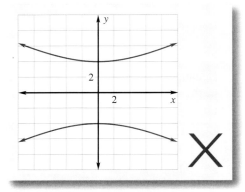

Write an equation of the hyperbola with the given foci and vertices.

8. Foci: $(6, 0)$, $(-6, 0)$ $\dfrac{x^2}{16} - \dfrac{y^2}{20} = 1$
Vertices: $(4, 0)$, $(-4, 0)$

9. Foci: $(0, 8)$, $(0, -8)$ $\dfrac{y^2}{49} - \dfrac{x^2}{15} = 1$
Vertices: $(0, 7)$, $(0, -7)$

10. Foci: $(0, -8)$, $(0, 8)$ $\dfrac{y^2}{25} - \dfrac{x^2}{39} = 1$
Vertices: $(0, -5)$, $(0, 5)$

11. Foci: $\left(0, -2\sqrt{5}\right)$, $\left(0, 2\sqrt{5}\right)$ $\dfrac{y^2}{16} - \dfrac{x^2}{4} = 1$
Vertices: $(0, -4)$, $(0, 4)$

12. Foci: $\left(\sqrt{13}, 0\right)$, $\left(-\sqrt{13}, 0\right)$ $\dfrac{x^2}{4} - \dfrac{y^2}{9} = 1$
Vertices: $(2, 0)$, $(-2, 0)$

13. Foci: $\left(0, \sqrt{61}\right)$, $\left(0, -\sqrt{61}\right)$ $\dfrac{y^2}{36} - \dfrac{x^2}{25} = 1$
Vertices: $(0, 6)$, $(0, -6)$

14. Foci: $(16, 0)$, $(-16, 0)$ $\dfrac{x^2}{196} - \dfrac{y^2}{60} = 1$
Vertices: $(14, 0)$, $(-14, 0)$

15. Foci: $(0, 12)$, $(0, -12)$ $\dfrac{y^2}{108} - \dfrac{x^2}{36} = 1$
Vertices: $\left(0, 6\sqrt{3}\right)$, $\left(0, -6\sqrt{3}\right)$

The equations of a parabola, an ellipse, and a hyperbola are given. Graph the equation. 16–18. See Additional Answers beginning on page AA1.

16. $25x^2 + 4y^2 = 100$

17. $25x^2 + 4y = 0$

18. $25x^2 - 4y^2 = 100$

19. **Machine Shop** A machine shop needs to make a small automotive part by drilling four holes of radius r from a flat circular piece of radius R. The area of the resulting part is eight square inches. Write an equation of a hyperbola in standard form that relates r and R. $\dfrac{R^2}{\left(\dfrac{8}{\pi}\right)} - \dfrac{r^2}{\left(\dfrac{2}{\pi}\right)} = 1$

UNIT 5

Exercise Set B

MM3G2b   Graph conic sections, identifying fundamental characteristics.

MM3G2c   Write equations of conic sections given appropriate information.

Graph the equation. Identify the vertices, foci, and asymptotes of the hyperbola. 1–6. See Additional Answers beginning on page AA1.

1. $\dfrac{x^2}{64} - \dfrac{y^2}{21} = 1$

2. $\dfrac{x^2}{32} - \dfrac{y^2}{48} = 1$

3. $\dfrac{y^2}{18} - \dfrac{x^2}{81} = 1$

4. $24x^2 - 13y^2 = 312$

5. $12y^2 - 40x^2 = 480$

6. $16y^2 - 9x^2 = 160$

Write an equation of the hyperbola with the given foci and vertices.

7. Foci: $(8, 0), (-8, 0)$ $\dfrac{x^2}{36} - \dfrac{y^2}{28} = 1$

Vertices: $(6, 0), (-6, 0)$

8. Foci: $\left(0, \dfrac{5}{2}\right), \left(0, -\dfrac{5}{2}\right)$ $\dfrac{y^2}{4} - \dfrac{4x^2}{9} = 1$

Vertices: $(0, 2), (0, -2)$

The equations of a parabola, an ellipse, and a hyperbola are given. Graph the equation. 9–11. See Additional Answers beginning on page AA1.

9. $121x^2 + 81y^2 = 9801$

10. $108y^2 - 81x = 0$

11. $121x^2 - 81y^2 = 9801$

Write an equation of the hyperbola with the given vertices and asymptotes.

12. Vertices: $(1, 0), (-1, 0)$ $x^2 - \dfrac{y^2}{9} = 1$

Asymptotes: $y = 3x, y = -3x$

13. Vertices: $(0, 4), (0, -4)$ $\dfrac{y^2}{16} - \dfrac{x^2}{4} = 1$

Asymptotes: $y = 2x, y = -2x$

14. Rope Pulley The center cross section of a rope pulley forms a hyperbolic shape for the outline of the concaved groove. The horizontal transverse axis of the hyperbolic outline has a distance of 8 centimeters from vertex to vertex and the foci are $2\sqrt{6}$ centimeters from the center. Write an equation that models the concaved groove. $\dfrac{x^2}{16} - \dfrac{y^2}{8} = 1$

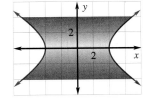

15. Multiple Representations A circular walkway is to be built around a fountain in a park. There is enough concrete available for the walkway to have an area of 500 square feet.   See Additional Answers beginning on page AA1.

a. Writing an Equation Let the inside and outside radii of the walkway be x feet and y feet, respectively. Draw a diagram of the situation. Then write an equation relating x and y.

b. Making a Table Give four possible pairs of dimensions x and y that satisfy the equation from part (a).

c. Drawing a Graph Graph the equation from part (a). What portion of the graph represents solutions that make sense in this situation?

d. Reasoning How does the width of the walkway, $y - x$, change as both x and y increase? *Explain* why this makes sense.

Translate and Classify Conic Sections

Georgia Performance Standards: MM3G2a, MM3G2b, MM3G2c

Goal Translate conic sections.

Vocabulary

Because parabolas, circles, ellipses, and hyperbolas are formed when a plane intersects a double-napped cone, they are called **conic sections** or **conics.**

In the following standard form of equations for translated conics, the point (h, k) is the *vertex* of the parabola and the *center* of other conics.

Circle $(x - h)^2 + (y - k)^2 = r^2$

	Horizontal axis	**Vertical axis**
Parabola	$(y - k)^2 = 4p(x - h)$	$(x - h)^2 = 4p(y - k)$
Ellipse	$\dfrac{(x - h)^2}{a^2} + \dfrac{(y - k)^2}{b^2} = 1$	$\dfrac{(x - h)^2}{b^2} + \dfrac{(y - k)^2}{a^2} = 1$
Hyperbola	$\dfrac{(x - h)^2}{a^2} - \dfrac{(y - k)^2}{b^2} = 1$	$\dfrac{(y - k)^2}{a^2} - \dfrac{(x - h)^2}{b^2} = 1$

Any conic can be described by a **general second-degree equation** in x and y: $Ax^2 + Bxy + Cy^2 + Dx + Ey + F = 0$. The expression $B^2 - 4AC$ is the **discriminant** of the equation and can be used to identify the type of conic.

Discriminant	**Type of Conic**
$B^2 - 4AC < 0$, $B = 0$, and $A = C$	Circle
$B^2 - 4AC < 0$ and either $B \neq 0$ or $A \neq C$	Ellipse
$B^2 - 4AC = 0$	Parabola
$B^2 - 4AC > 0$	Hyperbola

Example 1   Graph the equation of a translated ellipse

Graph $\dfrac{(x + 2)^2}{9} + \dfrac{(y - 1)^2}{16} = 1$.

STEP 1 **Compare** the given equation to the standard form of an ellipse. The graph is an ellipse with center at $(h, k) = (-2, 1)$.

STEP 2 **Plot** the center, vertices $(-2, 5)$ and $(-2, -3)$, and co-vertices $(-5, 1)$ and $(1, 1)$.

STEP 3 **Draw** the ellipse through the points.

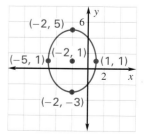

Guided Practice for Example 1

1–2. See Additional Answers beginning on page AA1.

Graph the equation. Identify the important characteristics of the graph.

1. $\dfrac{(x - 2)^2}{4} - \dfrac{(y - 2)^2}{5} = 1$

2. $(x - 4)^2 = 4(y + 1)$

Example 2   **Write an equation of a translated circle**

Write an equation of the circle with center at (3, −1) and radius $r = \sqrt{10}$.

STEP 1   **Determine** the form of the equation. The equation has the form $(x - h)^2 + (y - k)^2 = r^2$.

STEP 2   **Identify** h and k. The center is at $(3, -1)$, so $h = 3$ and $k = -1$.

STEP 3   **Find** r^2. Because $r = \sqrt{10}$, $r^2 = 10$.

The standard form of the equation is $(x - 3)^2 + (y + 1)^2 = 10$.

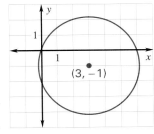

Example 3   **Classify a conic**

Classify the conic $4x^2 - 24x + 9y^2 = 0$. Then graph the equation.

Note that $A = 4$, $B = 0$, and $C = 9$, so the value of the discriminant is:

$$B^2 - 4AC = 0^2 - 4(4)(9) = -144$$

Because $B^2 - 4AC < 0$ and $A \neq C$, the conic is an ellipse.

To graph the ellipse, first complete the square in x.

$$4x^2 - 24x + 9y^2 = 0$$
$$4(x^2 - 6x) + 9y^2 = 0$$
$$4(x^2 - 6x + \underline{\ ?\ }) + 9y^2 = 0 + 4(\underline{\ ?\ })$$
$$4(x^2 - 6x + 9) + 9y^2 = 4(9)$$
$$4(x - 3)^2 + 9y^2 = 36$$
$$\frac{(x - 3)^2}{9} + \frac{y^2}{4} = 1$$

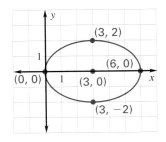

From the equation, the axis is horizontal, $(h, k) = (3, 0)$, $a = 3$, and $b = 2$. Use these facts to draw the ellipse.

Guided Practice for Examples 2 and 3

3.   Write an equation of a circle with center $(-4, 2)$ and radius $r = 3$.
$(x + 4)^2 + (y - 2)^2 = 9$

Classify the conic and write its equation in standard form. Then graph the equation.   4 and 5. See Additional Answers beginning on page AA1.

4. $x^2 + 4y^2 + 2x - 8y + 1 = 0$ **5.** $x^2 - 4x - 4y = 0$

UNIT 5

MM3G2a Convert equations of conics by completing the square.

MM3G2b Graph conic sections, identifying fundamental characteristics.

MM3G2c Write equations of conic sections given appropriate information.

Graph the equation. Identify the important characteristics of the graph.

1–12. See Additional Answers beginning on page AA1.

1. $x^2 + (y - 3)^2 = 9$

2. $\dfrac{(x - 4)^2}{16} + \dfrac{(y - 2)^2}{4} = 1$

3. $(x - 3)^2 = 8(y + 4)$

4. $\dfrac{(y + 2)^2}{18} - \dfrac{(x + 1)^2}{25} = 1$

5. $\dfrac{(x + 3)^2}{32} + \dfrac{(y - 4)^2}{36} = 1$

6. $(x - 5)^2 + (y + 2)^2 = 28$

7. $(x - 6)^2 + (y - 2)^2 = 4$

8. $\dfrac{(y - 8)^2}{16} - \dfrac{(x + 3)^2}{4} = 1$

9. $(y - 4)^2 = 3(x + 2)$

10. $\dfrac{(x + 1)^2}{16} + \dfrac{(y + 3)^2}{4} = 1$

11. $(x + 7)^2 + (y - 1)^2 = 1$

12. $(x + 7)^2 = 12(y - 3)$

Write an equation of the conic section.

13. Circle with center at $(2, -6)$ and a radius of 4 $(x - 2)^2 + (y + 6)^2 = 16$

14. Parabola with vertex at $(3, 3)$ and focus at $(3, 0)$ $(x - 3)^2 = -12(y - 3)$

15. Ellipse with vertices at $(-2, -1)$ and $(-2, 7)$ and co-vertices at $(-4, 3)$ and $(0, 3)$ $\dfrac{(x + 2)^2}{4} + \dfrac{(y - 3)^2}{16} = 1$

16. Hyperbola with vertices at $(2, 4)$ and $(8, 4)$ and foci at $(-2, 4)$ and $(12, 4)$ $\dfrac{(x - 5)^2}{9} - \dfrac{(y - 4)^2}{40} = 1$

17. Ellipse with vertices at $(2, -3)$ and $(2, 6)$ and foci at $(2, 0)$ and $(2, 3)$ $\dfrac{(x - 2)^2}{18} + \dfrac{(y - 1.5)^2}{20.25} = 1$

18. Parabola with vertex at $(-8, 1)$ and focus at $(-8, 3)$ $(x + 8)^2 = 8(y - 1)$

19. Circle with center at $(3, -4)$ and radius of $4\sqrt{3}$ $(x - 3)^2 + (y + 4)^2 = 48$

20. Hyperbola with vertices at $\left(0, -2\sqrt{6}\right)$ and $\left(0, 2\sqrt{6}\right)$ and foci at $(0, -5)$ and $(0, 5)$ $\dfrac{y^2}{24} - \dfrac{x^2}{1} = 1$

21. Parabola with vertex at $(6, 2)$ and directrix $x = 2$ $(y - 2)^2 = 16(x - 6)$

22. **Error Analysis** *Describe* and correct error in writing the standard form of an equation of the circle with center $(3, 7)$ and radius 5.

Center: $(h, k) = (3, 7)$; radius $= 5$

Equation: $(x + 3)^2 + (y + 7)^2 = 25$

The standard form of a circle is $(x - h)^2 + (y - k)^2 = r^2$, not $(x + h)^2 + (y + k)^2 = r^2$;

Equation: $(x - 3)^2 + (y - 7)^2 = 25$

Exercise Set A *(continued)*

Use the discriminant to classify the conic section.

23. $2x^2 + 5x + y + 14 = 0$ **parabola**

24. $4x^2 + 4y^2 - 6x + 8y - 10 = 0$ **circle**

25. $5x^2 - 5y^2 + 4x - 3y + 4 = 0$ **hyperbola**

26. $x^2 + 4y^2 - 8x - 12y - 2 = 0$ **ellipse**

27. $9x^2 + 4y^2 + 36x - 24y + 36 = 0$ **ellipse**

28. $x^2 - 4y^2 + 3x - 26y - 30 = 0$ **hyperbola**

29. $4x^2 - 9y^2 + 18y + 3x = 0$ **hyperbola**

30. $x^2 + y^2 - 10x - 2y = -10$ **circle**

31. $62x^2 + 81y^2 - 868x - 1984 = 0$ **ellipse**

32. $y^2 - 6x - 16y + 52 = 0$ **parabola**

33. $x^2 + y^2 + 14x - 2y + 49 = 0$ **circle**

34. $4x^2 - 25y^2 - 32x - 150y - 261 = 0$ **hyperbola**

**Classify the conic section and write its equation in standard form.
Then graph the equation.** 35–44. See Additional Answers beginning on page AA1.

35. $y^2 + 8x - 2y - 15 = 0$

36. $x^2 + y^2 - 12x + 2y + 15 = 0$

37. $x^2 - 9y^2 + 54y - 90 = 0$

38. $9x^2 + 36y^2 + 54x - 144y - 99 = 0$

39. $x^2 + 10x - 6y + 7 = 0$

40. $-2x^2 + 5y^2 + 24x - 20y - 102 = 0$

41. $y^2 - 12y + 4x + 4 = 0$

42. $x^2 + y^2 - 6x - 8y + 24 = 0$

43. $9x^2 - y^2 - 72x + 8y + 119 = 0$

44. $4x^2 + y^2 - 48x - 4y + 48 = 0$

45. Racetrack A race track is in the shape of a figure eight, which consists of two externally tangent circles. Write equations for the circles if each is 450 feet in diameter, the circles intersect at the origin, and the centers are on the y-axis. Then graph the equations. **See Additional Answers beginning on page AA1.**

46. Designing a Menu As part of the graphics art department, your job is to create various art pieces and graphical models for your documents. Your newest project is to design a menu that incorporates the picture of a tree. The equation used to model the tree trunk is $9x^2 - y^2 + 8y - 52 = 0$. Write this equation in standard form and then graph the equation. **See Additional Answers beginning on page AA1.**

47. Astronomy An asteroid's path is modeled by $20x^2 - 30y^2 - 60x - 55 = 0$ where x and y are in astronomical units from the sun. Classify the path and write its equation in standard form. Then graph the equation.
See Additional Answers beginning on page AA1.

48. Long Jump A competitor's first long jump can be modeled by $x^2 - 20x + 20y = 0$ where x and y are measured in feet, and the origin marks the start of the jump. Write the equation in standard form. How far was the first jump? $(x - 10)^2 = -20(y - 5)$; 20 ft

MM3G2a Convert equations of conics by completing the square.

MM3G2b Graph conic sections, identifying fundamental characteristics.

MM3G2c Write equations of conic sections given appropriate information.

Graph the equation. Identify the important characteristics of the graph.

1–8. See Additional Answers beginning on page AA1.

1. $(y + 4)^2 = -16(x - 5)$

2. $\dfrac{(x - 2)^2}{20} + \dfrac{(y + 5)^2}{9} = 1$

3. $(x - 3)^2 + (y + 4)^2 = 18$

4. $\dfrac{(y + 7)^2}{26} - \dfrac{(x - 4)^2}{12} = 1$

5. $\dfrac{(x + 6)^2}{11} + \dfrac{(y + 5)^2}{27} = 1$

6. $(x - 8)^2 = 6(y + 3)$

7. $\dfrac{(x - 5)^2}{100} + \dfrac{(y + 1)^2}{9} = 1$

8. $(x + 2)^2 + (y - 4.5)^2 = 16$

Write an equation of the conic section.

9. Ellipse with foci at $(3, -4)$ and $(5, -4)$ and vertices at $(-1, -4)$ and $(9, -4)$ $\dfrac{(x - 4)^2}{25} + \dfrac{(y + 4)^2}{624} = 1$

10. Parabola with vertex at $(3, -2)$ and focus at $(3, -4)$ $(x - 3)^2 = -8(y + 2)$

11. Circle with center at $(-3, -7)$ and radius of $\sqrt{7}$ $(x + 3)^2 + (y + 7)^2 = 7$

12. Parabola with vertex at $(2, 6)$ and directrix $y = 8$ $(x - 2)^2 = -8(y - 6)$

13. Ellipse with vertices at $(2, -1)$ and $(10, -1)$ and foci at $(6 - \sqrt{3}, -1)$ and $(6 + \sqrt{3}, -1)$ $\dfrac{(x - 6)^2}{16} + \dfrac{(y + 1)^2}{13} = 1$

14. Hyperbola with vertices at $(-3, 0)$ and $(-3, 4)$ and foci at $(-3, 2 - \sqrt{7})$ and $(-3, 2 + \sqrt{7})$ $\dfrac{(y - 2)^2}{4} - \dfrac{(x + 3)^2}{3} = 1$

15. Circle with center at $\left(-\dfrac{1}{2}, \dfrac{3}{4}\right)$ and radius of $\dfrac{2}{3}$ $\left(x + \dfrac{1}{2}\right)^2 + \left(y - \dfrac{3}{4}\right)^2 = \dfrac{4}{9}$

16. Hyperbola with vertices at $\left(-\dfrac{5}{6}, -1\dfrac{1}{3}\right)$ and $\left(-\dfrac{5}{6} \text{ and } 2\dfrac{2}{3}\right)$ and foci at $\left(-\dfrac{5}{6}, \dfrac{2}{3} - \sqrt{13}\right)$ and $\left(-\dfrac{5}{6}, \dfrac{2}{3} + \sqrt{13}\right)$ $\dfrac{\left(y - \dfrac{2}{3}\right)^2}{4} - \dfrac{\left(x + \dfrac{5}{6}\right)^2}{9} = 1$

Use the discriminant to classify the conic section.

17. $2x^2 + 8xy + y - 4 = 0$ **hyperbola**

18. $9x^2 - 4y^2 - x - 12y - 1 = 0$ **hyperbola**

19. $7x^2 + 7y^2 - 14x + 34 = 0$ **circle**

20. $3x^2 + 5y^2 + x - 2y = 0$ **ellipse**

21. $36x^2 + 16y^2 - 25x + 22y + 2 = 0$ **ellipse**

22. $9y^2 - x^2 + 2x + 54y + 62 = 0$ **hyperbola**

Exercise Set B *(continued)*

**Classify the conic section and write its equation in standard form.
Then graph the equation.** 23–28. See Additional Answers beginning on page AA1.

23. $x^2 - 14x - 9y + 22 = 0$

24. $x^2 + y^2 + 10x - 12y + 40 = 0$

25. $18x^2 + 10y^2 - 108x - 100y + 232 = 0$

26. $8x^2 - 25y^2 + 32x + 150y - 393 = 0$

27. $4x^2 + 14y^2 + 8x + 56y + 4 = 0$

28. $-32x^2 + 20y^2 + 256x - 280y - 172 = 0$

29. **Machining** As part of a computer program, the programmer must input an equation to tell a machine the exterior shape of the part the machine is producing. The equation used to model the shape is $9x^2 + 36y^2 - 108x - 216y + 324 = 0$. Classify the conic. Write the equation in standard form and then graph the equation. **See Additional Answers beginning on page AA1.**

30. **Golf Shot** A golfer has 125 yards left to the hole. The approach shot can be modeled by $2x^2 - 240x + 180y = 0$ where x and y are measured in yards, and the origin is the point of impact. Write the equation in standard form for the path of the shot. Assuming the shot was straight at the hole, how many yards from the hole does the ball land? $(x - 60)^2 = -90(y - 40)$; **5 yd from the hole**

31. **Multiple Representations** Each cable of a suspension bridge is suspended (in the shape of a parabola) between two towers that are 120 meters apart. The top of each tower is 30 meters above the roadway. The cables touch the roadway halfway between the towers. **See Additional Answers beginning on page AA1.**

a. **Drawing a Graph** Represent the situation described above using a parabola in a coordinate plane. Assume the base of one of the towers is located at the origin.

b. **Finding Coordinates** The directrix of the parabola is $y = -30$. Find the coordinates of the focus.

c. **Writing an Equation** Write an equation in standard form of the parabola.

d. **Finding the Height** What is the height of the suspension cable 30 meters from the base of a tower?

32. **Communication Towers** A cellular phone transmission tower has a range of 20 miles. A second tower that is located 5 miles south and 10 miles west of the first tower has a range of 15 miles. Write an inequality that describes each tower's range. Assume that the first tower is located at the origin. Do the regions covered by the towers overlap? *Explain* your reasoning. $x^2 + y^2 \leq 400$; $(x + 10)^2 + (y + 5)^2 \leq 225$; **Yes, the center of the second tower is within the region covered by the first tower, so the regions overlap.**

Solve Quadratic Systems

Georgia Performance Standards: MM3G1d, MM3G1e

Goal Solve quadratic systems.

....

Vocabulary

Systems that include one or more equations of conics are called **quadratic systems.**

Example 1 **Solve a linear-quadratic system by graphing**

Solve the system using a graphing calculator.

$$x^2 = 5x - y \qquad \text{Equation 1}$$

$$y - x = 0 \qquad \text{Equation 2}$$

STEP 1 **Solve** each equation for y.

$$x^2 = 5x - y \qquad\qquad\qquad y - x = 0$$

$$y = 5x - x^2 \quad \text{Equation 1} \qquad y = x \quad \text{Equation 2}$$

STEP 2 **Graph** the equations $y = 5x - x^2$ and $y = x$.
Use the *intersect* feature of the calculator to find
the coordinates of the intersection points. The
graphs of $y = 5x - x^2$ and $y = x$ intersect at
$(0, 0)$ and $(4, 4)$.

The solutions are $(0, 0)$ and $(4, 4)$. Check the
solutions by substituting the coordinates of the
points into each of the original equations.

Example 2 **Solve a linear-quadratic system by substitution**

Solve the system using substitution.

$$x^2 + y^2 = 25 \qquad \text{Equation 1}$$

$$y = x + 1 \qquad \text{Equation 2}$$

Solution

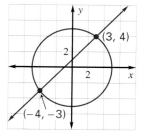

$$x^2 + y^2 = 25 \qquad\qquad \text{Equation 1}$$

$$x^2 + (x + 1)^2 = 25 \qquad\qquad \text{Substitute } x + 1 \text{ for } y.$$

$$2x^2 + 2x - 24 = 0 \qquad\qquad \text{Simplify.}$$

$$2(x + 4)(x - 3) = 0 \qquad\qquad \text{Factor trinomial.}$$

$$x = -4 \text{ or } x = 3 \qquad\qquad \text{Zero product property}$$

To find each y-coordinate, substitute each x-value in Equation 2. The solutions are
$(-4, -3)$ and $(3, 4)$. Check the solutions by graphing the equations of the system.

Georgia Performance Standards

MM3G1d Solve a system of equations involving a circle and a line.

MM3G1e Solve a system of equations involving two circles. ☑

Guided Practice for Examples 1 and 2

1. Solve the system consisting of the equations $y = x^2 - 2x + 3$ and $y = 2x - 1$ using a graphing calculator. **(2, 3)**

Solve the system using substitution.

2. $y = 5x - x^2$
$y = x$ **(0, 0), (4, 4)**

3. $4(x - 1)^2 + (y + 3)^2 = 4$
$y = -2x - 3$ **(0, −3), (1, −5)**

4. $x^2 + y^2 = 16$
$y = -x - 4$ **(0, −4), (−4, 0)**

Example 3   **Solve a quadratic system involving two circles**

Solve the system by elimination.

$x^2 + y^2 - 25 = 0$ Equation 1

$x^2 - 10x + y^2 + 10y + 25 = 0$ Equation 2

STEP 1 Multiply Equation 1 by -1 and add the equations to eliminate the x^2 and y^2 terms.

$$-x^2 - y^2 \qquad\qquad + 25 = 0 \qquad \text{Multiply Equation 1 by } -1.$$
$$\underline{x^2 + y^2 - 10x + 10y + 25 = 0}$$
$$-10x + 10y + 50 = 0 \qquad \text{Add.}$$
$$y = x - 5 \qquad \text{Solve for } y.$$

STEP 2 Substitute $x - 5$ for y in Equation 1 and solve for x.

$$x^2 + y^2 - 25 = 0 \qquad\qquad \text{Equation 1}$$
$$x^2 + (x - 5)^2 - 25 = 0 \qquad \text{Substitute for } y.$$
$$2x^2 - 10x = 0 \qquad\qquad \text{Simplify.}$$
$$2x(x - 5) = 0 \qquad\qquad \text{Factor binomial.}$$
$$x = 0 \quad \text{or} \quad x = 5 \quad \text{Zero product property}$$

STEP 3 Substitute for x in $y = x - 5$.

$$y = (0) - 5 = -5 \qquad \text{Substitute 0 for } x.$$
$$y = (5) - 5 = 0 \qquad \text{Substitute 5 for } x.$$

The solutions are $(0, -5)$ and $(5, 0)$. Check the solutions by graphing the equations of the system.

Guided Practice for Example 3

Solve the system by elimination.

5. $x^2 - y^2 - 4 = 0$ **(2, 0), (3, √5), (3, −√5)**
$x^2 + y^2 - 10x + 16 = 0$

6. $x^2 + y^2 - 14x + 2 = 0$ **(1, ±√11), (2, +√22)**
$x^2 - y^2 + 8x + 2 = 0$

MM3G1d   Solve a system of equations involving a circle and a line.

MM3G1e   Solve a system of equations involving two circles.

Solve the system using a graphing calculator.

1. $x^2 + (y - 3)^2 - 9 = 0$
$x + y - 1 = 0$
$(-2.87, 3.87), (0.87, 013)$

2. $2x^2 - y^2 + 4x - 6 = 0$
$2x + y + 4 = 0$ **no solution**

3. $x^2 - y - 4x + 2 = 0$
$x - 2y + 4 = 0$ **(0, 2), (4.5, 4.25)**

4. $6x^2 + y^2 = 12$
$3x + y = 1$
$(-0.68, 3.04), (1.08, -2.24)$

5. $(x - 2)^2 + y^2 = 16$ **(6, 0)**
$x = 6$

6. $x - 2x^2 - 3y = 1$
$9x^2 + 4y^2 = 36$
$(-1.41, -2.13), (1.67, -1.64)$

7. **Multiple Choice** Which ordered pair is a solution of the linear-quadratic system below? **C**

$$x^2 - 4x + 4y^2 - 8y = 8$$
$$2x + y = 7$$

A. $(1, 5)$ **B.** $(5, -1)$ **C.** $(2, 3)$ **D.** $(-3, 2)$

Solve the system using substitution.

8. $x^2 + y^2 = 45$ **(-3, -6), (3, 6)**
$y = 2x$

9. $x^2 - 3y - 3 = 0$ **(0, -1), (3, 2)**
$x - y = 1$

10. $x^2 - 2x + y^2 - 2y = 2$ **(1, 3), (3, 1)**
$x + y = 4$

11. $-x^2 + 2y^2 = 16$
$x - y = 0$ **(-4, -4), (4, 4)**

12. $3x + y^2 + 2 = 0$
$3x = y - 2$ **$(-1, -1), \left(\frac{2}{3}, 0\right)$**

13. $2x^2 + 6y^2 = 18$ **no solution**
$x + 4y + 8 = 0$

14. $2x^2 + y - 3 = 0$
$3x + y = -6$ **$\left(-\frac{3}{2}, -\frac{3}{2}\right), (3, -15)$**

15. $4x^2 - x - y^2 + 6 = 0$
$2x - y = 3$ **$\left(\frac{3}{11}, -\frac{27}{11}\right)$**

16. $2x + y^2 - 4y + 4 = 0$
$-x + y = 2$ **(-2, 0), (0, 2)**

Solve the system.

17. $x^2 - y^2 + 4x - 4 = 0$ **(1, 1), (1, -1)**
$-x^2 + y^2 - 3x + 3 = 0$

18. $x^2 + 2y^2 - 3y = 0$ **(-1, 1), (1, 1)**
$x^2 + y^2 - 2 = 0$

19. $2x^2 - y^2 - x - 4 = 0$ **$(-4, \pm 4\sqrt{2}), (2, \pm\sqrt{2})$**
$-x^2 + y^2 + 3x - 4 = 0$

20. $x^2 + y^2 = 1$ **(0, 1), (1, 0)**
$x^2 + y^2 + 4x + 4y - 5 = 0$

21. **Farming** A farmer has 1400 feet of fence to enclose a rectangular area that borders a river. No fence is needed along the river. Is it possible for the farmer to enclose five acres? (1 acre = 43,560 square feet) If possible, find the dimensions of the enclosure. **466.6 ft by 466.8 ft; or 233.4 ft by 933.2 ft**

22. **Radio** The range of a radio station is bounded by a circle given by the equation $x^2 + y^2 = 920$ where x and y are measured in miles. A straight highway that passes through the area can be modeled by the equation $y = \frac{1}{2}x + 20$. Find the length of the highway that lies within the range of the radio station. **about 49 mi**

LESSON 5.6

Exercise Set B

MM3G1d Solve a system of equations involving a circle and a line.

MM3G1e Solve a system of equations involving two circles.

Solve the system using a graphing calculator.

1. $(x + 2)^2 + (y - 3)^2 = 27$
    $x + y - 5 = 0$
    (−3.08, 8.08), (3.08, 1.92)

2. $x^2 + y^2 + 6x - 16 = 0$
    $2x + y - 1 = 0$
    (−1.94, 4.88), (1.54, −2.08)

3. $2x^2 - y^2 - 6y + 4 = 0$
    $3x - 4y + 2 = 0$
    (0.15, 0.61), (3.50, 3.13)

4. $12x^2 + y^2 = 34$
    $3x - y = 1$
    (1.40, 3.20), (−1.12, −4.36)

5. $3(x + 5)^2 + y = 6$
    $6x - 2y = 7$
    (−2.60, −11.30), (−8.40, −28.70)

6. $5x^2 - y^2 + 4y = 22$
    $2x^2 + 6y^2 = 42$ **(−2.66, −2.16),**
    (2.66, −2.16),
    (−1.91, 2.41),
    (1.91, 2.41)

7. **Multiple Choice** Which ordered pair is a solution of the quadratic system below? **D**

    $$x^2 - x + 5y^2 + 2y = 36$$
    $$3x^2 + 4y^2 = 43$$

    A. $(1, 5)$ **B.** $(5, -1)$ **C.** $(2, 3)$ **D.** $(-3, 2)$

Solve the system using substitution.

8. $x^2 + y = 16$
    $y = -2x + 1$ **(5, −9), (−3, 7)**

9. $x^2 - 3y - 4 = 0$
    $x - y = 2$ **(2, 0), (1, −1)**

10. $x^2 - 2x + y^2 - 2y = 6$
     $x + y = 2$ **(3, −1), (−1, 3)**

11. $-x^2 + y^2 = 13$
     $x - y = 1$ **(−6, −7)**

12. $x^2 + y^2 + 14 = 0$
     $x^2 = 7y - 2$ **no solution**

13. $x^2 - 8y^2 + 4 = 0$
     $x - 3y + 2 = 0$
     (16 + 6√7, 6 + 2√7),
     (16 − 6√7, 6 − 2√7)

14. $2x^2 + y - 3 = 0$
     $-9x + y = -15$ $\left(-\dfrac{3}{2}, -\dfrac{3}{2}\right)$,
     (−6, −69)

15. $5x^2 - x - y^2 - 25 = 0$
     $12x - y = 10$ **no solution**

16. $x + y^2 + 2y + 9 = 0$
     $-x + 4y = 3$
     (−15 + 4√3, −3 + √3),
     (−15 − 4√3, −3 − √3)

Solve the system.

17. $x^2 - y^2 + 7x - 12 = 0$ $\left(\dfrac{9}{5}, \pm\dfrac{4\sqrt{6}}{5}\right)$
     $-x^2 + y^2 - 2x + 3 = 0$

18. $2x^2 + 2y^2 + 4x - 6y = 0$ **no solution**
     $x^2 + y^2 + 2x - 3y = 1$

19. $5x^2 - y^2 - x + 2y + 2 = 0$ **(−2, 6), (−1, 4)**
     $-5x^2 + y^2 + 3x - y - 4 = 0$

20. $x^2 + y^2 + 7x - y = 12$ $\left(\dfrac{-46 + 2\sqrt{937}}{17}, \dfrac{-91 + \sqrt{937}}{34}\right)$,
     $x^2 + y^2 + 6x + 3y = 4$ $\left(\dfrac{-46 - 2\sqrt{937}}{17}, \dfrac{-91 - \sqrt{937}}{34}\right)$

21. **Radio** The range of a radio station is bounded by a circle given by the equation
     $x^2 + y^2 = 725$ where x and y are measured in miles. A straight highway that passes
     through the area can be modeled by the equation $y = \dfrac{2}{3}x - 5$. Find the length of the
     highway that lies within the range of the radio station. **about 53.2 mi**

22. **Aquarium** You want to construct an aquarium with 4 glass
     sides and a glass top and bottom. The aquarium must hold
     35 cubic feet of water and you only have 70 square feet
     of glass to work with. Is it possible to construct such
     an aquarium? If possible, find the dimensions of
     the aquarium. **yes; about 2.39 ft by 2.39 ft by 6.13 ft; or
     4.35 ft by 4.35 ft by 1.85 ft**

Georgia Performance Standards

MM3G1d   Solve a system of equations involving a circle and a line.

Technology Activity

Solve Quadratic Systems

Use after Lesson 5.6

Question

How can you use a graphing calculator to solve quadratic systems?

The solution(s) to a system is (are) the point(s) of intersection of the graphs of the equations. You can use a graphing calculator to find the point(s) of intersection.

Example

Solve the system of equations. $x^2 + y^2 = 9$
$3x - y = 3$

STEP 1* Solve for *y
Begin by solving each equation for y.

$x^2 + y^2 = 9$
$\quad y^2 = -x^2 + 9$
$\quad\quad y = \pm\sqrt{-x^2 + 9}$
$3x - y = 3$
$\quad\quad y = 3x - 3$

***STEP 2* Enter functions**

***STEP 3* Graph functions**
Graph the functions in an appropriate viewing window.

***STEP 4* Find points of intersection**
Use the *intersect* feature to find both points of intersection.

So, the solutions to the system of equations are (1.8, 2.4) and (0, −3).

Practice

Use a graphing calculator to solve the system of equations.

1. $x^2 + y^2 = 18$
$x - y = 0$ **(−3, −3), (3, 3)**

2. $-3x^2 + y^2 = 13$
$-3x + y = 1$ **(−2, −5), (1, 4)**

3. $x^2 + y^2 = 5$
$y = -2x$ **(−1, 2), (1, −2)**

4. $3x^2 - y^2 = -6$
$y = 2x + 1$ **(−5, −9), (1, 3)**

5. $x^2 + y^2 = 1$
$x + y = -1$ **(−1, 0), (0, −1)**

6. $x^2 = 6y$
$y = -x$ **(−6, 6), (0, 0)**

Use Figures in Three-Dimensional Space

Georgia Performance Standards: MM3G3a, MM3G3b, MM3G3c

Goal Understand the three-dimensional rectangular coordinate system.

Vocabulary

A **three-dimensional coordinate system** or **3-space** is formed by the intersection of an x-axis, a y-axis and a z-axis. The axes determine three coordinate planes: the xy-plane, the xz-plane, and the yz-plane. These planes divide the 3-space into eight octants.

Each point in a 3-space is represented by an ordered triple (x, y, z).

The distance d between (x_1, y_1, z_1) and (x_2, y_2, z_2) is

$$d = \sqrt{(x_2 - x_1)^2 + (y_2 - y_1)^2 + (z_2 - z_1)^2}.$$

Example 1 **Apply distance formula in 3-space**

> **Draw a rectangular prism having a diagonal with endpoints (1, 0, −2) and (2, −1, 3). Find the length of the diagonal.**

STEP 1 **Draw** the rectangular prism.

Plot and connect the points $(1, 0, -2)$ and $(2, -1, 3)$. Because the difference of the x-coordinates is $\left| 2 - 1 \right| = 1$, the prism has a length of 1 unit. Because the difference of the y-coordinates is $\left| -1 - 0 \right| = 1$, the prism has a width of 1 unit. Because the difference of the z-coordinates is $\left| 3 - (-2) \right| = 5$, the prism has a height of 5 units. Draw the rectangular prism.

STEP 2 **Find** the length of the diagonal.

Let $(x_1, y_1, z_1) = (1, 0, -2)$ and $(x_2, y_2, z_2) = (2, -1, 3)$.

$$d = \sqrt{(x_2 - x_1)^2 + (y_2 - y_1)^2 + (z_2 - z_1)^2}$$

$$= \sqrt{(2 - 1)^2 + (-1 - 0)^2 + [3 - (-2)]^2}$$

$$= \sqrt{(1)^2 + (-1)^2 + (5)^2}$$

$$= \sqrt{1 + 1 + 25}$$

$$= \sqrt{27} = 3\sqrt{3}$$

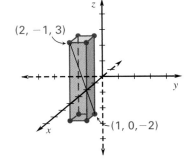

The length of the diagonal is $3\sqrt{3}$ units.

Guided Practice for Example 1

1. Draw a rectangular prism having a diagonal with endpoints (3, 2, 0) and (0, −1, 3). Find the length of the diagonal. **See Additional Answers beginning on page AA1.**

Georgia Performance Standards

MM3G3a Plot the point (x, y, z) and understand it as a vertex of a rectangular prism.

MM3G3b Apply the distance formula in 3-space.

MM3G3c Recognize and understand equations of planes and spheres.

Example 2 ## Recognize and graph the equation of a plane

Graph the equation $3x + 2y + 4z = 12$.

The graph of a linear equation in three variables is a *plane*. In order to sketch a plane, complete the following steps.

STEP 1 **Find** three points at which the plane intersects the axes.

Intersection of x-axis:

$3x + 2(0) + 4(0) = 12 \rightarrow x = 4$

The graph intersects the x-axis at $(4, 0, 0)$.

Intersection of y-axis:

$3(0) + 2y + 4(0) = 12 \rightarrow y = 6$

The graph intersects the y-axis at $(0, 6, 0)$.

Intersection of z-axis:

$3(0) + 2(0) + 4z = 12 \rightarrow z = 3$

The graph intersects the z-axis at $(0, 0, 3)$.

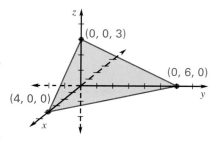

STEP 2 **Plot** and connect the points. Then shade the resulting region.

Example 3 ## Write an equation for a sphere

Write an equation of a sphere in standard form with center $(1, 5, -3)$ and radius $r = 5$.

STEP 1 **Write** the standard form of an equation for a sphere.

$$(x - x_0)^2 + (y - y_0)^2 + (z - z_0)^2 = r^2$$

STEP 2 **Identify** $x_0, y_0,$ and z_0. The center is at $(1, 5, -3)$, so $x_0 = 1, y_0 = 5,$ and $z_0 = -3$.

STEP 3 **Find** r^2. Because $r = 5, r^2 = 25$.

The standard form of the equation is $(x - 1)^2 + (y - 5)^2 + (z + 3)^2 = 25$.

Guided Practice for Examples 2 and 3

Graph the equation. 2 and 3. See Additional Answers beginning on page AA1.

2. $x + 2y - 4z = 16$

3. $2x + y - 5z = 10$

4. Write an equation of a sphere in standard form with center $(4, -2, 0)$ and radius $r = 7$. $(x - 4)^2 + (y + 2)^2 + z^2 = 49$

UNIT 5

LESSON
5.7

Exercise Set A

MM3G3a   Plot the point (x, y, z) and understand it as a vertex of a rectangular prism.

MM3G3b   Apply the distance formula in 3-space.

MM3G3c   Recognize and understand equations of planes and spheres.

Draw a rectangular prism having a diagonal with the given endpoints. Find the length of the diagonal. 1 and 2. See Additional Answers beginning on page AA1.

1. $(3, 0, 5)$ and $(0, 4, 0)$

2. $(1, 1, -8)$ and $(-3, 2, 0)$

Find the distances between the points.

3. $(6, 1, 0)$ and $(9, 4, 0)$ $3\sqrt{2}$

4. $(7, 4, 1)$ and $(1, 0, 11)$ $2\sqrt{38}$

5. $(-2, 9, 1)$ and $(4, 4, 2)$ $\sqrt{62}$

6. $(-1, -1, 6)$ and $(-5, -8, 4)$ $\sqrt{69}$

Graph the equation of the plane. 7–12. See Additional Answers beginning on page AA1.

7. $x + 6y + 2z + 18 = 0$

8. $2x - 3y + 9z + 36 = 0$

9. $3x + y - 5z - 15 = 0$

10. $-11x + y + 11z + 121 = 0$

11. $-4x + 3y + 2z + 12 = 0$

12. $4x - 5y - 2z - 40 = 0$

Determine whether the equation represents a *plane* or a *sphere*. If it is a plane, graph the equation. 13–16. See Additional Answers beginning on page AA1.

13. $x - 2y + z + 14 = 0$

14. $x^2 + y^2 + z^2 + 100 = 0$

15. $8x^2 + y^2 + z^2 + 8z + 32 = 0$

16. $-6x + 9y + z - 36 = 0$

Write an equation of the sphere in standard form with the given center and radius.

17. $(0, 2, 5)$; $r = 5$ $x^2 + (y - 2)^2 + (z - 5)^2 = 25$

18. $(2, 0, 3)$; $r = 8$ $(x - 2)^2 + y^2 + (z - 3)^2 = 64$

19. $(-1, -7, -2)$; $r = 9$
$(x + 1)^2 + (y + 7)^2 + (z + 2)^2 = 81$

20. $(5, 2, -7)$; $r = 4$
$(x - 5)^2 + (y - 2)^2 + (z + 7)^2 = 16$

21. Rectangular Prism Use the graph at the right to complete the following.
See Additional Answers beginning on page AA1.

   a. Find the length, width, and height of the rectangular prism.

   b. Find the surface area and the volume of the prism.

   c. Suppose the height of the solid is doubled. Give the new coordinates of each vertex.

   d. Sketch the new solid in a three-dimensional coordinate system.

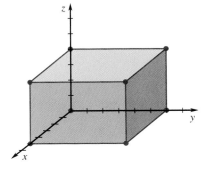

22. **Basketball** Suppose a basketball is sketched in a three-dimensional coordinate system with the origin at the center of the ball. Each axis is given in inches. The point $(0, 3.6, 2.7)$ lies on the surface of the basketball. What is the diameter of the basketball? **9 in.**

UNIT 5

MM3G3a	Plot the point (x, y, z) and understand it as a vertex of a rectangular prism.
MM3G3b	Apply the distance formula in 3-space.
MM3G3c	Recognize and understand equations of planes and spheres.

Draw a rectangular prism having a diagonal with the given endpoints. Find the length of the diagonal. 1 and 2. See Additional Answers beginning on page AA1.

1. $(2, 2, 3)$ and $(4, -5, 6)$

2. $(7, 5, 1)$ and $(10, 0, -1)$

Find the distance between the points.

3. $(-12, -4, 5)$ and $(-8, 0, -4)$ $\sqrt{113}$

4. $(-20, 6, 2)$ and $(4, 4, 1)$ $\sqrt{581}$

Graph the equation of the plane. 5–8. See Additional Answers beginning on page AA1.

5. $3x + 7y - 3z + 42 = 0$

6. $2x - 4y - 3z + 15 = 0$

7. $x + 2y + 0.5z + 3 = 0$

8. $10x - 5y + 11z + 55 = 0$

Write an equation of the sphere in standard form with the given center and radius. 9–14. See Additional Answers beginning on page AA1.

9. $(2, 2, -2); r = 6$

10. $(8, -2, 0); r = 12$

11. $(15, -1, 6); r = 1.2$

12. $(0, -4, -3); r = 4.5$

13. $(8, 2.5, 0); r = 8\sqrt{3}$

14. $(10, -2, 3); r = 3\sqrt{2}$

Complete the square to write the equation of the sphere in standard form. Identify the center and the radius. 15–18. See Additional Answers beginning on page AA1.

15. $x^2 + y^2 + z^2 - 2x + 6y + 8z + 1 = 0$

16. $x^2 + y^2 + z^2 + 9x - 2y + 10z = -10.25$

17. $9x^2 + 9y^2 + 9z^2 - 6x + 18y + 1 = 0$

18. $4x^2 + 4y^2 + 4z^2 - 4x - 32y + 8z + 33 = 0$

19. Storage Buildings A storage building has the shape of a hemisphere. An equation for the outer surface of the storage building is $x^2 + y^2 + z^2 - 40x - 30y + 400 = 0$ when $z \geq 0$. Each axis is given in feet. What is the volume of the storage building? (*Hint:* The volume of a sphere is $V = \frac{4}{3}\pi r^3$ where r is the radius.) 2250π ft³

20. Geometry The endpoints of a diameter of a sphere are $(2, 3, 8)$ and $(6, 3, 10)$. Find the center and the radius of the sphere. Then write an equation of the sphere in standard form. center: $(4, 3, 9)$; radius $\sqrt{5}$; $(x - 4)^2 + (y - 3)^2 + (z - 9)^2 = 5$

UNIT 5

TEST | for Unit 5

Graph the equation. 1–12. See Additional Answers beginning on page AA1.

1. $y^2 = 16x$

2. $x^2 + y^2 = 36$

3. $x^2 - 8y^2 = 8$

4. $9x^2 + 6y^2 = 18$

5. $(x + 2)^2 + (y - 3)^2 = 49$

6. $(x - 1)^2 = y - 3$

7. $\dfrac{(x + 1)^2}{100} - \dfrac{(y - 5)^2}{25} = 1$

8. $\dfrac{(x - 2)^2}{9} + \dfrac{y^2}{64} = 1$

9. $\dfrac{(y + 4)^2}{16} - x^2 = 1$

10. $-x + 4y + 2z + 8 = 0$

11. $4x - 2y - 5z - 20 = 0$

12. $3x - 6y - 3z + 24 = 0$

Write the standard form of the equation of the conic section with the given characteristics.

13. Parabola with vertex at $(0, 0)$ and directrix at $x = 5$ $\quad y^2 = -20x$

14. Parabola with vertex at $(-2, 4)$ and focus at $(3, 4)$ $\quad (y - 4)^2 = 20(x + 2)$

15. Circle with center at $(3, -1)$ and radius 4 $\quad (x - 3)^2 + (y + 1)^2 = 16$

16. Circle with center at $(0, 0)$ and passing through $(12, 9)$ $\quad x^2 + y^2 = 225$

17. Ellipse with foci at $(4, 2)$ and $(10, 2)$ and co-vertices at $(7, 0)$ and $(7, 4)$ $\quad \dfrac{(x - 7)^2}{13} + \dfrac{(y - 2)^2}{4} = 1$

18. Ellipse with center at $(0, 0)$, vertex at $(\pm 4, 0)$ and co-vertex at $(0, \pm 2)$ $\quad \dfrac{x^2}{16} + \dfrac{y^2}{4} = 1$

19. Hyperbola with vertex at $(0, 4)$, focus at $(0, 5)$, and center at $(0, 1)$ $\quad \dfrac{(y - 1)^2}{16} - \dfrac{x^2}{9} = 1$

20. Hyperbola with foci at $(0, \pm 5)$ and vertices at $(0, \pm 2)$ $\quad \dfrac{y^2}{4} - \dfrac{x^2}{21} = 1$

Classify the conic section and write its equation in standard form.

21. $y^2 - 8y - 8x = -24$ $\quad$ parabola; $(y - 4)^2 = 8(x - 1)$

22. $x^2 + y^2 - 4x + 2y - 11 = 0$ $\quad$ circle; $(x - 2)^2 + (y + 1)^2 = 16$

23. $4x^2 + y^2 - 8x - 8 = 0$ $\quad$ ellipse; $\dfrac{(x - 1)^2}{3} + \dfrac{y^2}{12} = 1$

24. $4x^2 - 25y^2 - 100y = 0$ $\quad$ hyperbola; $\dfrac{(y + 2)^2}{4} - \dfrac{x^2}{25} = 1$

Solve the system.

25. $x^2 + y^2 = 25$ $\quad$ $(0, 5), (5, 0)$

$x + y = 5$

26. $\dfrac{(x + 1)^2}{100} - \dfrac{(y - 6)^2}{25} = 1$ $\quad$ $(9, 6)$

$x - 2y = -3$

27. $x^2 + y^2 = 100$ $\quad$ $(10, 0)$

$(x - 14)^2 + y^2 = 16$

28. $\dfrac{x^2}{9} - y^2 = 1$ $\quad$ no solution

$2x + y = 0$

Find the distance between the points.

29. $(1, 0, 4)$ and $(0, 8, 0)$ $\quad$ 9

30. $(2, 2, -9)$ and $(-1, 6, 0)$ $\quad$ $\sqrt{106}$

31. $(3, 8, 1)$ and $(-2, 2, 1)$ $\quad$ $\sqrt{61}$

Write an equation of the sphere in standard form with the given center and radius.

32. $(0, 3, 2); r = 6$

$x^2 + (y - 3)^2 + (z - 2)^2 = 36$

33. $(4, 0, 2); r = 8$

$(x - 4)^2 + y^2 + (z - 2)^2 = 64$

34. $(-2, 7, 3); r = 7$

$(x + 2)^2 + (y - 7)^2 + (z - 3)^2 = 49$

35. Reflectors The cross section of a parabolic reflector is 25 feet across and the focus of the reflector is located 9 feet above the vertex. Write an equation for the cross section of a reflector opening upward with its vertex at (0, 0). What is the depth of the reflector? **$x^2 = 36y$; about 4.34 ft**

36. Delivery An appliance store advertises free delivery up to a 75 mile radius from the store. If a customer lives 65 miles north and 30 miles west of the store, does the customer qualify for free delivery? **yes**

37. Astronomy In its elliptical orbit, an asteroid ranges from 20 million miles to 36 million miles from the sun, which is at one focus of the orbit. **See Additional Answers beginning on page AA1.**

    a. Draw a sketch of the situation.

    b. Write an equation for the orbit of the asteroid.

38. Radar A radar system reports that a ship is 10 miles away. At the same time, a second station 6 miles east and 7 miles north of the first one reports that the ship is 1 mile away. Write and solve a system of equations to locate the ship relative to the first station. **$(x - 6)^2 + (y - 7)^2 = 1$, $x^2 + y^2 = 100$; (6, 8) or (6.99, 7.15); The ship is either 6 miles east and 8 miles north or about 6.99 miles east and about 7.15 miles north of the first station.**

Performance Task

Campus Parking

To be eligible for a parking pass on a college campus, a student must live at least 1 mile from the campus center.

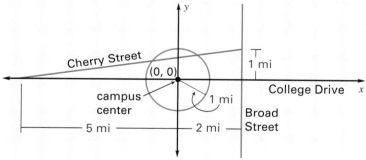

    a. Write equations that represent the circle and Cherry Street. **$x^2 + y^2 = 1$**   **$x - 7y = -5$**

    b. Solve the system that consists of the equations from part (a). **(−0.8, 0.6), (0.6, 0.8)**

    c. For what length of Cherry Street are students *not* eligible for a parking pass? **about 1.41 mi**

    d. Chestnut Lane follows a parabolic arc given by the equation $y = 0.5x^2 - 2x + 2$ when $-2 < x < 3$. Write the equation in standard form. Identify the focus and the directrix. **$(x - 2)^2 = 2y$; focus: $\left(2, \frac{1}{2}\right)$; directrix: $y = -\frac{1}{2}$**

    e. Sketch the circular region and the parabola in the same coordinate plane. Do students living along Chestnut Lane qualify for a parking pass? *Explain.*
    See Additional Answers beginning on page AA1.

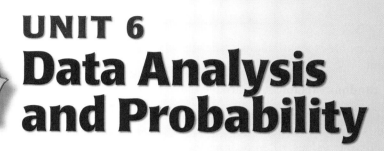

UNIT 6
Data Analysis and Probability

Construct and Interpret Binomial Distributions

Georgia Performance Standards: MM3D1

Goal Study probability distributions.

Vocabulary

A **random variable** is a variable whose value is determined by the outcomes of a random event.

A **discrete random variable** is a variable that can take on only a countable number of distinct values.

A **continuous random variable** is a variable that can take on an uncountable, infinite number of possible values, often over a specified interval.

A **probability distribution** is a function that gives the probability of each possible value of a random variable. The sum of all the probabilities in a probability distribution must equal 1.

A **binomial distribution** shows the probabilities of the outcomes of a binomial experiment.

A **binomial experiment** has n independent trials, with two possible outcomes (success or failure) for each trial. The probability for success is the same for each trial. The probability of exactly k successes in n trials is $P(k \text{ successes}) = {}_nC_k p^k (1-p)^{n-k}$.

A probability distribution is **symmetric** if a vertical line can be drawn to divide the histogram of the distribution into two parts that are mirror images.

A distribution that is not symmetric is called **skewed**.

Example 1 Construct a probability distribution

Let X be a random variable that represents the number of questions that students guessed correctly on a quiz with three true-false questions. Make a table and a histogram showing the probability distribution for X.

The possible values of X are the integers 0, 1, 2, and 3. The table shows how many outcomes of answering three questions on a quiz produce each value of X. Divide the number of outcomes for X by the total number of outcomes $1 + 3 + 3 + 1 = 8$ to find $P(X)$.

X (number correct)	0	1	2	3
Outcomes	1	3	3	1
P(X)	$\frac{1}{8}$	$\frac{3}{8}$	$\frac{3}{8}$	$\frac{1}{8}$

Georgia Performance Standards

MM3D1   Students will create probability histograms of discrete
random variables, using both experimental and
theoretical probabilities.

Example 2   **Interpret a probability distribution**

Use the probability distribution in Example 1 to find the probability
that a student guesses at least two questions correctly.

Solution

The probability that a student guesses at least two questions correctly is:

$P(X \geq 2) = P(X = 2) + P(X = 3)$

$$= \frac{3}{8} + \frac{1}{8} = \frac{4}{8} = \frac{1}{2} = 0.5$$

Example 3   **Construct a binomial distribution**

In a standard deck of cards, 25% are hearts. Suppose you choose a card
at random, note whether it is a heart, then replace it. You conduct the
experiment 5 times. Draw a histogram of the binomial distribution for
your experiment.

Solution

The probability that a randomly selected card is a heart is $p = 0.25$. Because you
conduct the experiment 5 times, $n = 5$.

$P(k = 0) = {_5}C_0(0.25)^0(0.75)^5 \approx 0.237$

$P(k = 1) = {_5}C_1(0.25)^1(0.75)^4 \approx 0.396$

$P(k = 2) = {_5}C_2(0.25)^2(0.75)^3 \approx 0.264$

$P(k = 3) = {_5}C_3(0.25)^3(0.75)^2 \approx 0.088$

$P(k = 4) = {_5}C_4(0.25)^4(0.75)^1 \approx 0.015$

$P(k = 5) = {_5}C_5(0.25)^5(0.75)^0 \approx 0.001$

A histogram of the distribution is shown.

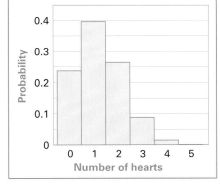

Guided Practice for Examples 1, 2, and 3

1. Use the data to construct a table and a histogram showing the probability
    distribution for *X*, a random variable that represents the number of cell phones
    per household. **See Additional Answers beginning on page AA1.**

X (number of cell phones)	0	1	2	3
Number of households	19	28	37	16

2. What is the probability that a household has at least two cell phones? **0.53**

3. In Example 3, $P(k = 1)$ is the greatest probability. Is this still the case if you
    conduct the experiment 8 times? *Explain.* **No; $P(k = 2) \approx 0.311$ is the greatest probability.**

| Example 4 | Construct a binomial distribution |

According to a survey, about 40% of residents on your street have a pet. Suppose you ask 3 random residents whether they have a pet. Draw a histogram of the binomial distribution showing the probability that exactly *k* of the residents have a pet.

Solution

The probability that a randomly selected resident has a pet is $p = 0.4$. Because you ask 3 residents, $n = 3$.

$$P(k = 0) = {}_3C_0(0.4)^0(0.6)^3 = 0.216$$

$$P(k = 1) = {}_3C_1(0.4)^1(0.6)^2 = 0.432$$

$$P(k = 2) = {}_3C_2(0.4)^2(0.6)^1 = 0.288$$

$$P(k = 3) = {}_3C_3(0.4)^3(0.6)^0 = 0.064$$

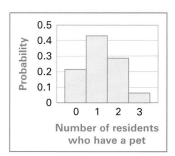

A histogram of the distribution is shown.

| Example 5 | Interpret and classify a binomial distribution |

Use the binomial distribution in Example 4 to answer each question.

   a. What is the least likely outcome of the survey?

   b. What is the probability that $k = 1$?

   c. Describe the shape of the binomial distribution.

Solution

   a. The least likely outcome is the value of k for which $P(k)$ is smallest. This probability is smallest for $k = 3$. So, the least likely outcome is that all 3 residents have a pet.

   b. The probability that $k = 1$ is 0.432.

   c. The distribution is skewed because it is not symmetric about any vertical line.

Guided Practice for Examples 4 and 5

In Exercises 4–6 use the following information. A binomial experiment consists of $n = 4$ trials with probability 0.1 of success on each trial.

  4. Construct a binomial distribution that shows the probability of exactly *k* successes and draw a histogram of the distribution. **See Additional Answers beginning on page AA1.**

  5. Find the most likely outcome. **$k = 0$**

  6. *Describe* the shape of the binomial distribution. **skewed**

MM3D1 Students will create probability histograms of discrete random variables, using both experimental and theoretical probabilities.

Decide whether the random variable *X* is discrete or continuous. *Explain*.

1. *X* represents the amount of time it takes to brush your teeth. **continuous; Length of time is a random variable that has an infinite number of possible values, so it is uncountable.**

2. *X* represents the number of days with a low temperature below freezing in January. **discrete; Number of days in a month is a random variable that is countable.**

Make a table and a histogram showing the probability distribution for the random variable. *Describe* the distribution as either *symmetric* or *skewed*.
3 and 4. See Additional Answers beginning on page AA1.

3. *B* = the number on an index card randomly chosen from a bag that contains 3 cards labeled "1", 4 cards labeled "2", and 3 cards labeled "3".

4. *D* = the absolute value of the difference when two eight-sided number cubes are rolled.

Calculate the probability of tossing a coin 25 times and getting the given number of heads.

5. 2 about 0.00000894   **6.** 10 about 0.0974   **7.** 18 about 0.0143   **8.** 25 about 0.00000003

Calculate the probability of *k* successes for a binomial experiment consisting of *n* trials with probability *p* of success on each trial.

9. $k \geq 4, n = 8, p = 0.16$ about 0.02667   **10.** $k \leq 5, n = 10, p = 0.45$ about 0.738

11. $k \geq 3, n = 5, p = 0.34$ about 0.2199   **12.** $k \leq 8, n = 12, p = 0.60$ about 0.775

Match the values of *n* and *p* for a binomial distribution with the histogram that shows the probability of exactly *k* successes.

13. $n = 4, p = 0.45$ **C**   **14.** $n = 5, p = 0.75$ **B**   **15.** $n = 6, p = 0.83$ **A**

A.

B.

C.
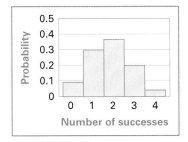

16. **Multiple Representations** A golden retriever has a litter of 7 puppies. Assume that the probability of a puppy being male is 0.5. Let *k* be the number of males. **See Additional Answers beginning on page AA1.**

   a. **Calculating Probabilities** Find *P(k)* for *k* = 0, 1, 2, . . . , 7.

   b. **Making a Table** Make a table showing the binomial distribution.

   c. **Making a Histogram** Make a histogram showing the binomial distribution. *Describe* the distribution as either *symmetric* or *skewed*.

In Exercises 1 and 2, make a table and a histogram showing the probability distribution for the random variable. *Describe* **the distribution as either** *symmetric* **or** *skewed*. 1 and 2. See Additional Answers beginning on page AA1.

1. C = the color of a marble chosen from a bag that contains 4 red marbles, 5 blue marbles, 8 green marbles, and 3 orange marbles.

2. X = the product of the numbers spun on two spinners with the numbers 0 through 4. (For each spinner, assume that the probability of spinning each number is the same.)

3. In Exercise 2, what is the probability that the product of the spins is greater than 5? **0.32**

Calculate the probability of tossing a coin 30 times and getting the given number of heads.

4. 8 about 0.00545
5. 15 about 0.144
6. 20 about 0.0280
7. 26 about 0.0000255

Calculate the probability of randomly guessing the given number of correct answers on a 30-question multiple choice exam that has choices A, B, C, and D for each question.

8. 10 about 0.0909
9. 20 about 0.00000154
10. 25 about 3.00×10^{-11}
11. 30 about 8.67×10^{-19}

Calculate the probability of k successes for a binomial experiment consisting of n trials with probability p of success on each trial.

12. $k \geq 3, n = 8, p = 0.42$ about 0.725
13. $k \leq 4, n = 7, p = 0.18$ about 0.997

A binomial experiment consists of n trials with probability p of success on each trial. Draw a histogram of the binomial distribution that shows the probability of exactly k successes. *Describe* **the distribution as either** *symmetric* **or** *skewed*. **Then find the most likely number of successes.**

14–16. See Additional Answers beginning on page AA1.

14. $n = 6, p = 0.76$
15. $n = 8, p = 0.245$
16. $n = 10, p = 0.066$

17. **Side Effects** According to a medical study, 40% of people will experience an adverse side effect within one hour after taking a particular experimental drug. Suppose you survey 15 people who participated in the study. What is the most likely number of these people who experienced an adverse effect in the study? **6**

18. **Entertainment** An entertainment system has n speakers. Each speaker will function properly with probability p, independent of whether the other speakers are functioning. The system will operate effectively if at least 50% of its speakers are functioning. For what values of p is a 4-speaker system more likely to operate than a 5-speaker system? **$p > 0$**

Georgia Performance Standards

MM3D1 Students will create probability histograms of discrete random variables, using both experimental and theoretical probabilities.

Technology Activity
Create a Binomial Distribution

Use after Lesson 6.1

Question

How can you use a graphing calculator to calculate binomial probabilities?

Some calculators have a binomial probability distribution function that you can use to calculate binomial probabilities. You can then use the calculator to draw a histogram of the distribution.

Example

Calculate binomial probabilities.

Football According to a recent survey, 62% of people agree with the statement that a team lost a football game because of poor officiating. Suppose you survey 5 people at random. Draw a histogram of the binomial distribution showing the probability that exactly k people agree with the statement. What is the most likely number of people in your survey who agree with the statement?

STEP 1 Enter values of k

Let $p = 0.62$ be the probability that a person agrees. Enter the k-values 0 through 5 into list L_1 on the graphing calculator.

STEP 2 Find values of $P(k)$

Enter the binomial probability command to generate $P(k)$ for all six k-values. Store the results in list L_2.

STEP 3 Draw histogram

Set up the histogram to use the numbers in L_1 as x-values and the numbers in L_2 as frequencies. Draw the histogram in a suitable viewing window.

From the histogram in Step 3, you can see that $k = 3$ is the most likely number of the 5 people surveyed who agree that the team lost the game because of poor officiating.

Practice

A binomial experiment consists of *n* trials with probability *p* of success on each trial. Use a graphing calculator to draw a histogram of the binomial distribution that shows the probability of exactly *k* successes. Then find the most likely number of successes.

1–3. See Additional Answers beginning on page AA1.

1. $n = 12, p = 0.28$ **2.** $n = 15, p = 0.56$ **3.** $n = 16, p = 0.825$

4. What If? In the example, how does the most likely number of people who agree change if you survey 10 adults at random? **increases to 6**

Georgia Performance Standards

MM3D2a   Determine intervals about the mean that include a given percent of data.

Investigating Math Activity

Explore a Normal Curve

Use before Lesson 6.2

> **Materials**   graph paper, salt, spray paint, newspaper, and music stand

Question

What is the percent of the area under a normal curve within 1, 2, and 3 standard deviations of the mean?

One type of probability distribution is a *normal distribution*. A *normal distribution* is modeled by a bell-shaped curve called a *normal curve* that is symmetric about the mean.

Explore

Create a normal curve.

STEP 1   Cover the music stand with newspaper. Place a piece of graph paper on the stand. Tilt the stand to the desired angle, and pour salt from a point near the middle of the graph paper until enough salt has accumulated to make a bell-shaped curve. Spray the grid and salt with the paint. Discard the salt.

STEP 2   Once the paint has dried, approximate and record the area under the curve by counting the squares and portions of squares on the graph paper.

STEP 3   The mean is the value corresponding to the highest point of the curve. Draw a vertical line at the approximate mean $\bar{x}$.

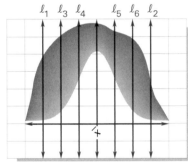

STEP 4   Draw vertical lines ℓ_1 and ℓ_2 at the ends of the curve. Lines ℓ_1 and ℓ_2 represent 3 standard deviations to the left and the right of the mean. Approximate and record the area under the curve that is within 3 standard deviations of the mean.

STEP 5   Draw two equally spaced vertical lines ℓ_3 and ℓ_4 between the mean and ℓ_1. Draw two equally spaced vertical lines ℓ_5 and ℓ_6 between the mean and ℓ_2. Lines ℓ_4 and ℓ_5 represent 1 standard deviation from the mean. Lines ℓ_3 and ℓ_6 represent 2 standard deviations from the mean. Approximate and record the area under the curve that is within 1 and 2 standard deviations of the mean.

Draw Conclusions

1.   Calculate the percent of the area under the normal curve that is within 1, 2, and 3 standard deviations of the mean. **68%; 95%; 99.7%**

2.   *Reasoning* *Compare* your answers with those of your classmates, and then write a rule describing the percent of the area under a normal curve that is within 1, 2, and 3 standard deviations of the mean. **See Additional Answers beginning on page AA1.**

Use Normal Distributions

Georgia Performance Standards: MM3D2a, MM3D2b, MM3D2c

Goal Study normal distributions.

Vocabulary

A **normal distribution** is modeled by a bell-shaped curve called a **normal curve** that is symmetric about the mean. A normal distribution with mean $\bar{x}$ and standard deviation σ has the following properties. The total area under the related normal curve is 1. The percent of the area covered by each standard deviation is shown in the graph.

The **standard normal distribution** is the normal distribution with mean 0 and standard deviation 1. The formula below can be used to transform x-values from a normal distribution with mean $\bar{x}$ and standard deviation σ into z-values having a standard normal distribution.

$$z = \frac{x - \bar{x}}{\sigma}$$

The z-value for a particular x-value is called the **z-score** for the x-value and is the number of standard deviations the x-value lies above or below the mean $\bar{x}$. To find the probability that z is less than or equal to some given value, use the standard normal table on page 248.

Example 1 Find a normal probability

A normal distribution has mean $\bar{x}$ and standard deviation σ. For a randomly selected x-value from the distribution, find $P(\bar{x} \le x \le \bar{x} + 3\sigma)$.

Solution

The probability that a randomly selected x-value lies between $\bar{x}$ and $\bar{x} + 3\sigma$ is the shaded area under the normal curve shown.

$P(\bar{x} \le x \le \bar{x} + 3\sigma) = 0.34 + 0.135 + 0.0235$

$\qquad = 0.4985$

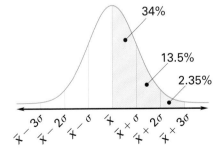

Guided Practice for Example 1

A normal distribution has mean $\bar{x}$ and standard deviation σ. Find the indicated probability for a randomly selected x-value from the distribution.

1. $P(x \le \bar{x} - 2\sigma)$ **2.5%**

2. $P(x \ge \bar{x} + 2\sigma)$ **2.5%**

3. $P(\bar{x} - 2\sigma \le x \le \bar{x} + \sigma)$
 81.5%

Georgia Performance Standards

MM3D2a	Determine intervals about the mean that include a given percent of data.	☑
MM3D2b	Determine the probability that a given value falls within a specified interval.	☑
MM3D2c	Estimate how many items in a population fall within a specified interval.	☑

Example 2   Interpret normally distributed data

Height The heights of 3000 women at a particular college are normally distributed with a mean of 65 inches and a standard deviation of 2.5 inches. About how many of these women have heights between 62.5 inches and 67.5 inches?

Solution

The heights of 62.5 inches and 67.5 inches represent one standard deviation on either side of the mean, as shown. So, about 68%, or 0.68(3000) = 2040, of the women at this particular college have heights between 62.5 inches and 67.5 inches.

College women's heights

Example 3   Use a *z*-score and the standard normal table

In Example 2, find the probability that a randomly selected college woman has a height of at most 68 inches.

Solution

STEP 1 **Find** the *z*-score corresponding to an *x*-value of 68.

$$z = \frac{x - \bar{x}}{\sigma} = \frac{68 - 65}{2.5} = 1.2$$

STEP 2 **Use** the standard normal table on page 248 to find $P(x \le 68) = P(z \le 1.2)$.

The table shows that $P(z \le 1.2) = 0.8849$. So, the probability that a randomly selected college woman has a height of at most 68 inches is 0.8849.

z	.0	.1	.2
−3	.0013	.0010	.0007
−2	.0228	.0179	.0139
−1	.1587	.1357	.1151
−0	.5000	.4602	.4207
0	.5000	.5398	.5793
1	.8413	.8643	.8849

Guided Practice for Examples 2 and 3

In the following exercises, refer to Example 2.

4. About what percent of college women have heights below 70 inches? **97.5%**

5. About how many of the college women have heights between 60 inches and 65 inches? **143**

6. Find the probability that a randomly selected college woman has a height of at most 61 inches. **0.0548**

UNIT 6

Exercise Set A

MM3D2a Determine intervals about the mean that include a given percent of data.

MM3D2b Determine the probability that a given value falls within a specified interval.

MM3D2c Estimate how many items in a population fall within a specified interval.

A normal distribution has mean $\bar{x}$ and standard deviation σ. Find the indicated probability for a randomly selected x-value from the distribution.

1. $P(x \leq \bar{x} + \sigma)$ **84%**

2. $P(x \geq \bar{x} - 2\sigma)$ **97.5%**

3. $P(\bar{x} - \sigma \leq x \leq \bar{x} + \sigma)$ **68%**

Give the percent of the area under the normal curve represented by the shaded region.

4.

16%

5.

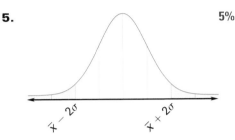

5%

A normal distribution has a mean of 25 and a standard deviation of 5. Find the probability that a randomly selected x-value from the distribution is in the given interval.

6. Between 20 and 30 **0.68**

7. Between 10 and 25 **0.4985**

8. Between 15 and 35 **0.95**

9. At least 20 **0.84**

10. At least 35 **0.025**

11. At most 30 **0.84**

A normal distribution has a mean of 70 and a standard deviation of 10. Use the standard normal table on page 248 to find the indicated probability for a randomly selected x-value from the distribution.

12. $P(x \leq 65)$ **0.3085**

13. $P(x \leq 47)$ **0.0107**

14. $P(x \leq 73)$ **0.6179**

15. $P(x \leq 91)$ **0.9821**

16. $P(x \leq 39)$ **0.0010**

17. $P(x \leq 101)$ **0.9990**

18. **Error Analysis** In a study, the wheat yields (in bushels) for several plots of land were normally distributed with a mean of 5 bushels and a standard deviation of 0.3 bushel. *Describe* and correct the error in finding the probability that a plot yielded at most 4.73 bushels. **Subtract the mean from the** x**-value;** $z = \frac{4.73 - 5}{0.3} = -0.9$**,** $P(z \leq -0.9) = 0.1841$

$$z = \frac{\bar{x} - x}{\sigma} = \frac{5 - 4.73}{0.3} = 0.9$$

From the standard normal table, $P(z \leq 0.9) = 0.8159$. So, the probability that a plot yielded at most 4.73 bushels is 0.8159.

19. **Biology** The weights of 1800 fish in a lake are normally distributed with a mean of 3 kilograms and a standard deviation of 0.6 kilogram. About how many of the fish have a weight less than or equal to 2.4 kilograms? **288**

UNIT 6

Exercise Set B

MM3D2a Determine intervals about the mean that include a given percent of data.

MM3D2b Determine the probability that a given value falls within a specified interval.

MM3D2c Estimate how many items in a population fall within a specified interval.

A normal distribution has mean $\bar{x}$ and standard deviation σ. Find the indicated probability for a randomly selected x-value from the distribution.

1. $P(x \le \bar{x} + 2\sigma)$ **97.5%**

2. $P(x \ge \bar{x} + 3\sigma)$ **0.15%**

3. $P(\bar{x} - 2\sigma \le x \le \bar{x} + 3\sigma)$ **97.35%**

Give the percent of the area under the normal curve represented by the shaded region.

4.

50%

5.
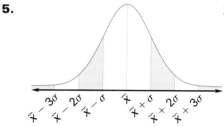
27.3%

A normal distribution has a mean of 64.6 and a standard deviation of 2.4. Find the probability that a randomly selected x-value from the distribution is in the given interval.

6. Between 64.6 and 69.4 **0.475**

7. Between 62.2 and 71.8 **0.8385**

8. Between 59.8 and 67 **0.815**

9. At least 67 **0.16**

10. At least 59.8 **0.975**

11. At most 69.4 **0.975**

A normal distribution has a mean of 112.8 and a standard deviation of 9.3. Use the standard normal table on page 248 to find the indicated probability for a randomly selected x-value from the distribution.

12. $P(x \le 104.3)$ **0.1841**

13. $P(x \le 79.6)$ **0.0002**

14. $P(x \le 127.1)$ **0.9332**

15. $P(x \ge 118.7)$ **0.2743**

16. $P(x \ge 140.7)$ **0.0013**

17. $P(x \ge 90.9)$ **0.9918**

18. $P(111 \le x \le 132.6)$ **0.5614**

19. $P(86.8 \le x \le 99.3)$ **0.0642**

20. $P(123.1 \le x \le 142.3)$ **0.135**

In Exercises 21–23, use the following information.

Fitness Two different one-mile run routes were set up for 1200 physical education students. The times to complete uphill course A are normally distributed with a mean of 480 seconds and a standard deviation of 90 seconds. The times to complete level course B are normally distributed with a mean of 420 seconds and a standard deviation of 75 seconds. All students ran both courses.

21. About how many students finished course A in 390 seconds or less? **192**

22. John completed course A in 525 seconds. Shawn completed course B in 470 seconds. Find the z-score for both runners. **John: 0.5; Shawn: about 0.667**

23. Which student had the better time? *Explain.* **John; In a standard normal distribution, John's time is lower which is better when running a mile.**

UNIT 6

Georgia Performance Standards

MM3D3   Students will understand the differences between experimental and observational studies by posing questions and collecting, analyzing, and interpreting data.

Investigating Math Activity
Collecting Data

Use before Lesson 6.3

Materials   paper, pencil, and a coin

Question

How can you collect and analyze data from an experiment?

Explore

A quiz has 6 true-false questions. You do not get to see the questions, but instead will flip a coin for each of your answers. Perform the following steps to see how many questions you can answer correctly without seeing the questions.

STEP 1 **Flip** a coin for each question. Let heads represent "true" and tails represent "false." Record your answers. How many of your answers do you think will be correct? What is the probability of answering the first question correctly? What is the probability of answering all 6 questions correctly?

STEP 2 **Determine** your quiz score. The correct answers for the quiz are:

1. true   **2.** true   **3.** false   **4.** true   **5.** false   **6.** false

Compare your score to the guess you made in Step 1.

STEP 3 **Collect** the individual scores from everyone in your class.

Draw Conclusions   1–3. Check student's work.

1. Use the scores collected from your class to make a table and a histogram that show the probability distribution.

2. From your results, what is the most likely number of questions to be answered correctly? What is the least likely number of questions to be answered correctly?

3. **Reasoning** *Compare* the experimental probabilities represented in your histogram with the theoretical probabilities of answering one question correctly, two questions correctly, and so on.

UNIT 6

Approximate Binomial Distributions and Test Hypotheses

Georgia Performance Standards: MM3D2b, MM3D2c, MM3D3

Goal Use normal distributions to approximate binomial distributions.

Vocabulary

Consider the binomial distribution consisting of n trials with probability p of success on each trial. If $np \geq 5$ and $n(1 - p) \geq 5$, then the binomial distribution can be approximated by a normal distribution with the following mean and standard deviation.

Mean: $\bar{x} = np$ **Standard Deviation:** $\sigma = \sqrt{np(1 - p)}$

To test a hypothesis about a statistical measure for a population, use the following steps:

STEP 1 **State** the hypothesis you are testing. The hypothesis should make a statement about some statistical measure of a population.

STEP 2 **Collect** data from a random sample of the population and compute the statistical measure of the sample.

STEP 3 **Assume** the hypothesis is true and calculate the resulting probability P of obtaining the sample statistical measure *or a more extreme* sample statistical measure. If this probability is small (typically $P < 0.05$), you should reject the hypothesis.

Example 1   Find a binomial probability

Surveys According to a survey conducted by the Harris Poll, 23% of adults in the United States favor abolishing the penny and making the nickel the lowest denomination coin. You are conducting a random survey of 500 adults. What is the probability that you will find at most 106 adults who favor abolishing the penny?

Solution

The number x of adults in your survey who favor abolishing the penny has a binomial distribution with $n = 500$ and $p = 0.23$. Solving the problem using the binomial probability formula is tedious. Instead, approximate the answer using a normal distribution with the mean and standard deviation calculated below.

$\bar{x} = np = 500(0.23) = 115$ Find mean.

$\sigma = \sqrt{np(1 - p)} = \sqrt{500(0.23)(0.77)} \approx 9$ Find standard deviation.

For this normal distribution, 106 is about one standard deviation to the left of the mean. So,

$P(x \leq 106) \approx 0.0015 + 0.0235 + 0.135 = 0.16.$

The probability that at most 106 of the people surveyed favor abolishing the penny is about 0.16.

0.16

88   97   106   115   124   133   142

People who favor abolishing penny

Georgia Performance Standards

MM3D2b	Determine the probability that a given value falls within a specified interval.	☑
MM3D2c	Estimate how many items in a population fall within a specified interval.	☑
MM3D3	Students will understand the differences between experimental and observational studies by posing questions and collecting, analyzing, and interpreting data.	☑

Example 2 Test a hypothesis

Consumer Spending A recent Harris Poll claimed that 44% of adults cut back on their spending in order to pay the increased price of gasoline. To test this finding, you survey 60 adults and find that 21 of them cut back on their spending in order to pay the increased price of gasoline. Should you reject the Harris Poll's findings? Explain.

STEP 1 State the hypothesis: 44% of adults cut back on their spending in order to pay the increased price of gasoline.

STEP 2 Collect data and calculate a statistical measure. In your survey, 21 out of 60, or 35%, cut back on their spending in order to pay the increased price of gasoline.

STEP 3 Assume that the hypothesis in Step 1 is true. Find the resulting probability that you could randomly select 21 *or fewer* adults out of 60 who have cut back on their spending to pay the increased price of gasoline. This probability is

$$P(x \le 21) = P(x = 0) + P(x = 1) + P(x = 2) + \cdots + P(x = 21)$$

where each term in the sum is a binomial probability with $n = 60$ and $p = 0.44$.

You can approximate the binomial distribution with a normal distribution having the following mean and standard deviation:

$$\bar{x} = np = 60(0.44) = 26.4 \qquad \sigma = \sqrt{np(1 - p)} = \sqrt{60(0.44)(0.56)} \approx 3.84$$

Using a z-score and the standard normal table on page 248 gives:

$$P(x \le 21) \approx P\left(z \le \frac{21 - 26.4}{3.84}\right) \approx P(z \le -1.4) = 0.0808$$

So, if it is true that *44% of adults cut back on their spending to pay the increased price of gasoline*, then there is about an 8% probability of finding 21 or fewer adults who cut back on their spending to pay the increased price of gasoline in a random sample of 60 adults. With a probability this large, you should *not* reject the hypothesis.

Guided Practice for Examples 1 and 2

1. Use the fact that hyperopia, or farsightedness, is a condition that affects approximately 25% of the adult population in the United States. Consider a random sample of 280 U.S. adults. What is the probability that 63 or more people are farsighted? What is the probability that 84 or fewer people are farsighted? **0.84; 0.975**

2. Rework Example 2 if 18 people in the survey cut back on their spending. **Yes; $P(x \le 18) \approx P(z \le -2.2) \approx 0.0139$ which is less than 0.05.**

MM3D2b	Determine the probability that a given value falls within a specified interval.
MM3D2c	Estimate how many items in a population fall within a specified interval.
MM3D3	Students will understand the differences between experimental and observational studies by posing questions and collecting, analyzing, and interpreting data.

Find the mean and standard deviation of a normal distribution that approximates the binomial distribution with *n* trials and probability *p* of success on each trial.

1. $n = 30, p = 0.4$ **12; about 2.7**
2. $n = 50, p = 0.6$ **30; about 3.5**
3. $n = 42, p = 0.3$ **12.6; about 3.0**

4. $n = 65, p = 0.15$ **9.75; about 2.9**
5. $n = 72, p = 0.2$ **14.4; about 3.4**
6. $n = 38, p = 0.7$ **26.6; about 2.8**

7. **Error Analysis** According to a medical study, 20% of all patients with high blood pressure have adverse side effects from a new medication. Suppose 220 patients are treated with the new medication. You want to find the probability that more than 50 patients will have adverse side effects. *Describe* and correct the error in finding the mean and standard deviation. **The value of *n* should be 220, not 50. So, $\bar{x} = 44$ and $\sigma \approx 6$.**

$$\bar{x} = np = 50(0.2) = 10$$
$$\sigma = \sqrt{np(1-p)}$$
$$= \sqrt{50(0.2)(0.8)} \approx 3 \quad \times$$

Use the fact that approximately 12% of people wear contact lenses. Consider a high school with 1075 students.

8. What is the probability that at least 151 students wear contact lenses? **about 0.025**

9. What is the probability that at most 118 students wear contact lenses? **about 0.16**

10. What is the probability that between 96 and 140 students wear contact lenses? **about 0.8385**

A bank loan application may be rejected if a borrower does not have enough assets or has too much debt based on their income. Suppose a bank rejects 15% of their loan applications. This month, there were 180 applications.

11. What is the probability that at most 22 applications will be rejected? **0.16**

12. What is the probability that at least 27 applications will be rejected? **0.5**

13. What is the probability that between 17 and 42 applications will be rejected? **0.9735**

Use the fact that approximately 30% of U.S. adults have high blood pressure. Consider a random sample of 190 U.S. adults.

14. What is the probability that 51 or more people have high blood pressure? **about 0.84**

15. What is the probability that 69 or fewer people have high blood pressure? **about 0.975**

16. What is the probability that between 45 and 75 people have high blood pressure? **about 0.9735**

17. **Class Rings** You read an article that claims 35% of seniors will buy a class ring. To test this claim, you survey 55 randomly selected seniors in your school and find that 11 are planning to buy a class ring. Should you reject the claim? *Explain.* **Yes; $P(x \le 11) \approx P(z \le -2.3) \approx 0.0107$, which is less than 0.05.**

UNIT 6

LESSON 6.3

Exercise Set B

MM3D2b	Determine the probability that a given value falls within a specified interval.
MM3D2c	Estimate how many items in a population fall within a specified interval.
MM3D3	Students will understand the differences between experimental and observational studies by posing questions and collecting, analyzing, and interpreting data.

Find the mean and standard deviation of a normal distribution that approximates the binomial distribution with _n_ trials and probability _p_ of success on each trial.

1. $n = 100, p = 0.37$ **37; about 4.8** **2.** $n = 135, p = 0.45$ **3.** $n = 150, p = 0.75$
60.75; about 5.8 **112.5; about 5.3**

4. $n = 120, p = 0.08$ **9.6; about 3.0** **5.** $n = 240, p = 0.01$ **6.** $n = 130, p = 0.79$
2.4; about 1.5 **102.7; about 4.6**

Use the fact that approximately 2% of people have blood type B−. Consider a random sample of 850 students.

7. What is the probability that at least 13 students have blood type B−? **about 0.84**

8. What is the probability that at most 9 students have blood type B−? **about 0.025**

9. What is the probability that between 17 and 25 students have blood type B−? **about 0.475**

10. Approximately 1% of people have blood type AB−. Consider a random sample of 450 students. Is it reasonable to use a normal approximation to find a probability using this information? _Explain._ **No; because $np = 450(0.01) = 4.5$, which is less than 5.**

According to a medical study, 24% of all patients with high cholesterol have adverse side effects from a certain kind of medication. Consider a random sample of 250 patients.

11. What is the probability that at most 46 patients have adverse side effects from the medication? **about 0.025**

12. What is the probability that at least 39 patients have adverse side effects from the medication? **about 0.9985**

13. What is the probability that between 53 and 67 patients have adverse side effects from the medication? **about 0.68**

14. **Surveys** A survey that asked people in the United States about their feelings of personal well-being found that 85% are generally happy. To test this finding, you question 110 people at random and find that 83 consider themselves generally happy. Would you reject the survey's findings? _Explain._
Yes; $P(x \leq 83) \approx P(z \leq -2.8) \approx 0.0026$, which is less than 0.05.

15. **Computers** A manufacturer of laptop computers claims that under normal work use only 2% of its computers will fail to operate at some point during a month. A business uses 500 of the manufacturer's computers under normal work use and has 15 failures in a month. Would you reject the manufacturer's claim? _Explain._
Yes; $P(x \geq 15) \approx 1 - P(z \leq 3.2) \approx 1 - 0.9993 = 0.0007$, which is less than 0.05.

16. **Energy Drink Preferences** A company that makes energy drinks has created a new brand of energy drink. The company claims that 80% of people prefer the new energy drink over a competitor's energy drink. A taste test is conducted to test this claim. Of 150 people, 108 prefer the new energy drink. Would you reject the company's claim? _Explain._
Yes; $P(x \leq 108) \approx P(z \leq -2.4) \approx 0.0082$, which is less than 0.05.

Select and Draw Conclusions from Samples

Georgia Performance Standards: MM3D3

Goal Study different sampling methods for collecting data.

Vocabulary

A **population** is a group of people or objects that you want information about.

A **sample** is a subset of the population.

In a *self-selected sample,* members of a population can volunteer to be in the sample.

In a *systematic sample,* a rule is used to select members of a population, such as selecting every other person.

In a *convenience sample,* easy-to-reach members of a population are selected, such as those in the first row.

In a *random sample,* each member of a population has an equal chance of being selected.

An **unbiased sample** is representative of the population you want information about. A sample that overrepresents or underrepresents part of the population is a **biased sample.**

The **margin of error** gives a limit on how much the responses of a sample would differ from the responses of a population. When a random sample of size n is taken from a large population, the margin of error is approximated by this formula:

$$\text{Margin of error} = \pm\frac{1}{\sqrt{n}}$$

This means that if the percent of the sample responding a certain way is p (expressed as a decimal), then the percent of the population that would respond the same way is likely to be between

$$p - \frac{1}{\sqrt{n}} \text{ and } p + \frac{1}{\sqrt{n}}.$$

Example 1   Classify samples

Education A teacher wants to find out how many hours students studied for a history quiz. Identify the type of sample described.

a. Before leaving the room, the teacher asks students to write the number of hours they studied for the quiz on the chalkboard if they want to participate.

b. The teacher selects students randomly from an alphabetical list and asks the selected students how many hours they studied for the quiz.

Solution

a. The students can choose whether or not to respond. So, the sample is a self-selected sample.

b. The teacher selects students randomly. So, the sample is a random sample.

Georgia Performance Standards

MM3D3 Students will understand the differences between experimental and observational studies by posing questions and collecting, analyzing, and interpreting data.

Example 2 Identify biased samples

Tell whether each sample in Example 1 is *biased* or *unbiased*. Explain your reasoning.

Solution

a. The sample is biased because the sample is self-selected and it may not be representative of the entire class.

b. The sample is not biased because it is representative of the population.

Example 3 Find a margin of error

Haircuts In a survey of 800 people, 20% said they get a haircut once per month.

a. What is the margin of error for the survey?

b. Give an interval that is likely to contain the exact percent of all people who get a haircut once per month.

Solution

a. Use the margin of error formula.

$$\text{Margin of error} = \pm \frac{1}{\sqrt{n}} \qquad \text{Write margin of error formula.}$$

$$= \pm \frac{1}{\sqrt{800}} \qquad \text{Substitute 800 for } n.$$

$$\approx \pm 0.035 \qquad \text{Use a calculator.}$$

The margin of error for the survey is about $\pm 3.5\%$.

b. To find the interval, subtract and add 3.5% to the percent of people who get a haircut once per month.

$20\% - 3.5\% = 16.5\% \qquad\qquad 20\% + 3.5\% = 23.5\%$

It is likely that the exact percent of all people who get a haircut once per month is between 16.5% and 23.5%.

Guided Practice for Examples 1, 2, and 3

1. An electronics company wants to know which aspect of their MP3 player is the consumers' favorite. Technicians are required to ask the question to all customers calling for technical support. Identify the type of sample described. **convenience**

2. Tell whether the sample in Exercise 1 is *biased* or *unbiased*. *Explain* your reasoning. **biased; The convenience sample is not representative of all consumers.**

3. In a survey of 1100 home buyers, 90% said they used a real-estate agent to research home listings. What is the margin of error? Give an interval that is likely to contain the exact percent of all home buyers who used a real-estate agent to research home listings. **about $\pm 3\%$; between 87% and 93%**

UNIT 6

Exercise Set A

MM3D3 Students will understand the differences between experimental and observational studies by posing questions and collecting, analyzing, and interpreting data.

Identify the type of sample described. Then tell if the sample is biased. _Explain_ your reasoning.

1. Kevin wants to find out the opinions of college students about the availability of parking spaces. He surveys students as they walk by his car. **convenience; biased; The sample is not representative of the population.**

2. A yearbook editor wants to know what type of cover the students prefer for the new yearbook. Every fifth student on an alphabetical list is surveyed. **systematic; unbiased; The sample is representative of the class.**

3. A mall supervisor wants to know how often people in the community shop at the mall. The supervisor randomly asks 50 people in the mall how often they shop at the mall. **random; biased; People at the mall are more likely to attend the mall than people in the community in general.**

Find the margin of error for a survey that has the given sample size. Round your answer to the nearest tenth of a percent.

4. 125 $\pm 8.9\%$
5. 250 $\pm 6.3\%$
6. 300 $\pm 5.8\%$
7. 1500 $\pm 2.6\%$

8. 3200 $\pm 1.8\%$
9. 585 $\pm 4.1\%$
10. 166 $\pm 7.8\%$
11. 4000 $\pm 1.6\%$

Find the sample size required to achieve the given margin of error. Round your answer to the nearest whole number, if necessary.

12. $\pm 3\%$ **1111**
13. $\pm 5\%$ **400**
14. $\pm 2.5\%$ **1600**
15. $\pm 0.8\%$ **15,625**

16. **Error Analysis** In a survey of students, 18% said they like all of their classes. The margin of error in the survey is $\pm 2\%$. _Describe_ and correct the error in calculating the sample size.
The wrong percentage was used;
$\pm 0.02 = \pm \frac{1}{\sqrt{n}}$, $0.0004 = \frac{1}{n}$, $n = 2500$

$$\pm 0.18 = \pm \frac{1}{\sqrt{n}}$$
$$0.0324 = \frac{1}{n}$$
$$n \approx 21$$

17. **Multiple Representations** A survey reported that 52% of respondents recommend a skateboarding game for teens 15 and older. **See Additional Answers beginning on page AA1.**

   a. **Calculating Sample Size** If 364 people recommend the game for teens 15 and older, how many people were surveyed?

   b. **Making a Circle Graph** If 126 people do not recommend the game for teens 15 and older, and the remaining replied to let the parents decide, make a circle graph that displays the results of the survey.

   c. **Drawing Conclusions** To the nearest tenth of a percent, what is the margin of error for the survey? Give an interval that is likely to contain the exact percent of people that recommend the skateboarding game for teens 15 and older.

UNIT 6

LESSON 6.4

Exercise Set B

MM3D3 Students will understand the differences between experimental and observational studies by posing questions and collecting, analyzing, and interpreting data.

Identify the type of sample described. Then tell if the sample is biased. *Explain* your reasoning.

1. A baseball league wants to know who the fans think was the league's best pitcher. Fans are asked to vote on the league's website. **self-selected; unbiased; People visiting the league website would not be biased toward any one particular player.**

2. The owner of a miniature golf course wants to find the number of times people in the community play a round of miniature golf each year. The owner has the front desk employee survey customers when they pay for a round. **convenience; biased; People about to play miniature golf are more likely to play than people in the community in general.**

3. An online vendor wants to know how people that purchased a new product feel about changes from the older models. A computer is used to randomly generate a list of 100 customers to survey from a list of all customers that bought the product. **random; unbiased; Selecting customers at random would eliminate bias.**

Find the margin of error for a survey that has the given sample size. Round your answer to the nearest tenth of a percent.

4. 482 **±4.6%**   5. 664 **±3.9%**   6. 801 **±3.5%**   7. 773 **±3.6%**

8. 1252 **±2.8%**   9. 2498 **±2.0%**   10. 3444 **±1.7%**   11. 8417 **±1.1%**

Find the sample size required to achieve the given margin of error. Round your answer to the nearest whole number.

12. ±1.8% **3086**   13. ±2.3% **1890**   14. ±4.8% **434**   15. ±3.7% **730**

16. ±6.2% **260**   17. ±2.9% **1189**   18. ±4.4% **517**   19. ±0.6% **27,778**

In Exercises 20 and 21, use the following information.

Computers A survey reported that 2048 respondents out of 3200 had detected a virus on their computer at least once during the last two years.

20. What is the margin of error for the survey? Round your answer to the nearest tenth of a percent. **±1.8%**

21. Give an interval that is likely to contain the exact percent of people that have detected a virus on their computer at least once during the last two years. **between 62.2% and 65.8%**

In Exercises 22 and 23, use the following information.

Environment A survey claims that the percent of the population that makes purchasing decisions based on the effect it will have on the environment is between 88.75% and 91.25%. The remainder of the people in the survey do not let effects on the environment influence their purchasing decisions.

22. How many people were surveyed? **6400 people**

23. Give an interval that is likely to contain the exact number of people in the population that do not let effects on the environment influence their purchasing decisions. **between 560 and 720 people**

Georgia Performance Standards

MM3D3   Students will understand the differences between experimental and observational studies by posing questions and collecting, analyzing, and interpreting data.

LESSON 6.4
Problem Solving Workshop

Problem In a survey of 1600 voters, 51% said they voted for candidate A. What is the margin of error? Give an interval that is likely to contain the exact percent of all voters who voted for candidate A.

STEP 1 Read and Understand

What do you know? The number of voters and the percent that voted for candidate A

What do you want to find out? The margin of error for the survey

STEP 2 Make a Plan
Use the formula for margin of error to solve the problem.

STEP 3 Solve the Problem
Use the formula for margin of error.

$$\text{Margin of error} = \pm\frac{1}{\sqrt{n}} \cdot \qquad \text{Write margin of error formula.}$$

$$= \pm\frac{1}{\sqrt{1600}} = \pm 0.025 \qquad \text{Substitute 1600 for } n \text{ and simplify.}$$

The margin of error is $\pm 2.5\%$.

To find the interval, subtract and add 2.5% to the percent of people surveyed who voted for candidate A (51%).

$$51\% - 2.5\% = 48.5\% \qquad\qquad 51\% + 2.5\% = 53.5\%$$

It is likely that the exact percent of all voters who voted for candidate A is between 48.5% and 53.5%.

STEP 4 Look Back
The answer seems reasonable. In Example 3 on page 229, there were 800 people surveyed and a margin of error of $\pm 3.5\%$. Because more people are surveyed in the problem above, the percent should be lower.

Practice

1. **Juice** In a survey of 400 people, 18% named grape as their favorite juice. What is the margin of error? Give an interval that is likely to contain the exact percent of all people who named grape as their favorite juice.
   $\pm 5\%$, 13% to 23%

2. **Gym Class** A survey of 2100 students found that 65% prefer having gym class during the last period of the day. What is the margin of error? Give an interval that is likely to contain the exact percent of all students who prefer to have gym class during the last period.
   $\pm 2.2\%$, 62.8% to 67.2%

3. **What If?** In Exercise 2, 35% of the students did not prefer gym class during the last period of the day. What is the margin of error? Give an interval that is likely to contain the exact percent of all students who did not prefer to have gym class during the last period.
   $\pm 2.2\%$, 32.8% to 37.2%

4. **Pizza Toppings** In a survey of 500 people, 64% said their favorite pizza topping was pepperoni. What is the margin of error? Give an interval that is likely to contain the exact percent of all people who said their favorite pizza topping was pepperoni.
   $\pm 4.5\%$, 59.5% to 68.5%

Experimental and Observational Studies

Georgia Performance Standards: MM3D3

Goal Identify types of studies and flaws in experiments.

Vocabulary

A study is often conducted with two groups. One group, called the **experimental group,** undergoes some procedure or treatment. The other group, called the **control group,** does not undergo the procedure or treatment.

In a well designed experiment, everything else about the experimental group and control group is as similar as possible so that the effect of the procedure or treatment can be determined.

In an **experimental study,** the investigator assigns the individuals to the experimental group or the control group.

In an **observational study,** the assignments of individuals to the experimental group and the control group are outside of the control of the investigator.

Example 1   **Identify studies**

Tell whether the study is an _experimental study_ or an _observational study_. Explain your reasoning.

a. You want to study the effects of regular exercise on a person's heart rate. You measure the heart rate of a person at rest and again after jogging in place for 5 minutes. The control group is students who are not on a school athletic team. The experimental group is students who are on a school athletic team.

b. You want to study the effects that music has on the ability to recall knowledge. Each individual in your study is given material to read on the same unfamiliar topic and then asked to take a factual quiz on the material. The control group is individuals who read the material and take the quiz in a quiet room. The experimental group is individuals who read the material and take the quiz in a room that has classical music playing.

Solution

a. This study is an observational study because the assignments of the individuals to the experimental group and the control group are outside of your control. The students "sort themselves" into the two groups based on their previously-made decisions about whether to participate in school sports.

b. This study is an experimental study because you are assigning individuals to the control group and the experimental group.

Georgia Performance Standards

MM3D3   Students will understand the differences between experimental and observational studies by posing questions and collecting, analyzing, and interpreting data.

Example 2   Identify flaws in an experiment

Research A manufacturing company conducts an experiment to test how effective a new foot cushion for shoes is at relieving back pain. The experimental group consists of young college athletes who are given the foot cushions to use during athletic practices and games. The control group consists of non-athletic college students who are not given the foot cushions.

The company finds that the people in the experimental group experience less back pain than those people in the control group. As a result, the company concludes that the foot cushions are effective. Identify any flaws in this experiment, and describe how they can be corrected.

Solution

College athletes are likely to be more physically active than non-athletic students. So, it could be physical activity rather than the foot cushions that explains why the experimental group had less back pain than the control group.

To correct this flaw, the manufacturing company could redesign the experiment so that the physical activity of the people in the experimental group is simiar to the physical activity of the people in the control group.

Guided Practice for Examples 1 and 2

In Exercises 1 and 2, tell whether the study is an *experimental study* or an *observational study*. *Explain* your reasoning.

1. A scientist wants to study the effects that a nutritional supplement has on the growth of mice. The weight of each mouse is recorded daily. The control group consists of mice that do not receive the supplement. The experimental group consists of mice that receive a safe amount of the supplement. **Experimental study; The scientist is assigning mice to the control group and the experimental group.**

2. You want to study the effects that using a calculator has on the time it takes to complete a math test. You record how long it takes a student to complete the test. The control group is students that choose not to use calculators. The experimental group is students that choose to use calculators.

   2. Observational study; The assignments of the students to the experimental group and the control group are outside of your control.

3. **Medicine** A researcher conducts an experiment to see if a new medication is effective in preventing strokes. An experimental group of lawyers suffers more strokes than a control group of professional tennis players. Identify any flaws in this experiment and describe how they can be corrected. **See Additional Answers beginning on page AA1.**

4. **Seat Belts** You conduct an experiment to see if parents make their children wear seat belts. You have a police officer ask the question to a large group of parents. Identify any flaws in the experiment, and describe how they can be corrected. **See Additional Answers beginning on page AA1.**

UNIT 6

LESSON 6.5

Exercise Set A

MM3D3 Students will understand the differences between experimental and observational studies by posing questions and collecting, analyzing, and interpreting data.

In Exercises 1–3, tell whether the study is an *experimental study* or an *observational study*. *Explain* your reasoning.

1. A professor wants to study the effects that teaching outdoors has on test scores. Each individual in the study is given the same lectures for a month and then tested. The control group is individuals who were lectured and tested indoors. The experimental group is individuals who were lectured and tested outdoors. **Experimental study; The professor is assigning individuals to the control group and the experimental group.**

2. You want to study the effects that yawning has on other individuals' yawning. Each individual in your study is placed in a room to watch an instructional video. You record the total number of yawns in each group. The control group is individuals who watch the video without a yawning scene. The experimental group is individuals who watch the same video with the addition of one yawning scene. **Experimental study; You are assigning individuals to the control group and the experimental group.**

3. Dr. Smith and Dr. Jones want to study the effects on a patient's arthritis that occur when the patient believes that he or she has used a new ointment. The control group consists of the patients that choose to visit Dr. Smith about arthritis and they receive an ointment with no medicinal value. The experimental group consists of the patients that choose to visit Dr. Jones about arthritis and they receive the new ointment. **See Additional Answers beginning on page AA1.**

4. **Math Anxiety** A company conducts an experiment to determine whether college students suffer from math anxiety. The experimental group consists of students enrolled in a mathematics program. The control group consists of students enrolled in an art history program. Identify any flaws in the experiment, and describe how they can be corrected. **See Additional Answers beginning on page AA1.**

5. **Government** A researcher conducts a survey to determine the approval rating of the current mayor of a city. The experimental group consists of registered voters in the same party as the mayor. The control group consists of registered voters in a different party from the mayor. Identify any flaws in the experiment, and describe how they can be corrected. **See Additional Answers beginning on page AA1.**

6. **Education** A company conducts an experiment to determine whether the use of educational software in an elementary classroom will increase test scores of students. The experimental group consists of students enrolled in third grade who are given the software. The control group consists of students enrolled in first grade who are not given the software.

   The company finds that the students in the experimental group test higher than the students in the control group and concludes that the educational software is effective at increasing test scores. Identify any flaws in the experiment, and describe how they can be corrected.
   Sample answer: **The flaw is that 3rd grade students are the experimental group and 1st grade students are the control group. The experimental and control groups should both be 3rd grade students or 1st grade students.**

LESSON 6.5

Exercise Set B

MM3D3   Students will understand the differences between experimental and observational studies by posing questions and collecting, analyzing, and interpreting data.

In Exercises 1–3, tell whether the study is an *experimental study* or an *observational study*. *Explain* your reasoning.

1. A health teacher at a large school wants to study the effects of regular swimming on a student's ability to hold his or her breath. The teacher measures the length of time that a student can hold his or her breath. The control group consists of students who are not on the swim team. The experimental group consists of students who are on the swim team. **Observational study; The assignments of the students to the experimental group and the control group are outside of the teacher's control.**

2. You want to study the ability of students to talk at a normal tone while listening to loud music with their MP3 player headphones. You measure how loud a student talks normally, then you measure how loud the student talks while listening to loud music with their MP3 player headphones. The control group is students who do not regularly use an MP3 player. The experimental group is students who regularly use an MP3 player. **Observational study; The assignments of the students to the experimental group and the control group are outside of your control.**

3. A manager wants to study the effects that positive reinforcement has on an employee's willingness to work overtime. The control group is employees who are given no reinforcement. The experimental group is employees who are given positive reinforcement during their weekly meeting with the manager. **Experimental study; The manager is assigning employees to the control group and the experimental group.**

4. **Health** A research company conducts a survey to determine how fast the cold virus would spread in a metropolitan area. The experimental group consists of trained medical professionals. The control group consists of college students. Identify any flaws in the experiment, and describe how they can be corrected. **See Additional Answers beginning on page AA1.**

5. **Statistics** A company that produces mathematics textbooks conducts an experiment to determine how effective an online help tutorial for their statistics book is for college students. The experimental group consists of first year mathematics majors. The control group consists of students from other majors required to take an introductory statistics course. Identify any flaws in the experiment, and describe how they can be corrected. **See Additional Answers beginning on page AA1.**

6. **Dance** A dance company conducts an experiment to determine whether the use of an instructional dance video will increase the skill level of dance students. The experimental group consists of fourth year dance students who are given the video. The control group consists of second year dance students who are not given the video.

    The company finds that the students' skill level in the experimental group has increased while the students' skill level in the control group has not increased. The company concludes that the instructional dance video is effective at increasing skill levels. Identify any flaws in the experiment, and describe how they can be corrected.
    Sample answer: **The flaw is that 4th year dance students are the experimental group and 2nd year dance students are the control group. The experimental and control groups should both be 4th year dance students or 2nd year dance students.**

TEST | for Unit 6

1. The random variable *C* represents the color of a pen chosen from a bag that contains 1 red pen, 5 black pens, and 4 blue pens. Make a table and a histogram showing the probability distribution for *C*. *Describe* the distribution as either *symmetric* or *skewed*.
See Additional Answers beginning on page AA1.

Calculate the probability of *k* successes for a binomial experiment consisting of *n* trials with probability *p* of success on each trial.

2. $k \leq 3, n = 6, p = 0.3$ about 0.930

3. $k \geq 6, n = 10, p = 0.55$ about 0.504

4. $k \leq 5, n = 8, p = 0.81$ about 0.181

5. $k \geq 2, n = 5, p = 0.12$ about 0.112

Give the percent of the area under the normal curve represented by the shaded region.

6. 47.65%

7. 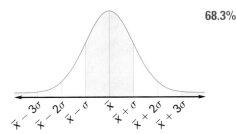 68.3%

Find the mean and standard deviation of a normal distribution that approximates the binomial distribution with *n* trials and probability *p* of success on each trial.

8. $n = 75, p = 0.15$
   11.25, about 3.1

9. $n = 96, p = 0.2$
   19.2, about 3.9

10. $n = 180, p = 0.75$
    135, about 5.8

Find the margin of error for a survey that has the given sample size. Round your answer to the nearest tenth of a percent.

11. 165 ±7.8%

12. 475 ±4.6%

13. 1450 ±2.6%

14. 3540 ±1.7%

Find the sample size required to achieve the given margin of error. Round your answer to the nearest whole number, if necessary.

15. ±1.4% 5102

16. ±3.8% 693

17. ±5.2% 370

18. ±0.5% 40,000

19. Tell whether the study below is an *experimental study* or an *observational study*. *Explain* your reasoning.

   You want to study the effects that prior playoff experience has on a player's ability to perform well in the playoffs. The performance of each individual in the playoffs is analyzed. The control group is individuals who have no prior playoff experience. The experimental group is individuals who have prior playoff experience.
   Observational study; The assignments of the players to the experimental group and the control group are outside of your control.

20. Fruit According to a farmer's study, 10% of his oranges are too damaged to sell. Which probability is greater: (a) the probability of choosing 40 oranges and getting 3 that are too damaged to sell, or (b) the probability of choosing 50 oranges and getting at most 3 that are too damaged to sell? **The probability in (b) is greater.**

In Exercises 21–23, use the fact that approximately 6% of people have blood type A−. Consider a class of 450 students.

21. What is the probability that 17 or fewer students have blood type A−? **about 0.025**

22. What is the probability that 32 or more students have blood type A−? **about 0.16**

23. What is the probability that between 12 and 37 students have blood type A−? **about 0.9735**

24. Paramedics The time paramedics take to arrive at the scene of an emergency is normally distributed with a mean of 7 minutes and a standard deviation of 1 minute.

a. What is the probability that the paramedics take at most 9 minutes to arrive at the scene of an emergency? **0.975**

b. What is the probability that the paramedics take between 5 minutes and 8 minutes to arrive at the scene of an emergency? **0.815**

25. Water Park A research company conducts a survey to determine how popular a new indoor water park is among residents. The experimental group consists of young adults from 16 to 29 years of age. The control group consists of adults from 30 to 50 years of age. Identify any flaws in the experiment, and describe how they can be corrected. **See Additional Answers beginning on page AA1.**

Performance Task

Restaurants

Surveys were conducted on two samples of 850 restaurant employees to determine their hand washing habits while working. Sample A consisted of individuals that completed and mailed in the survey. Sample B consisted of phone calls to random restaurant employees.

a. What type of sample is sample A? Sample B? Which is most appropriate for the survey? **Sample A: self-selected sample; Sample B: random sample; Sample B**

b. The question "Do you wash your hands every time you change duties at work?" was among the questions asked. In Sample B, there were 799 responses of "Yes" and the remaining replied "No." Find the margin of error. Round to the nearest tenth. Give an interval that is likely to contain the exact percent that responded "No." **±3.4%; between 2.6% and 9.4%**

c. If the question is asked to 50 more employees, what is the probability that fewer than 5 of these employees answer "No"? **about 0.821**

d. Identify a flaw in the experiment if the surveyed employees are not told that their responses will remain anonymous.

d. Employees would be more likely to reply "Yes" if they were not told their answers would remain anonymous.

Student Resources

Tables

Table of Symbols

Symbol	Meaning	Page
$\cdot$	multiplication, times	2
$\approx$	is approximately equal to	2
$-a$	opposite of a	3
(x, y)	ordered pair	6
$|x|$	absolute value of x	10
$<$	is less than	17
$>$	is greater than	17
$\leq$	is less than or equal to	17
$\geq$	is greater than or equal to	17
(x, y, z)	ordered triple	34
$\begin{bmatrix} 1 & 0 \\ 0 & 1 \end{bmatrix}$	matrix	38
$|A|$	determinant of matrix A	49
A^{-1}	inverse of matrix A	54
$x \to +\infty$	x approaches positive infinity	66
$x \to -\infty$	x approaches negative infinity	66
$\sqrt{a}$	the nonnegative square root of a	66
$[a, b]$	$a \leq x \leq b$	81
(a, b)	$a < x < b$	81
$[a, b)$	$a \leq x < b$	81
$(a, b]$	$a < x \leq b$	81
i	imaginary unit equal to $\sqrt{-1}$	94
$\sqrt[n]{a}$	nth root of a	108
e	irrational number ≈ 2.718	140
$\log_b y$	log base b of y	145
$\log x$	log base 10 of x	145
$\ln x$	log base e of x	145
$P(A)$	probability of event A	212
$_nC_r$	number of combinations of r objects chosen from n distinct objects	212
$\bar{x}$	x-bar, the mean of a data set	218
σ	sigma, the standard deviation of a data set	219

Time

60 seconds (sec) = 1 minute (min)	365 days
60 minutes = 1 hour (h)	52 weeks (approx.) ⎤ = 1 year
24 hours = 1 day	12 months ⎦
7 days = 1 week	10 years = 1 decade
4 weeks (approx.) = 1 month	100 years = 1 century

Measures

Metric	United States Customary
Length	**Length**
10 millimeters (mm) = 1 centimeter (cm)	12 inches (in.) = 1 foot (ft)
$\begin{matrix}100 \text{ cm}\\1000 \text{ mm}\end{matrix}\Big\rbrace$ = 1 meter (m)	$\begin{matrix}36 \text{ in.}\\3 \text{ ft}\end{matrix}\Big\rbrace$ = 1 yard (yd)
1000 m = 1 kilometer (km)	$\begin{matrix}5280 \text{ ft}\\1760 \text{ yd}\end{matrix}\Big\rbrace$ = 1 mile (mi)
Area	**Area**
100 square millimeters = 1 square centimeter (mm^2) (cm^2)	144 square inches (in.^{2}) = 1 square foot (ft^2)
	9 ft^2 = 1 square yard (yd^2)
10,000 cm^2 = 1 square meter (m^2)	$\begin{matrix}43{,}560 \text{ ft}^2\\4840 \text{ yd}^2\end{matrix}\Big\rbrace$ = 1 acre (A)
10,000 m^2 = 1 hectare (ha)	
Volume	**Volume**
1000 cubic millimeters = 1 cubic centimeter (mm^3) (cm^3)	1728 cubic inches (in.^{3}) = 1 cubic foot (ft^3)
1,000,000 cm^3 = 1 cubic meter (m^3)	27 ft^3 = 1 cubic yard (yd^3)
Liquid Capacity	**Liquid Capacity**
$\begin{matrix}1000 \text{ milliliters (mL)}\\1000 \text{ cubic centimeters (cm}^3)\end{matrix}\Big\rbrace$ = 1 liter (L)	8 fluid ounces (fl oz) = 1 cup (c)
	2 c = 1 pint (pt)
	2 pt = 1 quart (qt)
1000 L = 1 kiloliter (kL)	4 qt = 1 gallon (gal)
Mass	**Weight**
1000 milligrams (mg) = 1 gram (g)	16 ounces (oz) = 1 pound (lb)
1000 g = 1 kilogram (kg)	2000 lb = 1 ton
1000 kg = 1 metric ton (t)	
Temperature	**Temperature**
Degrees Celsius (°C)	**Degrees Fahrenheit (°F)**
0°C = freezing point of water	32°F = freezing point of water
37°C = normal body temperature	98.6°F = normal body temperature
100°C = boiling point of water	212°F = boiling point of water

Area and Volume Formulas

Area of an equilateral triangle	Area $= \frac{\sqrt{3}}{4}s^2$ where s is the length of a side	
Area of an ellipse	Area $= \pi ab$ where a and b are half the lengths of the major and minor axes of the ellipse	
Volume and surface area of a right rectangular prism	Volume $= \ell wh$ where ℓ is the length, w is the width, and h is the height Surface area $= 2(\ell w + wh + \ell h)$	
Volume and surface area of a right cylinder	Volume $= \pi r^2 h$ where r is the base radius and h is the height Lateral surface area $= 2\pi rh$ Surface area $= 2\pi r^2 + 2\pi rh$	
Volume and surface area of a right regular pyramid	Volume $= \frac{1}{3}Bh$ where B is the area of the base and h is the height Lateral surface area $= \frac{1}{2}ns\ell$ where n is the number of sides of the base, s is the length of a side of the base, and ℓ is the slant height Surface area $= B + \frac{1}{2}ns\ell$	
Volume and surface area of a right circular cone	Volume $= \frac{1}{3}\pi r^2 h$ where r is the base radius and h is the height Lateral surface area $= \pi r\ell$ where ℓ is the slant height Surface area $= \pi r^2 + \pi r\ell$	
Volume and surface area of a sphere	Volume $= \frac{4}{3}\pi r^3$ where r is the radius Surface area $= 4\pi r^2$	

Other Formulas

Name of Formula	Statement of Formula	Page
Determinant of a 2 × 2 matrix	$\det \begin{bmatrix} a & b \\ c & d \end{bmatrix} = \begin{vmatrix} a & b \\ c & d \end{vmatrix} = ad - cb$	49
Determinant of a 3 × 3 matrix	$\det \begin{bmatrix} a & b & c \\ d & e & f \\ g & h & i \end{bmatrix} = \begin{vmatrix} a & b & c \\ d & e & f \\ g & h & i \end{vmatrix} = (aei + bfg + cdh) - (gec + hfa + idb)$	49
Cramer's rule	Let $A = \begin{bmatrix} a & b \\ c & d \end{bmatrix}$ be the coefficient matrix of this linear system: $$ax + by = e$$ $$cx + dy = f$$ If $\det A \neq 0$, then the system has exactly one solution. The solution is $x = \dfrac{\begin{vmatrix} e & b \\ f & d \end{vmatrix}}{\det A}$ and $y = \dfrac{\begin{vmatrix} a & e \\ c & f \end{vmatrix}}{\det A}$.	49
Area of a triangle	The area of a triangle with vertices (x_1, y_1), (x_2, y_2), and (x_3, y_3) is given by $$\text{Area} = \pm\frac{1}{2}\begin{vmatrix} x_1 & y_1 & 1 \\ x_2 & y_2 & 1 \\ x_3 & y_3 & 1 \end{vmatrix}$$ where the appropriate sign ($\pm$) should be chosen to yield a positive value.	51
Inverse of a 2 × 2 matrix	The inverse of the matrix $A = \begin{bmatrix} a & b \\ c & d \end{bmatrix}$ is $$A^{-1} = \frac{1}{|A|}\begin{bmatrix} d & -b \\ -c & a \end{bmatrix} = \frac{1}{ad - cb}\begin{bmatrix} d & -b \\ -c & a \end{bmatrix} \text{ provided}$$ $ad - cb \neq 0$.	54
Discriminant of a general second-degree equation	Any conic can be described by a general second-degree equation in x and y: $Ax^2 + Bxy + Cy^2 + Dx + Ey + F = 0$. The expression $B^2 - 4AC$ is the discriminant of the conic equation and can be used to identify it. 	Discriminant	Type of Conic	 	---	---	 	$B^2 - 4AC < 0$, $B = 0$, and $A = C$	Circle	 	$B^2 - 4AC < 0$, and either $B \neq 0$ or $A \neq C$	Ellipse	 	$B^2 - 4AC = 0$	Parabola	 	$B^2 - 4AC > 0$	Hyperbola	 If $B = 0$, each axis of the conic is horizontal or vertical.	194

Other Formulas (continued)

Name of Formula	Statement of Formula	Page
Areas under a normal curve	A normal distribution with mean $\bar{x}$ and standard deviation σ has these properties: • The total area under the related normal curve is 1. • About 68% of the area lies within 1 standard deviation of the mean. • About 95% of the area lies within 2 standard deviations of the mean. • About 99.7% of the area lies within 3 standard deviations of the mean.	219
z-score formula	$z = \dfrac{x - \bar{x}}{\sigma}$ where x is a data value, $\bar{x}$ is the mean, and σ is the standard deviation	219

Theorems

Theorem or Corollary	Statement of Theorem or Corollary	Page
Remainder theorem	If a polynomial $f(x)$ is divided by $x - k$, then the remainder is $r = f(k)$.	85
Factor theorem	A polynomial $f(x)$ has a factor $x - k$ if and only if $f(k) = 0$.	85
Rational root theorem	If $f(x) = a_n x^n + \cdots + a_1 x + a_0$ has *integer* coefficients, then every rational zero of f has this form: $$\frac{p}{q} = \frac{\text{factor of constant term } a_0}{\text{factor of leading coefficient } a_n}$$	89
Fundamental theorem of algebra	If $f(x)$ is a polynomial of degree n where $n > 0$, then the equation $f(x) = 0$ has at least one solution in the set of complex numbers.	94
Corollary to the fundamental theorem of algebra	If $f(x)$ is a polynomial of degree n where $n > 0$, then the equation $f(x) = 0$ has exactly n solutions provided each solution repeated twice is counted as 2 solutions, each solution repeated three times is counted as 3 solutions, and so on.	94
Complex conjugates theorem	If f is a polynomial function with real coefficients, and $a + bi$ is an imaginary zero of f, then $a - bi$ is also a zero of f.	94
Irrational conjugates theorem	Suppose f is a polynomial function with rational coefficients, and a and b are rational numbers such that $\sqrt{b}$ is irrational. If $a + \sqrt{b}$ is a zero of f, then $a - \sqrt{b}$ is also a zero of f.	94
Descartes' rule of signs	Let $f(x) = a_n x^n + a_{n-1} x^{n-1} + \cdots + a_2 x^2 + a_1 x + a_0$ be a polynomial function with real coefficients. • The number of *positive real zeros* of f is equal to the number of changes in sign of the coefficients of $f(x)$ or is less than this by an even number. • The number of *negative real zeros* of f is equal to the number of changes in sign of the coefficients of $f(-x)$ or is less than this by an even number.	94

Properties of Matrices

Property	Statement of Property	Page
	Let A, B, and C be matrices, and let k be a scalar.	
Associative Property of Addition	$(A + B) + C = A + (B + C)$	38
Commutative Property of Addition	$A + B = B + A$	38
Distributive Property of Addition	$k(A + B) = kA + kB$	38
Distributive Property of Subtraction	$k(A - B) = kA - kB$	38
Associative Property of Matrix Multiplication	$(AB)C = A(BC)$	43
Left Distributive Property of Matrix Multiplication	$A(B + C) = AB + AC$	43
Right Distributive Property of Matrix Multiplication	$(A + B)C = AC + BC$	43
Associative Property of Scalar Multiplication	$k(AB) = (kA)B = A(kB)$	43
Multiplicative Identity	An $n \times n$ matrix with 1's on the main diagonal and 0's elsewhere is an identity matrix, denoted I. For any $n \times n$ matrix A, $AI = IA = A$.	54
Inverse Matrices	If the determinant of an $n \times n$ matrix A is nonzero, then A has an inverse, denoted A^{-1}, such that $A A^{-1} = A^{-1}A = I$.	54

Properties of Rational Exponents

Property	Statement of Property	Page
	Let a and b be real numbers, and let m and n be rational numbers.	
Product of Powers Property	$a^m \cdot a^n = a^{m+n}$	113
Power of a Power Property	$(a^m)^n = a^{mn}$	113
Power of a Product Property	$(ab)^m = a^m b^m$	113
Negative Exponent Property	$a^{-m} = \dfrac{1}{a^m}, a \neq 0$	113
Zero Exponent Property	$a^0 = 1, a \neq 0$	113
Quotient of Powers Property	$\dfrac{a^m}{a^n} = a^{m-n}, a \neq 0$	113
Power of a Quotient Property	$\left(\dfrac{a}{b}\right)^m = \dfrac{a^m}{b^m}, b \neq 0$	113

Properties of Radicals

Property	Statement of Property	Page
Number of Real nth Roots	Let n be an integer greater than 1, and let a be a real number. • If n is odd, then a has one real nth root: $\sqrt[n]{a} = a^{1/n}$. • If n is even and $a > 0$, then a has two real nth roots: $\pm \sqrt[n]{a} = \pm a^{1/n}$. • If n is even and $a = 0$, then a has one nth root: $\sqrt[n]{0} = 0^{1/n} = 0$. • If n is even and $a < 0$, then a has no real nth roots.	109
Radicals and Rational Exponents	Let $a^{1/n}$ be an nth root of a, and let m be a positive integer. • $a^{m/n} = (a^{1/n})^m = (\sqrt[n]{a})^m$ • $a^{-m/n} = \dfrac{1}{a^{m/n}} = \dfrac{1}{(a^{1/n})^m} = \dfrac{1}{(\sqrt[n]{a})^m}$, $a \neq 0$	109
Product and Quotient Properties of Radicals	Let n be an integer greater than 1, and let a and b be positive real numbers. Then $\sqrt[n]{a \cdot b} = \sqrt[n]{a} \cdot \sqrt[n]{b}$ and $\sqrt[n]{\dfrac{a}{b}} = \dfrac{\sqrt[n]{a}}{\sqrt[n]{b}}$.	113

Properties of Logarithms

Property	Statement of Property	Page
	Let a, b, c, m, n, x, and y be positive real numbers such that $b \neq 1$ and $c \neq 1$.	
Logarithms and Exponents	$\log_b y = x$ if and only if $b^x = y$	145
Special Logarithm Values	$\log_b 1 = 0$ because $b^0 = 1$ and $\log_b b = 1$ because $b^1 = b$	145
Common and Natural Logarithms	$\log_{10} x = \log x$ and $\log_e x = \ln x$	145
Product Property of Logarithms	$\log_b mn = \log_b m + \log_b n$	155
Quotient Property of Logarithms	$\log_b \dfrac{m}{n} = \log_b m - \log_b n$	155
Power Property of Logarithms	$\log_b m^n = n \log_b m$	155
Change of Base	$\log_c a = \dfrac{\log_b a}{\log_b c}$	156

TABLES

Table of Squares and Square Roots

No.	Square	Sq. Root	No.	Square	Sq. Root	No.	Square	Sq. Root
1	1	1.000	51	2601	7.141	101	10,201	10.050
2	4	1.414	52	2704	7.211	102	10,404	10.100
3	9	1.732	53	2809	7.280	103	10,609	10.149
4	16	2.000	54	2916	7.348	104	10,816	10.198
5	25	2.236	55	3025	7.416	105	11,025	10.247
6	36	2.449	56	3136	7.483	106	11,236	10.296
7	49	2.646	57	3249	7.550	107	11,449	10.344
8	64	2.828	58	3364	7.616	108	11,664	10.392
9	81	3.000	59	3481	7.681	109	11,881	10.440
10	100	3.162	60	3600	7.746	110	12,100	10.488
11	121	3.317	61	3721	7.810	111	12,321	10.536
12	144	3.464	62	3844	7.874	112	12,544	10.583
13	169	3.606	63	3969	7.937	113	12,769	10.630
14	196	3.742	64	4096	8.000	114	12,996	10.677
15	225	3.873	65	4225	8.062	115	13,225	10.724
16	256	4.000	66	4356	8.124	116	13,456	10.770
17	289	4.123	67	4489	8.185	117	13,689	10.817
18	324	4.243	68	4624	8.246	118	13,924	10.863
19	361	4.359	69	4761	8.307	119	14,161	10.909
20	400	4.472	70	4900	8.367	120	14,400	10.954
21	441	4.583	71	5041	8.426	121	14,641	11.000
22	484	4.690	72	5184	8.485	122	14,884	11.045
23	529	4.796	73	5329	8.544	123	15,129	11.091
24	576	4.899	74	5476	8.602	124	15,376	11.136
25	625	5.000	75	5625	8.660	125	15,625	11.180
26	676	5.099	76	5776	8.718	126	15,876	11.225
27	729	5.196	77	5929	8.775	127	16,129	11.269
28	784	5.292	78	6084	8.832	128	16,384	11.314
29	841	5.385	79	6241	8.888	129	16,641	11.358
30	900	5.477	80	6400	8.944	130	16,900	11.402
31	961	5.568	81	6561	9.000	131	17,161	11.446
32	1024	5.657	82	6724	9.055	132	17,424	11.489
33	1089	5.745	83	6889	9.110	133	17,689	11.533
34	1156	5.831	84	7056	9.165	134	17,956	11.576
35	1225	5.916	85	7225	9.220	135	18,225	11.619
36	1296	6.000	86	7396	9.274	136	18,496	11.662
37	1369	6.083	87	7569	9.327	137	18,769	11.705
38	1444	6.164	88	7744	9.381	138	19,044	11.747
39	1521	6.245	89	7921	9.434	139	19,321	11.790
40	1600	6.325	90	8100	9.487	140	19,600	11.832
41	1681	6.403	91	8281	9.539	141	19,881	11.874
42	1764	6.481	92	8464	9.592	142	20,164	11.916
43	1849	6.557	93	8649	9.644	143	20,449	11.958
44	1936	6.633	94	8836	9.695	144	20,736	12.000
45	2025	6.708	95	9025	9.747	145	21,025	12.042
46	2116	6.782	96	9216	9.798	146	21,316	12.083
47	2209	6.856	97	9409	9.849	147	21,609	12.124
48	2304	6.928	98	9604	9.899	148	21,904	12.166
49	2401	7.000	99	9801	9.950	149	22,201	12.207
50	2500	7.071	100	10,000	10.000	150	22,500	12.247

Standard Normal Table

If z is a randomly selected value from a standard normal distribution, you can use the table below to find the probability that z is less than or equal to some given value. For example, the table shows that $P(z \leq -0.6) = 0.2743$. You can find the value of $P(z \leq -0.6)$ in the table by finding the value where row -0 and column 6 intersect.

You can also use the standard normal table to find probabilities for any normal distribution by first converting values from the distribution to z-scores.

In the table, the value .0000+ means "slightly more than 0" and the value 1.0000− means "slightly less than 1."

z	.0	.1	.2	.3	.4	.5	.6	.7	.8	.9
−3	.0013	.0010	.0007	.0005	.0003	.0002	.0002	.0001	.0001	.0000+
−2	.0228	.0179	.0139	.0107	.0082	.0062	.0047	.0035	.0026	.0019
−1	.1587	.1357	.1151	.0968	.0808	.0668	.0548	.0446	.0359	.0287
−0	.5000	.4602	.4207	.3821	.3446	.3085	.2743	.2420	.2119	.1841
0	.5000	.5398	.5793	.6179	.6554	.6915	.7257	.7580	.7881	.8159
1	.8413	.8643	.8849	.9032	.9192	.9332	.9452	.9554	.9641	.9713
2	.9772	.9821	.9861	.9893	.9918	.9938	.9953	.9965	.9974	.9981
3	.9987	.9990	.9993	.9995	.9997	.9998	.9998	.9999	.9999	1.0000−

English-Spanish Glossary

A

asymptote (p. 130) A line that a graph approaches more and more closely.

asíntota (pág. 130) Recta a la que se aproxima una gráfica cada vez más.

The asymptote for the graph shown is the line $y = 3$.

La asíntota para la gráfica que se muestra es la recta $y = 3$.

average rate of change for a function (p. 149) For a function, the average rate of change between any two points (x_1, y_1) and (x_2, y_2) is the slope of the line through the two points.

$$\text{Average rate of change} = \frac{y_2 - y_1}{x_2 - x_1}$$

tasa de cambio promedio de una función (pág. 149) Para un función, la tasa de cambio promedio entre dos puntos cualesquiera (x_1, y_1) y (x_2, y_2) es la pendiente de la recta que atraviesa los dos puntos.

$$\text{Tasa de cambio promedio} = \frac{y_2 - y_1}{x_2 - x_1}$$

The average rate of change of $y = 2^x - 4$ from $(2, 0)$ to $(3, 4)$ is $\frac{4 - 0}{3 - 2}$, or 1.

La tasa de cambio promedio de $y = 2^x - 4$ de $(2, 0)$ a $(3, 4)$ es $\frac{4 - 0}{3 - 2}$, ó 1.

axis of symmetry of a parabola (p. 176) The line perpendicular to the parabola's directrix and passing through its focus and vertex.

See parabola.

eje de simetría de una parábola (pág. 176) La recta perpendicular a la directriz de la parábola y que pasa por su foco y su vértice.

Ver parábola.

B

biased sample (p. 228) A sample that overrepresents or underrepresents part of a population.

The members of a school's basketball team would form a biased sample for a survey about whether to build a new gym.

muestra sesgada (pág. 228) Muestra que representa de forma excesiva o insuficiente a parte de una población.

Los miembros del equipo de baloncesto de una escuela formarían una muestra sesgada si participaran en una encuesta sobre si quieren que se construya un nuevo gimnasio.

ENGLISH-SPANISH GLOSSARY

binomial distribution (p. 212) The probability distribution associated with a binomial experiment.

distribución binomial (pág. 212) La distribución de probabilidades asociada a un experimento binomial.

Binomial distribution for 8 trials with $p = 0.5$.

Distribución binomial de 8 pruebas con $p = 0.5$.

binomial experiment (p. 212) An experiment that meets the following conditions. (1) There are n independent trials. (2) Each trial has only two possible outcomes: success and failure. (3) The probability of success is the same for each trial.

experimento binomial (pág. 212) Experimento que satisface las siguientes condiciones. (1) Hay n pruebas independientes. (2) Cada prueba tiene sólo dos resultados posibles: éxito y fracaso. (3) La probabilidad de éxito es igual para cada prueba.

A fair coin is tossed 12 times. The probability of getting exactly 4 heads is as follows:

Una moneda normal se lanza 12 veces. La probabilidad de sacar exactamente 4 caras es la siguiente:

$$P(k = 4) = {}_nC_k p^k (1-p)^{n-k}$$
$$= {}_{12}C_4 (0.5)^4 (1-0.5)^8$$
$$= 495(0.5)^4(0.5)^8$$
$$\approx 0.121$$

C

center of a circle (p. 180) *See* circle.

centro de un círculo (pág. 180) *Ver* círculo.

The circle with equation $(x-3)^2 + (y+5)^2 = 36$ has its center at $(3, -5)$. *See also* circle.

El círculo con la ecuación $(x-3)^2 + (y+5)^2 = 36$ tiene el centro en $(3, -5)$. *Ver también* círculo.

center of a hyperbola (p. 190) The midpoint of the transverse axis of a hyperbola.

centro de una hipérbola (pág. 190) El punto medio del eje transverso de una hipérbola.

See hyperbola.

Ver hipérbola.

center of an ellipse (p. 186) The midpoint of the major axis of an ellipse.

centro de una elipse (pág. 186) El punto medio del eje mayor de una elipse.

See ellipse.

Ver elipse.

circle (p. 180) The set of all points (x, y) in a plane that are of distance r from a fixed point, called the center of the circle.

círculo (pág. 180) El conjunto de todos los puntos (x, y) de un plano que están a una distancia r de un punto fijo, llamado centro del círculo.

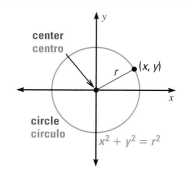

coefficient matrix (p. 49) The coefficient matrix of the linear system $ax + by = e$, $cx + dy = f$ is $\begin{bmatrix} a & b \\ c & d \end{bmatrix}$.

matriz coeficiente (pág. 49) La matriz coeficiente del sistema lineal $ax + by = e$, $cx + dy = f$ es $\begin{bmatrix} a & b \\ c & d \end{bmatrix}$.

$$9x + 4y = -6$$
$$3x - 5y = -21$$

coefficient matrix:
matriz coeficiente: $\begin{bmatrix} 9 & 4 \\ 3 & -5 \end{bmatrix}$

matrix of constants:
matriz de constantes: $\begin{bmatrix} -6 \\ -21 \end{bmatrix}$

matrix of variables:
matriz de variables: $\begin{bmatrix} x \\ y \end{bmatrix}$

common logarithm (p. 145) A logarithm with base 10. It is denoted by $\log_{10}$ or simply by log.

$\log_{10} 100 = \log 100 = 2$ because $10^2 = 100$.

logaritmo común (pág. 145) Logaritmo con base 10. Se denota por $\log_{10}$ ó simplemente por log.

$\log_{10} 100 = \log 100 = 2$ ya que $10^2 = 100$.

complex conjugates (p. 94) Two complex numbers of the form $a + bi$ and $a - bi$.

números complejos conjugados (pág. 94) Dos números complejos de la forma $a + bi$ y $a - bi$.

$2 + 4i$, $2 - 4i$

conic section (p. 194) A curve formed by the intersection of a plane and a double-napped cone. Conic sections are also called conics.

sección cónica (pág. 194) Una curva formada por la intersección de un plano y un cono doble. Las secciones cónicas también se llaman cónicas.

See circle, ellipse, hyperbola, *and* parabola.

Ver círculo, elipse, hipérbola y parábola.

consistent system (p. 6) A system of equations that has at least one solution.

sistema compatible (pág. 6) Sistema de ecuaciones que tiene al menos una solución.

$$y = 2 + 3x$$
$$6x + 2y = 4$$

The system above is consistent, with solution $(0, 2)$.

El sistema de arriba es compatible, con la solución $(0, 2)$.

constraints (p. 30) In linear programming, the linear inequalities that form a system.

See **linear programming.**

restricciones (pág. 30) En la programación lineal, las desigualdades lineales que forman un sistema.

Ver **programación lineal.**

---

continuous random variable (p. 212) A variable that can take on an uncountable, infinite number of possible values, often over a specified interval.

The weight of a person is a continuous random variable.

variable aleatoria continua (pág. 212) Una variable que puede tomar un número incontable e infinito de valores posibles, a menudo durante un intervalo especificado.

El peso de una persona es una variable aleatoria continua.

---

control group (p. 233) A group that does not undergo a procedure or treatment when an experiment is conducted. *See also* experimental group.

See **experimental group.**

grupo de control (pág. 233) Grupo que no se somete a ningún procedimiento o tratamiento durante la realización de un experimento. *Ver también* grupo experimental.

Ver **grupo experimental.**

---

co-vertices of an ellipse (p. 186) The points of intersection of an ellipse and the line perpendicular to the major axis at the center.

See **ellipse.**

puntos extremos del eje menor de una elipse (pág. 186) Los puntos de intersección de una elipse y la recta perpendicular al eje mayor en el centro.

Ver **elipse.**

Cramer's rule (p. 49) A method for solving a system of linear equations using determinants: For the linear system $ax + by = e$, $cx + dy = f$, let A be the coefficient matrix. If $\det A \neq 0$, the solution of the system is as follows:

$$x = \frac{\begin{vmatrix} e & b \\ f & d \end{vmatrix}}{\det A}, \quad y = \frac{\begin{vmatrix} a & e \\ c & f \end{vmatrix}}{\det A}$$

regla de Cramer (pág. 49) Método para resolver un sistema de ecuaciones lineales usando determinantes: Para el sistema lineal $ax + by = e$, $cx + dy = f$, sea A la matriz coeficiente. Si $\det A \neq 0$, la solución del sistema es la siguiente:

$$x = \frac{\begin{vmatrix} e & b \\ f & d \end{vmatrix}}{\det A}, \quad y = \frac{\begin{vmatrix} a & e \\ c & f \end{vmatrix}}{\det A}$$

$$9x + 4y = -6$$
$$3x - 5y = -21; \quad \begin{vmatrix} 9 & 4 \\ 3 & -5 \end{vmatrix} = -57$$

Applying Cramer's rule gives the following:

Al aplicar la regla de Cramer se obtiene lo siguiente:

$$x = \frac{\begin{vmatrix} -6 & 4 \\ -21 & -5 \end{vmatrix}}{-57} = \frac{114}{-57} = -2$$

$$y = \frac{\begin{vmatrix} 9 & -6 \\ 3 & -21 \end{vmatrix}}{-57} = \frac{-171}{-57} = 3$$

decay factor (p. 135) The quantity b in the exponential decay function $y = ab^x$ with $a > 0$ and $0 < b < 1$.

The decay factor for the function $y = 3(0.5)^x$ is 0.5.

factor de decrecimiento (pág. 135) La cantidad b de la función de decrecimiento exponencial $y = ab^x$, con $a > 0$ y $0 < b < 1$.

El factor de decrecimiento de la función $y = 3(0.5)^x$ es 0.5.

---

degree of a polynomial function (p. 66) The exponent in the term of a polynomial function where the variable is raised to the greatest power.

See polynomial function.

grado de una función polinómica (pág. 66) En una función polinómica, el exponente del término donde la variable se eleva a la mayor potencia.

Ver función polinómica.

---

dependent system (p. 6) A consistent system of equations that has infinitely many solutions.

sistema dependiente (pág. 6) Sistema compatible de ecuaciones que tiene infinitas soluciones.

$$2x - y = 3$$
$$4x - 2y = 6$$

Any ordered pair $(x, 2x - 3)$ is a solution of the system above, so there are infinitely many solutions.

Cualquier par ordenado $(x, 2x - 3)$ es una solución del sistema que figura arriba, por lo que hay infinitas soluciones.

---

determinant (p. 49) A real number associated with any square matrix A, denoted by det A or $|A|$.

determinante (pág. 49) Número real asociado a toda matriz cuadrada A, denotada por det A o $|A|$.

$$\det \begin{bmatrix} 5 & 4 \\ 3 & 1 \end{bmatrix} = 5(1) - 3(4) = -7$$

$$\det \begin{bmatrix} a & b \\ c & d \end{bmatrix} = ad - cb$$

---

dimensions of a matrix (p. 38) The dimensions of a matrix with m rows and n columns are $m \times n$.

A matrix with 2 rows and 3 columns has the dimensions 2×3 (read "2 by 3").

dimensiones de una matriz (pág. 38) Las dimensiones de una matriz con m filas y n columnas son $m \times n$.

Una matriz con 2 filas y 3 columnas tiene por dimensiones 2×3 (leído "2 por 3").

---

directrix of a parabola (p. 176) *See* parabola.

See parabola.

directriz de una parábola (pág. 176) *Ver* parábola.

Ver parábola.

---

discrete random variable (p. 212) A variable that can take on only a countable number of distinct values.

The Saturday night attendance at a movie theater is a discrete random variable.

variable aleatoria discreta (pág. 212) Una variable que puede tomar un número contable de valores diferenciados.

La asistencia de público al cine un sábado a la noche es una variable aleatoria discreta .

discriminant of a general second-degree equation (p. 194) The expression $B^2 - 4AC$ for the equation $Ax^2 + Bxy + Cy^2 + Dx + Ey + F = 0$. Used to identify which type of conic the equation represents.

discriminante de una ecuación general de segundo grado (pág. 194) La expresión $B^2 - 4AC$ para la ecuación $Ax^2 + Bxy + Cy^2 + Dx + Ey + F = 0$. Se usa para identificar qué tipo de cónica representa la ecuación.

For the equation
$4x^2 + y^2 - 8x - 8 = 0$,
$A = 4$, $B = 0$, and $C = 1$.

$$B^2 - 4AC = 0^2 - 4(4)(1) = -16$$

Because $B^2 - 4AC < 0$, $B = 0$, and $A \neq C$, the conic is an ellipse.

Para la ecuación
$4x^2 + y^2 - 8x - 8 = 0$,
$A = 4$, $B = 0$ y $C = 1$.

$$B^2 - 4AC = 0^2 - 4(4)(1) = -16$$

Debido a que $B^2 - 4AC < 0$, $B = 0$ y $A \neq C$, la cónica es un elipse.

E

edge of a vertex-edge graph (p. 59) A line segment connecting the vertices of a graph.

arista de una gráfica de aristas y vértices (pág. 59) Un segmento de recta que conecta los vértices de una gráfica.

See vertex-edge graph.

Ver gráfica de aristas y vértices.

element of a matrix (p. 38) Each number in a matrix.

elemento de una matriz (pág. 38) Cada número de una matriz.

See matrix.

Ver matriz.

elimination method (p. 13) A method of solving a system of equations by multiplying equations by constants, then adding the revised equations to eliminate a variable.

método de eliminación (pág. 13) Método para resolver un sistema de ecuaciones en el que se multiplican ecuaciones por constantes y se agregan luego las ecuaciones revisadas para eliminar una variable.

To use the elimination method to solve the system with equations $3x - 7y = 10$ and $6x - 8y = 8$, multiply the first equation by -2 and add the equations to eliminate x.

Para usar el método de eliminación a fin de resolver el sistema con las ecuaciones $3x - 7y = 10$ y $6x - 8y = 8$, multiplica la primera ecuación por -2 y suma las ecuaciones para eliminar x.

ellipse (p. 186) The set of all points P in a plane such that the sum of the distances between P and two fixed points, called the foci, is a constant.

elipse (pág. 186) El conjunto de todos los puntos P de un plano tales que la suma de las distancias entre P y dos puntos fijos, llamados focos, es una constante.

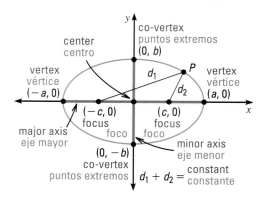

end behavior (p. 66) The behavior of the graph of a function as x approaches positive infinity $(+\infty)$ or negative infinity $(-\infty)$.

comportamiento (pág. 66) El comportamiento de la gráfica de una función al aproximarse x a infinito positivo $(+\infty)$ o a infinito negativo $(-\infty)$.

$f(x) \to +\infty$ **as** $x \to -\infty$
or as $x \to +\infty$.

$f(x) \to +\infty$ **según** $x \to -\infty$
o según $x \to +\infty$.

equal matrices (p. 38) Matrices that have the same dimensions and equal elements in corresponding positions.

matrices iguales (pág. 38) Matrices que tienen las mismas dimensiones y elementos iguales en posiciones correspondientes.

$$\begin{bmatrix} 6 & 0 \\ -\dfrac{4}{4} & \dfrac{3}{4} \end{bmatrix} = \begin{bmatrix} 3 \cdot 2 & -1 + 1 \\ -1 & 0.75 \end{bmatrix}$$

even function (p. 66) A function f is even if $f(-x) = f(x)$.

función par (pág. 66) Una función f es par si $f(-x) = f(x)$.

$f(x) = x^2 + 5$ **is an even function.**

$f(x) = x^2 + 5$ **es una función para.**

experimental group (p. 233) A group that undergoes some procedure or treatment when an experiment is conducted. *See also* control group.

grupo experimental (pág. 233) Grupo que se somete a algún procedimiento o tratamiento durante la realización de un experimento. *Ver también* grupo de control.

One group of headache sufferers, the experimental group, is given pills containing medication. Another group, the control group, is given pills containing no medication.

Un grupo de personas que sufren de dolores de cabeza, el grupo experimental, recibe píldoras que contienen el medicamento. Otro grupo, el grupo de control, recibe píldoras sin el medicamento.

experimental study (p. 233) A study in which the investigator assigns the individuals to the experimental group or the control group.

As part of a study on virus-protection software for computers, the investigator installs one brand of virus-protection software on half the computers and a different brand on the other half of the computers being used in the study.

estudio experimental (pág. 233) Un estudio en el cual el investigador asigna a los individuos al grupo experimental o al grupo de control.

Como parte de un estudio sobre software antivirus para computadoras, el investigador instala una marca de software antivirus en la mitad de las computadoras y otra marca en la otra mitad de las computadoras usadas en el estudio.

---

exponential decay function (p. 135) If $a > 0$ and $0 < b < 1$, then the function $y = ab^x$ is an exponential decay function with decay factor b.

función de decrecimiento exponencial (pág. 135) Si $a > 0$ y $0 < b < 1$, entonces la función $y = ab^x$ es una función de decrecimiento exponencial con factor de decrecimiento b.

$$y = 2\left(\frac{1}{4}\right)^x$$

---

exponential equation (p. 159) An equation in which a variable expression occurs as an exponent.

$4^x = \left(\frac{1}{2}\right)^{x-3}$ is an exponential equation.

ecuación exponencial (pág. 159) Ecuación que tiene como exponente una expresión algebraica.

$4^x = \left(\frac{1}{2}\right)^{x-3}$ es una ecuación exponencial.

---

exponential function (p. 130) A function of the form $y = ab^x$, where $a \neq 0$, $b > 0$, and $b \neq 1$.

See exponential growth function *and* exponential decay function.

función exponencial (pág. 130) Función de la forma $y = ab^x$, donde $a \neq 0$, $b > 0$ y $b \neq 1$.

Ver función de crecimiento exponencial *y* función de decrecimiento exponencial.

---

exponential growth function (p. 130) If $a > 0$ and $b > 1$, then the function $y = ab^x$ is an exponential growth function with growth factor b.

función de crecimiento exponencial (pág. 130) Si $a > 0$ y $b > 1$, entonces la función $y = ab^x$ es una función de crecimiento exponencial con factor de crecimiento b.

$$y = \frac{1}{2} \cdot 4^x$$

exponential inequality in one variable
(p. 163) An inequality that can be written in the form $ab^x + k < 0$, $ab^x + k > 0$, $ab^x + k \leq 0$, or $ab^x + k \geq 0$, where $a \neq 0$, $b > 0$, and $b \neq 1$.

desigualdad exponencial con una variable
(pág. 163) Una desigualdad que puede escribirse en la forma $ab^x + k < 0$, $ab^x + k > 0$, $ab^x + k \leq 0$, o $ab^x + k \geq 0$, donde $a \neq 0$, $b > 0$, y $b \neq 1$.

$3(2)^x - 5 \leq 0$ and $-5(0.8)^x + 2 > 0$ are exponential inequalities in one variable.

$3(2)^x - 5 \leq 0$ y $-5(0.8)^x + 2 > 0$ son desigualdades exponenciales con una variable.

factor by grouping (p. 76) To factor a polynomial with four terms by grouping, factor common monomials from pairs of terms, and then look for a common binomial factor.

factorizar por grupos (pág. 76) Para factorizar por grupos un polinomio con cuatro términos, factoriza unos monomios comunes a partir de los pares de términos y luego busca un factor binómico común.

$$\begin{aligned} x^3 - 3x^2 - 16x + 48 \\ = x^2(x - 3) - 16(x - 3) \\ = (x^2 - 16)(x - 3) \\ = (x + 4)(x - 4)(x - 3) \end{aligned}$$

factored completely (p. 76) A factorable polynomial with integer coefficients is factored completely if it is written as a product of unfactorable polynomials with integer coefficients.

completamente factorizado (pág. 76) Un polinomio que puede factorizarse y que tiene coeficientes enteros está completamente factorizado si está escrito como producto de polinomios que no pueden factorizarse y que tienen coeficientes enteros.

$3x(x - 5)$ is factored completely.

$(x + 2)(x^2 - 6x + 8)$ is *not* factored completely because $x^2 - 6x + 8$ can be factored as $(x - 2)(x - 4)$.

$3x(x - 5)$ está completamente factorizado.

$(x + 2)(x^2 - 6x + 8)$ *no* está completamente factorizado ya que $x^2 - 6x + 8$ puede factorizarse como $(x - 2)(x - 4)$.

feasible region (p. 30) In linear programming, the graph of the system of constraints.

región factible (pág. 30) En la programación lineal, la gráfica del sistema de restricciones.

See linear programming.

Ver programación lineal.

foci of a hyperbola (p. 190) *See* hyperbola.
focos de una hipérbola (pág. 190) *Ver* hipérbola.

See hyperbola.
Ver hipérbola.

foci of an ellipse (p. 186) *See* ellipse.
focos de una elipse (pág. 186) *Ver* elipse.

See ellipse.
Ver elipse.

focus of a parabola (p. 176) *See* parabola.
foco de una parábola (pág. 176) *Ver* parábola.

See parabola.
Ver parábola.

general second-degree equation in *x* and *y* (p. 194) The form $Ax^2 + Bxy + Cy^2 + Dx + Ey + F = 0$.

ecuación general de segundo grado en *x* e *y* (pág. 194) La forma $Ax^2 + Bxy + Cy^2 + Dx + Ey + F = 0$.

$16x^2 - 9y^2 - 96x + 36y - 36 = 0$ and $4x^2 + y^2 - 8x - 8 = 0$ are second-degree equations in x and y.

$16x^2 - 9y^2 - 96x + 36y - 36 = 0$ y $4x^2 + y^2 - 8x - 8 = 0$ son ecuaciones de segundo grado en x e y.

---

graph of a linear inequality in two variables (p. 17) The set of all points in a coordinate plane that represent solutions of the inequality.

gráfica de una desigualdad lineal con dos variables (pág. 17) El conjunto de todos los puntos de un plano de coordenadas que representan las soluciones de la desigualdad.

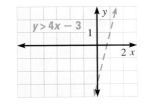

---

graph of a system of linear inequalities (p. 23) The graph of all solutions of the system.

gráfica de un sistema de desigualdades lineales (pág. 23) La gráfica de todas las soluciones del sistema.

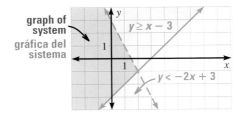

---

growth factor (p. 130) The quantity b in the exponential growth function $y = ab^x$ with $a > 0$ and $b > 1$.

factor de crecimiento (pág. 130) La cantidad b de la función de crecimiento exponencial $y = ab^x$, con $a > 0$ y $b > 1$.

The growth factor for the function $y = 8(3.4)^x$ is 3.4.

El factor de crecimiento de la función $y = 8(3.4)^x$ es 3.4.

---

half-life (p. 135) The time required for a substance or an amount to fall to half its initial value.

vida media (p. 135) El tiempo que requiere una sustancia o una cantidad para alcanzar la mitad de su valor inicial.

A sample of beryllium 11 will decay to half its size in 13.8 seconds. So, beryllium 11 has a half life of 13.8 seconds.

Una muestra de berilio 11 decaerá a la mitad de su tamaño en 13.8 segundos. Por lo tanto, el berilio 11 tiene una vida media de 13.8 segundos.

half-planes (p. 17) The two regions into which the boundary line of a linear inequality divides the coordinate plane.

semiplanos (pág. 17) Las dos regiones en que la recta límite de una desigualdad lineal divide al plano de coordenadas.

The solution of $y < 3$ is the half-plane consisting of all the points below the line $y = 3$.

La solución de $y < 3$ es el semi-plano que consta de todos los puntos que se encuentran debajo de la recta $y = 3$.

---

hyperbola (p. 190) The set of all points P in a plane such that the difference of the distances from P to two fixed points, called the foci, is constant.

hipérbola (pág. 190) El conjunto de todos los puntos P de un plano tales que la diferencia de distancias entre P y dos puntos fijos, llamados focos, es constante.

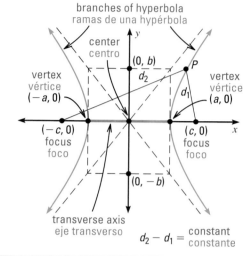

---

identity matrix (p. 54) The $n \times n$ matrix that has 1's on the main diagonal and 0's elsewhere.

matriz identidad (pág. 54) La matriz $n \times n$ que tiene los 1 en la diagonal principal y los 0 en las otras posiciones.

The 2×2 identity matrix is
$$\begin{bmatrix} 1 & 0 \\ 0 & 1 \end{bmatrix}.$$

La matriz identidad 2×2 es
$$\begin{bmatrix} 1 & 0 \\ 0 & 1 \end{bmatrix}.$$

---

inconsistent system (p. 6) A system of equations that has no solution.

sistema incompatible (pág. 6) Sistema de ecuaciones que no tiene solución.

$$x + y = 4$$
$$x + y = 1$$

The system above has no solution because the sum of two numbers cannot be both 4 and 1.

El sistema de arriba no tiene ninguna solución porque la suma de dos números no puede ser 4 y 1.

---

independent system (p. 6) A consistent system that has exactly one solution.

sistema independiente (pág. 6) Sistema compatible que tiene exactamente una solución.

The system consisting of $4x + y = 8$ and $2x - 3y = 18$ has exactly one solution, $(3, -4)$.

El sistema que consiste de $4x + y = 8$ y $2x - 3y = 18$ tiene exactamente una solución, $(3, -4)$.

ENGLISH-SPANISH GLOSSARY

index of a radical (p. 109) The integer n, greater than 1, in the expression $\sqrt[n]{a}$.

The index of $\sqrt[3]{-216}$ is 3.

índice de un radical (pág. 109) El número entero n, que es mayor que 1 y aparece en la expresión $\sqrt[n]{a}$.

El índice de $\sqrt[3]{-216}$ es 3.

interval notation (p. 81) A notation for representing an interval on a number line as a pair of numbers that are the endpoints of the interval. Parentheses are used to show that the endpoints are excluded, and brackets are used to show that the endpoints are included.

[4, 9) represents the interval between 4 and 9 that includes 4 and does not include 9. This interval can also be written as $4 \le x < 9$.

notación de intervalo (pág. 81) Una notación para representar un intervalo sobre una recta numérica como un par de números que son los extremos del intervalo. Los paréntesis se usan para indicar que los extremos se excluyen y los paréntesis cuadrados se usan para indicar que los extremos se incluyen.

[4, 9) representa el intervalo entre 4 y 9 que incluye el 4 y no incluye el 9. Este intervalo también puede escribirse como $4 \le x < 9$.

inverse matrices (p. 54) Two $n \times n$ matrices are inverses of each other if their product (in both orders) is the $n \times n$ identity matrix. *See also* identity matrix.

matrices inversas (pág. 54) Dos matrices $n \times n$ son inversas entre sí si su producto (de ambos órdenes) es la matriz identidad $n \times n$. *Ver también* matriz identidad.

$$\begin{bmatrix} -5 & 8 \\ 2 & -3 \end{bmatrix}^{-1} = \begin{bmatrix} 3 & 8 \\ 2 & 5 \end{bmatrix}$$

because
ya que

$$\begin{bmatrix} 3 & 8 \\ 2 & 5 \end{bmatrix}\begin{bmatrix} -5 & 8 \\ 2 & -3 \end{bmatrix} = \begin{bmatrix} 1 & 0 \\ 0 & 1 \end{bmatrix}$$

and
y

$$\begin{bmatrix} -5 & 8 \\ 2 & -3 \end{bmatrix}\begin{bmatrix} 3 & 8 \\ 2 & 5 \end{bmatrix} = \begin{bmatrix} 1 & 0 \\ 0 & 1 \end{bmatrix}.$$

L

leading coefficient (p. 66) The coefficient in the term of a polynomial function that has the greatest exponent.

See polynomial function.

coeficiente inicial (pág. 66) En una función polinómica, el coeficiente del término con el mayor exponente.

Ver función polinómica.

like radicals (p. 113) Radical expressions with the same index and radicand.

$\sqrt[4]{10}$ and $7\sqrt[4]{10}$ are like radicals.

radicales semejantes (pág. 113) Expresiones radicales con el mismo índice y el mismo radicando.

$\sqrt[4]{10}$ y $7\sqrt[4]{10}$ son radicales semejantes.

linear equation in three variables (p. 34) An equation of the form $ax + by + cz = d$ where a, b, and c are not all zero.

$2x + y - z = 5$ is a linear equation in three variables.

ecuación lineal con tres variables (pág. 34) Ecuación de la forma $ax + by + cz = d$, donde a, b y c no son todos cero.

$2x + y - z = 5$ es una ecuación lineal con tres variables.

linear inequality in two variables (p. 17) An inequality that can be written in one of the following forms: $Ax + By < C$, $Ax + By \leq C$, $Ax + By > C$, or $Ax + By \geq C$.

$5x - 2y \geq -4$ is a linear inequality in two variables.

desigualdad lineal con dos variables (pág. 17) Desigualdad que puede escribirse de una de las siguientes formas: $Ax + By < C$, $Ax + By \leq C$, $Ax + By > C$ o $Ax + By \geq C$.

$5x - 2y \geq -4$ es una desigualdad lineal con dos variables.

linear programming (p. 30) The process of maximizing or minimizing a linear objective function subject to a system of linear inequalities called constraints. The graph of the system of constraints is called the feasible region.

programación lineal (pág. 30) El proceso de maximizar o minimizar una función objetivo lineal sujeta a un sistema de desigualdades lineales llamadas restricciones. La gráfica del sistema de restricciones se llama región factible.

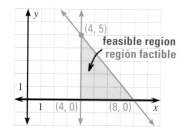

To maximize the objective function $P = 35x + 30y$ subject to the constraints $x \geq 4$, $y \geq 0$, and $5x + 4y \leq 40$, evaluate P at each vertex. The maximum value of 290 occurs at (4, 5).

Para maximizar la función objetivo $P = 35x + 30y$ sujeta a las restricciones $x \geq 4$, $y \geq 0$ y $5x + 4y \leq 40$, evalúa P en cada vértice. El valor máximo de 290 ocurre en (4, 5).

local maximum (p. 98) The y-coordinate of a turning point of a function if the point is higher than all nearby points.

máximo local (pág. 98) La coordenada y de un punto crítico de una función si el punto está situado más alto que todos los puntos cercanos.

The function $f(x) = x^3 - 3x^2 + 6$ has a local maximum of $y = 6$ when $x = 0$.

La función $f(x) = x^3 - 3x^2 + 6$ tiene un máximo local de $y = 6$ cuando $x = 0$.

local minimum (p. 98) The y-coordinate of a turning point of a function if the point is lower than all nearby points.

mínimo local (pág. 98) La coordenada y de un punto crítico de una función si el punto está situado más bajo que todos los puntos cercanos.

Minimum Minimo
X=-.56971   Y=-6.50858

The function $f(x) = x^4 - 6x^3 + 3x^2 + 10x - 3$ has a local minimum of $y \approx -6.51$ when $x \approx -0.57$.

La función $f(x) = x^4 - 6x^3 + 3x^2 + 10x - 3$ tiene un mínimo local de $y \approx -6.51$ cuando $x \approx -0.57$.

---

logarithm of y with base b (p. 145) Let b and y be positive numbers with $b \neq 1$. The logarithm of y with base b, denoted $\log_b y$ and read "log base b of y," is defined as follows: $\log_b y = x$ if and only if $b^x = y$.

logaritmo de y con base b (pág. 145) Sean b e y números positivos, con $b \neq 1$. El logaritmo de y con base b, denotado por $\log_b y$ y leído "log base b de y", se define de esta manera: $\log_b y = x$ si y sólo si $b^x = y$.

$\log_2 8 = 3$ because $2^3 = 8$.

$\log_{1/4} 4 = -1$ because $\left(\dfrac{1}{4}\right)^{-1} = 4$.

$\log_2 8 = 3$ ya que $2^3 = 8$.

$\log_{1/4} 4 = -1$ ya que $\left(\dfrac{1}{4}\right)^{-1} = 4$.

---

logarithmic equation (p. 159) An equation that involves a logarithm of a variable expression.

ecuación logarítmica (pág. 159) Ecuación en la que aparece el logaritmo de una expresión algebraica.

$\log_5 (4x - 7) = \log_5 (x + 5)$ is a logarithmic equation.

$\log_5 (4x - 7) = \log_5 (x + 5)$ es una ecuación logarítmica.

---

logarithmic function (p. 145) A function of the form $f(x) = \log_b x$.

función logarítmica (pág. 145) Una función de la forma $f(x) = \log_b x$.

$f(x) = \log_3 x$ is a logarithmic function.

$f(x) = \log_3 x$ es una función logarítmica.

---

logarithmic inequality in one variable (p. 163) An inequality that can be written in the form $\log_b x + k < 0$, $\log_b x + k > 0$, $\log_b x + k \leq 0$, or $\log_b x + k \geq 0$, where $b > 0$, $b \neq 1$.

desigualdad logarítmica con una variable (pág. 163) Una desigualdad que puede escribirse en la forma $\log_b x + k < 0$, $\log_b x + k > 0$, $\log_b x + k \leq 0$, or $\log_b x + k \geq 0$, donde $b > 0$, $b \neq 1$.

$\log_3 x > 0$ and $\log_5 x - 100 \leq 0$ are logarithmic inequalities in one variable.

$\log_3 x > 0$ y $\log_5 x - 100 \leq 0$ son desigualdades logarítmicas con una variable.

major axis of an ellipse (p. 186) The line segment joining the vertices of an ellipse.

See ellipse.

eje mayor de una elipse (pág. 186) El segmento de recta que une los vértices de una elipse.

Ver elipse.

---

margin of error (p. 228) The margin of error gives a limit on how much the response of a sample would be expected to differ from the response of the population.

If 40% of the people in a poll prefer candidate A, and the margin of error is ±4%, then it is expected that between 36% and 44% of the entire population prefer candidate A.

margen de error (pág. 228) El margen de error indica un límite acerca de cuánto se prevé que diferirían las respuestas obtenidas en una muestra de las obtenidas en la población.

Si el 40% de los encuestados prefiere al candidato A y el margen de error es ±4%, entonces se prevé que entre el 36% y el 44% de la población total prefiere al candidato A.

---

matrix, matrices (p. 38) A rectangular arrangement of numbers in rows and columns. Each number in a matrix is an element.

$$A = \begin{bmatrix} 4 & -1 & 5 \\ 0 & 6 & 3 \end{bmatrix}$$

Matrix A has 2 rows and 3 columns. The element in the second row and first column is 0.

matriz, matrices (pág. 38) Disposición rectangular de números colocados en filas y columnas. Cada numero de la matriz es un elemento.

La matriz A tiene 2 filas y 3 columnas. El elemento en la segunda fila y en la primera columna es 0.

---

matrix of constants (p. 54) The matrix of constants of the linear system $ax + by = e$, $cx + dy = f$ is $\begin{bmatrix} e \\ f \end{bmatrix}$.

See coefficient matrix.

matriz de constantes (pág. 54) La matriz de constantes del sistema lineal $ax + by = e$, $cx + dy = f$ es $\begin{bmatrix} e \\ f \end{bmatrix}$.

Ver matriz coeficiente.

---

matrix of variables (p. 54) The matrix of variables of the linear system $ax + by = e$, $cx + dy = f$ is $\begin{bmatrix} x \\ y \end{bmatrix}$.

See coefficient matrix.

matriz de variables (pág. 54) La matriz de variables del sistema lineal $ax + by = e$, $cx + dy = f$ es $\begin{bmatrix} x \\ y \end{bmatrix}$.

Ver matriz coeficiente.

---

minor axis of an ellipse (p. 186) The line segment joining the co-vertices of an ellipse.

See ellipse.

eje menor de una elipse (pág. 186) El segmento de recta que une los puntos extremos de una elipse.

Ver elipse.

multiplicity of roots (p. 98) The number of times a given polynomial equation has a value as a root. For the polynomial equation $f(x) = 0$, k is a repeated solution, or a root with a multiplicity greater than 1, if and only if the factor $x - k$ has an exponent greater than 1 when $f(x)$ is factored completely.

-1 is a repeated solution of the equation $(x + 1)^2(x - 3) = 0$. In this equation, -1 is a root with a multiplicity of 2.

multiplicidad de raíces (p. 98) El número de veces que una ecuación polinómica dada tiene un valor como raíz. Para la ecuación polinómica $f(x) = 0$, k es una solución repetida, o una raíz con multiplicidad mayor de 1, si y solo si el factor $x - k$ tiene un exponente mayor de 1 cuando $f(x)$ se descompone completamente en factores.

-1 es una solución repetida de la ecuación $(x + 1)^2(x - 3) = 0$. En esta ecuación, -1 es una raíz con una multiplicidad de 2.

N

natural base e (p. 140) An irrational number defined as follows: As n approaches $+\infty$, $\left(1 + \frac{1}{n}\right)^n$ approaches $e \approx 2.718281828$.

See natural logarithm.

base natural e (pág. 140) Número irracional definido de esta manera: Al aproximarse n a $+\infty$, $\left(1 + \frac{1}{n}\right)^n$ se aproxima a $e \approx 2.718281828$.

Ver logaritmo natural.

natural logarithm (p. 145) A logarithm with base e. It can be denoted $\log_e$, but is more often denoted by ln.

$\ln 0.3 \approx -1.204$ because $e^{-1.204} \approx (2.7183)^{-1.204} \approx 0.3$.

logaritmo natural (pág. 145) Logaritmo con base e. Puede denotarse $\log_e$, pero es más frecuente que se denote ln.

$\ln 0.3 \approx -1.204$ ya que $e^{-1.204} \approx (2.7183)^{-1.204} \approx 0.3$.

normal curve (p. 219) A smooth, symmetrical, bell-shaped curve that can model normal distributions and approximate some binomial distributions.

See normal distribution.

curva normal (pág. 219) Curva lisa, simétrica y con forma de campana que puede representar distribuciones normales y aproximar a algunas distribuciones binomiales.

Ver distribución normal.

normal distribution (p. 219) A probability distribution with mean $\bar{x}$ and standard deviation σ modeled by a bell-shaped curve with the area properties shown at the right.

distribución normal (pág. 219) Una distribución de probabilidad con media $\bar{x}$ y desviación normal σ representada por una curva en forma de campana y que tiene las propiedades vistas a la derecha.

nth root of _a_ (p. 109) For an integer _n_ greater than 1, if $b^n = a$, then _b_ is an _n_th root of _a_. Written as $\sqrt[n]{a}$.

$\sqrt[3]{-216} = -6$ because $(-6)^3 = -216$.

raíz enésima de _a_ (pág. 109) Para un número entero _n_ mayor que 1, si $b^n = a$, entonces _b_ es una raíz enésima de _a_. Se escribe $\sqrt[n]{a}$.

$\sqrt[3]{-216} = -6$ ya que $(-6)^3 = -216$.

O

objective function (p. 30) In linear programming, the linear function that is maximized or minimized.

See linear programming.

función objetivo (pág. 30) En la programación lineal, la función lineal que se maximiza o minimiza.

Ver programación lineal.

observational study (p. 233) A study in which the assignments of individuals to the experimental group and the control group are outside the control of the investigator.

In a study involving headache sufferers, participants are randomly assigned to the control group or the experimental group by a computer.

estudio observacional (p. 233) Un estudio en el cual las asignaciones de los individuos al grupo experimental y al grupo de control no son controladas por el investigador.

En un estudio que incluye personas que padecen jaquecas, los participantes son asignados aleatoriamente al grupo de control o al grupo experimental por la computadora.

odd function (p. 66) A function _f_ is odd if $f(-x) = -f(x)$.

$f(x) = x^3$ **is an odd function.**

función impar (p. 66) Una función _f_ es impar si $f(-x) = -f(x)$.

$f(x) = x^3$ **es una función impar.**

ordered triple (p. 34) A set of three numbers of the form (x, y, z) that represents a point in space.

The ordered triple $(2, 1, -3)$ is a solution of the equation $4x + 2y + 3z = 1$.

terna ordenada (pág. 34) Un conjunto de tres números de la forma (x, y, z) que representa un punto en el espacio.

La terna ordenada $(2, 1, -3)$ es una solución de la ecuación $4x + 2y + 3z = 1$.

P

parabola (p. 176) The set of all points equidistant from a point called the focus and a line called the directrix.

parábola (pág. 176) El conjunto de todos los puntos equidistantes de un punto, llamado foco, y de una recta, llamada directriz.

axis of symmetry
eje de simetría
focus
foco
vertex
vértice
directrix
directriz

polynomial (p. 66) A monomial or a sum of monomials, each of which is called a term of the polynomial.

-14, $x^4 - \frac{1}{4}x^2 + 3$, and $7b - \sqrt{3} + \pi b^2$ are polynomials.

polinomio (pág. 66) Monomio o suma de monomios, cada uno de los cuales se llama término del polinomio.

-14, $x^4 - \frac{1}{4}x^2 + 3$ y $7b - \sqrt{3} + \pi b^2$ son polinomios.

polynomial function (p. 66) A function of the form $f(x) = a_n x^n + a_{n-1}x^{n-1} + \cdots + a_1 x + a_0$ where $a_n \neq 0$, the exponents are all whole numbers, and the coefficients are all real numbers.

$f(x) = 11x^5 - 0.4x^2 + 16x - 7$ is a polynomial function. The degree of $f(x)$ is 5, the leading coefficient is 11, and the constant term is -7.

función polinómica (pág. 66) Función de la forma $f(x) = a_n x^n + a_{n-1}x^{n-1} + \cdots + a_1 x + a_0$ donde $a_n \neq 0$, los exponentes son todos números enteros y los coeficientes son todos números reales.

$f(x) = 11x^5 - 0.4x^2 + 16x - 7$ es una función polinómica. El grado de $f(x)$ es 5, el coeficiente inicial es 11 y el término constante es -7.

polynomial inequality in one variable (p. 81) An inequality that can be written in the form

$a_n x^n + a_{n-1}x^{n-1} + \ldots + a_1 x + a_0 < 0,$

$a_n x^n + a_{n-1}x^{n-1} + \ldots + a_1 x + a_0 > 0,$

$a_n x^n + a_{n-1}x^{n-1} + \ldots + a_1 x + a_0 \leq 0,$ or

$a_n x^n + a_{n-1}x^{n-1} + \ldots + a_1 x + a_0 \geq 0,$ where $a_n \neq 0$.

$3x^4 + 2x^3 + 5x - 4 < 0$ and $7x^3 - 8x^2 + 1 \geq 0$ are polynomial inequalities in one variable.

desigualdad polinómica con una variable (pág. 81) Una desigualdad que puede escribirse en la forma

$a_n x^n + a_{n-1}x^{n-1} + \ldots + a_1 x + a_0 < 0,$

$a_n x^n + a_{n-1}x^{n-1} + \ldots + a_1 x + a_0 < 0,$

$a_n x^n + a_{n-1}x^{n-1} + \ldots + a_1 x + a_0 \leq 0,$ ó

$a_n x^n + a_{n-1}x^{n-1} + \ldots + a_1 x + a_0 \geq 0,$ donde $a_n \neq 0$.

$3x^4 + 2x^3 + 5x - 4 < 0$ y $7x^3 - 8x^2 + 1 \geq 0$ son desigualdades polinómicas con una variable.

polynomial long division (p. 85) A method used to divide polynomials similar to the way you divide numbers.

división desarrollada polinómica (pág. 85) Método utilizado para dividir polinomios semejante a la manera en que divides números.

$$
\begin{array}{r}
x^2 + 7x + 7 \\
x - 2 \overline{)x^3 + 5x^2 - 7x + 2} \\
\underline{x^3 - 2x^2} \\
7x^2 - 7x \\
\underline{7x^2 - 14x} \\
7x + 2 \\
\underline{7x - 14} \\
16
\end{array}
$$

$$\frac{x^3 + 5x^2 - 7x + 2}{x - 2} = x^2 + 7x + 7 + \frac{16}{x - 2}$$

population (p. 228) A group of people or objects that you want information about.

A sportswriter randomly selects 5% of college baseball coaches for a survey. The population is all college baseball coaches. The 5% of coaches selected is the sample.

población (pág. 228) Grupo de personas u objetos acerca del cual deseas informarte.

Un periodista deportiva selecciona al azar al 5% de los entrenadores universitarios de béisbol para que participe en una encuesta. La población son todos los entrenadores universitarios de béisbol. El 5% de los entrenadores que resultó seleccionado es la muestra.

probability distribution (p. 212) A function that gives the probability of each possible value of a random variable. The sum of all the probabilities in a probability distribution must equal 1.

Let the random variable X represent the number showing after rolling a standard six-sided die.

distribución de probabilidades (pág. 212) Función que indica la probabilidad de cada valor posible de una variable aleatoria. La suma de todas las probabilidades de una distribución de probabilidades debe ser igual a 1.

Sea la variable aleatoria X el número que salga al lanzar un dado normal de seis caras.

Probability Distribution for Rolling a Die Distribución de probabilidad al lanzar un dado						
X	1	2	3	4	5	6
P(X)	$\frac{1}{6}$	$\frac{1}{6}$	$\frac{1}{6}$	$\frac{1}{6}$	$\frac{1}{6}$	$\frac{1}{6}$

Q

quadratic form (p. 76) The form $au^2 + bu + c$, where u is any expression in x.

The expression $16x^4 - 8x^2 - 8$ is in quadratic form because it can be written as $u^2 - 2u - 8$ where $u = 4x^2$.

forma cuadrática (pág. 76) La forma $au^2 + bu + c$, donde u es cualquier expresión en x.

La expresión $16x^4 - 8x^2 - 8$ está en la forma cuadrática ya que puede escribirse $u^2 - 2u - 8$, donde $u = 4x^2$.

quadratic system (p. 200) A system of equations that includes one or more equations of conics.

$y^2 - 7x + 3 = 0 \quad x^2 + 4y^2 + 8y = 16$
$2x - y = 3 \qquad 2x^2 - y^2 - 6x - 4 = 0$

sistema cuadrático (pág. 200) Sistema de ecuaciones que incluye una o más ecuaciones de cónicas.

The systems above are quadratic systems.

Los sistemas de arriba son sistemas cuadráticos.

R

radical conjugates (p. 94) The expressions $a + \sqrt{b}$ and $a - \sqrt{b}$ where a and b are rational numbers.

conjugados radical (pág. 94) Las expresiones $a + \sqrt{b}$ y $a - \sqrt{b}$ cuando a y b son números racionales.

The conjugate of $7 + \sqrt{2}$ is $7 - \sqrt{2}$.

El conjugado de $7 + \sqrt{2}$ es $7 - \sqrt{2}$.

---

radical equation (p. 122) An equation with one or more radicals that have variables in their radicands.

ecuación radical (pág. 122) Ecuación con uno o más radicales en cuyo radicando aparecen variables.

$$\sqrt[3]{2x + 7} = 3$$

---

radical function (p. 118) A function that contains a radical with a variable in its radicand.

función radical (pág. 118) Función que tiene un radical con una variable en su radicando.

$$f(x) = \tfrac{1}{2}\sqrt{x}, \; g(x) = -3\sqrt[3]{x + 5}$$

---

radius of a circle (p. 180) The distance from the center of a circle to a point on the circle. Also, a line segment that connects the center of a circle to a point on the circle. *See also* circle.

radio de un círculo (pág. 180) La distancia desde el centro de un círculo hasta un punto del círculo. También, es un segmento de recta que une el centro de un círculo con un punto del círculo. *Ver también* círculo.

The circle with equation $(x - 3)^2 + (y + 5)^2 = 36$ has radius $\sqrt{36} = 6$. *See also* circle.

El círculo con la ecuación $(x - 3)^2 + (y + 5)^2 = 36$ tiene el radio $\sqrt{36} = 6$. *Ver también* círculo.

---

random variable (p. 212) A variable whose value is determined by the outcomes of a random event.

variable aleatoria (pág. 212) Variable cuyo valor viene determinado por los resultados de un suceso aleatorio.

The random variable X representing the number showing after rolling a six-sided die has possible values of 1, 2, 3, 4, 5, and 6.

La variable aleatoria X que representa el número que sale al lanzar un dado de seis caras tiene como valores posibles 1, 2, 3, 4, 5 y 6.

---

repeated solution (p. 94) For the polynomial equation $f(x) = 0$, k is a repeated solution if and only if the factor $x - k$ has an exponent greater than 1 when $f(x)$ is factored completely.

solución repetida (pág. 94) Para la ecuación polinómica $f(x) = 0$, k es una solución repetida si y sólo si el factor $x - k$ tiene un exponente mayor que 1 cuando $f(x)$ está completamente factorizado.

-1 is a repeated solution of the equation $(x + 1)^2(x - 2) = 0$.

-1 es una solución repetida de la ecuación $(x + 1)^2(x - 2) = 0$.

sample (p. 228) A subset of a population.

See population.

muestra (pág. 228) Subconjunto de una población.

Ver población.

---

scalar (p. 38) A real number by which you multiply a matrix.

See scalar multiplication.

escalar (pág. 38) Número real por el que se multiplica una matriz.

Ver multiplicación escalar.

---

scalar multiplication (p. 38) Multiplication of each element of a matrix by a real number, called a scalar.

multiplicación escalar (pág. 38) Multiplicación de cada elemento de una matriz por un número real llamado escalar.

$$-2 \begin{bmatrix} 4 & -1 \\ 1 & 0 \\ 2 & 7 \end{bmatrix} = \begin{bmatrix} -8 & 2 \\ -2 & 0 \\ -4 & -14 \end{bmatrix}$$

---

simplest form of a radical (p. 113) A radical with index n is in simplest form if the radicand has no perfect nth powers as factors and any denominator has been rationalized.

$\sqrt[3]{135}$ in simplest form is $3\sqrt[3]{5}$.

$\dfrac{\sqrt[5]{7}}{\sqrt[5]{8}}$ in simplest form is $\dfrac{\sqrt[5]{28}}{2}$.

forma más simple de un radical (pág. 113) Un radical con índice n está escrito en la forma más simple si el radicando no tiene como factor ninguna potencia enésima perfecta y el denominador ha sido racionalizado.

$\sqrt[3]{135}$ en la forma más simple es $3\sqrt[3]{5}$.

$\dfrac{\sqrt[5]{7}}{\sqrt[5]{8}}$ en la forma más simple es $\dfrac{\sqrt[5]{28}}{2}$.

---

skewed distribution (p. 212) A probability distribution that is not symmetric. *See also* symmetric distribution.

distribución asimétrica (pág. 212) Distribución de probabilidades que no es simétrica. *Ver también* distribución simétrica.

---

solution of a linear inequality in two variables (p. 17) An ordered pair (x, y) that produces a true statement when the values of x and y are substituted into the inequality.

The ordered pair $(1, 2)$ is a solution of $3x + 4y > 8$ because $3(1) + 4(2) = 11$, and $11 > 8$.

solución de una desigualdad lineal con dos variables (pág. 17) Par ordenado (x, y) que produce un enunciado verdadero cuando x e y se sustituyen por sus valores en la desigualdad.

El par ordenado $(1, 2)$ es una solución de $3x + 4y > 8$ ya que $3(1) + 4(2) = 11$, y $11 > 8$.

solution of a system of linear equations in three variables (p. 34) An ordered triple (x, y, z) whose coordinates make each equation in the system true.

solución de un sistema de ecuaciones lineales en tres variables (pág. 34) Terna ordenada (x, y, z) cuyas coordenadas hacen que cada ecuación del sistema sea verdadera.

$$4x + 2y + 3z = 1$$
$$2x - 3y + 5z = -14$$
$$6x - y + 4z = -1$$

$(2, 1, -3)$ is the solution of the system above.

$(2, 1, -3)$ es la solución del sistema de arriba.

---

solution of a system of linear equations in two variables (p. 6) An ordered pair (x, y) that satisfies each equation of the system.

solución de un sistema de ecuaciones lineales en dos variables (pág. 6) Par ordenado (x, y) que satisface cada ecuación del sistema.

$$4x + y = 8$$
$$2x - 3y = 18$$

$(3, -4)$ is the solution of the system above.

$(3, -4)$ es la solución del sistema de arriba.

---

solution of a system of linear inequalities in two variables (p. 23) An ordered pair (x, y) that is a solution of each inequality in the system.

solución de un sistema de desigualdades lineales en dos variables (pág. 23) Par ordenado (x, y) que es una solución de cada desigualdad del sistema.

$$y > -2x - 5$$
$$y \leq x + 3$$

$(-1, 1)$ is a solution of the system above.

$(-1, 1)$ es una solución del sistema de arriba.

---

standard form of a polynomial function (p. 66) The form of a polynomial function that has terms written in descending order of exponents from left to right.

forma general de una función polinómica (pág. 66) La forma de una función polinómica en la que los términos se ordenan de tal modo que los exponentes disminuyen de izquierda a derecha.

The function $g(x) = 7x - \sqrt{3} + \pi x^2$ can be written in standard form as $g(x) = \pi x^2 + 7x - \sqrt{3}$.

La función $g(x) = 7x - \sqrt{3} + \pi x^2$ escrita en la forma general es $g(x) = \pi x^2 + 7x - \sqrt{3}$.

---

standard normal distribution (p. 219) The normal distribution with mean 0 and standard deviation 1. *See also* z-score.

distribución normal típica (pág. 219) La distribución normal con media 0 y desviación típica 1. *Ver también* puntuación z.

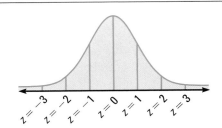

substitution method (p. 13) A method of solving a system of equations by solving one of the equations for one of the variables and then substituting the resulting expression in the other equation(s).

método de sustitución (pág. 13) Método para resolver un sistema de ecuaciones mediante la resolución de una de las ecuaciones para una de las variables seguida de la sustitución de la expresión resultante en la(s) otra(s) ecuación (ecuaciones).

$$2x + 5y = -5$$
$$x + 3y = 3$$

Solve equation 2 for x: $x = -3y + 3$. Substitute the expression for x in equation 1 and solve for y: $y = 11$. Use the value of y to find the value of x: $x = -30$.

Resuelve la ecuación 2 para x: $x = -3y + 3$. Sustituye la expresión para x en la ecuación 1 y resuelve para y: $y = 11$. Usa el valor de y para hallar el valor de x: $x = -30$.

---

symmetric distribution (p. 212) A probability distribution, represented by a histogram, in which you can draw a vertical line that divides the histogram into two parts that are mirror images.

distribución simétrica (pág. 212) Distribución de probabilidad representada por un histograma en la que se puede trazar una recta vertical que divida al histograma en dos partes; éstas son imágenes especulares entre sí.

---

synthetic division (p. 85) A method used to divide a polynomial by a divisor of the form $x - k$.

división sintética (pág. 85) Método utilizado para dividir un polinomio por un divisor en la forma $x - k$.

$$-3 \begin{array}{|rrrr} 2 & 1 & -8 & 5 \\ & -6 & 15 & -21 \\ \hline 2 & -5 & 7 & -16 \end{array}$$

$$\frac{2x^3 + x^2 - 8x + 5}{x + 3} = 2x^2 - 5x + 7 - \frac{16}{x + 3}$$

---

synthetic substitution (p. 66) A method used to evaluate a polynomial function.

sustitución sintética (pág. 66) Método utilizado para evaluar una función polinómica.

$$3 \begin{array}{|rrrrr} 2 & -5 & 0 & -4 & 8 \\ & 6 & 3 & 9 & 15 \\ \hline 2 & 1 & 3 & 5 & 23 \end{array}$$

The synthetic substitution above indicates that for $f(x) = 2x^4 - 5x^3 - 4x + 8$, $f(3) = 23$.

La sustitución sintética de arriba indica que para $f(x) = 2x^4 - 5x^3 - 4x + 8$, $f(3) = 23$.

system of linear inequalities in two variables (p. 23) A system consisting of two or more linear inequalities in two variables. *See also* linear inequality in two variables.

sistema de desigualdades lineales con dos variables (pág. 23) Sistema que consiste de dos o más desigualdades lineales con dos variables. *Ver también* desigualdad lineal con dos variables.

$$x + y \le 8$$
$$4x - y > 6$$

system of three linear equations in three variables (p. 34) A system consisting of three linear equations in three variables. *See also* linear equation in three variables.

sistema de tres ecuaciones lineales en tres variables (pág. 34) Sistema formado por tres ecuaciones lineales con tres variables. *Ver también* ecuación lineal con tres variables.

$$2x + y - z = 5$$
$$3x - 2y + z = 16$$
$$4x + 3y - 5z = 3$$

system of two linear equations in two variables (p. 6) A system consisting of two equations that can be written in the form $Ax + By = C$ and $Dx + Ey = F$ where x and y are variables, A and B are not both zero, and D and E are not both zero.

sistema de dos ecuaciones lineales con dos variables (pág. 6) Un sistema que consiste en dos ecuaciones que se pueden escribir de la forma $Ax + By = C$ y $Dx + Ey = F$, donde x e y son variables, A y B no son ambos cero, y D y E tampoco son ambos cero.

$$4x + y = 8$$
$$2x - 3y = 18$$

three-dimensional coordinate system (p. 205) Three-dimensional space defined by the x-, y-, and z-axes. The three dimensional coordinate system is also called 3-space.

sistema de coordenadas tridimensional (pág. 205) Espacio tridimensional definido por los ejes x, y, y z. El sistema de coordenadas tridimensional también llamado espacio tridimensional.

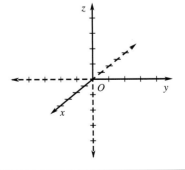

transverse axis of a hyperbola (p. 190) The line segment joining the vertices of a hyperbola.

eje transverso de una hipérbola (pág. 190) El segmento de recta que une los vértices de una hipérbola.

See hyperbola.

Ver hipérbola.

unbiased sample (p. 228) A sample that is representative of the population you want information about.

You want to poll members of the senior class about where to hold the prom. If every senior has an equal chance of being polled, then the sample is unbiased.

muestra no sesgada (pág. 228) Muestra que es representativa de la población acerca de la cual deseas informarte.

Quieres encuestar a algunos estudiantes de último curso sobre el lugar donde organizar el baile de fin de año. Si cada estudiante de último curso tiene iguales posibilidades de ser encuestado, entonces es una muestra no sesgada.

verbal model (p. 2) A word equation that represents a real-life problem.

Distance =	Rate	·	Time
(miles)	(miles/hour)		(hours)

modelo verbal (pág. 2) Ecuación expresada mediante palabras que representa un problema de la vida real.

Distancia =	Velocidad	·	Tiempo
(millas)	(millas/hora)		(horas)

vertex of a parabola (p. 176) The point on a parabola that lies on the axis of symmetry.

See parabola.

vértice de una parábola (pág. 176) El punto de una parábola que se encuentra en el eje de simetría.

Ver parábola.

vertex of a vertex-edge graph (p. 59) A point on a vertex-edge graph that is either the endpoint of an edge or not part of an edge.

See vertex-edge graph.

vértice de una gráfica de aristas y vértices (pág. 59) Un punto de una gráfica de aristas y vértices que es el extremo de una arista o que no es parte una arista.

Ver gráfica de aristas y vértices.

vertex-edge graph (p. 59) A collection of points and line segments connecting some (possibly empty) subset of the points.

gráfica de aristas y vértices (pág. 59) Una colección de puntos y segmentos de recta que conectan algún subconjunto (posiblemente vacío) de los puntos.

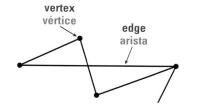

vertices of a hyperbola (p. 190) The points of intersection of a hyperbola and the line through the foci of the hyperbola.

See hyperbola.

vértices de una hipérbola (pág. 190) Los puntos de intersección de una hipérbola y la recta que pasa por los focos de la hipérbola.

Ver hipérbola.

vertices of an ellipse (p. 186) The points of intersection of an ellipse and the line through the foci of the ellipse.

See ellipse.

vértices de una elipse (pág. 186) Los puntos de intersección de una elipse y la recta que pasa por los focos de la elipse.

Ver elipse.

Z

zero of a function (p. 149) A number k is a zero of a function f if $f(k) = 0$.

The zeros of the function $f(x) = 2(x + 3)(x - 1)$ are -3 and 1.

cero de una función (pág. 149) Un número k es un cero de una función f si $f(k) = 0$.

Los ceros de la función $f(x) = 2(x + 3)(x - 1)$ son -3 y 1.

z-score (p. 219) The number z of standard deviations that a data value lies above or below the mean of the data set: $z = \frac{x - \bar{x}}{\sigma}$.

A normal distribution has a mean of 76 and a standard deviation of 9. The z-score for $x = 64$ is $z = \frac{x - \bar{x}}{\sigma} = \frac{64 - 76}{9} \approx -1.3$.

puntuación z (pág. 219) El número z de desviaciones típicas que un valor se encuentra por encima o por debajo de la media del conjunto de datos: $z = \frac{x - \bar{x}}{\sigma}$.

Una distribución normal tiene una media de 76 y una desviación típica de 9. La puntuación z para $x = 64$ es $z = \frac{x - \bar{x}}{\sigma} = \frac{64 - 76}{9} \approx -1.3$.

Index

Compound interest, 131–133, 161
  continuously, 141, 161
Conics, *See also* Conic section(s),
  194
Conic section(s), *See also*
  Circle(s); Ellipse(s);
  Hyperbola(s); Parabola(s)
  classifying, 194–199
  general second-degree
    equation, 194
  discriminant of, 194
  translating, 194–199
  equations of, 194–199
Conjugates, 113
Consistent system, 6
  dependent, 6
  independent, 6
Constant(s), matrix of, 54
Constraints, 30
  linear programming and, 30–33
**Continuously compounded
  interest,** 141, 161
Continuous random variable, 212
Control group, 233
Convenience sample, 228
Corollary, to the fundamental
  theorem of algebra, 94
Co-vertices, of an ellipse, 186
Cramer's rule, 49
  to solve linear systems, 49–52
Critical thinking, exercises, 70,
  79, 84, 92, 97, 103, 112
Critical x-value, 163, 165
Cube root function(s), 118–121

D

Data
  analyzing
    using binomial distribution,
      212–217, 224–227
    using break-even analysis, 7,
      9, 11
    finding margin of error,
      229–232
    identifying bias, 229–231
    using normal distribution,
      219–222, 224–227
  collecting
    identifying flaws in an
      experiment, 234–236

    identifying studies, 233–236
    sampling methods, 228–231
  displaying, in histograms,
    212–217
Decay factor, 135
Decay function(s), *See also*
  Exponential function(s)
  exponential, 135
    decay factor, 135
    depreciation and, 138, 139
  domain of, 136–138
  evaluating on a graphing
    calculator, 139
  graphing, 135–138
  half-life and, 136–138
  range of, 136–138
  translation and, 136–138
Decreasing on an interval,
  149–154
Degree of a polynomial function,
  66
Dependent system, 6
Depreciation, exponential decay
  functions and, 138, 139
Descartes' rule of signs, 94
Determinatant
  of a matrix, 49
    evaluating, 49–52
    rules for, 49
Dimensions of a matrix, 38
Directrix, 176
Discrete random variable, 212
Discriminant
  of an equation of a circle, 194
  of an equation of an ellipse,
    194
  of a general second-degree
    equation of a conic
    section, 194
  of an equation of a hyperbola,
    194
  of an equation of a parabola,
    194
Distance formula, 4
  equation of a circle and, 180
  to find distance in space, 205,
    207–208
Distance between two points
  in a coordinate plane, 180
  in three-dimensional space,
    205, 207–208

Distributive property of addition,
  38
  applied to matrices, 38–42
**Distributive property of
  subtraction,** 38
  applied to matrices, 38–42
Domain
  of an exponential growth
    function, 131–133
  of a function involving natural
    base e, 140–143
  of a logarithmic function,
    146–148
Doubling time, exponential growth
  functions and, 131, 132, 133
Draw conclusions, 12, 53, 93, 108,
  144, 185, 218, 223
Draw a diagram, problem-solving
  strategy, 3–5

E

Edge, of a vertex-edge graph, 59
Element(s), of a matrix, 38
Elimination method, for solving
  linear systems, 14–16, 34–37
Ellipse(s), *See also* Conic
  section(s), 186
  area of, 188
  center of, 186
  co-vertices of, 186
  discriminant of an equation of,
    194
  drawing, 185
  foci of, 186
  graphing equations of,
    186–189
  major axis of, 186
  minor axis of, 186
  vertices of, 186
  writing equations of, 186–189
End behavior
  of a polynomial function, 66
  describing, 68–70
Equal matrices, 38
Equation(s), *See also* Formulas;
  Function(s); Linear-quadratic
  system; Linear system(s);
  Quadratic system(s)
  of circles, 180–184
  of ellipses, 186–189

INDEX

involving natural base e, 140–143

linear objective, 30–33

logarithmic, 144–148, 150–154

natural base, 140–143, 151–152

objective, 30–33

odd, 66

radical, 118

   graphing, 118–121

square root, 118–121

Fundamental theorem of algebra, 94

applying, 94–97

corollary to, 94

General second-degree equation

of a conic section, 194

discriminant of, 194

Geometry, *See* Circle(s); Conic section(s); Ellipse(s); Formulas; Hyperbola(s); Parabola(s); Three-dimensional coordinate system

Graph(s)

of polynomial functions, analyzing, 98–104

vertex edge, 59

   using, 59–62

Graphing

absolute value inequalities, 18, 20, 21

   in a system, 24, 25, 27

equations

   of circles, 180–184

   of ellipses, 186–189

   of hyperbolas, 190–193

   of parabolas, 176–179

   of a plane, 206–208

functions

   cube root, 118–121

   exponential decay, 135–138

   exponential growth, 130–134

   involving natural base e, 140–143

   logarithmic, 146–148, 151–152

   natural base, 140–143

polynomial, 68–70, 71–75, 98–104

radical, 118–121

square root, 118–121

linear inequalities, 17–22

   systems of, 23–29

linear programming and, 30–33

linear systems, 6–11

to solve quadratic systems, 200–204

Graphing calculator

create a binomial distribution, 217

evaluating exponential decay models, 139

evaluating radicals and rational exponents, 108

finding the inverse of a matrix, 55, 57, 58

finding local maximums and minimums, 104

finding turning points, 98

finding zeros of a polynomial function, 93, 96, 97

graphing natural base functions, 141

graphing radical functions, 119

graphing systems of linear equations, 12

to make a table of values, 117

matrices representing vertex-edge graphs and, 60

maximizing a polynomial function, 99

to perform matrix operations, 48

to solve an exponential equation, 159

to solve an exponential inequality, 164

to solve a logarithmic equation, 160

to solve a logarithmic inequality, 166

to solve quadratic systems, 200, 202–204

solving polynomial equations using a graph, 80

solving radical equations using a graph, 126

Growth factor, 130

Growth function(s), *See also* Exponential function(s)

exponential, 130

   compound interest and, 131–133

   domain of, 131–133

   doubling time and, 131, 132, 133

   graphing, 130–134

   range of, 131–133

   translations and, 131–133

Half-life, 135

exponential decay functions and, 136–138

Half-plane, 17

Histogram, probability, 212–217

Hyperbola(s), *See also* Conic section(s), 190

center of, 190

discriminant of equation of, 194

foci of, 190

graphing equations of, 190–193

transverse axis of, 190

vertices of, 190

writing equations of, 191–193

Hypothesis (hypotheses), testing, 225–227

Identity matrix, 54

Inconsistent system, 6

Increasing on an interval, 149–154

Independent system, 6

Index of a radical, 108, 109

Inequalities, *See* Linear inequalities; Logarithmic inequality (inequalities); Polynomial inequality (inequalities); Systems of linear inequalities

Interest

compound, 131–133

continuously compounded, 141

INDEX

Multi-step problems, *Throughout.*
See for example 12, 13, 14, 18,
23, 24, 29, 31, 34, 35, 39, 44

N

Natural base *e*, 140
functions involving, 140–143
graphing, 140–143
Natural base expression(s),
simplifying, 140, 142, 143
Natural base function(s), 140–143
domain of, 140, 142, 143
graphing, 140–143
on a graphing calculator, 141
range of, 140, 142, 143
translations and, 140, 142, 143
Natural logarithm, 145
Normal curve, 218, 219
Normal distribution, 218, 219
to approximate binomial
distribution, 224–227
interpreting, 219–222
normal curve and, 218
probability and, 219–222,
224–227
standard, 219
*n***th root(s),** 108, 109
approximating, 109–112
evaluating, 108–112

O

Objective function, 30
linear programming and, 30–33
Observational study, 233
identifying, 233, 235, 236
Odd function, 66
Ordered pair, as solution of a
linear inequality, 17
Ordered triple, 205
as solution of a system with
three variables, 34

P

Parabola(s), See also Conic
section(s), 176
axis of symmetry of, 176
directrix of, 176

discriminant of an equation of,
194
focus of, 176
graphing equations of,
176–179
writing equations of, 177–179
Parent function
cube root, 118
square root, 118
Performance Tasks
art, 106
campus parking, 210
finance, 174
MP3 players, 64
park design, 128
restaurants, 238
Plane, graphing the equation of,
206–208
Polynomial(s), *See also*
Polynomial equation(s);
Polynomial function(s), 66
degree of, 66
dividing, 85–88
factoring, 76–79
using the factor theorem,
85–88
using the remainder theorem,
85–88
Polynomial curve fitting, 37
Polynomial equation(s)
multiplicity of a root of, 98
solving
by factoring, 77–79
using a graph, 80
Polynomial function(s), 66
characteristics of, 68–70
complex conjugates theorem
and, 94–97
Descartes' rule of signs and, 94
end behavior of, 66
describing, 68–70
evaluating, 66–70
even, 66
fundamental theorem of
algebra and, 94–97
graphing, 68–70, 98–104
as translations, 71–75
graphs of, analyzing, 98–104
identifying, 66, 69, 70
irrational conjugates theorem
and, 94–97

local maximum of, 98
finding, 98–104
local minimum of, 98
finding, 98–104
multiplicity of a root of, 98
odd, 66
repeated solution and, 94
standard form of, 66
translating, 71–75
zeros of
classifying, 94–97
finding, 86–97
**Polynomial inequality
(inequalities),** 81
solving
algebraically, 81, 83, 84
using a graph, 82–84
Polynomial long division, 85
using, 85–88
Population, 228
sampling, 228–231
Power property
of logarithms, 155
applying, 155–158
Probability
binomial distribution and,
212–217, 224–227
binomial experiment, 212–217
continuous random variable, 212
discrete random variable, 212
normal distribution and,
218–222
random variable, 212
Probability distribution(s), 212
binomial, 212–217, 224–227
histogram of, 212–217
normal, 218–222, 224–227
skewed, 212
symmetric, 212
Probability histogram, 212–217
Problem solving
break-even analysis, 7, 9, 11
strategies, 2–5
draw a diagram, 3–5
use a formula, 2, 4–5
look for a pattern, 2–5
Problem Solving Workshop, 29,
80, 117, 134, 184, 232
Product property of logarithms,
155
applying, 155–158

Selected Answers

UNIT 1

1.1 Exercise Set A (p. 4)

1. 315 mi **3.** 63 mi/h **5.** 54 ft^2 **7.** 13 m

9. In the table the inputs increase by 5. An equation that represents the table is $y = 2x + 9$.

11. $y = 3x + 34$ **13.** $y = 58 - 11x$ **15.** 5 **17.** 3

1.1 Exercise Set B (p. 5)

1. $y = 6x + 22$

3. a. $57; $62; $67; $72; *Sample answer:* 175 text messages **b.** $69.2 = 0.1x + 52$; 172 text messages. **c.** *Sample answer:* Yes; the estimate in part (a) was comparable to the exact answer in part (b).

5.

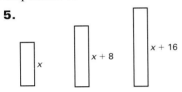

$3x + 24 = 84$; 20 in., 28 in., 36 in.

7.

$8x + 10 = 24$; $x = 1.75$; So the paintings should be 1.75 feet apart and the spaces on the left and right should be 3.5 feet.

1.2 Exercise Set A (pp. 8–9)

5.

$(-3, 1)$

7.

$(0, 3)$

9.

$(3, 4)$

11.

$(-3, -2)$

13.

$(-1, 2)$

15.

$(-5, 4)$

17. $(2, -1)$; consistent and independent

19. no solution; inconsistent **21.** infinitely many solutions; consistent and dependent **23.** (3, 0); consistent and independent **25.** $(2, -1)$; consistent and independent **27.** (2, 6); consistent and independent **29.** lifeguard; 8 h, cashier: 10 h

31. 60 tickets at $36; 140 tickets at $28

33. $R = 5500t$

35.

1.2 Exercise Set B (pp. 10–11)

1.

$(1, 3)$

3.

$(-1, -4)$

5.

$\left(\dfrac{1}{2}, 0\right)$

7.

$\left(\dfrac{1}{4}, \dfrac{1}{2}\right)$

9.

$\left(\dfrac{1}{3}, \dfrac{3}{2}\right)$

11. ; infinitely many solutions

13. $(3, 1)$; consistent and independent

15. $(1, -4)$; consistent and independent

17. $\left(\dfrac{4}{5}, -\dfrac{13}{5}\right)$; consistent and independent

19. infinitely many solutions; consistent and dependent

21. $\left(-\dfrac{16}{5}, \dfrac{7}{5}\right)$; consistent and independent

23. *Sample answer:*
$$x + y = 2$$
$$2x + 2y = 4$$

25.
no solution

27.
$(1.5, 0.5)$

29. ; $(10, 5)$ and $(-10, 5)$

31. $x + y = 20$
$4x + 6y = 100$

33. a. $y = 90.25x + 756$, where x represents the number of years, and y represents the cost; $y = 48.50x + 1424$, where x represents the number of years, and y represents the cost

b. ; 16 years

c. Yes, a washer can last 16 years.

35.

37. $R = 1.25x$

39.

1.3 Exercise Set A (p. 15)

1. $(2, 2)$ **3.** $(2, -1)$ **5.** $\left(\dfrac{2}{3}, -2\right)$ **7.** $(2, 3)$

9. $(-16, -5)$ **11.** $\left(-\dfrac{4}{5}, \dfrac{17}{10}\right)$ **13.** $(1, -1)$

15. no solution **17.** $(16, 6)$ **19.** infinitely many solutions **21.** $(6, -12)$ **23.** 60 of type A, 24 of type B

1.3 Exercise Set B (p. 16)

1. $(4, -3)$ **3.** infinitely many solutions

5. $(-3, 7)$ **7.** $(3, -4)$ **9.** $(1, -2)$ **11.** $(6, 2)$

13. $(10, 10)$ **15.** $\left(\dfrac{17}{7}, \dfrac{9}{7}\right)$ **17.** $\left(\dfrac{14}{3}, 0\right)$

19. plane: 150 mi/h, wind: 50 mi/h **21.** $20.00

1.4 Exercise Set A (pp. 19–20)

1. yes; yes **3.** no; no **5.** yes; yes

11.   **13.**

15.

17.

13.

15.

19.

21.

17.

19.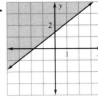

23. The other side of the boundary line should be shaded.

21. The other side of the boundary line should be shaded.

23. $y \le -\frac{3}{4}x + \frac{3}{2}$ **25.** $y \ge |x| + 2$

25. $y \le 5$

27.

27.

29. $20x + 10y \ge 1500$ **31.** $25x + 20y \le 550$

29. $c = 5t + 10$ **31.** no; The initial cost will be less but as the hours increase the cost will eventually surpass the music teachers cost due to the higher hourly rate.

33. 10

1.4 Exercise Set B (pp. 21–22)

1. yes **3.** yes

9.

11.

1.5 Exercise Set A (pp. 25–26)

5.

7.

9.

11.

13.   **15.**

17. Answers will vary. **19.** Answers will vary.

21. $y \le 4$
$y \ge -x - 2$
$y \ge x - 2$

23. Answers will vary.

25.
$x \ge 0, x \le 17,$
$y \ge 18, y \le 40$

17.   **19.**

21. Answers will vary. **23.** Answers will vary.

25. $t \le 3$
$d \le 55t$

27. a. $x + y \le 24, 7x + 6.5y \ge 100$

b.

c. *Sample answer:* 7 hours babysitting and 11 hours at the grocery store, 9 hours babysitting and 9 hours at the grocery store, 5 hours babysitting and 14 hours at the grocery store

27. a. $x \ge 20, x \le 65, y \ge 0.5(220 - x),$
$y \le 0.75(220 - x)$

b.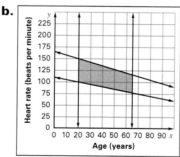

c. No, the person's heart rate is above the recommended range. A 36-year old person's heart rate should be between 92 and 138 heartbeats per minute.

1.5 Exercise Set B (pp. 27–28)

5.   **7.**

9.   **11.**

13.   **15.**

1.6 Exercise Set A (p. 32)

1. 1; 16 **3.** 270; 920 **5.** 10; 50 **7.** 24; 72
9. 9; 27 **11.** 30 inkjet printers, 30 laser printers

1.6 Exercise Set B (p. 33)

1. 46; 100 **3.** 0; 38 **5.** 0; no maximum

7. The graph should have a vertex at (3, 2), not (4, 2). The maximum value of C is 74. It occurs when $x = 2$ and $y = 14$.

1.7 Exercise Set A (p. 36)

1. no **3.** no **5.** $(2, 1, 4)$ **7.** $(3, 1, -2)$

9. $(5, -3, 6)$ **11.** $\left(-\dfrac{5}{2}z + \dfrac{19}{2}, 2z - 12, z\right)$

13. $0.5x + 0.75y + 0.4z = 2885$
$0.3x + 0.1y + 0.3z = 1335$
$0.2x + 0.15y + 0.3z = 1230$;
1st delivery: 1800, 2nd delivery: 1500,
3rd delivery: 2150

1.7 Exercise Set B (p. 37)

1. $(2, 1, -3)$ **3.** $\left(\dfrac{4}{13}z, \dfrac{11}{13}z, z\right)$ **5.** $\left(\dfrac{1}{2}, 1, -\dfrac{3}{2}\right)$

7. $\left(\dfrac{3}{2}, -2, -1\right)$ **9.** $(7, -21, 18)$ **11.** $\left(\dfrac{4}{3}, -\dfrac{1}{4}, -\dfrac{2}{3}\right)$

13. $(1, 1, 1, 1)$ **15.** $(2 - y, 0, y, -2)$

17. $a + b + c = -2$
$4a - 2b + c = 7$
$25a - 5b + c = -2$; $a = -1, b = -4, c = 3$

1.8 Exercise Set A (p. 41)

1. $\begin{bmatrix} 4 & 0 \\ 10 & 4 \end{bmatrix}$ **3.** $\begin{bmatrix} 2 & -1 & 7 \\ -4 & -4 & 2 \\ 2 & 3 & -6 \end{bmatrix}$

5. $\begin{bmatrix} 3 & 9 & 13 \\ 2 & 0 & -4 \\ 10 & 3 & 9 \end{bmatrix}$ **7.** $\begin{bmatrix} -12 & -6 \\ -9 & -6 \end{bmatrix}$

9. $\begin{bmatrix} -16 & -4 \\ 20 & 0 \\ -4 & 12 \end{bmatrix}$

11. $x = 2, y = -7$ **13.** 15,000 more **15.** more

1.8 Exercise Set B (p. 42)

1. $\begin{bmatrix} 5 & -2 \\ 4 & 8 \end{bmatrix}$ **3.** $\begin{bmatrix} -4 & -20 \\ 6 & -18 \end{bmatrix}$ **5.** $\begin{bmatrix} 1 \\ 1 \end{bmatrix}$

7. $\begin{bmatrix} \dfrac{5}{3} & 0 & 2 \\ \dfrac{4}{3} & 3 & 2 \\ \dfrac{19}{3} & \dfrac{26}{3} & 2 \end{bmatrix}$ **9.** $\begin{bmatrix} -4 & 18 \\ 33 & -20 \\ -1 & -24 \end{bmatrix}$

11. $x = -3, y = 1$

13. Store A $\begin{bmatrix} x & 2x & 3x - 150 \\ y & 1.5y + 220 & 3y - 60 \end{bmatrix}$
Store B

1.9 Exercise Set A (p. 46)

1. A: 3×2; B: 1×3; *not* defined

3. $\begin{bmatrix} 11 \end{bmatrix}$ **5.** $\begin{bmatrix} -2 & 6 \\ 1 & -3 \\ -3 & 9 \end{bmatrix}$ **7.** $\begin{bmatrix} -5 & 15 & -11 \\ 4 & 10 & 20 \\ 8 & 6 & 16 \end{bmatrix}$

9. $\begin{bmatrix} 1 \end{bmatrix}$ **11.** $\begin{bmatrix} -3 \\ -6 \\ -16 \\ 8 \end{bmatrix}$ **13.** $\begin{bmatrix} 8 & -10 \\ -2 & 6 \end{bmatrix}$

15. Game 1 $\begin{bmatrix} \$1361 \\ \$1625 \end{bmatrix}$
Game 2

1.9 Exercise Set B (p. 47)

1. $\begin{bmatrix} -2 & 6 \\ -2 & -1 \\ 9 & 8 \end{bmatrix}$ **3.** $\begin{bmatrix} 1 & 2 \\ -17 & 12 \\ -9 & 5 \end{bmatrix}$

5. $\begin{bmatrix} -4 & -8 \\ -2 & 3 \end{bmatrix}$ **7.** $\begin{bmatrix} -1 & -21 \\ 2 & 6 \\ -2 & -22 \end{bmatrix}$

9. $\begin{bmatrix} 14 & 35 \\ 8 & 2 \\ 8 & 30 \end{bmatrix}$ **11.** $x = 3, y = 4$

13. $AB = \begin{bmatrix} 0 & -2 & -4 \\ -1 & -3 & -1 \end{bmatrix}$;
reflection through the origin

1.10 Exercise Set A (p. 51)

1. -12 **3.** $-\dfrac{3}{2}$ **5.** -91 **7.** 6 **9.** 2 **11.** $(-5, 3)$

13. $(1, -1, 2)$ **15.** $\left(\dfrac{1}{2}, \dfrac{1}{4}, -1\right)$

17. Premium: \$2.15,
Regular: \$1.95

1.10 Exercise Set B (p. 52)

1. 22　**3.** -10　**5.** -72　**7.** 9　**9.** $(4, 6)$

11. $(7, -8)$　**13.** $\left(-\dfrac{61}{8}, \dfrac{3}{8}, \dfrac{43}{8}\right)$　**15.** $(-7, 3, 9)$

17. $(-3, -4, -1)$　**19.** $(297, 240, 1)$

1.11 Exercise Set A (p. 57)

1. $\begin{bmatrix} 2 & -7 \\ -1 & 4 \end{bmatrix}$　**3.** $\begin{bmatrix} \frac{1}{10} & \frac{1}{5} \\ -\frac{3}{10} & \frac{2}{5} \end{bmatrix}$　**5.** $\begin{bmatrix} 1 & 1 \\ -\frac{5}{2} & -2 \end{bmatrix}$

7. $\begin{bmatrix} 1 & -1 & 0 \\ 0 & \frac{1}{3} & -\frac{1}{3} \\ 0 & 0 & \frac{1}{5} \end{bmatrix}$　**9.** $\begin{bmatrix} 8 & 1 \\ -11 & -1 \end{bmatrix}$

11. $\begin{bmatrix} -1 & 4 & -1 \\ 4 & -8 & 1 \end{bmatrix}$　**13.** $(2, 2)$　**15.** $(1, -2, 4)$

17. a. $x + y + z = 1011$
$x + 2y + 3z = 1669$
$x - y = -305$

b. $\begin{bmatrix} 1 & 1 & 1 \\ 1 & 2 & 3 \\ 1 & -1 & 0 \end{bmatrix} \begin{bmatrix} x \\ y \\ z \end{bmatrix} = \begin{bmatrix} 1011 \\ 1669 \\ -305 \end{bmatrix}$

c. 1-point: 353, 2-point: 658, 3-point: 0

1.11 Exercise Set B (p. 58)

1. no inverse　**3.** $\begin{bmatrix} \frac{2}{13} & -\frac{7}{13} \\ \frac{1}{13} & \frac{3}{13} \end{bmatrix}$

5. $\begin{bmatrix} -0.2\overline{2} & 0.2\overline{7} & 0.8\overline{8} \\ -0.1\overline{1} & -0.1\overline{1} & 0.4\overline{4} \\ 0.1\overline{1} & 0.1\overline{1} & 0.5\overline{5} \end{bmatrix}$

7. $\begin{bmatrix} 18 & 30 & -44 \\ 7 & 11 & -\frac{31}{2} \end{bmatrix}$

9. $(-7, 7)$　**11.** $\left(\dfrac{1}{2}, -1\right)$

13. $(6, -7, 4)$　**15.** $A = \left(A^{-1}\right)^{-1}$

1.12 Exercise Set A (p. 61)

1. 5 vertices; 7 edges　**3.** 5 vertices; 8 edges

5. false

7. *Sample answer:* 2 tanks: one tank with gouramis, tetras, and black mollies; another tank with just angelfish; 2 tanks: one tank with gouramis and angelfish; another tank with tetras and black mollies

9. $\begin{array}{c} \\ C \\ D \\ E \\ F \\ G \end{array} \begin{array}{c} \begin{array}{ccccc} C & D & E & F & G \end{array} \\ \begin{bmatrix} 0 & 1 & 0 & 0 & 0 \\ 1 & 0 & 0 & 1 & 2 \\ 0 & 0 & 0 & 2 & 0 \\ 0 & 1 & 2 & 0 & 1 \\ 0 & 2 & 0 & 1 & 0 \end{bmatrix} \end{array}$

11. *Sample answer:*

1.12 Exercise Set B (p. 62)

1. false　**3.** true　**5.** The shortest route is to the pizza shop, to your friend's house, then to your cousin's house, a distance of 7 miles.

7. $\begin{array}{c} \\ R \\ S \\ T \\ U \\ V \end{array} \begin{array}{c} \begin{array}{ccccc} R & S & T & U & V \end{array} \\ \begin{bmatrix} 0 & 2 & 0 & 0 & 1 \\ 2 & 0 & 0 & 1 & 2 \\ 0 & 0 & 0 & 2 & 0 \\ 0 & 1 & 2 & 0 & 1 \\ 1 & 2 & 0 & 1 & 0 \end{bmatrix} \end{array}$

9. a. 4　**b.** 2　**c.** 3　**d.** 9

11. *Sample answer:*

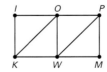

UNIT 2

2.1 Exercise Set A (p. 69)

1. yes; $f(x) = -2x + 7$; 1; -2

3. no　**5.** -283　**7.** 3　**9.** $-\infty, +\infty$

11. even; The graph is symmetric with respect to the y-axis.

13. odd; The graph is symmetric with respect to the origin.

15.

17. a.

b. domain: all real numbers; range: all real numbers

c. degree: 3; leading coefficient: -1

d. origin symmetry **e.** decreasing over all real numbers

19. a.

b. domain: all real numbers; range: all real numbers

c. degree: 3; leading coefficient: 3 **d.** no symmetry

e. increasing for $x < -2$ and $x > 2$; decreasing for $-2 < x < 2$

2.1 Exercise Set B (p. 70)

1. yes; $f(x) = x^3\sqrt{5} - 2x^2 + 7$; 3; $\sqrt{5}$

3. 32 **5.** $+\infty, -\infty$ **7.** $+\infty, +\infty$

9. odd; The graph is symmetric with respect to the origin.

11.   **13.**

15. a.

b. domain: all real numbers; range: $y \geq 6$

c. degree: 4; leading coefficient: 2

d. y-axis symmetry

e. increasing for about $-1 < x < 0$ and $x > 1$; decreasing for about $x < -1$ and $0 < x < 1$

17. *Sample answer:* $f(x) = -x^4 + 2x^3$

2.2 Exercise Set A (p. 74)

5. The graph of g is the graph of f translated down 6 units.

7.

The graph of g is the graph of f translated up 2 units; the domains and ranges of both functions are all real numbers; f has x- and y-intercepts of 0 and g has an x-intercept of about -1.3 and a y-intercept of 2; f is odd and symmetric with respect to the origin and g is neither even nor odd and has no symmetry.

9.

The graph of g is the graph of f translated up 3 units; the domains and ranges of both functions are all real numbers; f has x- and y-intercepts of 0 and g has an x-intercept of about 1.1 and a y-intercept of 3; f is odd and symmetric with respect to the origin and g is neither even nor odd and has no symmetry.

11.

The graph of *g* is the graph of *f* translated to the left 2 units and up 4 units; the domains and ranges of both functions are all real numbers; *f* has *x*- and *y*-intercepts of 0 and *g* has an *x*-intercept of about −0.75 and a *y*-intercept of −12; *f* is odd and symmetric with respect to the origin and *g* is neither even nor odd and has no symmetry.

13.

The graph of *g* is the graph of *f* translated down 5 units; the domain of *f* and *g* is all real numbers and the range of *f* is *y* ≥ 0 and the range of *g* is *y* ≥ −5; *f* has *x*- and *y*-intercepts of 0 and *g* has *x*-intercepts of about −1.5 and 1.5 and a *y*-intercept of −5; *f* and *g* are even and symmetric with respect to the *y*-axis.

15.

The graph of *g* is the graph of *f* translated down 2 units; the domain of *f* and *g* is all real numbers and the range of *f* is *y* ≥ 0 and the range of *g* is *y* ≥ −2; *f* has *x*- and *y*-intercepts of 0 and *g* has *x*-intercepts of about −1.6 and 1.6 and a *y*-intercept of −2; *f* and *g* are even and symmetric with respect to the *y*-axis.

17.

The graph of *g* is the graph of *f* translated to the right 1 unit and up 1 unit; the domain of *f* and *g* is all real numbers and the range of *f* is *y* ≥ 0 and the range of *g* is *y* ≥ 1; *f* has *x*- and *y*-intercepts of 0 and *g* has a *y*-intercept of $\frac{4}{3}$; *f* is even and symmetric with respect to the *y*-axis and *g* is neither even nor odd and has no symmetry.

19. $y = (x + 5)^4$

2.2 Exercise Set B (p. 75)

1. The graph of *g* is the graph of *f* translated down 7 units. **3.** The graph of *g* is the graph of *f* translated to the left 3 units and down 1 unit.

5.

The graph of *g* is the graph of *f* translated up 4 units; the domains and ranges of both functions are all real numbers; *f* has *x*- and *y*-intercepts of 0 and *g* has an *x*-intercept of about 1.6 and a *y*-intercept of 4; *f* is odd and symmetric with respect to the origin and *g* is neither even nor odd and has no symmetry.

7.

The graph of *g* is the graph of *f* translated to the right 5 units and up 1 unit; the domains and ranges of both functions are all real numbers; *f* has *x*- and *y*-intercepts of 0 and *g* has an *x*-intercept of 6 and a *y*-intercept of 126; *f* is odd and symmetric with respect to the origin and *g* is neither even nor odd and has no symmetry.

9.

The graph of g is the graph of f translated to the right 4 units; the domains and ranges of both functions are all real numbers; f has x- and y-intercepts of 0 and g has an x-intercept of 4 and a y-intercept of -96; f is odd and symmetric with respect to the origin and g is neither even nor odd and has no symmetry.

11.

The graph of g is the graph of f translated to the right 3 units; the domain of f and g is all real numbers and the range of f and g is $y \geq 0$; f has x- and y-intercepts of 0 and g has an x-intercept of 3 and a y-intercept of 81; f is even and symmetric with respect to the y-axis and g is neither even nor odd and has no symmetry.

13.

The graph of g is the graph of f translated to the left 3 units and down 5 units; the domain of f and g is all real numbers and the range of f is $y \geq 0$ and the range of g is $y \geq -5$; f has x- and y-intercepts of 0 and g has x-intercepts of about -4.5 and -1.5 and a y-intercept of 76; f is even and symmetric with respect to the y-axis and g is neither even nor odd and has no symmetry.

15.

The graph of g is the graph of f translated to the right 6 units; the domain of f and g is all real numbers and the range of f and g is $y \geq 0$; f has x- and y-intercepts of 0 and g has an x-intercept of 6 and a y-intercept of 648; f is even and symmetric with respect to the y-axis and g is neither even nor odd and has no symmetry.

17. The student described the direction of the translation incorrectly. The graph of $g(x) = -2(x - 5)^3 + 4$ is the graph of $f(x) = -2x^3$ translated right 5 units and up 4 units. **19.** $y = 3(x + 7)^4 + 1$

2.3 Exercise Set A (p. 78)

1. $(x + 5)(x^2 - 5x + 25)$

3. $(4n - 3)(16n^2 + 12n + 9)$

5. $(w + 3)(w^2 - 3w + 9)$ **7.** $(r^2 + 6)(r - 3)$

9. $(c + 3)(c - 3)(c + 4)$ **11.** $(x^2 - 6)(x^2 + 6)$

13. $(2y^3 + 1)(3y^3 - 4)$ **15.** $(d^2 - 5)(d^2 - 2)$

17. $(a^3 + 6)(a + 1)(a^2 - a + 1)$

19. $2(b + 7)(b - 2)(b^2 + 2b + 4)$ **21.** $0, \dfrac{9}{4}$

23. $-5, -\sqrt{3}, \sqrt{3}$ **25.** $-1, 0, 1$

27. 6 ft by 3 ft by 1 ft

2.3 Exercise Set B (p. 79)

1. $(x - 8)(x^2 + 8x + 64)$

3. $7(h + 4)(h^2 - 4h + 16)$ **5.** $(6x^2 + 1)(2x - 1)$

7. $(n + 4)(n - 4)(3n - 10)$

9. $(y^2 + 9)(y + 3)(y - 3)$

11. $(3a^2 - 1)(2a^2 + 5)$

13. $(r - 1)(r^2 + r + 1)(r^2 + 1)$

15. $(a^2b + 5)(a^4b^2 - 5a^2b + 25)$

17. -10 **19.** 4 **21.** $-\dfrac{3}{5}, 1$ **23.** $-\dfrac{1}{3}, \dfrac{1}{3}$

25. $-1, 0, 1$ **27.** $-\dfrac{\sqrt{6}}{2}, 0, \dfrac{\sqrt{6}}{2}$

29. *Sample answer:*
$x^4 + 5x^3 + x + 5; (x + 5)(x + 1)(x^2 - x + 1)$

2.4 Exercise Set A (p. 83)

1. $(-\infty, 5)$ and $(0, 4)$ **3.** $(-\infty, -2)$ and $(2, \infty)$
5. $(-\infty, -2)$ and $(2, \infty)$ **7.** $[-4, 1]$ and $[4, \infty)$
9. $\left(-4, \dfrac{3}{2}\right)$ and $(4, \infty)$ **11.** $[-3, -1.4]$ and $[1.4, 3]$
13. $(-2.4, 0)$ and $(2.4, \infty)$ **15.** $(-\infty, 0]$ and $\left[\dfrac{2}{3}, \dfrac{5}{2}\right]$
17. $(-\infty, -0.5]$ and $[0.5, 8]$ **19.** The open dots on the graph mean that the values do not satisfy the inequality. The solution set is $(0, 1)$ and $(3, \infty)$.
21. a. $1000(1 + r)^3 > 1200$ **b.** The interest rate must be greater than 6.3%.

2.4 Exercise Set B (p. 84)

1. $(-4, 2)$ and $(6, \infty)$ **3.** $\left[-2, -\dfrac{1}{2}\right]$ and $\left[\dfrac{1}{2}, 2\right]$
5. $\left(-3, -\dfrac{3}{2}\right)$ and $(3, \infty)$ **7.** $(-4, 2)$ and $(7, \infty)$
9. $(-\infty, -1.6]$ and $[-0.4, 1.5]$ **11.** $(-2.4, -1.3)$ and $(1, \infty)$ **13.** $(4, \infty)$ **15.** $[6, \infty)$
17. $(-\infty, -0.3]$ and $[0.3, 1]$ **19.** If $<$ is replaced with $\le$, then the solution set changes from $(-\infty, -7)$ and $(-1, 1)$ to $(-\infty, -7]$ and $[-1, 1]$.
21. The height of the box is greater than 3 inches and less than 9.6 inches.

2.5 Exercise Set A (p. 87)

1. $x + 7$ **3.** $x^2 - 3x + 10$ **5.** $8x + 5 + \dfrac{12x + 25}{x^2 - 3}$
7. $x + 3$ **9.** $x^3 + 2x^2 - 3x + 3 - \dfrac{4}{x - 2}$
11. $2x^3 - 5x^2 + 6$ **13.** $(x - 6)(x + 1)(x + 2)$
15. $(x - 9)(x - 2)(x - 7)$
17. $(x - 1)(2x + 3)(2x - 3)$ **19.** 2   **21.** $-5, -\dfrac{1}{2}$
23. 5   **25.** $x - 2$

2.5 Exercise Set B (p. 88)

1. $2x^2 - 4x + 9 - \dfrac{28}{2x + 3}$ **3.** $2x - \dfrac{9}{x^3 + x^2 - 5}$
5. $x^3 + 2x^2 - 8x + 20 - \dfrac{56}{x + 3}$
7. $2x^2 + 5x - 1$ **9.** $(x - 5)(x + 3)(x + 11)$

11. $(x + 7)(2x - 1)(2x^2 + 3)$
13. $-\dfrac{5 - \sqrt{17}}{2}, -\dfrac{5 + \sqrt{17}}{2}$
15. a. $1, -8$ **b.** $x - 4, x - 1, x + 8$
c. $x = 4, x = 1, x = -8$

2.6 Exercise Set A (p. 91)

1. $\pm 1, \pm 3, \pm 7, \pm 21$
3. $\pm 1, \pm 2, \pm 5, \pm 10, \pm\dfrac{1}{5}, \pm\dfrac{2}{5}$
5. $-2, 1, 4$ **7.** $-4, 3, 6$ **9.** $-\dfrac{3}{2}, \dfrac{1}{2}, 3$
11. $-2, -1, 1$ **13.** $-3, -1, \dfrac{1}{2}, 1$
15. a. $t^4 - 18t^3 + 89t^2 - 32t - 400$
b. 1, 2, 4, 5, 8   **c.** 4; 1999
d. about 6.4 or 2001

2.6 Exercise Set B (p. 92)

1. $-2, 1, 5$ **3.** $-3, -\sqrt{2}, -1, \sqrt{2}$
5. $-3 - 2\sqrt{2}, -1, -3 + 2\sqrt{2}, 3$ **7.** $-\dfrac{3}{4}, -\dfrac{1}{2}, \dfrac{1}{3}, 2$
9. $-\sqrt{3}, -\dfrac{5}{3}, \dfrac{1}{2}, \sqrt{3}$
11. *Sample answer:* $f(x) = 6x^3 - 7x^2 + 10x + 2$
13. a. for each function: $-5, -1, 4$ **b.** The zeros of $f(x)$ are also the zeros of $af(x)$.   **c.** To apply the rational zero theorem, the coefficients must be integers.   **d.** $-3, -\dfrac{1}{4}, 1$

2.7 Exercise Set A (p. 96)

1. 3   **3.** 7   **5.** $-1, 1, 3$ **7.** $-5, -i, i$
9. $-3, 2 + \sqrt{3}, 2 - \sqrt{3}$ **11.** $f(x) = x^2 + 11x + 28$
13. $f(x) = x^3 + 2x^2 - 3x$
15. $f(x) = x^4 + 5x^3 + 4x^2 + 20x$
17. The polynomial function should be written as a product of three factors because $2 - i$ must also be a zero by the complex conjugates theorem.
$$f(x) = (x - 3)[x - (2 + i)][x - (2 - i)]$$
$$= (x - 3)(x^2 - 4x + 5)$$
$$= x^3 - 7x^2 + 17x - 15$$
19. $-0.62, -0.50, 1.62$
21. $-4.09, -0.98, 1.47, 4.60$
23. 3 and 9 years after opening

2.7 Exercise Set B (p. 97)

1. $-3, -1, 3$ **3.** $-2, 0, 2 + i\sqrt{3}, 2 - i\sqrt{3}$

5. $-3, -1, 3, \frac{9}{2}$ **7.** $-i, i, -1 + \sqrt{2}, -1 - \sqrt{2}$

9. $f(x) = 2x^4 - 4x^3 - 32x^2 + 64x$

11. $f(x) = 2x^3 + 10x^2 - 6x - 30$

13. $f(x) = 2x^4 - 22x^3 + 80x^2 - 116x + 56$

15. 2 or 0; 1; 2 or 0 **17.** 4, 2, or 0; 1; 4, 2, or 0

19. $-0.75, 0.75$ **21.** $-1.06, 3.98$

23. *Sample answer:* One zero is a repeated zero.

25. a. $R = -315t^5 + 5554t^4 + 1932t^3 - 709,619t^2 + 6,441,145t + 49,246,365$ **b.** 2001

2.8 Exercise Set A (pp. 100–101)

1. The error is in calling -6 a factor. The correct statement is *If -6 is a solution of the polynomial equation $f(x) = 0$, then $(x + 6)$ is a factor of $f(x)$.*

3. 4 **5.** 3 **7.** $-4, 6, 8$ **9.** $-5, -1, 7$ **11.** 8

13. zeros: -2 (multiplicity 2), 5; turning points: 2

15. zeros: -6 (multiplicity 2), $\frac{2}{3}$ (multiplicity 2); turning points: 3 **17.** zeros: 0 (multiplicity 2),

$-4, \frac{3}{2}$ (multiplicity 3); turning points: 5

19.   **21.**

23.

25. $(-2, 0)$: min, $(-0.5, 5)$: max, $(1, 0)$: min; $-2, 1; 4$

27.

x-int: $-1.79, 0.11, 1.67$; max: $(-1, 7)$; min: $(1, -5)$

29.

x-int: $-2.83, 0, 2.83$; max: $(-2, 4), (2, 4)$; min: $(0, 0)$

31.

x-int: $-2, -1, 0, 1, 2$; max: $(-1.64, 3.63)$, $(0.54, 1.42)$; min: $(-0.54, -1.42), (1.64, -3.63)$

33. about 5 in. by 7 in. by 1.5 in.; about 52.5 in.^{3}

35. a.

b. $(25.33, 222.93)$; *Sample answer:* From 1970 to 1995, per capita egg consumption decreased to about 223 eggs, then began to increase again.

2.8 Exercise Set B (pp. 102–103)

1. 8

3. zeros: -2 (multiplicity 2), 3, $\frac{9}{2}$; turning points: 3

5. zeros: 0 (multiplicity 3), -1 (multiplicity 2), 1; turning points: 5 **7.** zeros: $-3, -2, 2$ (multiplicity 2); turning points: 3

9.

11.

domain: $-\infty < x < \infty$
range: $-\infty < y < \infty$

domain: $-\infty < x < \infty$
range: $y \geq -4.489$

13.

15.

domain: $-\infty < x < \infty$
range: $-\infty < y < \infty$

domain: $-\infty < x < \infty$
range: $y \geq -22.9$

17. $(-2, 2.4)$: max, $(0, -1.2)$: min, $(1, -1)$: max, $(2.4, -2)$: min; $-2.5, -1, 2.6$; 5

19. $(-1.5, -2.25)$: min, $(0, 3)$: max, $(2, -3)$: min, $(3.5, 2)$: max; $-2, -1, 1, 3, 4$; 5

21.

x-int: 0, 1.2; max: $(-1.19, 4.09)$; min: $(-1.77, 3.8)$, $(0.71, -2.93)$

23.

x-int: $-2, -1, 0, 1, 2$; max: $(-1.64, 3.63)$, $(0.54, 1.42)$; min: $(-0.54, -1.42)$, $(1.64, -3.63)$

25.

x-int: $-5, 0, 1.2$; max: $(0.42, 1.38)$; min: $(-3.57, -116.16)$, $(1.2, 0)$

27. *Sample answer:* $f(x) = x^3 - 6x^2 + 5x + 12$, $g(x) = x^4 - 5x^3 - x^2 + 17x + 12$, $h(x) = x^5 - 8x^4 + 14x^3 + 20x^2 - 39x - 36$

29. 2, 4

31. If n is even, there is a turning point. If n is odd, the graph passes through the x-axis.;

33. a.

b. $(6.6, 63.9)$, $(19.8, 34.0)$; the high temperature for the 24-hour period was 63.9°F, which occurred at about 12:36 P.M. and the low temperature for the 24-hour period was 34°F, which occurred at about 1:48 A.M. **c.** $34 \leq y \leq 63.9$

UNIT 3

3.1 Exercise Set A (p. 111)

1. $7^{1/3}$ **3.** $14^{4/5}$ **5.** $11^{7/8}$ **7.** $\sqrt[3]{17}$ **9.** $\left(\sqrt[3]{33}\right)^2$
11. $\left(\sqrt[5]{-28}\right)^7$ **13.** 4 **15.** 81 **17.** 32 **19.** 625
21. -8 **23.** 2.20 **25.** 3.00 **27.** 2.88 **29.** 26.15
31. 5.2 cm **33.** -1.58 **35.** 601.75 cm^3; 8.44 cm

3.1 Exercise Set B (p. 112)

1. $63^{3/5}$ **3.** $124^{7/6}$ **5.** $\left(\sqrt{13}\right)^3$ **7.** 9 **9.** 16
11. $\dfrac{1}{125}$ **13.** $-\dfrac{1}{8}$ **15.** $-\dfrac{1}{3125}$ **17.** 22.89
19. 132.26 **21.** 32 **23.** 0.09 **25.** 4.21

27. 0.18, 5.82 **29.** ±2.06 **31.** 1.32
33. −3.58 **35.** 1.81 in.

3.2 Exercise Set A (p. 115)

1. $7^{5/3}$ **3.** $6^{1/2}$ **5.** 2 **7.** $11^{3/4}$ **9.** 27 **11.** 2

13. x^3 **15.** $x^{1/7}$ **17.** $2x\sqrt[3]{2x}$ **19.** $x^{3/5}$

21. $x^{5+\sqrt{3}}$ **23.** $\dfrac{x^{2\sqrt{3}}}{2}$ **25.** $8\sqrt[3]{5}$ **27.** $-6\sqrt{3}$

29. $2xy^6$ **31.** $xy^2\sqrt[4]{3x^3yz^3}$ **33.** $\dfrac{3\sqrt[3]{3xy^2z^2}}{2yz}$

35. 10 ft

3.2 Exercise Set B (p. 116)

1. $16 \cdot 5^{9/4}$ **3.** $7^{6/5}$ **5.** 4 **7.** $\dfrac{\sqrt{6}}{3}$ **9.** $\dfrac{\sqrt{70}}{35}$

11. $\dfrac{x^4\sqrt[4]{x}}{y^2}$ **13.** $x^{1/3}y^{1/6}$ **15.** $\dfrac{\sqrt{3}z^{1/4}}{x^{1/2}y^{1/3}}$

17. $9x^4\sqrt[4]{x^3}$

19. Addition was used to combine the exponents instead of subtraction; $\dfrac{y^{1/2}}{y^{-3/4}} = y^{1/2-(-3/4)} = y^{5/4}$

21. $3x^2z\sqrt[3]{xyz^2}$ **23.** $\dfrac{\sqrt[3]{50x + 25\sqrt{x}}}{5}$

25. $4x^2z\sqrt{xyz}$ **27.** 4.3 in.

3.3 Exercise Set A (p. 120)

1.
domain: $x \geq 0$,
range: $y \geq -2$

3.
domain: $x \geq -1$,
range: $y \geq 0$

5.
domain: $x \geq 1$,
range: $y \geq 1$

7.
domain and range:
all real numbers

9.
domain and range:
all real numbers

11.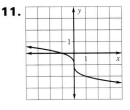
domain and range:
all real numbers

13. domain: $t \geq -273$, range: $V \geq 0$

15. domain: $h \leq 200$; range: $0 \leq t \leq 3.5$

17. a. $v_t = 33.7\sqrt{\dfrac{175}{A}}$

b. *Sample answer:*

A	2	4	6	8	10
v_t	315.23	222.90	182.00	157.62	140.98

c.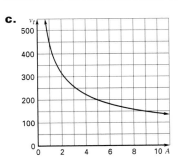

3.3 Exercise Set B (p. 121)

1.
domain: $x \geq -4$,
range: $y \geq -2$

3.
domain: $x \geq 0$,
range: $y \leq 3$

5.
domain and range:
all real numbers

7.
domain and range:
all real numbers

9. ; domain and range: all real numbers

11. $(0, 0)$ and $(1, 1)$

13.

15. On the interval $(-1, 1)$, the larger the root, the steeper the graph. On the intervals $(-\infty, -1)$ and $(1, \infty)$, the larger the root, the less steep the graph.

17. domain: $h \le 175$; range: $0 \le t \le 3.3$ **19.** 31 ft

3.4 Exercise Set A (p. 124)

1. 81 **3.** 2 **5.** 3 **7.** 173 **9.** 26 **11.** $-\dfrac{1}{8}$

13. -68 **15.** $-\dfrac{8}{27}$ **17.** $\dfrac{26}{5}$ **19.** 27 **21.** -8

23. -1 **25.** 4 **27.** $\dfrac{5}{2}$ **29.** 4 **31.** 1

33. 45.87 m **35.** 120.97 m

3.4 Exercise Set B (p. 125)

1. $\dfrac{15}{2}$ **3.** -4 **5.** $\pm\sqrt{39}$ **7.** -6 **9.** 120 **11.** $\dfrac{397}{81}$

13. 25 **15.** 9 **17.** no solution **19.** 3 **21.** -5

23. no solution **25.** 0 **27.** no solution **29.** 12 in.

UNIT 4

4.1 Exercise Set A (p. 132)

5. ; domain: all real numbers; range: $y > 0$

7. ; domain: all real numbers; range: $y < 0$

9. ; domain: all real numbers; range: $y > 1$

11. ; domain: all real numbers; range: $y > -5$

13. The function was not evaluated correctly when $x = 0$. The correct point is $(0, 0.5)$, not $(0, 1)$.

15. a. $E = 1350(1.09)^t$; about 1748 students
b. 2016

4.1 Exercise Set B (p. 133)

1. ; domain: all real numbers; range: $y > 0$

3. ; domain: all real numbers; range: $y < 0$

5. ; domain: all real numbers; range: $y > -7$

7. ; domain: all real numbers; range: $y > -1$

9. ; domain: all real numbers; range: $y > -2$

11. $4660.05

13. a. $P = 494{,}290(1.03)^t$; 664,284

b.

domain: $0 \le t \le 10$;
range: $494{,}290 \le P \le 664{,}284$

c. 1993

15. a. $n = 41(1.089)^t$

b.

n	0	1	2	3
t	41	44.65	48.62	52.95

c.   **d.** 1985

4.2 Exercise Set A (p. 137)

1. exponential decay   **3.** exponential decay

7. ; domain: all real numbers; range: $y > 0$

9. ; domain: all real numbers; range: $y < 0$

11. ; domain: all real numbers; range: $y > 2$

13. 3 h

4.2 Exercise Set B (p. 138)

1. ; domain: all real numbers; range: $y > 0$

3. ; domain: all real numbers; range: $y < 0$

5. ; domain: all real numbers; range: $y < 0$

7. ; domain: all real numbers; range: $y < -2$

9. ; domain: all real numbers; range: $y > -2$

11. The decay factor should be $1 - 0.03 = 0.97$, not 0.03. **13. a.** 400 g **b.** 243.8 g **c.** 28 days

4.3 Exercise Set A (p. 142)

1. $\dfrac{1}{e^3}$ **3.** $\dfrac{1}{e^{12}}$ **5.** $\dfrac{e^2}{4}$ **7.** $6e^{5x}$ **9.** $\dfrac{1}{e^x}$ **11.** 1096.633

13. 1.822 **15.** exponential growth

17. exponential decay **19.** exponential decay

21. ; domain: all real numbers; range: $y > 0$

23. ; domain: all real numbers; range: $y < 3$

25. ; domain: all real numbers; range: $y > -3$

27. $3444.50

4.3 Exercise Set B (p. 143)

1. $4e^{10}$ **3.** $27e^{12}$ **5.** $\dfrac{e^{9x-3}}{8}$ **7.** 148.413 **9.** 0.202

11. ; domain: all real numbers; range: $y > -3$

13. ; domain: all real numbers; range: $y < 2$

15. ; domain: all real numbers; range: $y > -4$

17. exponential growth **19.** 3 **21.** 21

4.4 Exercise Set A (p. 147)

1. $7^2 = 49$ **3.** $5^3 = 125$ **5.** $4^{-1} = \dfrac{1}{4}$ **7.** 2

9. -1 **11.** $\dfrac{1}{3}$ **13.** 0.805 **15.** -0.693

17. $f^{-1}(x) = e^x$ **19.** $f^{-1}(x) = 2(10^x)$

21. $f^{-1}(x) = 3^{x-2}$

23. ; domain: $x > -2$; range: all real numbers

25. 129

4.4 Exercise Set B (p. 148)

1. $4^{1/2} = 2$ **3.** $\left(\dfrac{1}{4}\right)^{-3} = 64$ **5.** $\dfrac{3}{2}$ **7.** $\dfrac{2}{3}$

9. $\dfrac{3}{2}$ **11.** 7.974 **13.** $f^{-1}(x) = 7^x$

15. $f^{-1}(x) = \left(\dfrac{1}{2}\right)^{x-2}$ **17.** $f^{-1}(x) = e^{x+3} + 1$

19. ; domain: $x > -2$; range: all real numbers

21. ; domain: $x > 1$; range: all real numbers

23.

Number of years since 1900

4.5 Exercise Set A (p. 153)

1. a. y-intercept: $(0, 1)$; no x-intercept; no zeros **b.** increasing: $(-\infty, \infty)$ **c.** C and D

3. The zero is the x-coordinate of the x-intercept, not the y-coordinate of the y-intercept. The zero is $x = 2$.

5.

; domain: $x > 0$; range: all real numbers

7. a. no zeros **b.** decreasing: $(-\infty, \infty)$

9. a. $x = 1$ **b.** decreasing: $(0, \infty)$

4.5 Exercise Set B (p. 154)

1. a. $x = 0$ **b.** increasing: $(-\infty, \infty)$ **c.** C and D

3. a. no zeros **b.** increasing: $(-\infty, \infty)$

5. a. no zeros **b.** increasing: $(-\infty, \infty)$

7. a. $x = 9$ **b.** increasing: $(-1, \infty)$

9.

domain: $x > -1.2$; range: all real numbers

11.

; domain: $x > -7.8$; range: all real numbers

13. a.

; $x \approx 3.35$

b. increasing: $(4, \infty)$; The alligator's length increases as its weight increases.

4.6 Exercise Set A (p. 157)

5. 1.447 **7.** 1.204 **9.** -0.602

11. $2 \log_7 x + \log_7 y$ **13.** $\log 5 + \frac{1}{3} \log x$

15. $\log_9 2 + 3 \log_9 x - \frac{1}{2}$ **17.** $\log_3 16$

19. $\log \frac{2x^2}{3}$ **21.** 1.277 **23.** 0.139 **25.** 2.018

27. a. $\text{pH} = 6.1 + \log B - \log C$ **b.** 7.38 **c.** just below normal

4.6 Exercise Set B (p. 158)

1. 3.332 **3.** 2.772 **5.** 1.659

7. $3 \log_2 x - \log_2 y - 2 \log_2 z$

9. $\log 2 + \frac{1}{2} \log x - 2 \log y$

11. $5[\log_9 2 + 2 \log_9 x + \log_9 y + \log_9 z]$

13. $\log_3 \frac{5}{3}$ **15.** $\log_2 \frac{9}{x^3 y}$ **17.** $\log \frac{\sqrt{(x+4)^3}}{6x^3}$

19. 1.869 **21.** 2.665

4.7 Exercise Set A (p. 161)

1. 0 **3.** 1.544 **5.** 0.462 **7.** $\frac{5}{2}$ **9.** 2.243 **11.** 5

13. 2 **15.** $\frac{4}{5}$ **17.** 2.730 **19.** 0.327

21. no solution **23.** 54.598 **25.** $\frac{1}{3}$ **27.** 30.375

29. 39.121 **31.** $\frac{10}{7}$ **33.** 4 **35.** 36.399

39. 28.1 yr **41.** 22.88

4.7 Exercise Set B (p. 162)

1. 1.609 **3.** 0.973 **5.** 2.096 **7.** 2.473 **9.** 6.091

11. -4.420 **13.** -0.135 **15.** 0 **17.** $-\frac{9}{2}$

19. 9998 **21.** 12 **23.** 1 **25.** 1 **27.** no solution

29. $2, \frac{5}{2}$ **31.** $4, 8$ **33.** 0.656 **35.** -9.110

37. $\$206,400$

4.8 Exercise Set A (p. 167)

1. $(-\infty, 3)$ **3.** $(-\infty, 4)$ **5.** $(2, \infty)$

7. $(-\infty, 3.409]$ **9.** $(-\infty, 2]$ **11.** $(0, 5]$ **13.** $(0, 8]$

15. $(0, 6)$ **17.** $(5.04, \infty)$ **19.** after about 4.5 years
21. a. $C = P(1.04)^t$ **b.** $0.99 < 0.99\,(1.04)^t < 1.5$;
in the first 10.6 years, $(0, 10.6)$ **c.** $0.99\,(1.04)^t > 2$;
over 17.9 years, $(17.9, \infty)$

4.8 Exercise Set B (p. 168)

1. $(-\infty, 2.21]$ **3.** $[2.42, +\infty)$ **5.** $(0.85, +\infty)$
7. $(-\infty, -2.32)$ **9.** $(-16.82, +\infty)$
11. $[2.72, +\infty)$ **13.** $[28, +\infty)$ **15.** $(0, 70.29]$
17. $(0, 49.47)$
19. $200e^{-0.00043t} < 10$; after about 6966.8 years
21. $80 \le p \le 196.36$

4.9 Exercise Set A (p. 171)

1. $y = \dfrac{1}{2}(3)^x$ **3.** $y = 3(4)^x$ **5.** $y = 5\left(\dfrac{2}{3}\right)^x$
7. $y = 37.86(6.85)^x$ **9.** $y = 62.12(0.03)^x$
11. $y = 3x^3$ **13.** $y = 2x^{1.5}$ **15.** $y = \dfrac{1}{4}x^{0.5}$
17. $y = 12.94x^{3.3}$ **19.** $y = 93.34x^2$
21. $y = 0.81x^{0.79}$; $6.14

4.9 Exercise Set B (p. 172)

1. $y = 1.2(2.4)^x$ **3.** $y = 2.7(4.2)^x$
5. $y = 0.9(4^x)$

7. $y = 2.1x^{3.7}$
9. $y = 2.2x^{0.13}$

11. $y = 2.233x^{0.129}$

UNIT 5

5.1 Exercise Set A (p. 178)

3. left

5.

$(-1, 0)$; $x = 1$

7.

$\left(\dfrac{3}{2}, 0\right)$; $x = -\dfrac{3}{2}$

9.

$\left(0, \dfrac{1}{8}\right)$; $y = -\dfrac{1}{8}$

11. $y^2 = 8x$ **13.** $y^2 = -4x$ **15.** $y^2 = 12x$
17. $y^2 = -12x$ **19.** $y^2 = 4x$ **21.** $y^2 = -x$
23. $x^2 = 10y$

5.1 Exercise Set B (p. 179)

1.

$(0, 3)$; $y = -3$

3.

$\left(0, -\dfrac{1}{32}\right)$; $y = \dfrac{1}{32}$

5.

$\left(0, -\dfrac{1}{16}\right)$; $y = \dfrac{1}{16}$

7.

$(0, 10)$; $y = -10$

9.

$\left(0, \dfrac{1}{3}\right)$; $y = -\dfrac{1}{3}$

11. $x^2 = 24y$ **13.** $y^2 = 20x$ **15.** $x^2 = -\dfrac{3}{2}y$

17. $y^2 = -6x$ **19.** $y^2 = -8x$ **21.** $y^2 = 24x$

23. $y^2 = -16x$ **25.** $x^2 = -\dfrac{5}{2}y$ **27.** $x^2 = 10y$

29. 7238.2 ft^3

5.2 Exercise Set A (p. 182)

1.

3

3.

8

5.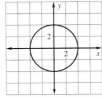

4

7. The radius of the circle should be 4, not 16.

9. $x^2 + y^2 = 80$ **11.** $x^2 + y^2 = 7$

13. $x^2 + y^2 = 90$ **15.** $x^2 + y^2 = 25$

17. $x^2 + y^2 = 13$ **19.** $x^2 + y^2 = 52$

21.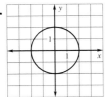

23. $y = -\dfrac{1}{4}x + \dfrac{17}{4}$ **25.** $x^2 + y^2 = 2304$

5.2 Exercise Set B (p. 183)

1.

10

3.

7

5.

$3\sqrt{2}$

7. $x^2 + y^2 = 13$ **9.** $x^2 + y^2 = 272$

11. $x^2 + y^2 = 104$ **13.** $x^2 + y^2 = 20$

15. $x^2 + y^2 = \dfrac{101}{4}$ **17.** $y = \dfrac{-\sqrt{6}}{2}x + 10$

19. a.   **b.** $x^2 + y^2 \le 400$
$x^2 + y^2 \le 1225$

c. The rating is between 4.2 and 4.6. The location is outside of the circle with a rating of 4.2, but inside the circle with a rating of 4.6.

5.3 Exercise Set A (p. 188)

1. ; vertices: $(0, \pm6)$;
co-vertices: $(\pm4, 0)$;
foci: $(0, \pm2\sqrt{5})$

3. ; vertices: $(0, \pm10)$;
co-vertices: $(\pm8, 0)$;
foci: $(0, \pm6)$

5. ; vertices: $(0, \pm 4)$;
co-vertices: $(\pm 1, 0)$;
foci: $(0, \pm\sqrt{15})$

7. ; vertices: $(0, \pm 3)$;
co-vertices: $(\pm 2, 0)$;
foci: $(0, \pm\sqrt{5})$

9. ; vertices: $(\pm 9, 0)$;
co-vertices: $(0, \pm 2)$;
foci: $(\pm\sqrt{77}, 0)$

11. $\dfrac{x^2}{1} + \dfrac{y^2}{25} = 1$ **13.** $\dfrac{x^2}{4} + \dfrac{y^2}{16} = 1$ **15.** $\dfrac{x^2}{64} + \dfrac{y^2}{36} = 1$

17.

19. $\dfrac{x^2}{64} + \dfrac{y^2}{100} = 1$

21. a. $\dfrac{x^2}{62{,}500} + \dfrac{y^2}{22{,}500} = 1$ **b.** $37{,}500\pi$ yd^2

5.3 Exercise Set B (p. 189)

1. ; vertices: $(\pm 3, 0)$;
co-vertices: $(0, \pm 1)$;
foci: $(\pm 2\sqrt{2}, 0)$

3. ; vertices: $(\pm 12, 0)$;
co-vertices: $(0, \pm 9)$;
foci: $(\pm 3\sqrt{7}, 0)$

5. ; vertices: $(0, \pm 2\sqrt{3})$;
co-vertices: $(\pm 2\sqrt{2}, 0)$;
foci: $(0, \pm 2)$

7. $\dfrac{x^2}{64} + \dfrac{y^2}{25} = 1$ **9.** $\dfrac{x^2}{169} + \dfrac{y^2}{31} = 1$

11. $\dfrac{x^2}{169} + \dfrac{y^2}{81} = 1$ **13.** $\dfrac{x^2}{16} + \dfrac{y^2}{36} = 1$

15. a. The greatest distance the boat can travel
between islands is 20 miles, going straight out
to a point and then straight to the other island.
This is the definition of an ellipse.
b. Island 1: $(-6, 0)$; Island 2: $(6, 0)$
c. 20 mi; $(\pm 10, 0)$
d. $\dfrac{x^2}{100} + \dfrac{y^2}{64} = 1$

5.4 Exercise Set A (p. 192)

1. ; vertices: $(\pm 4, 0)$;
foci: $(\pm 2\sqrt{5}, 0)$;
asymptotes: $y = \pm\dfrac{1}{2}x$

3. ; vertices: $(0, \pm 5)$;
foci: $(0, \pm\sqrt{29})$;
asymptotes: $y = \pm\dfrac{5}{2}x$

5. ; vertices: $(0, \pm 2\sqrt{5})$;
foci: $(0, \pm 2\sqrt{6})$;
asymptotes: $y = \pm\sqrt{5}x$

7. The transverse axis should
be horizontal, not vertical.

9. $\dfrac{y^2}{49} - \dfrac{x^2}{15} = 1$ **11.** $\dfrac{y^2}{16} - \dfrac{x^2}{4} = 1$

13. $\dfrac{y^2}{36} - \dfrac{x^2}{25} = 1$ **15.** $\dfrac{y^2}{108} - \dfrac{x^2}{36} = 1$

b. *Sample answer:* (2, 14.0), (4, 14.4), (6, 15.1), (8, 16.0)

17.

c. ; the part of the hyperbola in the first quadrant

19. $\dfrac{R^2}{\left(\dfrac{8}{\pi}\right)} - \dfrac{r^2}{\left(\dfrac{2}{\pi}\right)} = 1$

d. It gets smaller; because the area of the concrete remains constant as the radii increase, the width decreases.

5.4 Exercise Set B (p. 193)

1. 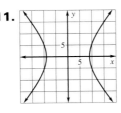 ; vertices: $(\pm 8, 0)$; foci: $\left(\pm\sqrt{85}, 0\right)$; asymptotes: $y = \pm\dfrac{\sqrt{21}}{8}x$

5.5 Exercise Set A (pp. 196–197)

1. ; center: (0, 3); radius: 3

3. ; vertices: $\left(0, \pm 3\sqrt{2}\right)$; foci: $\left(0, \pm 3\sqrt{11}\right)$; asymptotes: $y = \pm\dfrac{\sqrt{2}}{3}x$

3. ; vertex: (3, −4); focus: (3, −2)

5. ; vertices: $\left(0, \pm 2\sqrt{10}\right)$; foci: $\left(0, \pm 2\sqrt{13}\right)$; asymptotes: $y = \pm\dfrac{\sqrt{30}}{3}x$

5. ; center: (−3, 4); vertices: (−3, 10), (−3, −2); co-vertices: $\left(-3 \pm 4\sqrt{2}, 4\right)$; foci: (−3, 2), (−3, 6)

7. $\dfrac{x^2}{36} - \dfrac{y^2}{28} = 1$

7. ; center: (6, 2); radius: 2

9. **11.**

9. ; vertex: (−2, 4); focus: (−1.25, 4)

13. $\dfrac{y^2}{16} - \dfrac{x^2}{4} = 1$

15. a. 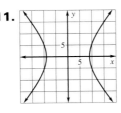 $\pi y^2 - \pi x^2 = 500$

11. ; center: $(-7, 1)$; radius: 1

13. $(x - 2)^2 + (y + 6)^2 = 16$

15. $\dfrac{(x + 2)^2}{4} + \dfrac{(y - 3)^2}{16} = 1$

17. $\dfrac{(x - 2)^2}{18} + \dfrac{(y - 1.5)^2}{20.25} = 1$

19. $(x - 3)^2 + (y + 4)^2 = 48$

21. $(y - 2)^2 = 16(x - 6)$ **23.** parabola

25. hyperbola **27.** ellipse **29.** hyperbola

31. ellipse **33.** circle

35. parabola; $(y - 1)^2 = -8(x - 2)$

37. hyperbola; $\dfrac{x^2}{9} - \dfrac{(y - 3)^2}{1} = 1$

39. parabola; $(x + 5)^2 = 6(y + 3)$

41. parabola; $(y - 6)^2 = -4(x - 8)$

43. hyperbola; $\dfrac{(x - 4)^2}{1} - \dfrac{(y - 4)^2}{9} = 1$

45. $x^2 + (y + 225)^2 = 50{,}625$; $x^2 + (y - 225)^2 = 50{,}625$

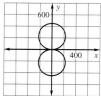

47. hyperbola; $\dfrac{(x - 1.5)^2}{5} - \dfrac{y^2}{\left(\frac{10}{3}\right)} = 1$

5.5 Exercise Set B (pp. 198–199)

1. ; vertex: $(5, -4)$; focus: $(1, -4)$

3. ; center: $(3, -4)$; radius: $3\sqrt{2}$

5. ; center: $(-6, -5)$; vertices: $(-6, -5 \pm 3\sqrt{3})$; co-vertices: $(-6 \pm \sqrt{11}, -5)$; foci: $(-6, -9), (-6, -1)$

7. ; center: $(5, -1)$;
vertices: $(15, -1)$ and
$(-5, -1)$;
co-vertices: $(5, 2)$ and $(5, -4)$;
foci: $(5 \pm \sqrt{91}, -1)$\

9. $\dfrac{(x-4)^2}{25} + \dfrac{(y+4)^2}{624} = 1$

11. $(x+3)^2 + (y+7)^2 = 7$

13. $\dfrac{(x-6)^2}{16} + \dfrac{(y+1)^2}{13} = 1$

15. $\left(x + \dfrac{1}{2}\right)^2 + \left(y - \dfrac{3}{4}\right)^2 = \dfrac{4}{9}$

17. hyperbola **19.** circle **21.** ellipse
23. parabola; $(x-7)^2 = 9(y+3)$

25. ellipse; $\dfrac{(x-3)^2}{10} + \dfrac{(y-5)^2}{18} = 1$

27. ellipse; $\dfrac{(x+1)^2}{14} + \dfrac{(y+2)^2}{4} = 1$

29. ellipse; $\dfrac{(x-6)^2}{36} + \dfrac{(y-3)^2}{9} = 1$

31. a.   **b.** $(60, 30)$
c. $(x-60)^2 = 120y$
d. 7.5 m

5.6 Exercise Set A (p. 202)

1. $(-2.87, 3.87)$, $(0.87, 0.13)$ **3.** $(0, 2)$, $(4.5, 4.25)$
5. $(6, 0)$ **9.** $(0, -1)$, $(3, 2)$ **11.** $(-4, -4)$, $(4, 4)$
13. no solution **15.** $\left(\dfrac{3}{11}, -\dfrac{27}{11}\right)$ **17.** $(1, 1)$, $(1, -1)$
19. $(-4, \pm 4\sqrt{2})$, $(2, \pm\sqrt{2})$ **21.** 466.6 ft by 466.8 ft; or 233.4 ft by 933.2 ft

5.6 Exercise Set B (p. 203)

1. $(-3.08, 8.08)$, $(3.08, 1.92)$ **3.** $(0.15, 0.61)$, $(3.50, 3.13)$ **5.** $(-2.60, -11.30)$, $(-8.40, -28.70)$
9. $(2, 0)$, $(1, -1)$ **11.** $(-6, -7)$
13. $(16 + 6\sqrt{7}, 6 + 2\sqrt{7})$, $(16 - 6\sqrt{7}, 6 - 2\sqrt{7})$
15. no solution **17.** $\left(\dfrac{9}{5}, \pm\dfrac{4\sqrt{6}}{5}\right)$
19. $(-2, 6)$, $(-1, 4)$ **21.** about 53.2 mi

5.7 Exercise Set A (p. 207)

1. $5\sqrt{2}$

3. $3\sqrt{2}$ **5.** $\sqrt{62}$

7.   **9.**

11.

13. plane;

15. sphere **17.** $x^2 + (y - 2)^2 + (z - 5)^2 = 25$

19. $(x + 1)^2 + (y + 7)^2 + (z + 2)^2 = 81$

21. a. length = 6; width = 5; height = 5

b. $SA = 148$ units^2; $V = 120$ units^3

c. (0, 0, 0), (0, 6, 0), (5, 6, 0), (5, 0, 0), (0, 0, 8), (0, 6, 8), (5, 6, 8), (5, 0, 8)

d.

5.7 Exercise Set B (p. 208)

1.

3. $\sqrt{113}$
$\sqrt{62}$

5. 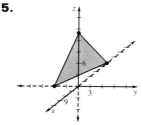 **7.**

9. $(x - 2)^2 + (y - 2)^2 + (z + 2)^2 = 36$

11. $(x - 15)^2 + (y + 1)^2 + (z - 6)^2 = 1.44$

13. $(x - 8)^2 + (y - 2.5)^2 + z^2 = 192$

15. $(x - 1)^2 + (y + 3)^2 + (z + 4)^2 = 25$; center: (1, −3, −4); radius: 5

17. $\left(x - \dfrac{1}{3}\right)^2 + (y + 1)^2 + z^2 = 1$;

center: $\left(\dfrac{1}{3}, -1, 0\right)$; radius: 1

19. 2250π ft^3

UNIT 6

6.1 Exercise Set A (p. 215)

1. continuous; Length of time is a random variable that has an infinite number of possible values, so it is uncountable.

3.

B	1	2	3
P(B)	0.3	0.4	0.3

 ; symmetric

5. about 0.00000894 **7.** about 0.0143

9. about 0.02667 **11.** about 0.2199

6.1 Exercise Set B (p. 216)

1.

C	red	blue	green	orange
P(C)	0.2	0.25	0.4	0.15

 ; skewed

3. 0.32 **5.** about 0.144 **7.** about 0.0000255

9. about 0.00000154 **11.** about 8.67×10^{-19}

13. about 0.997

15. 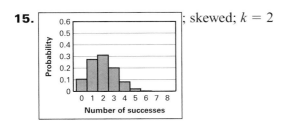 ; skewed; $k = 2$

17. 6

6.2 Exercise Set A (p. 221)

1. 84% **3.** 68% **5.** 5% **7.** 0.4985

9. 0.84 **11.** 0.84 **13.** 0.0107 **15.** 0.9821

17. 0.9990 **19.** 288

6.2 Exercise Set B (p. 222)

1. 97.5% **3.** 97.35% **5.** 27.3% **7.** 0.8385

9. 0.16 **11.** 0.975 **13.** 0.0002 **15.** 0.2743

17. 0.9918 **19.** 0.0642 **21.** 192 **23.** John; In a standard normal distribution, John's time is lower which is better when running a mile.

6.3 Exercise Set A (p. 226)

1. 12; about 2.7 **3.** 12.6; about 3.0

5. 14.4; about 3.4 **7.** The value of n should be 220, not 50. So, $\bar{x} = 44$ and $\sigma \approx 6$. **9.** about 0.16

11. 0.16 **13.** 0.9735 **15.** about 0.975

17. Yes; $P(x \leq 11) \approx P(z \leq -2.3) \approx 0.0107$, which is less than 0.05.

6.3 Exercise Set B (p. 227)

1. 37; about 4.8 **3.** 112.5; about 5.3

5. 2.4; about 1.5 **7.** about 0.84 **9.** about 0.475

11. about 0.025 **13.** about 0.68

15. Yes; $P(x \geq 15) \approx 1 - P(z \leq 3.2) \approx 1 - 0.9993 = 0.0007$, which is less than 0.05.

6.4 Exercise Set A (p. 230)

1. convenience; biased; The sample is not representative of the population. **3.** random; biased; People at the mall are more likely to attend the mall than people in the community in general.

5. ±6.3% **7.** ±2.6% **9.** ±4.1% **11.** ±1.6%

13. 400 **15.** 15,625

17. a. 700

b.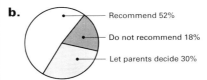

Recommend 52%

Do not recommend 18%

Let parents decide 30%

c. ±3.8%; between 48.2% and 55.8%

6.4 Exercise Set B (p. 231)

1. self-selected; unbiased; People visiting the league website would not be biased toward any one particular player. **3.** random; unbiased; Selecting customers at random would eliminate bias.

5. ±3.9% **7.** ±3.6% **9.** ±2.0% **11.** ±1.1%

13. 1890 **15.** 730 **17.** 1189 **19.** 27,778

21. between 62.2% and 65.8%

23. between 560 and 720 people

6.5 Exercise Set A (p. 235)

1. Experimental study; The professor is assigning individuals to the control group and the experimental group.

3. Observational study; The assignments of the patients to the experimental group and the control group are outside the doctor's control.

5. *Sample answer:* The approval rating of the registered voters in the same party as the mayor is likely to be higher than that of the registered voters in a different party from the mayor. To correct the flaw, the company should redesign the experiment so that the political affiliations in both groups are similar.

6.5 Exercise Set B (p. 236)

1. Observational study; The assignments of the students to the experimental group and the control group are outside of the teacher's control.

3. Experimental study; The manager is assigning employees to the control group and the experimental group.

5. *Sample answer:* The mathematical knowledge of the students enrolled as math majors is likely to be higher than that of the mathematical knowledge of students enrolled in other majors. To correct the flaw, the company should redesign the experiment so that the mathematical backgrounds in both groups are similar.

Additional Answers

UNIT 1

1.1 Guided Practice (pp. 2–3)

5. $x + (x + 16) = 50$; 17 in.

6. 18 in.

1.1 Exercise Set B (p. 5)

5.

$3x + 24 = 84$; 20 in., 28 in., 36 in.

7.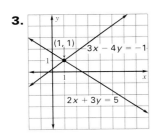

$8x + 10 = 24$; $x = 1.75$; So the paintings should be 1.75 feet apart and the spaces on the left and right should be 3.5 feet.

1.2 Guided Practice (pp. 6–7)

1.   **2.**

3.

1.2 Exercise Set A (pp. 8–9)

4.   **5.**

$(4, 0)$ $(-3, 1)$

6.   **7.**

$(2, -1)$ $(0, 3)$

8.   **9.**

$(-1, -2)$ $(3, 4)$

10.   **11.**

$(2, -1)$ $(-3, -2)$

12.   **13.**

$(-1, 4)$ $(-1, 2)$

14.   **15.**

$(3, 4)$ $(-5, 4)$

16. The solution was not checked in the second equation; $1 + 4(-2) = -5, -7 \neq -5, (1, -2)$ is not a solution of the system.

20. infinitely many solutions; consistent and dependent **21.** infinitely many solutions; consistent and dependent **22.** $(4, 5)$; consistent and independent **23.** $(3, 0)$; consistent and independent **24.** $(-4, 4)$; consistent and independent **25.** $(2, -1)$; consistent and independent **26.** infinitely many solutions; consistent and dependent **27.** $(2, 6)$; consistent and independent **28.** $(1, 4)$; consistent and independent

32. a. $y = 50x + 800$, where x represents the number of years, and y represents the cost; $y = 40x + 1300$, where x represents the number of years, and y represents the cost.

b. 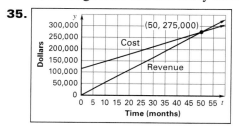 ; 50 years

c. No, a refrigerator will not likely last 50 years.

35.

1.2 Exercise Set B (pp. 10–11)

1.

$(1, 3)$

2.

$(2, -1)$

3.

$(-1, -4)$

4.

$(-2, 5)$

5.

$\left(\dfrac{1}{2}, 0\right)$

6.

$\left(2, -\dfrac{1}{3}\right)$

7.

$\left(\dfrac{1}{4}, \dfrac{1}{2}\right)$

8.

$\left(-\dfrac{2}{3}, \dfrac{3}{4}\right)$

9.

$\left(\dfrac{1}{3}, \dfrac{3}{2}\right)$

10.

infinitely many solutions

11.

infinitely many solutions

12.

$\left(\dfrac{1}{2}, \dfrac{1}{3}\right)$

13. $(3, 1)$; consistent and independent

14. $(-2, -1)$; consistent and independent

15. $(1, -4)$; consistent and independent

16. $\left(-\dfrac{5}{2}, 3\right)$; consistent and independent

17. $\left(\dfrac{4}{5}, -\dfrac{13}{5}\right)$; consistent and independent

18. no solution; inconsistent

19. infinitely many solutions; consistent and dependent

20. $\left(-\dfrac{2}{5}, -\dfrac{8}{5}\right)$; consistent and independent

21. $\left(-\dfrac{16}{5}, \dfrac{7}{5}\right)$; consistent and independent

25.

no solution

26.

(2, 2)

27.

(1.5, 0.5)

28.

no solution

29.

(10, 5) and (−10, 5)

30.

(0, 3)

33. a. $y = 90.25x + 756$, where x represents the number of years, and y represents the cost; $y = 48.50x + 1424$, where x represents the number of years, and y represents the cost

b. ; 16 years

c. Yes, a washer can last 16 years.

35.

39.

1.3 Investigating Math Activity (p. 12)

1.

no solutions

2.

infinite number of solutions

3.

infinite number of solutions

4. parallel; In the Explore, if you multiply the coefficients of x and y by 3 in the first equation, the result will be the coefficients of x and y in the second equation. In Exercise 1, if you multiply the coefficients of x and y by 4 in the first equation, the result will be the coefficients of x and y in the second equation. There is no relationship between the constants.

5. coinciding lines; In Exercise 2, if you multiply the first equation by 2, the result will be the second equation. In Exercise 3, if you multiply the first equation by −1.5, the result will be the second equation.

6. A linear system of parallel lines has no solution. A linear system of coinciding lines has an infinite number of solutions.

1.4 Guided Practice (pp. 17–18)

3.

4.

5.

6.

(5, 6)
(6, 5)
(9, 4)

7.

8.

9.

1.4 Exercise Set A (pp. 19–20)

10.

11.

12.

13.

14.

15.

16.

17.

18.

19.

20.

21.

22. The boundary line should be a dashed line.

23. The other side of the boundary line should be shaded.

26.

27.

28.

29. $20x + 10y \geq 1500$

31. $25x + 20y \leq 550$

34. a. $12x + 30y \leq 140$;

b. *Sample answer:* 2 days canoeing and 3 days biking, 3 days canoeing and 3 days biking, 4 days canoeing and 2 days biking

c. $12x + 30y \leq 113$; *Sample answer:* 2 days canoeing and 2 days biking, 3 days canoeing and 2 days biking, 5 days canoeing and 1 day biking

1.4 Exercise Set B (pp. 21–22)

8.

9.

10.

11.

12.

13.

14.

15.

16.

17.

18.

19.

20. The boundary line should be a dashed line.

21. The other side of the boundary line should be shaded.

27.

30. $c < 5t + 10$

1.5 Guided Practice (pp. 23–24)

1.

2.

3.

4.

5.

6.

7.

8.

9.

10.

11.

12.

1.5 Exercise Set A (pp. 25–26)

4. The shading of the second inequality is incorrect.

5.

6.

7.

8.

9.

10.

11.

12.

13.

14.

15.

16.

17.

18.

19.

27. a. $x + y \le 24$, $7x + 6.5y \ge 100$

b.

c. *Sample answer:* 7 hours babysitting and 11 hours at the grocery store, 9 hours babysitting and 9 hours at the grocery store, 5 hours babysitting and 14 hours at the grocery store

28. a. $x \ge 4$, $y \ge 4$, $x + y \le 12$, $x + y \ge 9$

b.

c. *Sample answer:* 4 juniors, 6 seniors; 5 juniors, 5 seniors

1.5 Exercise Set B (pp. 27–28)

4.

5.

6.

7.

8.

9.

10.

11.

12.

13.

14.

15.

20. $x \le 5$
$y \ge -1$
$x \le 2$
$x \ge -2$

21. $y \le 4$
$y \ge -x - 2$
$y \ge x - 2$

22. $y < \frac{1}{2}x + \frac{3}{2}$
$y < -2x + 4$
$y > -\frac{1}{3}x - 1$

25.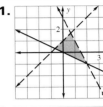
$x \ge 0$, $x \le 17$, $y \ge 18$, $y \le 40$

26. a. $x \ge 15$
$y \le 0.8x$
$y \ge 0.5x$

b.

c. $22.50 to $36.00

27. a. $x \geq 20$, $x \leq 65$, $y \geq 0.5(220 - x)$, $y \leq 0.75(220 - x)$

b.

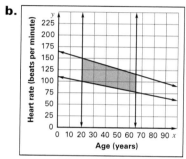

c. No, the person's heart rate is above the recommended range. A 36-year old person's heart rate should be between 92 and 138 heartbeats per minute.

28. $x \geq 500$, $y \geq 500$, $|y - 1000| > |x - 1000|$;

1.5 Problem Solving Workshop (p. 29)

1. $x \geq 100$, $x \leq 330$, $y \geq 0.65x$, $y \leq 0.9x$;

; from $130 to $180, inclusive

2. $2\ell + 2w \leq 500$, $\ell > 50$, $w > 25$;

; $25 \text{ ft} < w \leq 130 \text{ ft}$

1.6 Exercise Set B (p. 33)

7. The graph should have a vertex at (3, 2), not (4, 2). The maximum value of C is 74. It occurs when $x = 2$ and $y = 14$.

1.8 Exercise Set A (p. 41)

1. $\begin{bmatrix} 4 & 0 \\ 10 & 4 \end{bmatrix}$ **2.** $\begin{bmatrix} 3 & 6 \\ 5 & 2 \\ 4 & 1 \end{bmatrix}$ **3.** $\begin{bmatrix} 2 & -1 & 7 \\ -4 & -4 & 2 \\ 2 & 3 & -6 \end{bmatrix}$

4. Not possible because the matrices do not have the same dimensions.

5. $\begin{bmatrix} 3 & 9 & 13 \\ 2 & 0 & -4 \\ 10 & 3 & 9 \end{bmatrix}$ **6.** $\begin{bmatrix} 11 & -4 & 6 \\ 7 & -10 & -6 \\ -1 & 2 & -12 \end{bmatrix}$

7. $\begin{bmatrix} -12 & -6 \\ -9 & -6 \end{bmatrix}$ **8.** $\begin{bmatrix} -6 & 0 & 2 \\ -1 & 12 & -8 \\ -14 & 2.5 & -18 \end{bmatrix}$

9. $\begin{bmatrix} -16 & -4 \\ 20 & 0 \\ -4 & 12 \end{bmatrix}$

1.8 Exercise Set B (p. 42)

1. $\begin{bmatrix} 5 & -2 \\ 4 & 8 \end{bmatrix}$ **2.** $\begin{bmatrix} 15 & 17 \\ 5 & -6 \\ 2 & 22 \end{bmatrix}$ **3.** $\begin{bmatrix} -4 & -20 \\ 6 & -18 \end{bmatrix}$

4. Not possible because the matrices do not have the same dimensions.

5. $\begin{bmatrix} 1 \\ 1 \end{bmatrix}$

6. Not possible because the matrices do not have the same dimensions.

7. $\begin{bmatrix} \frac{5}{3} & 0 & 2 \\ \frac{4}{3} & 3 & 2 \\ \frac{19}{3} & \frac{26}{3} & 2 \end{bmatrix}$ **8.** $\begin{bmatrix} 0 & -4 \\ 1 & 6 \end{bmatrix}$

9. $\begin{bmatrix} -4 & 18 \\ 33 & -20 \\ -1 & -24 \end{bmatrix}$ **10.** $\begin{bmatrix} -\frac{19}{2} & \frac{9}{4} \\ -\frac{7}{2} & -\frac{45}{4} \end{bmatrix}$

1.9 Exercise Set B (p. 47)

1. $\begin{bmatrix} -2 & 6 \\ -2 & -1 \\ 9 & 8 \end{bmatrix}$

2. The matrices cannot be multiplied because the number of columns in $\begin{bmatrix} 3 & -1 & 0 \\ 2 & 5 & -4 \end{bmatrix}$ does not equal the number of rows in $\begin{bmatrix} 1 & 0 \\ 0 & 1 \end{bmatrix}$.

3. $\begin{bmatrix} 1 & 2 \\ -17 & 12 \\ -9 & 5 \end{bmatrix}$ **4.** $\begin{bmatrix} -4 & -6 & 6 \\ -2 & -3 & 1 \\ 6 & 9 & -3 \\ 8 & 12 & -4 \end{bmatrix}$

5. $\begin{bmatrix} -4 & -8 \\ -2 & 3 \end{bmatrix}$ **6.** $\begin{bmatrix} 4 & 7 \\ 1 & -\frac{1}{2} \\ 3 & \frac{13}{2} \end{bmatrix}$ **7.** $\begin{bmatrix} -1 & -21 \\ 2 & 6 \\ -2 & -22 \end{bmatrix}$

8. $\begin{bmatrix} -2 & 3 \\ 35 & -14 \\ 13 & -8 \end{bmatrix}$ **9.** $\begin{bmatrix} 14 & 35 \\ 8 & 2 \\ 8 & 30 \end{bmatrix}$

10. $\begin{bmatrix} -35 & -17 \\ 30 & 22 \\ 5 & 1 \end{bmatrix}$

1.9 Technology Activity (p. 48)

1. $\begin{bmatrix} 3 & -4 \\ 9 & 0 \end{bmatrix}$ **2.** $\begin{bmatrix} 40.6 & 27.3 & -14.7 \\ -2.1 & 18.9 & -7.35 \end{bmatrix}$

3. $\begin{bmatrix} -4 & 19 & 14 \\ -12 & -1 & -7 \\ 7 & 2 & 2 \end{bmatrix}$ **4.** $\begin{bmatrix} -6 & -8 \\ 50 & -10 \\ 2 & -62 \end{bmatrix}$

1.11 Guided Practice (pp. 54–56)

4. $\begin{bmatrix} 16 & 4 \\ -10 & 0 \end{bmatrix}$ **5.** $\begin{bmatrix} 3 & 5 \\ -2 & -3 \end{bmatrix}$ **6.** $\begin{bmatrix} -12 & -9 \\ 27 & 20 \end{bmatrix}$

1.11 Exercise Set A (p. 57)

17. a. $x + y + z = 1011$
$x + 2y + 3z = 1669$
$x - y = -305$

b. $\begin{bmatrix} 1 & 1 & 1 \\ 1 & 2 & 3 \\ 1 & -1 & 0 \end{bmatrix} \begin{bmatrix} x \\ y \\ z \end{bmatrix} = \begin{bmatrix} 1011 \\ 1669 \\ -305 \end{bmatrix}$

c. 1-point: 353, 2-point: 658, 3-point: 0

1.11 Exercise Set B (p. 58)

4. $\begin{bmatrix} -0.1 & 0.5 & 0.2 \\ 0.05 & 0.25 & -0.1 \\ 0.6 & -1 & -0.2 \end{bmatrix}$

5. $\begin{bmatrix} -0.2\overline{2} & 0.2\overline{7} & 0.8\overline{8} \\ -0.1\overline{1} & -0.1\overline{1} & 0.4\overline{4} \\ 0.1\overline{1} & 0.1\overline{1} & 0.5\overline{5} \end{bmatrix}$

6. $\begin{bmatrix} 0.05 & 0.3 & -0.1 \\ -0.15 & 0.1 & 0.3 \\ 0.75 & -0.5 & -0.5 \end{bmatrix}$

16. a. $x + y + z = 500{,}000$
$x - 8y = 0$
$0.2x + 0.2y - z = 0$

b. $\begin{bmatrix} 1 & 1 & 1 \\ 1 & -8 & 0 \\ 0.2 & 0.2 & -1 \end{bmatrix} \begin{bmatrix} x \\ y \\ z \end{bmatrix} = \begin{bmatrix} 500{,}000 \\ 0 \\ 0 \end{bmatrix}$

c. salaries: \$370,370.37, insurance: \$46,296.30, general expenses: \$83,333.33

1.12 Guided Practice (pp. 59–60)

1. *Sample answer:*

2. $\begin{bmatrix} 0 & 3 & 2 & 0 \\ 3 & 0 & 0 & 2 \\ 2 & 0 & 0 & 1 \\ 0 & 2 & 1 & 0 \end{bmatrix}$; number of ways you can fly from one city to another using exactly three flights

3. There is a 0 in the first row, first column of A because there would not be a flight leaving Bedford for Bedford. There is a 2 in the first row, first column of A^2 because there are exactly 2 two-flight trips that would land you back in Bedford. You could fly from Bedford to Columbia and back, or you could fly from Bedford to Dunwich and back.

1.12 Exercise Set A (p. 61)

10. *Sample answer:*

11. *Sample answer:*

12. *Sample answer:*

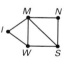

1.12 Exercise Set B (p. 62)

7.

	R	S	T	U	V
R	0	2	0	0	1
S	2	0	0	1	2
T	0	0	0	2	0
U	0	1	2	0	1
V	1	2	0	1	0

8.

	R	S	T	U	V
R	5	2	0	3	4
S	2	9	2	2	3
T	0	2	4	0	2
U	3	2	0	6	2
V	4	3	2	2	6

10. *Sample answer:*

11. *Sample answer:*

12. *Sample answer:*

Unit Test 1 (pp. 63–64)

5.

6.

7.

8.

9.

10.

15. $\begin{bmatrix} -1 & 7 \\ 2 & -3 \end{bmatrix}$ **16.** $\begin{bmatrix} 10 & -9 & 11 \\ 9 & -10 & 6 \\ -1 & -7 & -15 \end{bmatrix}$

17. $\begin{bmatrix} 16 & -21 \\ 43 & -35 \end{bmatrix}$ **18.** $\begin{bmatrix} 41 & -56 \\ 101 & -98 \end{bmatrix}$

27. $x \geq 3, y \geq 3, x + y \geq 7, x + y \leq 10$

Two possible solutions: 4 juniors, 5 seniors; 5 juniors, 5 seniors

30. *Sample answer:*

Performance Task (p. 64)

a. **Total Number Shipped (M)**

	M	M/P	M/P/V
Warehouse 1	27,000	32,000	18,000
Warehouse 2	24,000	28,000	15,000

b. $\begin{bmatrix} 13{,}500 & 16{,}000 & 9000 \\ 12{,}000 & 14{,}000 & 7500 \end{bmatrix}$;
the average number of units shipped to each warehouse over the two months

c. **Total Value Shipped**

Warehouse 1	12,959,230
Warehouse 2	11,189,330

d. $x + y + z = 64$
$99.99x + 179.99y + 249.99z = 9339.36$
$x = 2y$
36 music only, 18 music/photo, 10 music/photo/video

UNIT 2

2.1 Guided Practice (pp. 67–68)

1. not a polynomial; The leading coefficient is not a real number.   **2.** not a polynomial; The term x^{-1} has an exponent that is not a whole number.

3. is a polynomial already in standard form with degree 2 and leading coefficient of 3π **4.** -30

5. $f(x) \to +\infty$ as $x \to -\infty$; $f(x) \to +\infty$ as $x \to +\infty$ **6.** $f(x) \to -\infty$ as $x \to -\infty$; $f(x) \to +\infty$ as $x \to +\infty$

7.

The domain is all real numbers and the range is all real numbers. The degree is odd and the leading coefficient is positive. The graph has origin symmetry. The graph increases for about $x < -0.5$ and $x > 1.25$. The graph decreases for about $-0.5 < x < 1.25$.

2.1 Exercise Set A (p. 69)

11. even; The graph is symmetric with respect to the y-axis.   **12.** odd; The graph is symmetric with respect to the origin.   **13.** odd; The graph is symmetric with respect to the origin.

14.

15.

16.

17. a.

b. domain: all real numbers; range: all real numbers

c. degree: 3; leading coefficient: -1

d. origin symmetry   **e.** decreasing over all real numbers

18. a.

b. domain: all real numbers; range: $y \geq 1$
c. degree: 4; leading coefficient: -1 **d.** y-axis symmetry   **e.** increasing for $x > 0$; decreasing for $x < 0$

19. a.

b. domain: all real numbers; range: all real numbers
c. degree: 3; leading coefficient: 3 **d.** no symmetry
e. increasing for $x < -2$ and $x > 2$; decreasing for $-2 < x < 2$

20. a.

Years since 1986

b. 1996

c. about 5715 million ft²; *Sample answer:* No. The function starts to decrease after 2007, and the amount of retail space will probably continue to increase over time.

2.1 Exercise Set B (p. 70)

8. even; The graph is symmetric with respect to the *y*-axis. **9.** odd; The graph is symmetric with respect to the origin. **10.** even; The graph is symmetric with respect to the *y*-axis.

11.   **12.**

13.

14. a.

b. domain: all real numbers; range: $y \le 9$
c. degree: 4; leading coefficient: -1
d. *y*-axis symmetry

e. increasing for $x < -1.7$ and $0 < x < 1.7$; decreasing for $-1.7 < x < 0$ and $x > 1.7$

15. a.

b. domain: all real numbers; range: $y \ge 6$
c. degree: 4; leading coefficient: 2 **d.** *y*-axis symmetry **e.** increasing for about $-1 < x < 0$ and $x > 1$; decreasing for about $x < -1$ and $0 < x < 1$

16. a.

b. domain: all real numbers; range: all real numbers
c. degree: 3; leading coefficient: -1 **d.** no symmetry
e. increasing for about $0.5 < x < 1.5$; decreasing for about $x < 0.5$ and $x > 1.5$

18. a. about 6 in.

b.

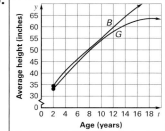
Age (years)

c. *Sample answer:* Female; According to the models, the average 14-year-old male is about 64 inches, and the average 14-year-old female is about 61 inches. Because 60 inches is closer to 61 inches than to 64 inches, it is more likely the 14-year-old is female.

2.2 Guided Practice (pp. 72–73)

1.

The graph of g is the graph of f translated up
1 unit; the domains and ranges of both functions
are all real numbers; f has x- and y-intercepts of 0
and g has an x-intercept of −1 and a y-intercept of
1; f is odd and symmetric with respect to the origin
and g is neither even nor odd and has no symmetry.

2.

The graph of g is the graph of f translated down
4 units; the domains and ranges of both functions
are all real numbers; f has x- and y-intercepts
of 0 and g has an x-intercept of about 1.5 and a
y-intercept of −4; f is odd and symmetric with
respect to the origin and g is neither even nor odd
and has no symmetry.

3.

The graph of g is the graph of f translated down
3 units; the domain of f and g is all real numbers
and the range of f is y ≥ 0 and the range of g is
y ≥ −3; f has x- and y-intercepts of 0 and g has
x-intercepts of about −1.3 and 1.3 and a y-intercept
of −3; f and g are even and symmetric with respect
to the y-axis.

4.

The graph of g is the graph of f translated up
2 units; the domain of f and g is all real numbers
and the range of f is y ≥ 0 and the range of g is
y ≥ 2; f has x- and y-intercepts of 0 and g has a
y-intercept of 2; f and g are even and symmetric
with respect to the y-axis.

5.

The graph of g is the graph of f translated to the
right 1 unit; the domains and ranges of both
functions are all real numbers; f has x- and
y-intercepts of 0 and g has an x-intercept of 1 and
a y-intercept of −1; f is odd and symmetric with
respect to the origin and g is neither even nor odd
and has no symmetry.

6.

The graph of g is the graph of f translated to the
left 4 units; the domain of f and g is all real
numbers and the range of f and g is y ≥ 0; f has
x- and y-intercepts of 0 and g has an x-intercept
of −4 and a y-intercept of 256; f is even and
symmetric with respect to the y-axis and g is
neither even nor odd and has no symmetry.

7.

The graph of *g* is the graph of *f* translated to the right 3 units; the domain of *f* and *g* is all real numbers and the range of *f* and *g* is $y \geq 0$; *f* has *x*- and *y*-intercepts of 0 and *g* has an *x*-intercept of 3 and a *y*-intercept of 243; *f* is even and symmetric with respect to the *y*-axis and *g* is neither even nor odd and has no symmetry.

8.

The graph of *g* is the graph of *f* translated to the left 2 units; the domains and ranges of both function are all real numbers; *f* has *x*- and *y*-intercepts of 0 and *g* has an *x*-intercept of −2 and a *y*-intercept of 4; *f* is odd and symmetric with respect to the origin and *g* is neither even nor odd and has no symmetry.

9.

The graph of *g* is the graph of *f* translated to the left 4 units and down 2 units; the domains and ranges of both function are all real numbers; *f* has *x*- and *y*-intercepts of 0 and *g* has an *x*-intercept of about −2.7 and a *y*-intercept of 62; *f* is odd and symmetric with respect to the origin and *g* is neither even nor odd and has no symmetry.

10.

The graph of *g* is the graph of *f* translated to the right 1 unit and up 3 units; the domains and ranges of both function are all real numbers; *f* has *x*- and *y*-intercepts of 0 and *g* has an *x*-intercept of about 2.3 and a *y*-intercept of 4.5; *f* is odd and symmetric with respect to the origin and *g* is neither even nor odd and has no symmetry.

11.

The graph of *g* is the graph of *f* translated to the right 2 units and up 1 unit; the domain of *f* and *g* is all real numbers and the range of *f* is $y \leq 0$ and the range of *g* is $y \leq 1$; *f* has *x*- and *y*-intercepts of 0 and *g* has *x*-intercepts of 1 and 3 and a *y*-intercept of −15; *f* is even and symmetric with respect to the *y*-axis and *g* is neither even nor odd and has no symmetry.

12.

The graph of *g* is the graph of *f* translated to the left 2 units and down 2 units; the domain of *f* and *g* is all real numbers and the range of *f* is $y \geq 0$ and the range of *g* is $y \geq -2$; *f* has *x*- and *y*-intercepts of 0 and *g* has *x*-intercepts of about −3.3 and −0.7 and a *y*-intercept of $\frac{26}{3}$; *f* is even and symmetric with respect to the *y*-axis and *g* is neither even nor odd and has no symmetry.

2.2 Exercise Set A (p. 74)

6.

The graph of g is the graph of f translated down 1 unit; the domains and ranges of both functions are all real numbers; f has x- and y-intercepts of 0 and g has an x-intercept of 1 and a y-intercept of −1; f is odd and symmetric with respect to the origin and g is neither even nor odd and has no symmetry.

7.

The graph of g is the graph of f translated up 2 units; the domains and ranges of both functions are all real numbers; f has x- and y-intercepts of 0 and g has an x-intercept of about −1.3 and a y-intercept of 2; f is odd and symmetric with respect to the origin and g is neither even nor odd and has no symmetry.

8.

The graph of g is the graph of f translated to the right 4 units; the domains and ranges of both functions are all real numbers; f has x- and y-intercepts of 0 and g has an x-intercept of 4 and a y-intercept of −64; f is odd and symmetric with respect to the origin and g is neither even nor odd and has no symmetry.

9.

The graph of g is the graph of f translated up 3 units; the domains and ranges of both functions are all real numbers; f has x- and y-intercepts of 0 and g has an x-intercept of about 1.1 and a y-intercept of 3; f is odd and symmetric with respect to the origin and g is neither even nor odd and has no symmetry.

10.

The graph of g is the graph of f translated to the right 1 unit; the domains and ranges of both functions are all real numbers; f has x- and y-intercepts of 0 and g has an x-intercept of 1 and a y-intercept of 2; f is odd and symmetric with respect to the origin and g is neither even nor odd and has no symmetry.

11.

The graph of g is the graph of f translated to the left 2 units and up 4 units; the domains and ranges of both functions are all real numbers; f has x- and y-intercepts of 0 and g has an x-intercept of about −0.75 and a y-intercept of −12; f is odd and symmetric with respect to the origin and g is neither even nor odd and has no symmetry.

12.

The graph of g is the graph of f translated to the left 1 unit; the domain of f and g is all real numbers and the range of f and g is $y \geq 0$; f has x- and y-intercepts of 0 and g has an x-intercept of -1 and a y-intercept of 1; f is even and symmetric with respect to the y-axis and g is neither even nor odd and has no symmetry.

13.

The graph of g is the graph of f translated down 5 units; the domain of f and g is all real numbers and the range of f is $y \geq 0$ and the range of g is $y \geq -5$; f has x- and y-intercepts of 0 and g has x-intercepts of about -1.5 and 1.5 and a y-intercept of -5; f and g are even and symmetric with respect to the y-axis.

14.

The graph of g is the graph of f translated to the right 3 units; the domain of f and g is all real numbers and the range of f and g is $y \geq 0$; f has x- and y-intercepts of 0 and g has an x-intercept of 3 and a y-intercept of 81; f is even and symmetric with respect to the y-axis and g is neither even nor odd and has no symmetry.

15.

The graph of g is the graph of f translated down 2 units; the domain of f and g is all real numbers and the range of f is $y \geq 0$ and the range of g is $y \geq -2$; f has x- and y-intercepts of 0 and g has x-intercepts of about -1.6 and 1.6 and a y-intercept of -2; f and g are even and symmetric with respect to the y-axis.

16.

The graph of g is the graph of f translated to the left 3 units; the domain of f and g is all real numbers and the range of f and g is $y \geq 0$; f has x- and y-intercepts of 0 and g has an x-intercept of -3 and a y-intercept of 27; f is even and symmetric with respect to the y-axis and g is neither even nor odd and has no symmetry.

17.

The graph of g is the graph of f translated to the right 1 unit and up 1 unit; the domain of f and g is all real numbers and the range of f is $y \geq 0$ and the range of g is $y \geq 1$; f has x- and y-intercepts of 0 and g has a y-intercept of $\frac{4}{3}$; f is even and symmetric with respect to the y-axis and g is neither even nor odd and has no symmetry.

20. a.

The graph of V_2 is the graph of V_1 translated to the left 2 units.

b. $V_1 = 216 \text{ ft}^3$; $V_2 = 512 \text{ ft}^3$

2.2 Exercise Set B (p. 75)

1. The graph of g is the graph of f translated down 7 units.   **2.** The graph of g is the graph of f translated to the left 6 units.   **3.** The graph of g is the graph of f translated to the left 3 units and down 1 unit.

4. the graph of g is the graph of f translated to the right 1 unit and up 0.5 unit.

5.

The graph of g is the graph of f translated up 4 units; the domains and ranges of both functions are all real numbers; f has x- and y-intercepts of 0 and g has an x-intercept of about 1.6 and a y-intercept of 4; f is odd and symmetric with respect to the origin and g is neither even nor odd and has no symmetry.

6.

The graph of g is the graph of f translated to the left 2 units; the domains and ranges of both functions are all real numbers; f has x- and y-intercepts of 0 and g has an x-intercept of -2 and a y-intercept of -8; f is odd and symmetric with respect to the origin and g is neither even nor odd and has no symmetry.

7.

The graph of g is the graph of f translated to the right 5 units and up 1 unit; the domains and ranges of both functions are all real numbers; f has x- and y-intercepts of 0 and g has an x-intercept of 6 and a y-intercept of 126; f is odd and symmetric with respect to the origin and g is neither even nor odd and has no symmetry.

8.

The graph of g is the graph of f translated down 2 units; the domains and ranges of both functions are all real numbers; f has x- and y-intercepts of 0 and g has an x-intercept of about 1.1 and a y-intercept of -2; f is odd and symmetric with respect to the origin and g is neither even nor odd and has no symmetry.

9.

The graph of g is the graph of f translated to the right 4 units; the domains and ranges of both functions are all real numbers; f has x- and y-intercepts of 0 and g has an x-intercept of 4 and a y-intercept of -96; f is odd and symmetric with respect to the origin and g is neither even nor odd and has no symmetry.

10.

The graph of g is the graph of f translated to the left 1 unit and down 3 units; the domains and ranges of both functions are all real numbers; f has x- and y-intercepts of 0 and g has an x-intercept of about −0.25 and a y-intercept of −1.5; f is odd and symmetric with respect to the origin and g is neither even nor odd and has no symmetry.

11.

The graph of g is the graph of f translated to the right 3 units; the domain of f and g is all real numbers and the range of f and g is y ≥ 0; f has x- and y-intercepts of 0 and g has an x-intercept of 3 and a y-intercept of 81; f is even and symmetric with respect to the y-axis and g is neither even nor odd and has no symmetry.

12.

The graph of g is the graph of f translated up 4 units; the domain of f and g is all real numbers and the range of f is y ≥ 0 and the range of g is y ≥ 4; f has x- and y-intercepts of 0 and g has a y-intercept of 4; f and g are even and symmetric with respect to the y-axis.

13.

The graph of g is the graph of f translated to the left 3 units and down 5 units; the domain of f and g is all real numbers and the range of f is y ≥ 0 and the range of g is y ≥ −5; f has x- and y-intercepts of 0 and g has x-intercepts of about −4.5 and −1.5 and a y-intercept of 76; f is even and symmetric with respect to the y-axis and g is neither even nor odd and has no symmetry.

14.

The graph of g is the graph of f translated up 1 unit; the domain of f and g is all real numbers and the range of f is y ≥ 0 and the range of g is y ≥ 1; f has x- and y-intercepts of 0 and g has a y-intercept of 1; f and g are even and symmetric with respect to the y-axis.

15.

The graph of g is the graph of f translated to the right 6 units; the domain of f and g is all real numbers and the range of f and g is y ≥ 0; f has x- and y-intercepts of 0 and g has an x-intercept of 6 and a y-intercept of 648; f is even and symmetric with respect to the y-axis and g is neither even nor odd and has no symmetry.

16.

The graph of g is the graph of f translated to the right 2 units and up 3 units; the domain of f and g is all real numbers and the range of f is $y \geq 0$ and the range of g is $y \geq 3$; f has x- and y-intercepts of 0 and g has a y-intercept of 11; f is even and symmetric with respect to the y-axis and g is neither even nor odd and has no symmetry.

17. The student described the direction of the translation incorrectly. The graph of $g(x) = -2(x - 5)^3 + 4$ is the graph of $f(x) = -2x^3$ translated right 5 units and up 4 units.

20. a. $V_2 = \frac{4}{3}\pi(r + 1)^3$

b.

c. The graph of V_2 is the graph of V_1 translated to the left 1 unit. **d.** $V_1 \approx 381.7$ in.^{3}; $V_2 \approx 696.9$ in.^{3}

2.3 Guided Practice (p. 77)

1. $7x^2(x - 2)(x^2 + 2x + 4)$

2. $2(4y^2 + 1)(16y^4 - 4y^2 + 1)$

3. $(x + 2)(x - 2)(x - 3)$

4. $(y - 3)(y + 3)(y + 7)$ **5.** $3b^2(b^2 + 1)^2$

6. $(z^4 + 4)(z^2 + 2)(z^2 - 2)$

2.4 Guided Practice (pp. 81–82)

1. $[-2, 0]$ and $[2, \infty]$ **2.** $\left[-\frac{2}{3}, 0\right]$, $[4, \infty)$

3. $(-\infty, -1)$ and $(1, 3)$

2.4 Exercise Set A (p. 83)

10. $(-2, -1)$ and $(2, \infty)$

11. $[-3, -1.4]$ and $[1.4, 3]$

12. $[-1.4, 1.4]$ **13.** $(-2.4, 0)$ and $(2.4, \infty)$

14. $(-\infty, -1]$ and $[0, 3]$ **15.** $(-\infty, 0]$ and $\left[\frac{2}{3}, \frac{5}{2}\right]$

16. $(-1.9, 1.9)$ **17.** $(-\infty, -0.5]$ and $[0.5, 8]$

18. $(-\infty, -1.9)$ and $(0.5, 1.6)$

2.4 Exercise Set B (p. 84)

1. $(-4, 2)$ and $(6, \infty)$ **2.** $[-6, 2]$

3. $\left[-2, -\frac{1}{2}\right]$ and $\left[\frac{1}{2}, 2\right]$

4. $(-\infty, -\sqrt{2})$ and $(0, \sqrt{2})$

5. $\left(-3, -\frac{3}{2}\right)$ and $(3, \infty)$

6. $(-\infty, -\sqrt{2})$, $[-1, 0]$, and $[\sqrt{2}, \infty)$

22. a. $M(x) - E(x) < 0$ or $-0.07x^3 - 0.04x^2 + 62.6x - 528 < 0$

b.

x	0	1	2
M(x) − E(x)	−528	−465.51	−403.52

x	3	4	5
M(x) − E(x)	−342.45	−282.72	−224.75

x	6	7	8
M(x) − E(x)	−168.96	−115.77	−65.6

x	9	10	11
M(x) − E(x)	−18.87	24	62.59

x	12	13	14
M(x) − E(x)	96.48	125.25	148.48

x	15
M(x) − E(x)	165.75

$[0, 9]$; The number of morning newspapers in the United States was less than the number of evening newspapers in the years 1990–1999. **c.** $[0, 9]$

2.5 Exercise Set A (p. 87)

7. $x + 3$ **8.** $x^2 - 2x + 6 + \dfrac{1}{x - 1}$

9. $x^3 + 2x^2 - 3x + 3 - \dfrac{4}{x - 2}$

10. $2x^3 - 3x^2 + 3x - 3 + \dfrac{7}{x + 1}$

11. $2x^3 - 5x^2 + 6$

12. $x^3 + x^2 + 7x + 9 + \dfrac{96}{x - 7}$

26. Answers may vary depending on rounding.

$A = 0.001x^2 + 0.0823x - 6.8943 + \dfrac{1909}{3x + 267}$

2.5 Exercise Set B (p. 88)

1. $2x^2 - 4x + 9 - \dfrac{28}{2x + 3}$

2. $5x^2 + 20 + \dfrac{8x + 71}{x^2 - 4}$

3. $2x - \dfrac{9}{x^3 + x^2 - 5}$

4. $8x^2 - 8x + 34 - \dfrac{70x - 111}{x^2 + x - 3}$

5. $x^3 + 2x^2 - 8x + 20 - \dfrac{56}{x + 3}$

6. $3x^3 + 9x^2 + 26x + 84 + \dfrac{252}{x - 3}$

7. $2x^2 + 5x - 1$

8. $3x^4 + 3x^3 + 5x^2 + 5x + \dfrac{1}{x - 1}$

13. $-\dfrac{5 - \sqrt{17}}{2}, -\dfrac{5 + \sqrt{17}}{2}$ **14.** $1 \pm i\sqrt{7}$

2.6 Guided Practice (p. 90)

7. $3 = \frac{1}{3}x^2(x - 2)$; $\pm 1, \pm 3, \pm 9$; When $x = 3$, the sides have length 3 and the height is 1.

2.6 Exercise Set A (p. 91)

1. $\pm 1, \pm 3, \pm 7, \pm 21$

2. $\pm 1, \pm 2, \pm 3, \pm 5, \pm 6, \pm 10, \pm 15, \pm 30,$ $\pm\frac{1}{2}, \pm\frac{3}{2}, \pm\frac{5}{2}, \pm\frac{15}{2}$

3. $\pm 1, \pm 2, \pm 5, \pm 10, \pm\frac{1}{5}, \pm\frac{2}{5}$

4. $\pm 1, \pm 2, \pm 4, \pm\frac{1}{9}, \pm\frac{2}{9}, \pm\frac{1}{3}, \pm\frac{4}{9}, \pm\frac{2}{3}, \pm\frac{4}{3}$

2.7 Guided Practice (p. 95)

6. positive: 1, negative: 2 or 0, imaginary: 0 or 2

7. positive: 1 or 3, negative: 1, imaginary: 2 or 0

2.7 Exercise Set A (p. 96)

17. The polynomial function should be written as a product of three factors because $2 - i$ must also be a zero by the complex conjugates theorem.

$f(x) = (x - 3)[x - (2 + i)][x - (2 - i)]$
$= (x - 3)(x^2 - 4x + 5)$
$= x^3 - 7x^2 + 17x - 15$

2.7 Exercise Set B (p. 97)

1. $-3, -1, 3$ **2.** $-1, 1, 2 + \sqrt{3}, 2 - \sqrt{3}$

3. $-2, 0, 2 + i\sqrt{3}, 2 - i\sqrt{3}$ **4.** $-4, -2, \frac{5}{2}, 4$

5. $-3, -1, 3, \frac{9}{2}$ **6.** $1, \dfrac{-3 \pm i\sqrt{19}}{2}$

7. $-i, i, -1 + \sqrt{2}, -1 - \sqrt{2}$

8. $1 + 4i, 1 - 4i, \sqrt{3}, -\sqrt{3}$

9. $f(x) = 2x^4 - 4x^3 - 32x^2 + 64x$

10. $f(x) = 2x^4 + 58x^2 + 200$

11. $f(x) = 2x^3 + 10x^2 - 6x - 30$

12. $f(x) = 2x^3 - 12x^2 + 50x$

13. $f(x) = 2x^4 - 22x^3 + 80x^2 - 116x + 56$

14. $f(x) = 2x^6 - 26x^5 + 120x^4 - 200x^3 + 118x^2 - 174x$

23. *Sample answer:* One zero is a repeated zero.

25. a. $R = -315t^5 + 5554t^4 + 1932t^3 - 709,619t^2 + 6,441,145t + 49,246,365$ **b.** 2001

2.8 Guided Practice (p. 99)

1. ; x-intercepts: $(-2, 0)$, $(4, 0)$; maximum: $(-2, 0)$, minimum: $(2, -16)$

2. ; *x*-intercepts: $(-3, 0)$, $(-1, 0)$; maximum: $(-2.33, 1.19)$, minimum: $(-1, 0)$

2.8 Exercise Set A (pp. 100–101)

12. zeros: 0 (multiplicity 2), -1; turning points: 2

13. zeros: -2 (multiplicity 2), 5; turning points: 2

14. zeros: 4 (multiplicity 3), 1; turning points: 3

15. zeros: -6 (multiplicity 2), $\frac{2}{3}$ (multiplicity 2); turning points: 3

16. zeros: 0, $-\frac{3}{4}$, 8 (multiplicity 2); turning points: 3

17. zeros: 0 (multiplicity 2), -4, $\frac{3}{2}$ (multiplicity 3); turning points: 5

18.   **19.**

20.   **21.**

22.   **23.**

24. $(-0.5, 0.5)$: max, $(0.3, -0.3)$: min; $-0.6, 0, 0.6$; 3

25. $(-2, 0)$: min, $(-0.5, 5)$: max, $(1, 0)$: min; $-2, 1$; 4

26. $(-2.8, 2.1)$: max, $(0, 0.25)$: min, $(2, 1)$: max; $-3.8, 2.8$; 4

27.

x-int: $-1.79, 0.11, 1.67$; max: $(-1, 7)$; min: $(1, -5)$

28.

x-int: $-2, 1$; max: $(1, 0)$; min: $\left(-1, -\frac{4}{3}\right)$

29.

x-int: $-2.83, 0, 2.83$; max: $(-2, 4)$, $(2, 4)$; min: $(0, 0)$

30.

x-int: $-1.73, 0, 1.73$; max: $(-1.73, 0)$, $(0.77, 4.46)$; min: $(-0.77, -4.46)$, $(1.73, 0)$

31.

x-int: $-2, -1, 0, 1, 2$; max: $(-1.64, 3.63)$, $(0.54, 1.42)$; min: $(-0.54, -1.42)$, $(1.64, -3.63)$

32.

x-int: -1.53, -0.35, 1.88, 2; max: $(0.61, 3.62)$;
min: $(-1.05, -3.03)$, $(1.94, -0.03)$

35. a.

b. $(25.33, 222.93)$; *Sample answer:* From 1970
to 1995, per capita egg consumption decreased to
about 223 eggs, then began to increase again.

36. a. $\ell = \dfrac{600}{\pi r} - r$ **b.** $V = 300r - 0.5\pi r^3$

c. 1596 ft^3; $r \approx 7.98$ ft, $\ell \approx 15.95$ ft

2.8 Exercise Set B (pp. 102–103)

3. zeros: -2 (multiplicity 2), 3, $\dfrac{9}{2}$; turning points: 3

4. zeros: -4 (multiplicity 2), $\dfrac{5}{3}$ (multiplicity 2);
turning points 3

5. zeros: 0 (multiplicity 3), -1 (multiplicity 2), 1;
turning points: 5

6. zeros: 0, -6, -3, $\dfrac{1}{2}$ (multiplicity 2);
turning points: 4

7. zeros: -3, -2, 2 (multiplicity 2);
turning points: 3

8. zeros: -2 (multiplicity 2), $-\dfrac{3}{2}$, 0, 1;
turning points: 4

9.

domain: $-\infty < x < \infty$
range: $-\infty < y < \infty$

10.

domain: $-\infty < x < \infty$
range: $-\infty < y < \infty$

11.

domain: $-\infty < x < \infty$
range: $y \geq -4.489$

12.

domain: $-\infty < x < \infty$
range: $y \leq 0.8$

13.

domain: $-\infty < x < \infty$
range: $-\infty < y < \infty$

14.

domain: $-\infty < x < \infty$
range: $-\infty < y < \infty$

15.

domain: $-\infty < x < \infty$
range: $y \geq -22.9$

16.

domain: $-\infty < x < \infty$
range: $-\infty < y < \infty$

17. $(-2, 2.4)$: max, $(0, -1.2)$: min, $(1, -1)$:
max, $(2.4, -2)$: min; -2.5, -1, 2.6; 5

18. $(-2, -1)$: max, $(0, -2.2)$: min, $(1, -2)$:
max; none; 4

19. $(-1.5, -2.25)$: min, $(0, 3)$: max, $(2, -3)$:
min, $(3.5, 2)$: max; -2, -1, 1, 3, 4; 5

20.

x-int: -0.34, 1.43, 2.1; max: $(0.7, 2.44)$; min: $(1.83, -1.55)$

21.

x-int: 0, 1.2; max: $(-1.19, 4.09)$; min: $(-1.77, 3.8)$, $(0.71, -2.93)$

22.

x-int: -1.58, 0.78; min: $(-1, -4)$

23.

x-int: -2, -1, 0, 1, 2; max: $(-1.64, 3.63)$, $(0.54, 1.42)$; min: $(-0.54, -1.42)$, $(1.64, -3.63)$

24.

x-int: -0.88, 1.08, 1.41; max: $(1.26, 0.08)$; min: $(0, -0.88)$

25.

x-int: -5, 0, 1.2; max: $(0.42, 1.38)$; min: $(-3.57, -116.16)$, $(1.2, 0)$

27. *Sample answer:* $f(x) = x^3 - 6x^2 + 5x + 12$, $g(x) = x^4 - 5x^3 - x^2 + 17x + 12$, $h(x) = x^5 - 8x^4 + 14x^3 + 20x^2 - 39x - 36$

31. If n is even, there is a turning point. If n is odd, the graph passes through the x-axis.;

32. a. $h = \dfrac{500 - 2\pi r^2}{\pi r}$

b. $V = 500r - \dfrac{4}{3}\pi r^3$

c.

about 2103 ft^3; $r \approx 6.31$ ft, $h \approx 12.6$ ft

33. a.

b. $(6.6, 63.9)$, $(19.8, 34.0)$; the high temperature for the 24-hour period was $63.9°$F, which occurred at about 12:36 P.M. and the low temperature for the 24-hour period was $34°$F, which occurred at about 1:48 A.M. **c.** $34 \le y \le 63.9$

2.8 Technology Activity (p. 104)

1. local maximum: $(0.37, 13.51)$; local minima: $(-1.83, -12.66)$, $(2.96, -27.04)$

2. local maximum: $(-2.54, 0.88)$; local minimum: $(-0.13, -6.06)$ **3.** local maximum: $(0, 36)$; local minima: $(-2.55, -6.25)$, $(2.55, -6.25)$

4. local maximum $(-2.67, 29.63)$; local minimum: $(2.0, -72)$ **5.** local maxima: $(-1.57, 1.92)$, $(2.25, 8.63)$; local minimum: $(0.07, -4.02)$ **6.** local maximum: $(-4.19, 16.16)$; local minimum: $(2.86, -54.08)$

Unit 2 Test (pp. 105–106)

3. a.

b. domain: all real numbers; range: all real numbers
c. degree: 3; leading coefficient: 1   **d.** no symmetry
e. increasing for $x < -0.5$ and $x > 1.2$; decreasing for $-0.5 < x < 1.2$

4. a.

b. domain: all real numbers; range: $y \geq 12$

c. degree: 4; leading coefficient: $\frac{1}{4}$

d. y-axis symmetry   **e.** increasing for $-2 < x < 0$ and $x > 2$; decreasing for $x < -2$ and $0 < x < 2$

5. a.

b. domain: all real numbers; range: all real numbers
c. degree: 3; leading coefficient: -2

d. no symmetry   **e.** increasing for $\frac{1}{2} < x < \frac{3}{2}$;

decreasing for $x < \frac{1}{2}$ and $x > \frac{3}{2}$

6.

The graph of g is the graph of f translated up 2 units; the domain of f and g is all real numbers and the range of f is $y \geq 0$ and the range of g is $y \geq 2$; f has x- and y-intercepts of 0 and g has a y-intercept of 2; f and g are even and symmetric with respect to the y-axis.

7.

The graph of g is the graph of f translated to the right 1 unit; the domain of f and g is all real numbers and the range of f and g is $y \geq 0$; f has x- and y-intercepts of 0 and g has an x-intercept of 1 and a y-intercept of $\frac{1}{2}$; f is even and symmetric with respect to the y-axis and g is neither even nor odd and has no symmetry.

8.

The graph of g is the graph of f translated to the left 4 units and down 3 units; the domain of f and g is all real numbers and the range of f is $y \geq 0$ and the range of g is $y \geq -3$; f has x- and y-intercepts of 0 and g has x-intercepts of about -5.6 and -2.4 and a y-intercept of 125; f is even and symmetric with respect to the y-axis and g is neither even nor odd and has no symmetry

13. $\left(-\infty, -\frac{1}{2}\right]$ and $[0, 3]$

14. $\left(-\sqrt{3}, -1\right)$ and $\left(1, \sqrt{3}\right)$

15. $(-\infty, -1.9)$ and $(1.9, \infty)$

18. $-9, -1, 4$ **19.** $-5, -\frac{3}{2}, 2$

20. $-3, \dfrac{-1 + \sqrt{17}}{4}, \dfrac{-1 - \sqrt{17}}{4}, 1$

21. $-\dfrac{7}{2}, -3, -\dfrac{1}{3}, 1$

22. $f(x) = x^3 - 8x^2 + 4x + 48$

23. $f(x) = x^3 - 5x^2 + 5x + 3$

24. $f(x) = x^4 + x^3 + x^2 + x$

25. $f(x) = x^4 + x^3 - 5x^2 + 23x - 20$

26. zeros: 0 (multiplicity 3), -4; turning points: 3

27. zeros: 9 (multiplicity 2), 1; turning points: 2

28. zeros: 0 (multiplicity 2), -2 (multiplicity 3), 7; turning points: 5

29. zeros: -1 (multiplicity 2), $\dfrac{3}{4}$ (multiplicity 2); turning points: 3

30.

x-int: -1.82; max: $(0.11, -2.94)$; min: $(-1, -5)$

31.

x-int: $-1.68, -0.42, 0.42, 1.68$; max: $(0, 1)$, min: $(-1.22, -3.5), (1.22, -3.5)$

32. a. quartic polynomial

b.

x	0	3	5	7	8
T	20	19.67	20.94	23.53	24.20

c.

Sample answer: No, because as $x \to +\infty$, $T \to -\infty$.

Permormance Task (p. 106)

a.

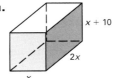

b. $V = 2x^3 + 20x^2$

c.

$x \approx 2.4$ in. when $V = 144$ in.^{3}

e. $\pm 1, \pm\dfrac{3}{2}, \pm 2, \pm 3, \pm 4, \pm\dfrac{9}{2}, \pm 6, \pm 8, \pm 9, \pm 12,$ $\pm 16, \pm 18, \pm 24, \pm 36, \pm 48, \pm 72; x \approx 2.4$ in.

f. The answers are the same. The dimensions of the sculpture are about 4.8 in. by 2.4 in. by 12.4 in.

g. No, only positive answers make sense in this situation and as $x \to +\infty$, $V \to +\infty$

UNIT 3

3.1 Investigating Math Activity (p. 108)

3. To rewrite a radical expression as an exponential expression, write an expression where the radicand is the base, the index is the denominator of the rational exponent, and 1 is the numerator of the rational exponent.

5. To rewrite a radical expression as an exponential expression, write an expression where the radicand is the base, the index is the denominator of the rational exponent, and the power to which the expression is raised is the numerator of the rational exponent. **a.** $8^{2/3}$ **b.** $32^{4/5}$

3.2 Problem Solving Workshop (p. 117)

4. about 1.59; The surface area of the Canadian lynx is about 1.59 times as great as the surface area of an average house cat.

3.3 Guided Practice (pp. 118–119)

1.

domain: $x \geq 0$,
range: $y \geq 0$

2.

domain: $x \geq 0$,
range: $y \leq 0$

3. ; domain: all real numbers,
range: all real numbers

4. ; domain: all real numbers,
range: all real numbers

6. ; domain: $x \geq -1$,
range: $y \leq 3$

7. ; domain: all real numbers,
range: all real numbers

3.3 Exercise Set A (p. 120)

1.

domain: $x \geq 0$,
range: $y \geq -2$

2.

domain: $x \geq 2$,
range: $y \geq 0$

3.

domain: $x \geq -1$,
range: $y \geq 0$

4.

domain: $x \geq -2$,
range: $y \geq -2$

5.

domain: $x \geq 1$,
range: $y \geq 1$

6.

domain: $x \geq 3$,
range: $y \geq 0$

7.

domain and range:
all real numbers

8.

domain and range:
all real numbers

9.

domain and range:
all real numbers

10.

domain and range:
all real numbers

11.

domain and range:
all real numbers

12.

domain and range:
all real numbers

17. a. $v_t = 33.7\sqrt{\dfrac{175}{A}}$

b. *Sample answer:*

A	2	4	6	8	10
v_t	315.23	222.9	182	157.62	140.98

c.

3.3 Exercise Set B (p. 121)

1.

domain: $x \geq -4$,
range: $y \geq -2$

2.

domain: $x \geq 2$,
range: $y \geq 3$

3.

domain: $x \geq 0$,
range: $y \leq 3$

4.

domain: $x \geq -2$,
range: $y \leq 2$

5.

domain and range:
all real numbers

6.

domain and range:
all real numbers

7.

domain and range:
all real numbers

8.

domain and range:
all real numbers

9. ; domain and range: all real
numbers

13.

15. On the interval $(-1, 1)$, the larger the root, the steeper the graph. On the intervals $(-\infty, -1)$ and $(1, \infty)$, the larger the root, the less steep the graph.

16.

Unit 3 Test (pp. 127–128)

25.

domain: $x \geq 0$,
range: $y \geq 5$

26.

domain: $x \geq 4$,
range: $y \geq 6$

27.
domain and range:
all real numbers

28.
domain: $x \geq -2$,
range: $y \geq -2$

29.
domain and range:
all real numbers

30.
domain and range:
all real numbers

31.
domain: $x \geq -3$,
range: $y \leq 1$

32.
domain and range:
all real numbers

33.
domain and range:
all real numbers

Performance Task (p. 128)

d. ;

The domain and range are both the same. The graph of $y = \sqrt{\dfrac{x}{\pi}}$ is a vertical shrink of the graph of $y = \sqrt{x}$ by a factor of $\sqrt{\dfrac{1}{\pi}}$.

UNIT 4
4.1 Guided Practice (p. 131)

1. ; domain: all real numbers;
range: $y > 0$

2. ; domain: all real numbers;
range: $y < 0$

3. ; domain: all real numbers;
range: $y > 4$

4.1 Exercise Set A (p. 132)

4. ; domain: all real numbers;
range: $y > 0$

5. ; domain: all real numbers;
range: $y > 0$

6. ; domain: all real numbers;
range: $y > 0$

7. ; domain: all real numbers;
range: $y < 0$

8. ; domain: all real numbers; range: $y > 0$

9. ; domain: all real numbers; range: $y > 1$

10. ; domain: all real numbers; range: $y < 1$

11. ; domain: all real numbers; range: $y > -5$

12. ; domain: all real numbers; range: $y > -6$

4.1 Exercise Set B (p. 133)

1. ; domain: all real numbers; range: $y > 0$

2. ; domain: all real numbers; range: $y > 0$

3. ; domain: all real numbers; range: $y < 0$

4. ; domain: all real numbers; range: $y < 0$

5. ; domain: all real numbers; range: $y > -7$

6. ; domain: all real numbers; range: $y > 3$

7. ; domain: all real numbers; range: $y > -1$

8. ; domain: all real numbers; range: $y < 2$

9. ; domain: all real numbers; range: $y > -2$

13. a. $P = 494{,}290(1.03)^t$; 664,284

b.

domain: $0 \le t \le 10$;
range: $494{,}290 \le P \le 664{,}284$

c. 1993

14. a. $v = 325(1.05)^t$; $358.31

b. ; domain: $t \ge 0$;
range: $v \ge 325$; 2022

15. a. $n = 41(1.089)^t$

b.

n	0	1	2	3
t	41	44.65	48.62	52.95

c.   **d.** 1985

4.2 Guided Practice (p. 134)

1. ; domain: all real numbers;
range: $y > 0$

2. ; domain: all real numbers;
range: $y < 0$

3. ; domain: all real numbers;
range: $y > -1$

4.2 Exercise Set A (p. 137)

7. ; domain: all real numbers;
range: $y > 0$

8. ; domain: all real numbers;
range: $y > 1$

9. ; domain: all real numbers;
range: $y < 0$

10. ; domain: all real numbers;
range: $y < 0$

11. ; domain: all real numbers;
range: $y > 2$

12. ; domain: all real numbers;
range: $y > -2$

4.2 Exercise Set B (p. 138)

1. ; domain: all real numbers; range: $y > 0$

2. ; domain: all real numbers; range: $y < 0$

3. ; domain: all real numbers; range: $y < 0$

4. ; domain: all real numbers; range: $y > -4$

5. ; domain: all real numbers; range: $y < 0$

6. ; domain: all real numbers; range: $y < -5$

7. ; domain: all real numbers; range: $y < -2$

8. ; domain: all real numbers; range: $y > 1$

9. ; domain: all real numbers; range: $y > -2$

10. a. $y = 200(0.75)^t$

b.

y	0	1	2	3
t	200	150	112.5	84.38

c.

d. 5 yr

4.3 Guided Practice (p. 141)

5. ; domain: all real numbers, range: $y > -1$

6. ; domain: all real numbers, range: $y > 0$

7. ; domain: all real numbers, range: $y > 2$

4.3 Exercise Set A (p. 142)

21. ; domain: all real numbers; range: $y > 0$

22. ; domain: all real numbers; range: $y > 0$

23. ; domain: all real numbers; range: $y < 3$

24. ; domain: all real numbers; range: $y > 1$

25. ; domain: all real numbers; range: $y > -3$

26. ; domain: all real numbers; range: $y > 2$

4.3 Exercise Set B (p. 143)

11. ; domain: all real numbers; range: $y > -3$

12. ; domain: all real numbers; range: $y > 1$

13. ; domain: all real numbers; range: $y < 2$

14. ; domain: all real numbers; range: $y > 1$

15. ; domain: all real numbers; range: $y > -4$

16. ; domain: all real numbers; range: $y > -3$

18.

4.4 Investigating Math Activity (p. 144)

1. a. 9 **b.** $\frac{1}{8}$ **c.** 1 **d.** 36 **2.** They are the same.

3. They are the same. **4.** To rewrite an exponential equation as a logarithmic equation, begin by writing *log* followed by a subscript, which is the base in the exponential equation. Next, write the value of the exponential equation followed by an equal sign. Finally, write the exponent.

a. $\log_2 32 = 5$ **b.** $\log_4 \frac{1}{16} = -2$ **c.** $\log_3 81 = 4$

4.4 Guided Practice (p. 146)

15. ; domain: $x > 4$; range: all real numbers

4.4 Exercise Set A (p. 147)

22. ; domain: $x > 0$; range: all real numbers

23. ; domain: $x > -2$; range: all real numbers

24. ; domain: $x > 0$; range: all real numbers

4.4 Exercise Set B (p. 148)

19. ; domain: $x > -2$; range: all real numbers

20. ; domain: $x > -2$; range: all real numbers

21. ; domain: $x > 1$; range: all real numbers

23.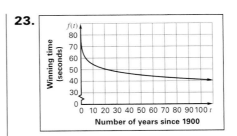

4.5 Guided Practice (pp. 150–152)

1. a. y-intercept: $(0, 1)$; no x-intercept; no zeros
b. increasing $(-\infty, \infty)$ **c.** C and D

2. a. no y-intercept; x-intercept: $(1, 0)$; zero $x = 1$
b. increasing $(0, \infty)$ **c.** A and B

3. ; domain: $x > 8$; range: all real numbers

4. ; domain: $x > -4$; range: all real numbers

5. ; domain: $x > 0$; range: all real numbers

6. ; domain: $x > -2$; range: all real numbers

7. ; domain: $x > 0$; range: all real numbers

8. ; domain: $x > 4$;
range: all real numbers

10. domain: $x > 0.5$;
range: all real numbers

4.5 Exercise Set A (p. 153)

4. ; domain: $x > -12$;
range: all real numbers

11. ; domain: $x > -7.8$;
range: all real numbers

5. ; domain: $x > 0$;
range: all real numbers

12. a.

V	0	1	2
t	250	275	302.50

V	3	4	5
t	332.75	366.03	402.63

6. ; domain: $x > 1$;
range: all real numbers

b. ; no zeros; The value of the table
is never $0.

10. a. no zeros; decreasing: $(-\infty, \infty)$; the value of
the car is constantly falling, and it is never worth $0.
b. years 1 and 2; The value of the car decreases at a
lower rate, as the years go on.

c. increasing: $(0, \infty)$; The value of the chair is
constantly increasing. **d.** years 4 and 5; The value
of the chair increases at a higher rate, as the years
go on.

4.5 Exercise Set B (p. 154)

3. a. no zeros **b.** increasing: $(-\infty, \infty)$

4. a. no zeros **b.** decreasing: $(-\infty, \infty)$

5. a. no zeros **b.** increasing: $(-\infty, \infty)$

6. a. $x \approx 0.0014$ **b.** increasing: $(0, \infty)$

7. a. $x = 9$ **b.** increasing: $(-1, \infty)$

8. a. $x = 1$ **b.** increasing: $(0, \infty)$

9. domain: $x > -1.2$;
range: all real numbers

13. a. ; $x \approx 3.35$

b. increasing: $(4, \infty)$; The alligator's length
increases as its weight increases.

4.6 Exercise Set B (p. 158)

13. $\log_3 \frac{5}{3}$ **14.** $\log \frac{25y}{x^2}$ **15.** $\log_2 \frac{9}{x^3 y}$

16. $\ln \frac{(x-3)^2}{6(x+2)^3}$ **17.** $\log \frac{\sqrt{(x+4)^3}}{6x^3}$

18. $\ln \sqrt{\frac{3x^4}{(x+1)^2}}$

4.8 Exercise Set A (p. 167)

21. a. $C = P(1.04)^t$ **b.** $0.99 < 0.99(1.04)^t < 1.5$; in the first 10.6 years, $(0, 10.6)$ **c.** $0.99(1.04)^t > 2$; over 17.9 years, $(17.9, \infty)$

4.8 Exercise Set B (p. 168)

20. a. $130 < (140)e^{-0.03t} + 72 < 140$

b. between 24.1 and 29.4 minutes, $(24.1, 29.4)$

c. no; There is a horizontal asymptote at $y = 72$, so the temperatures will never drop below 72°.

4.9 Guided Practice (p. 170)

1. $y = 4(2^x)$ **2.** $y = \frac{1}{2}(4^x)$ **3.** $y = 3(5^x)$

4.9 Exercise Set A (p. 171)

10.
$y = 1.2(2.8)^x$

20.
$y = 2.1x^{1.8}$

4.9 Exercise Set B (p. 172)

4.
$y = 3(1.8)^x$

5.
$y = 0.9(4^x)$

9.
$y = 2.2x^{0.13}$

Unit 4 Test (pp. 173–174)

1. ; domain: all real numbers; range: $y > 0$

2. ; domain: all real numbers; range: $y < 0$

3. ; domain: all real numbers; range: $y > 0$

4. ; domain: all real numbers; range: $y > 0$

5. ; domain: all real numbers; range: $y > -3$

6. ; domain: all real numbers; range: $y > 1$

10. ; domain: $x > 0$; range: all real numbers

11. ; domain: $x > 1$;
range: all real numbers

12. ; domain: $x > 0$;
range: all real numbers

34. ; about 269 bacteria

Performance Task (p. 174)

a. $A = 500\left(1 + \dfrac{0.05}{12}\right)^{12t}$

b.

t	0	2	4	6
A	500	552.47	610.45	674.51

t	8	10	12	14
A	745.29	823.50	909.92	1005.40

; about 14 years

c. no zeros; increasing: $(0, \infty)$; *Sample answer:*
The balance in the account is increasing, and it is
never worth $0.

d. 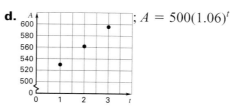 ; $A = 500(1.06)^t$

e. after about 7 years; The second bank is a better
choice because your money willl increase at a
faster rate.

UNIT 5

5.1 Guided Practice (pp. 176–177)

1. ; focus: $\left(0, \dfrac{1}{16}\right)$;

directrix: $y = -\dfrac{1}{16}$;

axis of symmetry: y-axis

2. ; focus: $\left(-\dfrac{1}{2}, 0\right)$;

directrix: $x = \dfrac{1}{2}$;

axis of symmetry: x-axis

3. ; focus: $\left(\dfrac{1}{2}, 0\right)$;

directrix: $x = -\dfrac{1}{2}$;

axis of symmetry: x-axis

4. ; focus: $\left(0, -\dfrac{3}{4}\right)$;

directrix: $y = \dfrac{3}{4}$;

axis of symmetry: y-axis

5.1 Exercise Set A (p. 178)

4.

$(0, 3); y = -3$

5.

$(-1, 0); x = 1$

6.

$\left(0, -\dfrac{1}{4}\right); y = \dfrac{1}{4}$

7.

$\left(\dfrac{3}{2}, 0\right); x = -\dfrac{3}{2}$

8.

$(0, -2); y = 2$

9.

$\left(0, \dfrac{1}{8}\right); y = -\dfrac{1}{8}$

10. The parabola should open to the right rather than up.

7.

$(0, 10); y = -10$

8.

$(-5, 0); x = 5$

9.

$\left(0, \dfrac{1}{3}\right); y = -\dfrac{1}{3}$

5.2 Guided Practice (pp. 180–181)

1. ; 4 **2.** ; 9

3. ; 3

5.1 Exercise Set B (p. 179)

1.

$(0, 3); y = -3$

2.

$(-4, 0); x = 4$

3.

$\left(0, -\dfrac{1}{32}\right); y = \dfrac{1}{32}$

4.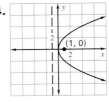

$(1, 0); x = -1$

5.

$\left(0, -\dfrac{1}{16}\right); y = \dfrac{1}{16}$

6.

$\left(0, \dfrac{3}{8}\right); y = -\dfrac{3}{8}$

5.2 Exercise Set A (p. 182)

1.

3

2.

$2\sqrt{5}$

3.

8

4.

$5\sqrt{2}$

5.

4

6.

$2\sqrt{10}$

7. The radius of the circle should be 4, not 16.

20.

21.

22.

5.2 Exercise Set B (p. 183)

1.

10

2.

6

3.

7

4.

$2\sqrt{6}$

5.

$3\sqrt{2}$

6.

$2\sqrt{7}$

19. a.

b. $x^2 + y^2 \le 400$
$x^2 + y^2 \le 1225$

c. The rating is between 4.2 and 4.6. The location is outside of the circle with a rating of 4.2, but inside the circle with a rating of 4.6.

5.3 Investigating Math Activity (p. 185)

4. The sum of the distances from the foci to any point on the ellipse must be constant. An ellipse is a set of all points such that the sum of the distances between the foci and any point on the ellipse is constant.

5.3 Guided Practice (p. 187)

1. ; vertices: $(0, \pm 5)$;
co-vertices: $(\pm 4, 0)$;
foci: $(0, \pm 3)$

2. ; vertices: $(\pm 6, 0)$;
co-vertices: $(0, \pm 3)$;
foci: $(\pm 4, 0)$

3. ; vertices: $(\pm 3, 0)$;
co-vertices: $(0, \pm 2)$;
foci: $(\pm\sqrt{5}, 0)$

5.3 Exercise Set A (p. 188)

1. ; vertices: $(0, \pm 6)$;
co-vertices: $(\pm 4, 0)$;
foci: $(0, \pm 2\sqrt{5})$

2. ; vertices: $(\pm 7, 0)$;
co-vertices: $(0, \pm 2)$;
foci: $(\pm 3\sqrt{5}, 0)$

3. ; vertices: $(0, \pm 10)$;
co-vertices: $(\pm 8, 0)$;
foci: $(0, \pm 6)$

4. ; vertices: $(0, \pm 9)$;
co-vertices: $(\pm 5, 0)$;
foci: $(0, \pm 2\sqrt{14})$

5. ; vertices: $(0, \pm 4)$;
co-vertices: $(\pm 1, 0)$;
foci: $(0, \pm \sqrt{15})$

6. ; vertices: $(0, \pm 7)$;
co-vertices: $(\pm 2, 0)$;
foci: $(0, \pm 3\sqrt{5})$

7. ; vertices: $(0, \pm 3)$;
co-vertices: $(\pm 2, 0)$;
foci: $(0, \pm \sqrt{5})$

8. ; vertices: $(\pm 5, 0)$;
co-vertices: $(0, \pm 4)$;
foci: $(\pm 3, 0)$

9. ; vertices: $(\pm 9, 0)$;
co-vertices: $(0, \pm 2)$;
foci: $(\pm \sqrt{77}, 0)$

16.

17.

18.

5.3 Exercise Set B (p. 189)

1. ; vertices: $(\pm 3, 0)$;
co-vertices: $(0, \pm 1)$;
foci: $(\pm 2\sqrt{2}, 0)$

2. ; vertices: $\left(0, \pm \dfrac{5}{2}\right)$;
co-vertices: $\left(\pm \dfrac{4}{3}, 0\right)$;
foci: $\left(0, \pm \dfrac{\sqrt{161}}{6}\right)$

3. ; vertices: $(\pm 12, 0)$;
co-vertices: $(0, \pm 9)$;
foci: $(\pm 3\sqrt{7}, 0)$

4. ; vertices: $(\pm\sqrt{10}, 0)$;
co-vertices: $(0, \pm2\sqrt{2})$;
foci: $(\pm\sqrt{2}, 0)$

5. ; vertices: $(0, \pm2\sqrt{3})$;
co-vertices: $(\pm2\sqrt{2}, 0)$;
foci: $(0, \pm2)$

6. ; vertices: $\left(\pm\dfrac{9}{2}, 0\right)$;

co-vertices: $\left(0, \pm\dfrac{5}{3}\right)$;

foci: $\left(\pm\dfrac{\sqrt{629}}{6}, 0\right)$

5.4 Guided Practice (p. 191)

1. ; vertices: $(\pm4, 0)$;
foci: $(\pm2\sqrt{5}, 0)$;
asymptotes: $y = \pm\dfrac{1}{2}x$

5.4 Exercise Set A (p. 192)

1. ; vertices: $(\pm4, 0)$;
foci: $(\pm2\sqrt{5}, 0)$;
asymptotes: $y = \pm\dfrac{1}{2}x$

2. ; vertices: $(\pm3, 0)$;
foci: $(\pm3\sqrt{5}, 0)$;
asymptotes: $y = \pm2x$

3. ; vertices: $(0, \pm5)$;
foci: $(0, \pm\sqrt{29})$;
asymptotes: $y = \pm\dfrac{5}{2}x$

4. ; vertices: $(\pm2, 0)$;
foci: $(\pm\sqrt{5}, 0)$;
asymptotes: $y = \pm\dfrac{1}{2}x$

5. ; vertices: $(0, \pm2\sqrt{5})$;
foci: $(0, \pm2\sqrt{6})$;
asymptotes: $y = \pm\sqrt{5}x$

6. ; vertices: $(0, \pm2)$;
foci: $(0, \pm2\sqrt{5})$;
asymptotes: $y = \pm\dfrac{1}{2}x$

7. The transverse axis should
be horizontal, not vertical.

16.

17.

18.

5.4 Exercise Set B (p. 193)

1. ; vertices: $(\pm8, 0)$;
foci: $(\pm\sqrt{85}, 0)$;
asymptotes: $y = \pm\dfrac{\sqrt{21}}{8}x$

2. ; vertices: $(\pm 4\sqrt{2}, 0)$;
foci: $(\pm 4\sqrt{5}, 0)$;
asymptotes: $y = \pm\dfrac{\sqrt{6}}{2}x$

3. ; vertices: $(0, \pm 3\sqrt{2})$;
foci: $(0, \pm 3\sqrt{11})$;
asymptotes: $y = \pm\dfrac{\sqrt{2}}{3}x$

4. 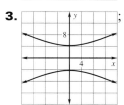 ; vertices: $(\pm\sqrt{13}, 0)$;
foci: $(\pm\sqrt{37}, 0)$;
asymptotes: $y = \pm\dfrac{2\sqrt{78}}{13}x$

5. ; vertices: $(0, \pm 2\sqrt{10})$;
foci: $(0, \pm 2\sqrt{13})$;
asymptotes: $y = \pm\dfrac{\sqrt{30}}{3}x$

6. ; vertices: $(0, \pm\sqrt{10})$;
foci: $\left(0, \pm\dfrac{5\sqrt{10}}{3}\right)$;
asymptotes: $y = \pm\dfrac{3}{4}x$

9. **10.**

11.

15. a. $\pi y^2 - \pi x^2 = 500$

b. *Sample answer:* (2, 14.0), (4, 14.4), (6, 15.1), (8, 16.0)

c. ; the part of the hyperbola in the first quadrant

d. It gets smaller; because the area of the concrete remains constant as the radii increase, the width decreases.

5.5 Guided Practice (pp. 194-195)

1. ; center: (2, 2);
vertices: (0, 2), (4, 2);
foci: (−1, 2), (5, 2);
asymptotes:
$y = 2 \pm \dfrac{\sqrt{5}}{2}(x - 2)$

2. ; vertex: (4, −1);
focus: (4, 0);
directrix: $y = -2$

4. ellipse; $\dfrac{(x + 1)^2}{4} + \dfrac{(y - 1)^2}{1} = 1$

5. parabola; $4(y + 1) = (x - 2)^2$

5.5 Exercise Set A (pp. 196–197)

1. ; center: $(0, 3)$;
radius: 3

2. ; center: $(4, 2)$;
vertices: $(0, 2), (8, 2)$;
co-vertices: $(4, 0), (4, 4)$;
foci: $(4 \pm 2\sqrt{3}, 2)$

3. ; vertex: $(3, -4)$;
focus: $(3, -2)$

4. ; center: $(-1, -2)$;
vertices: $(-1, -2 \pm 3\sqrt{2})$;
foci: $(-1, -2 \pm \sqrt{43})$

5. ; center: $(-3, 4)$;
vertices: $(-3, 10), (-3, -2)$;
co-vertices: $(-3 \pm 4\sqrt{2}, 4)$;
foci: $(-3, 2), (-3, 6)$

6. ; center: $(5, -2)$;
radius: $2\sqrt{7}$

7. ; center: $(6, 2)$;
radius: 2

8. ; center: $(-3, 8)$;
vertices: $(-3, 12)$ and
$(-3, 4)$;
foci: $(-3, 8 \pm 2\sqrt{5})$

9. ; vertex: $(-2, 4)$;
focus: $(-1.25, 4)$

10. ; center: $(-1, -3)$;
vertices: $(3, -3)$ and
$(-5, -3)$;
co-vertices: $(-1, 1)$ and
$(-1, -5)$;
foci: $(-1, -3 \pm 2\sqrt{3})$

11. ; center: $(-7, 1)$;
radius: 1

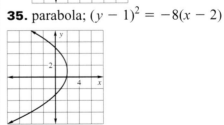

12. ; vertex: $(-7, 3)$;
focus: $(-7, 6)$

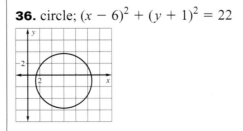

35. parabola; $(y - 1)^2 = -8(x - 2)$

36. circle; $(x - 6)^2 + (y + 1)^2 = 22$

37. hyperbola; $\dfrac{x^2}{9} - \dfrac{(y-3)^2}{1} = 1$

38. ellipse; $\dfrac{(x+3)^2}{36} + \dfrac{(y-2)^2}{9} = 1$

39. parabola; $(x+5)^2 = 6(y+3)$

40. hyperbola; $\dfrac{(y-2)^2}{10} - \dfrac{(x-6)^2}{25} = 1$

41. parabola; $(y-6)^2 = -4(x-8)$

42. circle; $(x-3)^2 + (y-4)^2 = 1$

43. hyperbola; $\dfrac{(x-4)^2}{1} - \dfrac{(y-4)^2}{9} = 1$

44. ellipse; $\dfrac{(x-6)^2}{25} + \dfrac{(y-4)^2}{100} = 1$

45. $x^2 + (y+225)^2 = 50{,}625;$
$x^2 + (y-225)^2 = 50{,}625$

46. $\dfrac{x^2}{4} - \dfrac{(y-4)^2}{36} = 1$

47. hyperbola; $\dfrac{(x-1.5)^2}{5} - \dfrac{y^2}{\left(\dfrac{10}{3}\right)} = 1$

5.5 Exercise Set B (pp. 198-199)

1. ; vertex: $(5, -4)$;
focus: $(1, -4)$

2. ; center: $(2, -5)$;
vertices: $(2 \pm 2\sqrt{5}, -5)$;
co-vertices: $(2, -2), (2, -8)$;
foci: $(2 \pm \sqrt{11}, -5)$

3. ; center: $(3, -4)$; radius: $3\sqrt{2}$

4. ; center: $(4, -7)$;
vertices: $(4, -7 \pm \sqrt{26})$;
foci: $(4, -7 \pm \sqrt{38})$

5. ; center: $(-6, -5)$;
vertices: $(-6, -5 \pm 3\sqrt{3})$;
co-vertices: $(-6 \pm \sqrt{11}, -5)$;
foci: $(-6, -9), (-6, -1)$

6. ; vertex: $(8, -3)$;
focus: $\left(8, -\dfrac{3}{2}\right)$

7. ; center: $(5, -1)$;
vertices: $(15, -1)$ and
$(-5, -1)$;
co-vertices: $(5, 2)$ and $(5, -4)$;
foci: $(5 \pm \sqrt{91}, -1)$

8. ; center: $(-2, 4.5)$;
radius: 4

23. parabola; $(x - 7)^2 = 9(y + 3)$

24. circle; $(x + 5)^2 + (y - 6)^2 = 21$

25. ellipse; $\dfrac{(x - 3)^2}{10} + \dfrac{(y - 5)^2}{18} = 1$

26. hyperbola; $\dfrac{(x + 2)^2}{25} - \dfrac{(y - 3)^2}{8} = 1$

27. ellipse; $\dfrac{(x + 1)^2}{14} + \dfrac{(y + 2)^2}{4} = 1$

28. hyperbola; $\dfrac{(y-7)^2}{32} - \dfrac{(x-4)^2}{20} = 1$

29. ellipse; $\dfrac{(x-6)^2}{36} + \dfrac{(y-3)^2}{9} = 1$

31. a.   **b.** $(60, 30)$
   c. $(x-60)^2 = 120y$
   d. 7.5 m

5.7 Guided Practice (pp. 205-206)

1.   ; $3\sqrt{3}$

2.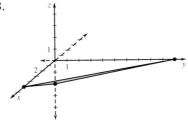

3.

5.7 Exercise Set A (p. 207)

1.   ; $5\sqrt{2}$

(3, 0, 5)

(0, 4, 0)

2. 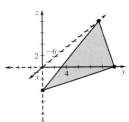   ; 9

(−3, 2, 0)

(1, 1, −8)

7.   **8.**

9.

10.

11.

12. (image)

13. plane;

14. sphere   **15.** sphere

16. plane;

21. a. length = 6; width = 5; height = 5

b. $SA = 148$ units^2; $V = 120$ units^3

c. (0, 0, 0), (0, 6, 0), (5, 6, 0), (5, 0, 0), (0, 0, 8), (0, 6, 8), (5, 6, 8), (5, 0, 8)

d.

5.7 Exercise Set B (p. 208)

1. (4, −5, 6)   (2, 2, 3) $\sqrt{62}$

2. $\sqrt{38}$ (7, 5, 1)   (10, 0, −1)

5.   **6.**

7.

8.

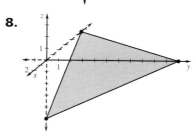

9. $(x - 2)^2 + (y - 2)^2 + (z + 2)^2 = 36$

10. $(x - 8)^2 + (y + 2)^2 + z^2 = 144$

11. $(x - 15)^2 + (y + 1)^2 + (z - 6)^2 = 1.44$

12. $x^2 + (y + 4)^2 + (z + 3)^2 = 20.25$

13. $(x - 8)^2 + (y - 2.5)^2 + z^2 = 192$

14. $(x - 10)^2 + (y + 2)^2 + (z - 3)^2 = 18$

15. $(x - 1)^2 + (y + 3)^2 + (z + 4)^2 = 25$;
center: $(1, -3, -4)$; radius: 5

16. $(x + 4.5)^2 + (y - 1)^2 + (z + 5)^2 = 36$;
center $(-4.5, 1, -5)$; radius: 6

17. $\left(x - \dfrac{1}{3}\right)^2 + (y + 1)^2 + z^2 = 1$;

center: $\left(\dfrac{1}{3}, -1, 0\right)$; radius: 1

18. $\left(x - \dfrac{1}{2}\right)^2 + (y - 4)^2 + (z + 1)^2 = 9$;

center: $\left(\dfrac{1}{2}, 4, -1\right)$; radius: 3

Unit 5 Test (pp. 209–210)

1.

2.

3.

4.

5.

6.

7.

8.

9.

10.

11.

12.

37. a. *Sample answer:*
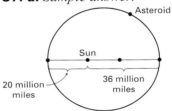

b. $\dfrac{x^2}{784} + \dfrac{y^2}{720} = 1$

Performance Task (p. 210)

e.

Yes, the students living along Chestnut Lane do qualify for a parking pass because the graphs do not intersect. So, it does not lie within the circular region.

UNIT 6

6.1 Guided Practice (pp. 212–214)

1.

X (number of cell phones)	0	1	2	3
Number of households	19	28	37	16
P(X)	$\frac{19}{100}$	$\frac{28}{100}$	$\frac{37}{100}$	$\frac{16}{100}$

4. $P(k = 0) = 0.6561$, $P(k = 1) = 0.2916$, $P(k = 2) = 0.0486$, $P(k = 3) = 0.0036$, $P(k = 4) = 0.0001$

6.1 Exercise Set A (p. 215)

3.

B	1	2	3
P(B)	0.3	0.4	0.3

 ; symmetric

4.

D (difference)	0	1	2	3
Outcomes	8	14	12	10
P(D)	$\frac{1}{8}$	$\frac{7}{32}$	$\frac{3}{16}$	$\frac{5}{32}$

D (difference)	4	5	6	7
Outcomes	8	6	4	2
P(D)	$\frac{1}{8}$	$\frac{3}{32}$	$\frac{1}{16}$	$\frac{1}{32}$

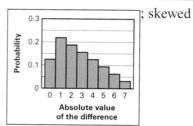 ; skewed

16. a. $P(k = 0) \approx 0.008$, $P(k = 1) \approx 0.055$, $P(k = 2) \approx 0.164$, $P(k = 3) \approx 0.273$, $P(k = 4) \approx 0.273$, $P(k = 5) \approx 0.164$, $P(k = 6) \approx 0.055$, $P(k = 7) \approx 0.008$

k	0	1	2	3
P(k)	0.008	0.055	0.164	0.273

k	4	5	6	7
P(k)	0.273	0.164	0.055	0.008

c. 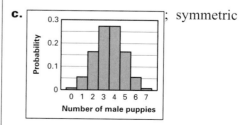 ; symmetric

6.1 Exercise Set B (p. 215)

1.

C	red	blue	green	orange
P(C)	0.2	0.25	0.4	0.15

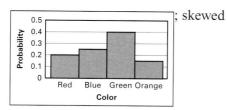

; skewed

2.

X (product)	0	1	2	3	4
Outcomes	9	1	2	2	3
P(X)	$\frac{9}{25}$	$\frac{1}{25}$	$\frac{2}{25}$	$\frac{2}{25}$	$\frac{3}{25}$

X (product)	6	8	9	12	16
Outcomes	2	2	1	2	1
P(X)	$\frac{2}{25}$	$\frac{2}{25}$	$\frac{1}{25}$	$\frac{2}{25}$	$\frac{1}{25}$

; skewed

14. ; skewed; $k = 5$

15. 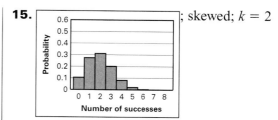 ; skewed; $k = 2$

16. 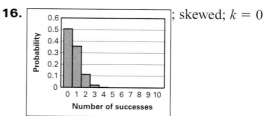 ; skewed; $k = 0$

6.1 Technology Activity (p. 217)

1. $k = 3$

2. $k = 8$

3. $k = 14$

6.2 Investigating Math Activity (p. 218)

2. About 68% of the area under a normal curve lies within 1 standard deviation of the mean. About 95% of the area under a normal curve lies within 2 standard deviations of the mean. About 99.7% of the area under a normal curve lies within 3 standard deviations of the mean.

6.4 Exercise Set A (p. 230)

17. a. 700

b.

Recommend 52%

Do not recommend 18%

Let parents decide 30%

c. ±3.8%; between 48.2% and 55.8%

6.5 Guided Practice (pp. 233–234)

3. *Sample answer:* The average age of the lawyers is likely to be higher than that of the tennis players. To correct the flaw, the company should redesign the experiment so that the ages and activity level in both groups are similar.

4. Having a police officer ask the question is a flaw; *Sample answer:* The person asking the question should not be involved in law enforcement.

6.5 Exercise Set A (p. 235)

3. Observational study; The assignments of the patients to the experimental group and the control group are outside the doctor's control.

4. *Sample answer:* The math anxiety level of the students enrolled in a mathematics program is likely to be lower than that of the math anxiety level of students enrolled in an art/history program. To correct the flaw, the company should redesign the experiment so that the mathematical backgrounds in both groups are similar.

5. *Sample answer:* The approval rating of the registered voters in the same party as the mayor is likely to be higher than that of the registered voters in a different party from the mayor. To correct the flaw, the company should redesign the experiment so that the political affiliations in both groups are similar.

6.5 Exercise Set B (p. 236)

4. *Sample answer:* The opinions of trained medical professionals are likely to be more accurate than the opinions of college students. To correct the flaw, the company should redesign the experiment so that the medical knowledge in both groups is similar.

5. *Sample answer:* The mathematical knowledge of the students enrolled as math majors is likely to be higher than that of the mathematical knowledge of students enrolled in other majors. To correct the flaw, the company should redesign the experiment so that the mathematical backgrounds in both groups are similar.

Unit 6 Test (pp. 237–238)

1.

C	red	black	blue
P(C)	0.1	0.5	0.4

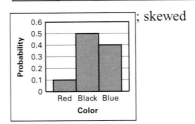

; skewed

25. *Sample answer:* The flaw is that young adults from 16 to 29 years of age are the experimental group and adults from 30 to 50 years of age are the control group. The experimental and control groups should consist of people from 16 to 50 years of age.